Management Innovation and Information Technology

Volume I: Information Technology

WIT*PRESS*

WIT Press publishes leading books in Science and Technology.
Visit our website for the current list of titles.
www.witpress.com

WIT*eLibrary*

Home of the Transactions of the Wessex Institute.
Papers contained in this title are archived in the WIT elibrary in volume 61 of
WIT Transactions on Information and Communication Technologies (ISSN 1743-3517).
The WIT electronic-library provides the international scientific community with immediate
and permanent access to individual papers presented at WIT conferences.
http://library.witpress.com

WIT Transactions

Transactions Editor

Carlos Brebbia
Wessex Institute of Technology
Ashurst Lodge, Ashurst
Southampton SO40 7AA, UK

Editorial Board

L M C **Godinho** University of Coimbra, Portugal

F **Gomez** Universidad Politecnica de Valencia, Spain

R **Gomez Martin** University of Granada, Spain

D **Goulias** University of Maryland, USA

K G **Goulias** Pennsylvania State University, USA

F **Grandori** Politecnico di Milano, Italy

W E **Grant** Texas A & M University, USA

S **Grilli** University of Rhode Island, USA

R H J **Grimshaw** Loughborough University, UK

D **Gross** Technische Hochschule Darmstadt, Germany

R **Grundmann** Technische Universitat Dresden, Germany

A **Gualtierotti** IDHEAP, Switzerland

O T **Gudmestad** University of Stavanger, Norway

R C **Gupta** National University of Singapore, Singapore

J M **Hale** University of Newcastle, UK

K **Hameyer** Katholieke Universiteit Leuven, Belgium

C **Hanke** Danish Technical University, Denmark

K **Hayami** University of Tokyo, Japan

Y **Hayashi** Nagoya University, Japan

L **Haydock** Newage International Limited, UK

A H **Hendrickx** Free University of Brussels, Belgium

C **Herman** John Hopkins University, USA

I **Hideaki** Nagoya University, Japan

D A **Hills** University of Oxford, UK

W F **Huebner** Southwest Research Institute, USA

J A C **Humphrey** Bucknell University, USA

M Y **Hussaini** Florida State University, USA

W **Hutchinson** Edith Cowan University, Australia

T H **Hyde** University of Nottingham, UK

M **Iguchi** Science University of Tokyo, Japan

D B **Ingham** University of Leeds, UK

L **Int Panis** VITO Expertisecentrum IMS, Belgium

N **Ishikawa** National Defence Academy, Japan

J **Jaafar** UiTm, Malaysia

W **Jager** Technical University of Dresden, Germany

Y **Jaluria** Rutgers University, USA

C M **Jefferson** University of the West of England, UK

P R **Johnston** Griffith University, Australia

D R H **Jones** University of Cambridge, UK

N **Jones** University of Liverpool, UK

N **Jovanovic** CSIR, South Africa

D **Kaliampakos** National Technical University of Athens, Greece

N **Kamiya** Nagoya University, Japan

D L **Karabalis** University of Patras, Greece

A **Karageorghis** University of Cyprus

M **Karlsson** Linkoping University, Sweden

T **Katayama** Doshisha University, Japan

K L **Katsifarakis** Aristotle University of Thessaloniki, Greece

J T **Katsikadelis** National Technical University of Athens, Greece

E **Kausel** Massachusetts Institute of Technology, USA

H **Kawashima** The University of Tokyo, Japan

B A **Kazimee** Washington State University, USA

S **Kim** University of Wisconsin-Madison, USA

D **Kirkland** Nicholas Grimshaw & Partners Ltd, UK

E **Kita** Nagoya University, Japan

A S **Kobayashi** University of Washington, USA

T **Kobayashi** University of Tokyo, Japan

D **Koga** Saga University, Japan

S **Kotake** University of Tokyo, Japan

A N **Kounadis** National Technical University of Athens, Greece

W B **Kratzig** Ruhr Universitat Bochum, Germany

T **Krauthammer** Penn State University, USA

C-H **Lai** University of Greenwich, UK

M **Langseth** Norwegian University of Science and Technology, Norway

B S **Larsen** Technical University of Denmark, Denmark

F Lattarulo Politecnico di Bari, Italy
A Lebedev Moscow State University, Russia
L J Leon University of Montreal, Canada
D Lesnic University of Leeds, UK
D Lewis Mississippi State University, USA
S Ighobashi University of California Irvine, USA
K-C Lin University of New Brunswick, Canada
A A Liolios Democritus University of Thrace, Greece
S Lomov Katholieke Universiteit Leuven, Belgium
J W S Longhurst University of the West of England, UK
G Loo The University of Auckland, New Zealand
J Lourenco Universidade do Minho, Portugal
J E Luco University of California at San Diego, USA
H Lui State Seismological Bureau Harbin, China
C J Lumsden University of Toronto, Canada
L Lundqvist Division of Transport and Location Analysis, Sweden
T Lyons Murdoch University, Australia
Y-W Mai University of Sydney, Australia
M Majowiecki University of Bologna, Italy
D Malerba Università degli Studi di Bari, Italy
G Manara University of Pisa, Italy
S Mambretti Politecnico di Milano, Italy
B N Mandal Indian Statistical Institute, India
Ü Mander University of Tartu, Estonia
H A Mang Technische Universitat Wien, Austria
G D Manolis Aristotle University of Thessaloniki, Greece
W J Mansur COPPE/UFRJ, Brazil
N Marchettini University of Siena, Italy
J D M Marsh Griffith University, Australia
J F Martin-Duque Universidad Complutense, Spain
T Matsui Nagoya University, Japan
G Mattrisch DaimlerChrysler AG, Germany
F M Mazzolani University of Naples "Federico II", Italy

K McManis University of New Orleans, USA
A C Mendes Universidade de Beira Interior, Portugal
R A Meric Research Institute for Basic Sciences, Turkey
J Mikielewicz Polish Academy of Sciences, Poland
N Milic-Frayling Microsoft Research Ltd, UK
R A W Mines University of Liverpool, UK
C A Mitchell University of Sydney, Australia
K Miura Kajima Corporation, Japan
A Miyamoto Yamaguchi University, Japan
T Miyoshi Kobe University, Japan
G Molinari University of Genoa, Italy
T B Moodie University of Alberta, Canada
D B Murray Trinity College Dublin, Ireland
G Nakhaeizadeh DaimlerChrysler AG, Germany
M B Neace Mercer University, USA
D Necsulescu University of Ottawa, Canada
F Neumann University of Vienna, Austria
S-I Nishida Saga University, Japan
H Nisitani Kyushu Sangyo University, Japan
B Notaros University of Massachusetts, USA
P O'Donoghue University College Dublin, Ireland
R O O'Neill Oak Ridge National Laboratory, USA
M Ohkusu Kyushu University, Japan
G Oliveto Universitá di Catania, Italy
R Olsen Camp Dresser & McKee Inc., USA
E Oñate Universitat Politecnica de Catalunya, Spain
K Onishi Ibaraki University, Japan
P H Oosthuizen Queens University, Canada
E L Ortiz Imperial College London, UK
E Outa Waseda University, Japan
A S Papageorgiou Rensselaer Polytechnic Institute, USA
J Park Seoul National University, Korea
G Passerini Universita delle Marche, Italy
F Patania University of Catania, Italy
B C Patten University of Georgia, USA

Management Innovation and Information Technology

Volume I: Information Technology

Editors

Zhenyu Du

*Information Technology and Industrial Engineering
Research Center, Hong Kong*

&

Maozhu Jin
Sichuan University, China

WITPRESS Southampton, Boston

Editors:

Zhenyu Du
Information Technology and Industrial Engineering Research Center, Hong Kong

Maozhu Jin
Sichuan University, China

Published by

WIT Press
Ashurst Lodge, Ashurst, Southampton, SO40 7AA, UK
Tel: 44 (0) 238 029 3223; Fax: 44 (0) 238 029 2853
E-Mail: witpress@witpress.com
http://www.witpress.com

For USA, Canada and Mexico

Computational Mechanics International
25 Bridge Street, Billerica, MA 01821, USA
Tel: 978 667 5841; Fax: 978 667 7582
E-Mail: infousa@witpress.com
http://www.witpress.com

British Library Cataloguing-in-Publication Data

A Catalogue record for this book is available
from the British Library

Volume I ISBN: 978-1-84564-976-0
Volume II ISBN: 978-1-84564-977-7

Set ISBN: 978-1-84564-940-1
Set eISBN: 978-1-84564-941-8
ISSN: (print) 1746-4463
ISSN: (on-line) 1743-3517

The texts of the papers in this volume were set individually by the authors or under their supervision. Only minor corrections to the text may have been carried out by the publisher.

Preface

The 2013 International Conference on Management Innovation and Information Technology is sponsored by the Information Technology & Industrial Engineering Research Center. It is the most international academic conference per year in Management Innovation and Information Technology area. MIIT 2013 is a forum for presentation of new research results and demonstration of new systems and techniques in the broad field of information systems, information technology, information management, and their applications in industrial engineering. The forum aims to bring together researchers, developers, and users from around the world in both industry and academia for sharing state-of-art results, for exploring new areas of research and development, and to discuss emerging issues facing business organizations in the knowledge economy. The Conference was held on December 7-8, 2013 in Wuhan, China.

In this conference, we had received more than 400 submissions from 5 countries and regions. Each of the papers was reviewed carefully by two famous specialists in this field. After received the revised papers on the basis of the specialists' advice, finally we collected about 260 papers into the proceedings. In addition to the regular publications of the papers, we have also invited several specialists and scholars in this field to make keynote speech at the conference. We would like to take this opportunity to express our thanks to the individuals and organizations for their efforts to serve the conference. We'd like to extend our thanks to members of academic committee for their effort to the conference; especially, we'd like to thank to members of organizing committee for their hard working; finally, we would like to express our appreciations to the participants of this conference.

Maozhu Jin & Zhenyu Du
Wuhan, China 2014

Contents

Volume II: Management science

Volume I
Information technology

Financial prediction system based on technology combining genetic algorithm with BP neural network

Laixing Chen
Huangshi Polytechnic College, Huangshi, China

Abstract

Neural network has the powerful ability of dealing with the nonlinear system and mapping, which is applied widely on the financial prewarning and financial forecast. The coupling of the neutral network and genetic algorithm for the financial parameters of forecast system is based on the intelligent simulation algorithm. The key for the algorithm is that the genetic algorithm weights the value of the neutral network prediction financial system among the topology structure layers. We have proved that the coupling of genetic algorithm and neutral network can improve the efficiency and the prediction accuracy of the network system, which realizes the integrated coupling for the two intelligent simulation methods.
Keywords: Genetic algorithm, neural networks, financial forecast.

1 Introduction

Disclosing the financial report form for the listing enterprise on the basis of the objective and justice, constructing the reasonable financial forecast and prewarning model, acquisition of the prediction value about the financial status and financial parameters from the listing enterprise, such as the debt ratio for the enterprise, obtaining the deterioration of the financial situation of the listing enterprise prewarning signal are very important realistic significance for the investors, operators, and regulators. These years, many scholars have constructed a variety of financial prediction model. The earliest discriminant model and enterprise financial prewarning analysis model is the Z.Score, which proposed by Breaver [1] in 1966. Ohlson [2] has proposed the logistic regression model in

1980. Currently, the multivariate linear judging method is usually adopted, especially the logistic regression method.

The neural network has excellent nonlinear approximation properties and the learning and inductive ability, which make it widely used in the applications of modelling, pattern recognitions, signal processing and controlling, especially, in some tough problems, such as facing the lack of physical or statistical understanding, the existence of statistical difference in observing data, and data from the nonlinear mechanism. In Ref. [3], it has reported the application for the BP neural network on the financial prewarning about the listing enterprise. Simultaneously, in Ref. [4], the failure prewarning problem of the complex listing enterprise has been investigated. Among them, the most representative is multilayer feed forward neural network (BPNN), which is based on BP learning algorithm. However, BPNN is easily falling into the local optimal value in the process of the training of weights. Furthermore, it is quite slow in the process of network training; therefore, the accuracy is needed to be improved in the forecast. In recent years, the integration of genetic algorithm (GA) and the neural network has made great progress. In Ref. [5], it was proposed the improved weight value, related parameters, and structure, where genetic algorithm training neural network. The incorporation of genetic algorithm and the neural network is used on the weight value and related parameters in the processing of training the radial basis function [6]. In Refs. [7,8], it is proposed the basis of BP network and genetic algorithm.

In this paper, we have designed forecast system in the financial field neural network based on the coupling of genetic algorithm and BP neural network. Firstly, we have improved weights in the fittest evolutionary from the hidden layer to the output layer among the network topology layers, and then found the optimal weight setting. Lastly, we have employed the BP algorithm to connect the weights learning and then incorporate into the genetic algorithm to optimize the weight value group, so as to improve the accuracy of the output layer financial parameters in the neural network system prediction.

2 The prediction model based on the coupling of GA–BP

2.1 The model of GA–BP system

BP neural network is a powerful learning system, which has been widely used in the economic field. The learning system is quite simple and easy to program. In the specific application, the most important is to determine the network structure, while the key for the network structure is the hidden layer and the numbers of node. From the data and sample in Ref. [4], we have employed the four layers neural network as shown in Figure 1. The prediction model for the incorporation of GA–BP is a mixed model, which connects the genetic algorithm with the neural network, based on the four layers BP neural network.

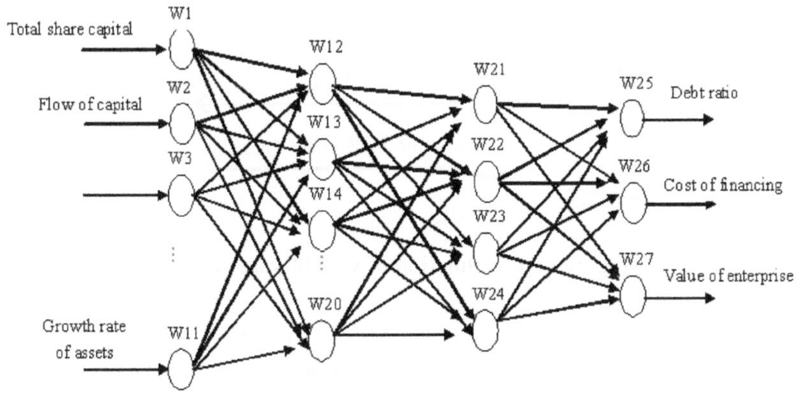

Figure 1: The structure of BP neural network.

Table 1: The Nodes of GA–BP Model.

No. of Node (Input Layer)	Name of Node (Input Layer)	Hidden Layer 1	Hidden Layer 2	No. of Node (Output Layer)	Name of Node (Output Layer)
1	Total share capital				
2	Flow of capita			25	Debt ratio
3	Net share assets				
4	Income tax rates				
5	Rate of return on assets	A total of nine nodes	A total of four nodes	26	Cost of financing
6	Return on equity				
7	Total assets				
8	Turnover				
9	Turnover rate				
10	Net profit growth rate			27	Value of enterprise
11	Asset growth rate				

2.2 The component content of GA–BP model

According to the related theories of the financial management, the financial ratio can combine the balance sheet, income statement, and cash flow statement. From the content of training sample and testing prewarning sample in Ref. [4], we have extracted 11 as the input for the GA–BP model, namely the training sample index, as shown in Table 1.

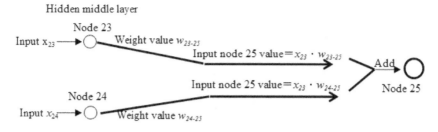

Figure 2: The function of weight value w.

Training samples input nodes: 1, total share capital; 2, flow of capital; 3, net share assets; 4, income tax rate; 5, rate of return on assets; 6, return on equity; 7, total assets; 8, turnover; 9, turnover rate; 10, net profit growth rate; 11, asset growth rate, respectively.

Training testing output nodes: 25- Debt ratio; 26- Cost of financing; 27- Value of enterprise.

2.3 The set of training sample for GA–BP

The formation of the set of sample is linearly transforming the required financial index x and the upper and lower limit value of X_{max} and X_{min}, which mapping to the [0,1] interval. To remove the influence of specification and diversification, the system will normalize the training data into the [−1,0.0,+1] interval value, and the normalized formula can be listed as following Eq. (1):

$$x = \frac{x - x_{min}}{x_{max} - x_{min}} \tag{1}$$

After Eq. (1) transformed, we can incorporate x into the forming training sample file (.nna). According to the data from Ref. [4], it can form two sampled files, training sample I and training sample II, respectively.

3 The coupling of prediction model

3.1 The weight value among the model nodes

The genetic algorithm used the survival of the fittest way, got rid of the negative variation, and inherited the useful variation. And this algorithm has been penetrated into various fields and research projects. BP neutral network mode is consists of input layer, middle hidden layer, and output layer. For the layer-in-layer, after training, the apparent weight value is the discounted value for the layer of the input value (as shown in Figure 2).

In this paper, the genetic algorithm is applied to the BP neural network prediction system, improves the survival of the fittest evolutionary in the network

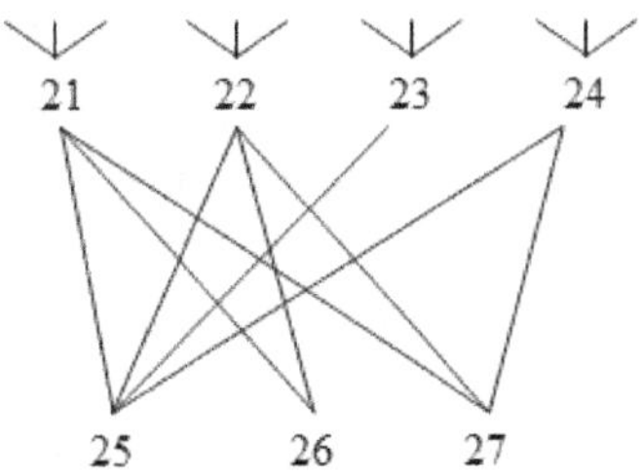

Figure 3: The weigh value for the layer of BPF after the sample I/II of training.

Table 2: The Parent Source Sample Weight Value of the Genetic Evolution.

	Sample	W_{21-25}	W_{22-25}	W_{23-25}	W_{24-25}	W_{21-26}	W_{22-26}	W_{23-26}	W_{24-26}	W_{21-27}	W_{22-27}	W_{23-27}	W_{24-27}
The parent source	Sample I	1.0591	0.2902	−1.1115	−1.0058	0.2074	0.0909	0.4455	−1.3447	−0.4110	−1.3147	0.0154	0.4862
	Sample II	1.3377	0.3189	−0.9779	−0.8504	0.0152	0.146	0.4115	−1.4942	−0.4092	−1.2939	0.1219	0.5543

Breakpoint a   Breakpoint b

topology structure layer from the hidden layer to the output layer, and finds out the optimal weights value set. Then, the genetic algorithm connects the weight learning using BP algorithm and couples the optimal of genetic algorithm into the group of weight coefficient value, which can effectively enhance the accuracy of GA–BP prediction of the output layer parameters.

3.2 The formation of weight value for the source sample

To solve the objective of practical problem using GA, it is needed to change the related parameters into the binary of quantitative processing. The weight value in BP network system such as 0.9412 can be directly incorporated into the parent source sample in the GA. For the BP network, after the generation training samples in the part of 2.3, it can obtain the weight value in the hidden layer 2 nodes to output node: W_{21-25}, W_{22-25}, W_{23-25}, and W_{24-25} (as shown in Figure 3). These weight values are listed in Table 2, which is regarded as the parent source sample in the genetic evolution.

3.3 The process of genetic evolution

3.3.1 Screening the quality of the population sample
Employing the breeding probability from Eq. (2), screening the population sample:

$$p = \frac{F_i}{\sum\limits_{j=1}^{n} F_j} \tag{2}$$

where $i = 1,2,3,\ldots,n$, n is the number of the population source; F_j is the adaptive value for the sample, namely, fitness. Generally, $F_j = \sum \min(Yp - Tp)^2$; Y_p is

Table 3: The Content of Source Mating Offspring.

The Offspring	$I_{w21\text{-}25}$	$I_{w22\text{-}25}$	$I_{w23\text{-}25}$	$I_{w24\text{-}25}$	$II_{w21\text{-}26}$	$II_{w22\text{-}26}$	$II_{w23\text{-}26}$	$II_{w24\text{-}26}$	$I_{w21\text{-}27}$	$I_{w22\text{-}27}$	$I_{w23\text{-}27}$	$I_{w24\text{-}27}$
After Mating	1.0591	0.2902	−1.1115	−1.0058	0.0152	−0.0146	0.4115	−1.4942	−0.4110	−1.3147	0.0154	0.4862

Table 4: The Weight Values of the Evolution and Mutation Progeny (Adaptive Value < 0.07).

Variation of Evolution of Offspring	$I_{w21\text{-}25}$	$I_{w22\text{-}25}$	$I_{w23\text{-}25}$	$I_{w24\text{-}25}$	$II_{w21\text{-}26}$	$II_{w22\text{-}26}$	$II_{w23\text{-}26}$	$II_{w24\text{-}26}$	$I_{w21\text{-}27}$	$I_{w22\text{-}27}$	$I_{w23\text{-}27}$	$I_{w24\text{-}27}$
	1.0591	0.2902	−1.1115	−1.0058	0.2152	−0.3146	0.7115	−0.8442	−0.4110	−1.3147	0.0154	0.4862

the actual output value, namely, the actual input debt ratio for the network system; T_p is the ideal output value or the existing debt ratio; $\Delta = Y_p - T_p \rightarrow \min$, it means that the error is small, but the debt ratio could not demand too small error. In this paper, $\Delta \leq 0.07$ in GA–BP network system.

3.3.2 The population mating

We can choose the preferred parent source sample to adapt to the enterprise environment from the above calculation adaptive value. For the selection of GA–BP system in Table 2, a and b is the double breakpoint mating method. The mating method is that take a and b from the source I away to the left and right gene (weight coefficient value w) and source II in the genetic code (weight coefficient value w'), which the two are composed of offspring (as shown in Table 3).

3.3.3 Variation generating new species

According to Table 3, each employs the random numerical from [0,1] to implement the variation operation. We add 0.2, −0.3, 0.3, and 0.6 into $II_{w21\text{-}26}$, $II_{w22\text{-}26}$, $II_{w23\text{-}26}$, $II_{w24\text{-}26}$ (as shown in Table 4), respectively.

However, according to the error between the forecast of financial parameters and the actual value, the adaptive value is less than that of 0.07. Calculated from the Eq. (2), it was found that the mating probability $[P_o]$ is in the range from 0.4 to 0.9, while the variation probability $[P_m]$ is in the range from 0.001 to 0.02. In order to evolve, $[P_o]$, $[P_m]$, and parent source are incorporated into genetic algorithm. Finally, converge to an adaptation of the above formula supporting adaptive value to optimize the offspring individuals. This is the optimal BP network weight value, which is coupling into GA–BP network forecasting system. At last, we need to test the above samples again.

4 Verification and testing for the system

We use the preferred offspring weight value of the above adaptive value p to replace the weight value from the original sample training value in GA–BP system (as shown in Table 4). And then employ the testing sample LiYi1.nna to test. At this time, the test sample debt ratio is 0.0000, and then gaining the prediction value is shown in Table 6, and then the original testing sample 0.0000 is changed into 0.756334.

Table 5: The Test Sample of GA–BP Network Prediction Debt Ratio (Unit: Million%).

Total Share Capital	Flow of Capital	Net Share Assets	Income Tax Rates	Rate of Return on Assets	Return on Equity	Total Assets
31312 (0.5042)	13300 (0.9339)	3.76 (0.8257)	0.075 (0.2777)	0.0214 (0.1709)	0.032 (0.1696)	175712.22 (0.4344)
Turnover (log)	Turnover rate	Net profit growth rate	Asset growth rate	Cost of financing	Value of enterprise	Prediction of debt ratio
Ln26172.5 (0.5601)	0.5387 (0.4113)	0.1552 (0.3407)	0.277 (0.1546)	0.0215 (0.1715)	173271.15 (0.2818)	(0.0000)

Table 6: Comparison of the Prediction of the Listing Enterprise Debt Ratio for GA–BP System.

	BP Neutral Network		GA–BP System
	Sample I training BP system	Sample II training BP system	Liyi1.nna acqusition
Prediction value	0.503481	0.326262	0.756334
Prediction the original value	35.5%	27.6%	46.7%
Actual value	46.4%	46.4%	46.4%
Error	0.23	0.40	0.06

5 Conclusions

This paper has designed a GA–BP prediction system in the financial field based on the coupling of the genetic algorithm and BP neural network. Using the genetic algorithm, it has improved the survival of the fittest evolutionary in the network topology structure layer from the hidden layer to the output layer, and finds out the optimal weights value set. And then training based on the BP algorithm to enhance the prediction accuracy of the GA-BP output layer parameters.

Acknowledgments

The research work was supported by Social Science Research Project Foundation of Huangshi under Grant No. 201201.

References

[1] W.H. Breaver, Financial rations as predictions of failure. *Supplement to Journal of Accounting Research*, **4(1)**, pp. 77–111, 1966.

[2] A.J. Ohlson, Financial ratios and the probabilistic prediction of bankruptcy. *Journal of Accounting Research*, **18(1)**, pp. 109–131, 1980.

[3] ZHANG Gen-ming, XIANG Xiao-ji, WANG Shu-wei, Financial crisis warning research based o BP neural network. *Chinese Journal of Management Science*, **14(Special)**, pp. 227–231, 2006.

[4] LIU Hong, HE Guangjun, Research on early warning of the failure of the artificial neural network method based on listing corporation operation. *Accounting Research*, **2**, pp. 42–46, 2004.

[5] Frank H.F. Leung, H.K. Lam, S.H. Ling, Tuning of the structure and parameters of a neural network using an improved genetic algorithm. *IEEE Transactions on Neural Networks*, **14(1)**, pp. 79–88, 2003.

[6] Steve A. Billings, Guang L. Zheng, Radial basis function network configuration using genetic algorithms. *Neural Network*, **8(6)**, pp. 877–890, 1995.

[7] LI Wei-chao, SONG Da-meng, CHENG Bin, Artificial neural network based on genetic algorithm. *Computer Engineering and Design*, **27(2)**, pp. 316–318, 2006.

[8] ZHOU Hui-ren, TANG Wan-sheng, REN Xianling, HGA-BP-based financial crisis warning method. *Journal of Systems and Management*, **19(1)**, pp. 1–6, 2010.

A multiobjective model for closed-loop supply chain network

Hongwei Jiang

School of Information Management, Beijing Information Science and Technology University, Beijing, China

Abstract

Due to the increased environmental concern and the competitive advantages, closed-loop supply chain network design has spurred an interest among researchers. This paper proposes a multiobjective model for closed-loop supply chain network. The model is designed for multiple products, plants, distribution centres, demand markets, and collection centres. The first objective function is minimization of the total cost of facility location, production, disposal, and transportation associated with forward and reverse supply chains in the network. The second objective function is maximization of the responsiveness of the closed-loop supply chain network.

Keywords: Multiobjective programming, closed-loop supply chain network, reverse logistics.

1 Introduction

Supply chain management (SCM) has received a lot of attentions. There are two types of supply chains: forward and reverse supply chains. The forward supply chain (FSC) contains of series of activities which result in the conversion of raw materials to finished products. Managers try to improve FSC performances in areas such as demand management, procurement, and order fulfillment. Reverse supply chain (RSC) is defined as the activities of the collection and recovery of product returns in SCM. The path toward sustainability to demonstrate environmental and social responsibility has led to an increasing attention to the value-added activities in RSC. Such as Xerox focused on recovery activities and they have achieved significant successes in this area [1]. The integration of a FSC and a RSC results in a closed-loop supply chain (CLSC). In other words, there are both forward and reverse logistics in CLSC networks.

In the recent years, CLSC has achieved considerable concern in industry and the academic community [2,3]. One of the most important and strategic issues in CLSC is the configuration of the CLSC network that has a significant effect on the total performance of the CLSC. CLSC network design decisions include determining the numbers, locations, and capacities of facilities and the quantity of flow between them.

In most of the past researches, the design of FSC and RSC networks is considered separately, but the configuration of the RSC network has a strong influence on the FSC network and vice versa. Separating the design may result in suboptimality, therefore the design of the FSC and RSC network should be integrated [4,5].

It is important to note that the design of the integrated CLSC network may involve a trade-off between the total costs and the network's responsiveness. In some cases, companies may decide to open more facilities to increase the responsiveness for higher customer satisfaction, which may lead to a greater investment cost. Thus, it is necessary to jointly take network costs and network responsiveness into account during the design of CLSC network [6].

2 Discussed problem

The CLSC discussed in this paper is a single period, multiproduct, multistage network including plants, distribution centres, demand markets, collection centres, and disposal centres, which is described in Figure 1. The products are sent to demand markets by plants and distribution centres. Then, the returned products are sent to collection centres. Collection centres have the following responsibilities: collecting of used products from demand markets, determining the condition of the returns by inspection and/or separation to find out whether they are recoverable or not, sending recoverable returns to the plants, sending the unrecoverable returns (because of economic and/or technological reasons) to the disposal centre. All of the returned products from demand markets are collected in collection centres. Locations of demand markets are fixed. Locations and capacities of plants, distribution centres, and collection centres are known in advance. The objective is to know how many and which plants, distribution centres, and collection centres should be open, and which products and in which quantities should be stock in them.

3 Multiobjective model

The problem above can be formulated as a multiobjective model. Sets, parameters, and decision variables are defined as follows:

Sets
I = set of products (1 ... i ... I)
J = set of potential manufacturing and remanufacturing plants locations (1 ... j ... J)

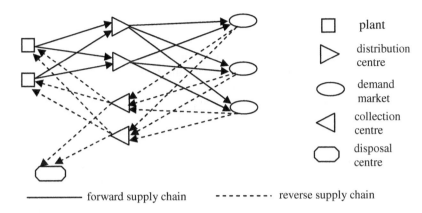

Figure 1: The CLSC network.

K = set of distribution centres locations (1 ... k ... K)
L = set of demand markets locations (1 ... l ... L)
O = set of potential collection centres locations (1 ... o ... O)

Parameters

A_i = production cost of product i

B_i = transportation cost of product i per km between plants and distribution centres

C_i = transportation cost of product i per km between distribution centres and demand markets

D_i = transportation cost of product i per km between demand markets and collection centres

E_i = transportation cost of product i per km between collection centres and plants

F_i = transportation cost of product i per km between collection centres and disposal centre

G_j = fixed cost for opening plant j

H_k = fixed cost for opening distribution centre k

β_o = fixed cost for opening collection centre o

M_i = cost saving of product i (because of product recovery)

N_i = disposal cost of product i

P_{ij} = capacity of plant j for product i

Q_{ik} = capacity of distribution centre k for product i

R_{io} = capacity of collection centre o for product i

t_{jk} = the distance between location j and k generated based on the Euclidean method (t_{kl}, t_{lo}, and t_{oj} are defined in the same way). t_o is the distance between collection centre o and disposal centre

d_{il} = demand of customer l for product i

r_{il} = return of customer l for product i

α_i = minimum disposal fraction of product i

ρ = weighting factor (importance) for the forward responsiveness in the second objective function; $(1-\rho)$ denotes the weight for the reverse responsiveness

Variables

X_{ijk} = quantity of product i produced by plant j for distribution centres k

Y_{ikl} = quantity of product i from distribution centres k to demand market l

Z_{ilo} = quantity of returned product i from demand market l to collection centre o

S_{ioj} = quantity of returned product i from collection centre o to plant j

T_{io} = quantity of returned product i from collection centre o to disposal centre

U_j = 1, if a plant is located and set up at potential site j, 0, otherwise

V_k = 1, if a distribution centre is located and set up at potential site k, 0, otherwise

W_o = 1, if a collection centre is located and set up at potential site o, 0, otherwise

The first objective function of the presented model is to minimize the total cost of the CLSC network as follows.<comp: make "Min" roman>

$$Min\ z_1 = \sum_j G_j U_j + \sum_k H_k V_k + \sum_o \beta_o W_o + \sum_i \sum_j \sum_k \left(A_i + B_i t_{jk} \right) X_{ijk} + \sum_i \sum_k \sum_l C_i t_{kl} Y_{ikl}$$
$$+ \sum_i \sum_l \sum_o D_i t_{lo} Z_{ilo} + \sum_i \sum_o \sum_j \left(-M_i + E_i t_{oj} \right) S_{ioj} + \sum_i \sum_o \left(N_i + F_i t_o \right) T_{io}$$

The first, second, and third parts show the fixed costs of opening plants, distribution centres, and collection centres, respectively. The fourth part represents the production cost of new products and the transportation cost of new products from plants to distribution centres. The fifth part represents the transportation cost of new products from distribution centres to demand markets. The sixth part is related to the transportation costs of returned products from demand markets to collection centres. The seventh part represents the total recovery and transportation costs of returned products from collection centres to plants. Besides, the eighth part calculates disposal cost and transportation cost from collection centres to disposal centre.

The second objective function of the presented model is to maximize the responsiveness of the CLSC network as follows.<comp: make "Max" roman>

$$Max\ z_2 = \rho \left(\sum_i \sum_k \sum_l Y_{ikl} \right) \Big/ \sum_i \sum_l d_{il} + (1 - \rho) \left(\sum_i \sum_l \sum_o Z_{ilo} \right) \Big/ \sum_i \sum_l r_{il}$$

The first part represents the weighted responsiveness of FSC. The second part shows the weighted responsiveness of RSC.

The following is a representation of the constraints of the presented model.

$$\sum_i \sum_j X_{ijk} \geq \sum_i \sum_l Y_{ikl} \qquad \forall k \tag{1}$$

$$\sum_k Y_{ikl} \geq d_{il} \qquad \forall i, l \tag{2}$$

$$\sum_i \sum_k X_{ijk} + \sum_o \sum_i S_{ioj} \leq U_j \sum_i P_{ij} \qquad \forall j \tag{3}$$

$$\sum_o Z_{ilo} \leq \sum_k Y_{ikl} \qquad \forall i, l \tag{4}$$

$$\alpha_i \sum_l Z_{ilo} \leq T_{io} \qquad \forall i, o \tag{5}$$

$$\sum_i \sum_j X_{ijk} \leq V_k \sum_i Q_{ik} \qquad \forall k \tag{6}$$

$$\sum_i \sum_l Z_{ilo} \leq W_o \sum_i R_{io} \qquad \forall o \tag{7}$$

$$\sum_l Z_{ilo} = \sum_j S_{ioj} + T_{io} \qquad \forall i, o \tag{8}$$

$$\sum_o Z_{iol} = r_{il} \qquad \forall i, l \tag{9}$$

$$U_i, V_k, W_o \in \{0, 1\} \qquad \forall i, k, o \tag{10}$$

$$X_{ijk}, Y_{ikl}, Z_{ilo}, S_{ioj}, T_{io} \geq 0 \qquad \forall i, j, k, l, o \tag{11}$$

The constraint (1) ensures that the quantity of new products from plants to distribution centres is equal to or greater than the quantity of new products from distribution centres to demand markets for each distribution centre. The constraint (2) ensures that the total number of each manufactured product for each demand market is equal or greater than the demand. Constraint (3) is a capacity constraint of plants. Constraint (4) represents that forward flow is greater than reverse flow. Constraint (5) enforces a minimum disposal fraction for each product. Constraint (6) is capacity constraint of distribution centre. Constraint (7) is capacity constraint of collection centres. Constraint (8) shows that the quantity of returned products from demand market is equal to the quantity of returned products to plants and quantity of products in disposal centre for each collection centre and each product. Constraint (9) shows the returned products. Constraint (10) ensures the binary nature of decision variables while constraint (11) preserves the nonnegativity restriction on the decision variables.

4   Conclusions

Because of the increasing importance of network costs and network responsiveness, this paper presents a multiobjective mixed integer nonlinear programming

(MINLP) model for CLSC network design. The proposed model has been designed for a single period. The further research direction is to extend this model to multiperiod. Another future research is to develop heuristic approaches such as genetic algorithm, particle swarm optimization, and artificial bee colony algorithm because it is hard to solve large problems in a reasonable time. In addition, addressing the demand uncertainty in a CLSC network is a promising research avenue with significant practical relevance. Finally, it is valuable to apply the model in real cases and analyze the results.

Acknowledgments

The research work was supported by Foundation for Distinguished Young Talents of Beijing Municipal Education Commission (Grant No. CIT&TCD201304118).

References

[1] W. Kerr, C. Ryan, Eco-efficiency gains from remanufacturing. A case study of photocopier remanufacturing at Fuji Xerox Australia. *Journal of Cleaner Production*, **9(1)**, pp. 275–281, 2001.

[2] V. Daniel R. Guide Jr., Luk N. Van Wassenhove, The evolution of closed-loop supply chain research. *Operation Research*, **57(1)**, pp. 10–18, 2009.

[3] R.C. Savaskan, S. Bhattacharya, L.N. Van Wassenhove, Closed-loop supply chain models with product remanufacturing. *Management Science*, **50(2)**, pp. 239–252, 2004.

[4] H. Uster, G. Easwaran, E. Akcali, et al., Benders decomposition with alternative multiple cuts for a multi-product closed-loop supply chain network design model. *Naval Research Logistics*, **54**, pp. 890–907, 2007.

[5] E. Akcali, S. Cetinkaya, H. Uster, Network design for reverse and closed-loop supply chains: an annotated bibliography of models and solution approaches. *Networks*, **53**, pp. 231–248, 2009.

[6] Mir Saman Pishvaee, Reza Zanjirani Farahani, Wout Dullaert, A memetic algorithm for bi-objective integrated forward/reverse logistics network design. *Computers and Operations Research*, **37**, pp. 1100–1112, 2010.

Research and application of an improved algorithm of decision tree–SVM based on the merging of decision tree and SVM in default detection system

Haoming Guo, Xingsheng Xie
Automation Department, University of Science and Technology of China, Hefei, China

Abstract

For large data sets with many training examples, lots of support vector machine (SVM) implementations quickly become infeasible especially in their memory and time complexities. On the basis of existing methods that use a decision tree to decompose a large data set and train SVMs on the decomposed regions (DT–SVM), an Improved Decision Tree–SVM (IDT–SVM) is developed. By taking the strategy of only using Decision Tree as rough classifier of data samples, it reduces the time of training for large data sets effectively and can take full advantage of parallel/concurrent processing capabilities as well. In addition, by the test-accuracy-rate-oriented joint optimization of SVM parameters and decision tree trimming, this algorithm is also able to effectively guarantee the accuracy in its classification. Experiments to predict the Probability of Default (PD) of customers' repaying loans of commercial banks are conducted. The results show that the IDT–SVM is as accurate as existing enhanced SVM implementations and can handle much larger data sets than existing SVM methods.
Keywords: Large-scale data, support vector machines (SVMs), decision tree, the probability of default (PD).

1 Introduction

Support vector machines (SVMs) have proven very effective for solving pattern classification problems and some general implementation toolkits such as

SVM^{light} or LIBSVM have been developed [1–5]. Because of the growing tendency to apply them to various fields of interest, including knowledge discovery, pattern recognition, and data mining, the size of data sets continues to increase at a rapid rate. At the same time, there is an unremitting effort to accelerate the SVM training. In this paper, two categories called the numerical technique and data reduction [1,2,6,7] have been proposed to deal with large sample processing. The numerical technique, also named working set method, seeks efficient solutions to the SVM optimization problems, which breaks a large problem into a series of small problems and reduces the amount of memory required for computation. A different type of approach, called data reduction, decreases a large training set to one or several small sets, and all results of these data sets are combined into the final classifier. The difficulty of data reduction is how the child SVM classifiers effectively joint together. In addition to this, neither of these two methods has adequately taken the problem of parameter optimization into consideration [1,2].

To handle problems created by large data sets, Fu Chang et al. raise an algorithm called DT–SVM (the Decision Tree–SVM) that employs a decision tree to decompose a given data set and trains SVMs on the decomposed regions [1]. For this purpose, in this paper, an improved DT–SVM algorithm is proposed to solve the problem of predicting probability of default with large data set problem through massive capital flow based on SVM.

2 The IDT–SVM method

2.1 Main idea of algorithm

Existing DT–SVM [8,9] algorithm is basically a simple combination of the decision tree and SVM. Samples are classified by decision tree, SVM subclassifiers are trained in leaf nodes whose purity of the class does not reach the specified threshold. However, it mostly ignores the cost to build the decision tree. In the massive data environment, if trimming is not effectively controlled when constructing a decision tree, it may result in lots of nodes in the tree. This paper proposes an improved DT–SVM algorithm to refine the practicability of DT–SVM in uncertain data size situations. Algorithm design considerations are as follows:

(i) Strategically weaken the role of the decision tree. It only serves as a rough classification of sample data. The size of the decision tree is mandatorily limited: the depth of available maximum tree does not exceed eight layers, the number leaf node samples is less than 1000 and when the purity of a leaf node of a class is more than 95%, it is necessary to stop building SVM subclassifiers.

(ii) Because of up to 128 leaf nodes in an eight-layer binary tree, a separate thread of training SVM can be created at each node, which can fully take advantage of machine's concurrent and parallel capacity and improve IDT–SVM training overall performance.

(iii) Accuracy of the algorithm is guaranteed by the strategy of test-accuracy-rate-oriented joint optimization of SVM parameters and decision tree trimming. This paper uses RBF kernel when undertaking SVM training and combination of parameters $<\delta, C>$ denotes respectively the kernel parameters and normalization factor of controlling the sample misclassification penalty degree.

After the above optimization program is applied, the construction of decision tree and trimming time are both controlled perfectly. At the same time, combining the process of parameter optimization of SVM and DT trimming not only simplifies the DT trimming program, but solves the problem of parameter optimization of SVM as well, which improves the prediction accuracy of the algorithm.

2.2 IDT–SVM algorithm

Algorithm 1: Main
01 BEGIN
02   Data pre-process, getting prepared for training and verifying data samples;
03   Train the initial decision tree using training data set,
        Use the following conditions as the termination of tree branch growing:
        1) The depth of the tree is less than 8, or
        2) The number of leaf node is less than 1000
     //Train the sub-classifiers at each leaf node of the initial decision tree;
04   FOR each *lnode* ∈ {initial DT leaf node set} DO
05   Count various types of sample's proportion;
06   IF (Max ratio of one type>=95%) THEN
07   Set the type flag 1 or -1 as the current leaf node *lnode* //1 or -1;
08   ELSE
09   Create a separate thread; invoke "**Generic SVM modelling tools**" to train *lnode* classifier;
10   Store optimization parameter group θ of *lnode*;
11   Set the flag of *lnode* as class of uncertain identity (value 0);
12   END IF;
13   END FOR;
     //Verify the accuracy of each leaf node of the initial decision tree
14   FOR each *pt* ∈ {validation sample point set} DO
15   Search the position pt for the leaf node-->*cnode*;
        //No need to deal with leaf nodes that have been marked(1|-1)
16   IF (cnode.y≠0) THEN CONTINUE;
17   u = cnode.svmf(pt); //Use the sub-classifier to predict which class *pt* belongs
22   IF (u==pt.y) THEN   //Right
23   cnode.err_cnt ++; //Right number + 1
24   ELSE
25   cnode.cor_cnt ++; //Wrong number + 1

26   END IF
27   END FOR;
28   Invoke: algorithm 2, optimize parameters in the whole SVM and trimming of DT
29 END BEGIN;

Algorithm 2: IDT-SVM parameters optimization combined with Decision Tree trimming algorithm
01 BEGIN
02   From sub-classifier in each leaf node of initial DT, the 10 best verifying accuracy groups θ are selected and stored.
03   Leaf nodes whose class purity is less than 95% and numbers of which are less than 2000 are marked as "**to be optimized**";
         //Optimize the decision tree and retrain related sub-classifiers in the leaf node;
04   LOOP over *cnode* ∈ {current set of leaf nodes to be optimized}
05   tnode = cnode.parent;//Parent node
         //Merge training and verifying samples into *tnode*;
06   tnode.points = tnode.lchild.points + tnode.rchild.points;
07   tnode.v_points=tnode.lchild.v_points + tnode.rchild.v_points;
08   IF samples of *tnode* >=1500 THEN
09   Set flag of *cnode* as **optimized**;
10   Remove *cnode* from {current set of leaf nodes to be optimized};
11   CONTINUE;
12   ENDIF
12   Use 10 best verifying accuracy groups θ to train the *tnode* of SVM;
13   Keep the best of verifying accuracy and restore the new θ';
14   IF (best verifying accuracy - original verifying accuracy) > 0.5% THEN
             //shape and modify
15   Modify the *tnode* as the leaf node and add it into the leaf node set as to be optimized;
16   Remove the lower sub-node of *tnode*;
17   Use the new θ' to replace the smallest one among the original 10 verifying accuracy;
18   ELSE
19   Set flag of *cnode* as **optimized** and remove it from {current set of leaf nodes to be optimized};
20   END IF
21   UNTIL {current set of leaf nodes to be optimized}=Φ
22 END BEGIN;

2.3 Complexity analysis

The time complexity of constructing initial decision tree using C4.5 is $O(nm^2L)$, with n is the total number of training samples, m is the number of attributes in the dataset, and L is the internal nodes of decision tree. When there is a total number of n training samples invoking SVM tools, the time complexity tends to be $O(n^2)$ [2,4,5]. Suppose the number of samples in a single leaf node is σ (less than 10,000) and the average number of leaf nodes is n/σ, the total average time of IDT–SVM algorithm training the leaf nodes of initial decision tree is

$$O\left(\frac{n}{\sigma p}\sigma^2\right) = O\left(\frac{n}{p}\sigma\right),$$ with p is concurrency/parallelism factor. Fusion optimization processing time is determined as 10 times of total training time of initial leaf nodes, that is, $10O\left(\frac{n}{p}\sigma\right)$. Therefore, in case of sample properties less than 10 with employing rough decision tree strategy, the time complexity of training sample with the algorithm of IDT–SVM is $O(n) + 11O\left(\frac{n}{p}\sigma\right)$. If the parallelism factor p of the classifier is large enough, main term $O\left(\frac{n}{p}\sigma\right)$ would be nearly linear, which makes the whole algorithm demonstrate a good linear scalability.

3 Application and analysis of results

3.1 Main idea of algorithm

In order to verify the effectiveness of IDT–SVM algorithm, an application scenario with large-scale data is chosen, which is the Probability of Default (PD) prediction of a provincial commercial bank with 25,922 loans. Table 1 summarizes a group of illegal trading characteristics as model input properties.

Among them, the purpose of the additional dimension of 0 attribute is to make the model indirectly integrate the influence factor of customer financial conditions. Table 2 gives the normalized value of the main attribute by credit grading summary and the percentage of overdue default or nonperforming loan which is defined by the bank. According to this table, the credit rating level and the overdue default are not distinctly correlated.

3.2 Experiment comparison

In the experiment, 1500 samples are set aside as verifying samples, 500 samples are test samples, and others are classified as training sample candidate set. The following experiments based on four kinds of algorithms are conducted. (i) SVM[light+] toolkit (v6.0.1, 2002), (ii) LIBSVM toolkit (v3.14, 2012 for Java), (iii) IDT + SVM[light+] toolkit, (iv) IDT + LIBSVM toolkit. All these algorithms are modelled with 23,922 samples.

Table 1: Model Input Properties Design.

Attribute Number	Attribute Name	Attribute Value	Characteristics and Significance Description
1	Spending involving courts or administrative fines	Amount in total	Enterprise or business may be in financial trouble.
2	Spending involving high-risk investments	Amount in total	Total amount which is transferred to real estate, stock, securities, or futures market.
3	Spending different from the use of loans as stipulated	Amount in total	Expenditure of wage payments, management fees, insurance costs, interest on the debt, a purchase of financial products, and transferring to a fixed account.
4	Spending involving connected transactions	Amount in total	Amount that is transferred to the parent company or other related parties with equity relationship.
5	Trading spending involving transfer between two accounts with the same owner/contra flow/small chunks	Amount in Total	Transaction spending with the risk of circumventing monitoring and the conversion of credit funds to its own.
0	Customer credit grading	0–9	It stands for manually verified data, once for a year. The greater the value, the lower the rating. AAA, AA,A,BBB,BB,B,CCC,CC,C,D

Table 2: Attribute Value, Overdue Rate, and Defect Rate Classified by Credit Grading.

	Record Number	Attribute 1	Attribute 2	Attribute 3	Attribute 4	Attribute 5	Overdue Rate %
AAA	3	0	0	0	0	0.631	33.33
AA	39	0	0.073	0.187	0.026	0.430	51.28
A	233	0.013	0.031	0.125	0.031	0.629	36.91
BBB	569	0	0.023	0.094	0.007	0.218	44.82
BB	456	0.002	0.018	0.032	0.022	0.196	45.18
B	82	0	0	0.016	0	0.143	52.44
CCC	1	0	0	0	0	0	0
CC	5	0	0	0	0	0.200	0
D	3	0	0.00003	0	0.027	0.333	100

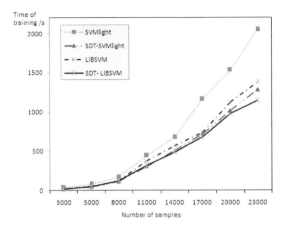

Figure 1: Training time comparison of IDT–LIBSVM and other algorithms.

Table 3: Time and Validation Accuracy of Four Algorithms.

Numbers of Samples	SVM^{light}		IDT–SVM^{light}			LIBSVM		IDT–LIBSVM		
	Training time	Accuracy rate	Training time	Accuracy rate*	Accuracy rate	Training time	Accuracy rate	Training time	Accuracy rate*	Accuracy rate
3000	37	88.2	18	88.1	92.6	21	89.9	19	89.6	92.1
5000	81	88.5	52	87.3	91.9	53	88.4	48	87.9	91.4
8000	171	88.9	116	87.9	91.7	122	89.4	122	88.9	92.2
11,000	443	89.1	306	87.8	91.2	376	90.2	320	88.9	92.9
14,000	676	88.0	508	89.2	90.4	567	90.1	489	89.8	92.4
17,000	1165	88.7	718	86.9	89.7	743	89.9	678	89.2	91.7
20,000	1532	89.0	1012	87.1	90.2	1121	90.6	979	90.0	92.1
23,000	2051	89.2	1283	88.9	92.0	1381	90.4	1143	89.9	92.4

All the kernel function of SVM training is selected as Radical Base Function (RBF). And default cross-validation functions and grid iterative search method is used when modelling.

3.3 Experiment result

Table 3 gives that the time (s) and validation accuracy (%) of IDT–LIBSVM and three other algorithms. Figure 1 depicts the training time comparison chart of the above algorithm in different sample sets.

It is clearly observed that the training time of SVM^{light} algorithm increases as the number of samples grows. In addition, IDT–LIBSVM is the greatest among three other methods and with the scale of samples increase, the advantage is more obvious, which indicates that from the perspective of numerical methods, LIBSVM improves the performance of large sample training by introducing the working set reduction, cache technology, convergence proof, and so on [4].

In order to analyze the overall parameters optimization effect, columns with "*" are added in Table 3, which indicates the direct validation accuracy based on the initial tree and initial leaf node classifier. It is easy to observe that the new validation accuracy is enhanced about 2% relative to the original value.

4 Conclusions

DT–SVM trains and tests samples with the same DT could avoid the problem of constructing joint classifier using general data chunking. In this paper, an improved algorithm which can adapt to large-scale data better is presented. Through weakening decision tree, which means only a rough classification of samples with decision tree strategy is implemented; it not only can effectively reduce the time cost in the construction phase, but also help to make full use of concurrent/parallel processing. Meantime, the test-accuracy-rate-oriented joint optimization of SVM parameters and decision tree trimming has ensured the accuracy of the algorithm. Experimental results show that this algorithm can maintain or even slightly better than the accuracy of the original LIBSVM and, at the same time, effectively shortens the training time and improves scalability and practicality of the algorithm for large-scale samples.

References

[1] F. Chang, C. Y. Guo, X. R. Lin, et al., Tree decomposition for large-scale SVM problems. *The Journal of Machine Learning Research*, **9999**, pp. 2935–2972, 2010.

[2] A. K. Menon, *Large-Scale Support Vector Machines: Algorithms and Theory*. University of California, San Diego, pp. 1–17, 2009.

[3] Y. M. Wen, Y. N. Wang, B. L. Lv, et al., Survey of applying support vector machines to handle large-scale problems. *Computer Science*, **36(7)**, pp. 20–27, 2009.

[4] C. C. Chang, C. J. Lin, LIBSVM: a library for support vector machines. *ACM Transactions on Intelligent Systems and Technology (TIST)*, **2(3)**, pp. 27, 2011.

[5] R. E. Fan, K. W. Chang, C. J. Hsieh, et al., LIBLINEAR: a library for large linear classification. *The Journal of Machine Learning Research*, **9**, pp. 1871–1874, 2008.

[6] Q. Xu, S. Geng, A fast SVM classification learning algorithm used to large training set. *Proceedings of the 2012 Second International Conference on Intelligent System Design and Engineering Application*. IEEE Computer Society, Sanya, pp. 15–19, 2012.

[7] W. Anna, Z. Fengyun, L. Yunlu, et al., Research on new reduction strategy of SVM used to large-scale training sample set. *Proceedings of 2011 International Conference on Electronics and Optoelectronics*. IEEE, Dalian, pp. V2-5, 2011.

[8] A. Lopez-Chau, L. L. Garcia, J. Cervantes, et al., Data selection using decision tree for SVM classification. *Proceedings of the 24th International Conference on Tools with Artificial Intelligence*. IEEE, Athens, pp. 742–749, 2012.

[9] J. Cui, Q. Li, Y. Liu, et al., Fast SVM classification method based on the decision tree. *Systems Engineering and Electronics*, **33(11)**, pp. 2558–2563, 2011.

Applied research in water source heat pump system construction based on systems engineering

Bu Zhang, Xiaoli Dai
School of Automation, Northwestern Polytechnical University, Xi'an, China

Abstract

Exploiting and harnessing new resources is one of the most important ways to cope with energy shortage in the light of the energy supply challenges facing China. In this context, this paper, based on the systems engineering theory, first analyzes how the theory is applied to water source heat pump (WSHP) system and then uses the WSHP central air-conditioning project planned for the Culture & Sports Center of Xi'an Daxing New District as a case study, in which a WSHP system was designed in an attempt to save energy and reduce emissions through integrated use of resources.

Keywords: Systems engineering, WSHP, central air-conditioning, construction.

1 Introduction

Since the late 1970s, China has experienced rapid economic and social development with remarkable achievements, but the approaching energy crisis is likely to pose a threat to the development in the future. In view of that, it has become a great necessity to protect the environment and maintain sustainable development while keeping the economy growing in a rapid manner. In order to improve energy efficiency, energy-efficient equipment and technologies should be promoted, and new energy resources should be exploited and harnessed as an important way to cope with the energy crisis.

WIT Transactions on Information and Communication Technologies, Vol. 61, © 2014 WIT Press
www.witpress.com, ISSN 1743-3517 (on-line)
doi:10.2495/MIIT130041

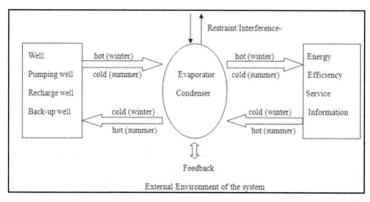

Figure 1: Schematic diagram of the system.

2 Application of systems engineering in a WSHP system

A system is a set of interacting or interdependent components forming an integrated whole, which has particular functions and is part of a larger system. Systems engineering, which is a general approach applicable to all systems, focuses on the organization and management of the design, research, planning, building, test, and use of systems. It is characterized by integration, interconnectivity, objectives, environment, and adaptability [1]. Since the theory took shape, it has been extensively applied in various fields.

A WSHP, which shares all the characteristics of all systems, is an artificial, open, dynamic, and complex system. Like the other systems, the WSHP has the functionality of input, transfer, and output. Input and output functions enable the system to communicate with the external environment and make them become mutually dependent. The basic mode of a WSHP is as shown in Figure 1.

3 A brief introduction to WSHP technology

The groundwater source heat pump technology is to use the low-temperature and low-lying heat resource formed by the solar energy and geothermal energy absorbed by shallow groundwater and transfer it from low to high positions through a power supply at a high electric potential based on the working theory of heat pumps [2]. A groundwater source pump can be an open or a closed system according to different ways to use groundwater. The former draws water from the ground and discharges it directly after it goes through a heat exchanger while the latter is a set of heat exchange tubes that form a closed loop located on one side of the water source.

A WSHP air-conditioning system recharges the groundwater that has gone through the heating/cooling appliance to the stratum from which it was drawn. The quality of the discharged water after heating/cooling is almost the same as that when it was drawn except the temperature. Recharging the water back to the stratum can maintain the quality and amount of groundwater and reduce air

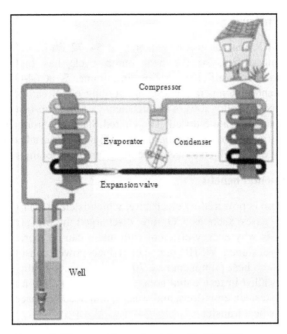

Figure 2: The working principle of a WSHP system.

pollution and energy consumption caused by heating boilers. Therefore, a WSHP air-conditioning system is an energy-efficient and environmental-friendly solution to heating/cooling in compliance with related regulations regarding the use of groundwater. The working principle of the WSHP system is as shown in Figure 2.

4   Advantages and drawbacks of the WSHP system

4.1 Advantages

As it uses surface water as heating/cooling source of air-conditioning units, the WSHP system has the following advantages.

4.1.1 Use of renewable energy

The WSHP system uses the solar energy stored in water on the earth as a heat source (in winter) or a heat sink (in summer) to exchange heat. The water media can be groundwater or water from rivers, lakes, or seas. The earth's surface and water is a huge solar energy container which is able to collect 47% solar energy, more than 500 times of the energy a man consumes each year. This makes it possible to use the almost infinite solar or geothermal energy, which is clean renewable [3].

WIT Transactions on Information and Communication Technologies, Vol. 61, © 2014 WIT Press
www.witpress.com, ISSN 1743-3517 (on-line)

4.1.2 Energy efficiency

The water a WSHP unit can use in winter is at 54–72°F (12–22°C), higher than ambient air temperatures, so the heat pump cycle has higher evaporating temperatures and energy efficiency ratios; in summer is at 64–95°F (18–35°C), lower than ambient air temperatures, so the cooling effect can be better than air cooled condensers or cooling towers and efficiency of the units can be improved as condensing temperatures are reduced. The United States Environmental Protection Agency (EPA) estimates that an appropriately designed and installed WSHP system can help users save 30–40% on costs of operating air-conditioning systems.

4.1.3 Environmental benefit

The WSHP system is powered by electricity, which is clean energy but pollutants and greenhouse gases such as CO_2 are discharged in the process of power generation. That is why energy-efficient equipment can be more environmental-friendly. A well-designed WSHP unit can reduce power consumption by over 30% than air-source heat pumps and by 70% than electric heating. WSHP units, which can be installed in residential areas, produce no pollution as they have no combustion, smokestack emissions, and wastes, and need no space for fuel wastes and long-distance heat transfer.

4.1.4 Wide application scope

The WSHP system, which can be used for heat supply, air-conditioning, and domestic hot water generation, has a wide application scope. Such a system can take the place of both boiler and air-conditioning units/systems. It has obvious advantages, especially for buildings requiring both beating and cooling.

4.2 Drawbacks

As a new solution to heating/cooling, the WSHP system has been full-fledged in terms of technology and can operate well. However, problems may arise when the WSHP heating and/or cooling system is promoted in China because of the following reasons.

4.2.1 Policies toward use of water sources

The Chinese government has enacted the *Water Law of the People's Republic of China*, and each city has also issued their *Regulations for Urban Water Management* in order to protect limited water resources. All polices require approval and charge for water use, but the existing approval standards do not include requirements for the WSHP technology or the like. Therefore, the use of the WSHP system is likely to be restricted when users shall be charged for both drawing and discharging water in some regions even though they get approvals. Moreover, costs and expenses may be increased as there is no universal water charging standards across the nation. In these situations where water charge increased may outnumber cost saved due to energy efficiency, the WSHP system has a comparatively low economical efficiency.

4.2.2 Technology for and costs of water sources identification

The technology for water sources, especially urban water sources identification, should be updated in China. One of the prerequisites to apply the WSHP system is a good knowledge of the local water resources. That means an on-site inspection must be carried out so as to identify where the water is located, if the water is sufficient and whether the ground meets the standards of well-sinking and recharge. To improve technology and reduce costs is considered a way to promote wider application of the WSHP system [4].

4.2.3 Groundwater recharge technology

Recharge must be considered if the WSHP system uses groundwater. Appropriate recharging techniques must be adopted according to local geological conditions.

5   Case study

5.1 Project description

The WSHP central air-conditioning project carried out for the Culture & Sports Center of Xi'an Daxing New District is a typical case. Located in the southeast of the intersection of Daxing East Road and Taoyuan North Road, the Center takes up a total floor area of 26,700 m^2. The project, which involves 8436 m^2, including six floors above the ground and two below, provides air-conditioning and hot water to the buildings by applying the WSHP technology, rather than using municipal heat supply. The Center has great potential to exploit and utilize groundwater as it is situated in an area where massive overdraft has not occurred.

5.2 Design of the WSHP system

5.2.1 Design items

The Center, with an area of 28,000 m^2 for business operation, requires a cooling load of 3120 kW and a heating load of 2496 kW. The central air-conditioning system uses deep groundwater as a heat source in winter and a heat sink in summer, and the WSHP unit provides heating and cooling supply for the buildings. Ten wells need to dug, three for pumping, six for recharge, and one for backup, with a depth range from 80 to 200 m. Each pumping well is expected to produce a water yield of 80 m^3/h, amounting to 240 m^3/h. The project needs a total investment of approximately 13.6 million yuan.

5.2.2 Heating and cooling load estimates

Heating and cooling loads are estimated through a unit floor area load index. The loads of each functional zone are calculated separately according to their specific function, and then total heating and cooling loads can be calculated. It is estimated that the project requires a total cooling load of approximately 2821.75 kW and a heating load of 1988.88 kW. Estimates of each functional zone are given in Table 1.

Table 1: Heating/Cooling Load Estimates.

Functional Zone	Floor Area (m²)	Heating Load Index (W/m²)	Heating Load (kW)	Cooling Load Index (W/m²)	Cooling Load (kW)
Sports and fitness area	3100	150	465.00	240	744.00
Swimming and bathing area	1570	150	235.50	200	314.00
Coffee and tea area	2010	140	281.40	160	321.60
Catering area (not include the staff canteen)	3520	140	492.80	200	704.00
Personal care area	1325	100	132.50	130	172.25
Rest area	1120	100	112.00	130	145.60
Office area	4005	65	260.33	100	400.50
Staff canteen	110	85	9.35	180	19.80
TOTAL	16,760		1988.88		2821.75

5.2.3 Operation and benefit

The system is estimated to consume electric power of 1.6 million yuan each year if running at full capacity. Provided that it depends on heat pump heat recovery and sewage heat collection in 9 months and heat generated by small gas-fired boilers in the other 3 months, it would consume gas of 0.15 million yuan each year. Therefore, the system's annual energy consumption would amount to 1.75 million yuan in total.

If a low-carbon central air-conditioning system is not adopted, a conventional cooling installation would consume power of 1.28 million yuan each year; the Center uses a heat-supply pipe network for heating, which costs 0.77 million yuan. Plus 1.12 million yuan spent on domestic hot water, the total energy expenses would reach 3.17 million yuan. By comparison, the WSHP system is able to save 1.43 million yuan, achieving 45% energy efficiency.

5.3 Benefits of the WSHP system

5.3.1 Energy efficiency

The WSHP system can help Xi'an enhance socioeconomic efficiency through optimizing resource allocation and adopting energy-efficient equipment with advanced technologies. When the WSHP system is built, it is expected to save

2.6 kg/a·m^2 coal and reduce CO_2 emission by 7.09 kg/a·m^2 while SO_2, smokestack, and NO_X by 0.1 kg/a·m^2, respectively.

5.3.2 Water resources conservation

The WSHP system is a new technique which uses heat contained in groundwater for heating and/or cooling and recharges the water back to the ground after heat exchange. The whole process usually does no harm to water quality and causes little effect on annual average water temperature and level, since the heat exchange and water transfer are done in closed pipelines without solute exchange.

6 Conclusion and suggestions

The WSHP system, as a kind of energy-saving application, only consumes half of the energy used by conventional systems, achieving approximately 45% energy efficiency. However, the system has not received strong support from the Chinese government and faces the problem of sizable one-time investment. In order to promote the wide application of the system in construction projects, three suggestions are put forward as follows.

6.1 More government support for energy-efficient technologies

Today the Chinese government has devoted much effort to application of energy-efficient technologies. For example, projects adopting energy-saving technologies will be given special financial support. However, companies are unwilling to increase investment in such technologies since their upfront investments often far outnumber the government support. That's why application of the WSHP system is restricted. The government should provide more support for use of new energy resources and energy-efficient facilities while making policies for application of energy-saving practices in construction projects.

6.2 Reducing cost through further research

Reducing cost is a key way to promote application of the WSHP system since returns on sizable upfront investments will not come until a few years later. Since the application of the WSHP technology is at an initial stage in China with considerable untapped potential, institutes for WSHP research should redouble their efforts to facilitate wide application of the technology at lower cost.

6.3 Technology promotion

The government should make policies to encourage use of the WSHP system according to the development demand of each city in view of the high energy efficiency and low carbon emission the system can bring. Wide application of the technology to urban construction can facilitate in building green cities, saving energy and reducing emissions, and improving the environment to the long-term benefit of urban development.

WIT Transactions on Information and Communication Technologies, Vol. 61, © 2014 WIT Press
www.witpress.com, ISSN 1743-3517 (on-line)

References

[1] D. Q. Zhou, *An Introduction to Systems Engineering*. Science Press, Beijing, pp. 50–55, 2011.
[2] X. Y. Wang & S. G. Shi, Principles and application of water source heat pumps. *Fujian Building Materials*, **28(2)**, pp. 88–89, 2009.
[3] C. Wu & S. J. You, Engineering application of water source heat pumps to office buildings. *Gas and Heat*, **27(3)**, pp. 58–60, 2007.
[4] Q. C. Zhao, The application prospect of water source heat pumps and problems. *Sci-Tech Information Development and Economy*, **16(16)**, pp. 245–246, 2006.

Research and design of culture decision support system

Fulian Yin[1], Jianping Chai[1], Hanlei Wang[1], Jiecong Lin[2]
[1]*Information Engineering School, Communication University of China, Beijing, China*
[2]*Beijing Institute of Computer Application, Beijing, China*

Abstract

A decision support system (DSS) for culture is proposed in this paper. It combines the intelligence of people and the ability of computer. Its configuration is divided into consumer layer, business layer, application layer, and data layer, which includes data base, model base, method base, and knowledge base. The culture DSS is a computer system to help national culture macroscopic decision department to enhance culture decision quality.

Keywords: Decision support system, culture; data base, model base, method base, knowledge base.

1 Introduction

Decision support system (DSS) [1,2] was originated in the 1970s by American scientist Keen and Scott Morton. Then it had a great development in the 1980s. Now, it has developed from traditional DSS with three bases which are data base, model base, method base to four bases which are data base, model base, method base, and knowledge base. Furthermore, new DSS developed to a novel DSS which consists of data warehouse, online analytical processing, and data mining. Its typical feature is to get information which could assist making decisions from a large amount of data.

DSS becomes more and more imperative with high standard of unified business, scientific decision, and efficient management which based on accurate data. It has been used in a wide range of area such as insurance, investment industry, enterprise operation, securities industry, and so on. Especially, for the area of telecommunication, DSS has already matured as the most important part

WIT Transactions on Information and Communication Technologies, Vol. 61, © 2014 WIT Press
www.witpress.com, ISSN 1743-3517 (on-line)
doi:10.2495/MIIT130051

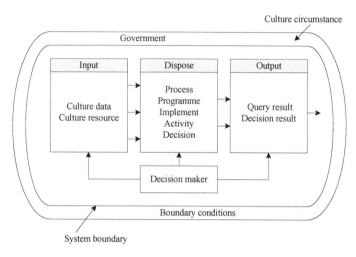

Figure 1: Overall design on culture DSS.

of Business and operation support system (BOSS) [3]. Besides, with the accelerated steps to "integration of three networks," broadcasting and television DSS has been developing steadily [4].

Nowadays, culture exchanges frequently all over the world. So, how to maintain the security and enhance the soft ability of national culture becomes more and more essential with the difference of thinking activity [5,6]. At present, the blank of DSS in culture area has not been filled. In order to solve the problem of prospective of culture development strategy, policies and regulations, and so on, this paper proposes a culture DSS and introduces its configuration with consumer layer, business layer, application layer, and data layer.

2 The configuration of culture decision support system

The outer environment of culture DSS is very complex. The manpower shortage and the material shortage used for scientific support calls prospective and systematic research of culture development strategy and policy. The quick feedback for new culture, the foresight for cultural trend, and the reply for the emergency response should also be considered. Besides, effective data collection, analysis, investigation and research will affect the scientific nature, democracy, and maneuverability seriously. To design the architecture of that, this paper only considers the boundary conditions which service for government only. The proposed culture DSS is a software application system to do structured, half-structured, and nonstructured decision by demand analysis with relative data, model, method, and knowledge. Figure 1 gives the basic idea of configuration design on culture DSS.

There are three indispensable parts of culture DSS. The first part of that is input which means a wide variety of culture data and culture resource. Then, the

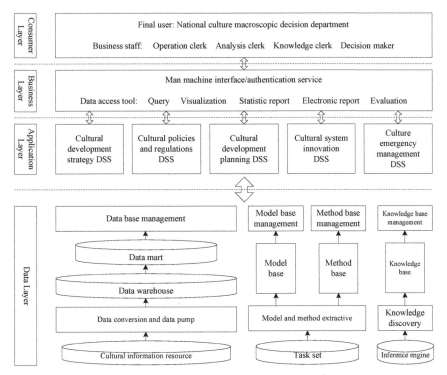

Figure 2: The configuration of culture DSS.

ultimate goal of that is to give service using the block of dispose. Finally is the output such as query result and decision result.

In accordance with the basic idea of overall design, the configuration of culture DSS analyzes the government demand with relevant data, model, method, and knowledge to realize service through man–computer interaction. The most important function of culture DSS is to transmit information after analysis and decision for final users and business staffs. As shown in Figure 2, the configuration of culture DSS consists of four layers which are access layer, business layer, application layer, and data layer.

2.1 Consumer layer

Consumer layer is the user and the operator for culture DSS. Here, it's divided into final user which considers the national culture macroscopic decision department only, and the business staffs who include operation clerk, analysis clerk, knowledge clerk, and decision maker. Wherein, business layer is the only interface between consumers and decision support system. The consumers select the decision problem and control the decision support system by business layer only. Simultaneously, the system allows inputting necessary information by consumers.

2.2 Business layer

Business layer is the important and the only display form for culture DSS. On the one hand, it controls the man–machine interface and discusses the authentication service. For final consumer user and business staff, each consumer has some special demands. So, the business layer offers different access tools such as query, visualization, statistic report, electronic report, and evaluation.

2.3 Application layer

Application layer is the core embodiment of problems that can be supported by culture DSS. The DSS service is divided into five parts which are culture development strategy DSS, cultural policies and regulations DSS, cultural development planning DSS, cultural system innovation DSS and culture emergency management DSS. And each part could contain some use cases itself.

2.4 Data layer

Data layer is the core of use case solving for culture DSS which consists of data base management, model base management, method base management, and knowledge base management supported by data base, model base, method base, and knowledge base. Especially, each use case has a corresponding model type which includes a set of unique methods and knowledge for that solution. So, model is the most hardly gettable part, and method and knowledge are the spirit.

3 The data base of culture decision support system

The data base not only collects the original data, but also stores the processed data to create data base. Figure 3 gives the data base of culture DSS. There are some characteristics for the data base of national culture macroscopic DSS, such as subject orientation, integration, time variable, nonvolatile, summarization, nonstandardized, and so on.

As shown in Figure 3, cultural information resources are obtained from the form of handiwork data, cultural media data, cultural text data, and culture regulation data through source data pretreatment and data format check. Especially, data warehouse and data mart are two important parts of data base. And, data mart is the subset of data warehouse by data conversion and data pump. Here, data mart includes a only single subject such as important speech and report library, cultural policies and regulation library, cultural development planning library, cultural system innovation library, cultural development strategy library, cultural industry library, public culture service library, cultural heritage library, foreign culture library, national culture security library, literature library, cultural audio library, and cultural video library.

Figure 4 gives the data processing of data warehouse for culture DSS. To form data warehouse, the cultural data prepared should be selected, extracted, converted, integrated, and maintained sequentially. The data warehouse could

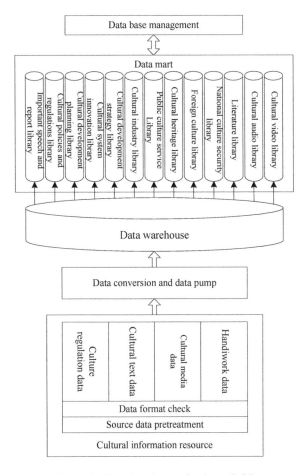

Figure 3: The data base of culture DSS.

already be used by report for final user and business staff. Furthermore, data mart is extracted by copying a specific meaning part of data warehouse. It is stressed that, metadata is very important for culture DSS. It should accord the rule of data warehouse, could be derived from one data to another data, and also would be modified easily with the changes of environment.

4　The model base and method base of culture decision support system

The proposed culture DSS is a software application system to do structured, half-structured, and nonstructured decision by consumer demand analysis with relative data, model, method, and information. This paper builds a model base of culture DSS as shown in Figure 5. There are three parts to follow in this architecture. At the stage of gathering information, building the model base includes organization

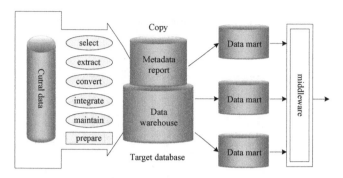

Figure 4: The data processing of data warehouse for culture DSS.

goal, search procedure, cultural data gathering, question identification, question of ownership, question classification, and question solving. Then, at the stage of designing, building the model base should process model, set standard, search scheme, and even predict consequence. Besides, at the stage of choosing, building the model base should find the model, do sensitive analysis, select the best scheme, and execute plan. This model has already feedback mechanism to optimize the change of external environment.

The methods in method base are corresponded to the models in model base. But, in order to make the theory clearly, method base is isolated of model base, as shown in Figure 2.

5 The knowledge base of culture decision support system

Besides data base, model base, and method base, knowledge base is another spirit of culture DSS. To solve the structured demand, method base is used to store the fixed arithmetic without human factor. But for half-structured demand and nonstructured demand, there exists a certain rule or absolutely no rule to follow. Their determination is hold by the wisdom, instinct, sense, in sight, and so on of culture final user and business staff.

Figure 6 gives the knowledge base of culture DSS. The idea of cultural expert is stored to knowledge base by knowledge obtaining and then converted to computer knowledge base by coding. So, the computer knowledge could finally be used by cultural decision maker through expert tool. Besides, knowledge engineer is an important technical person for each step of above by advice, collect, edit, manage, validate, educate, and so on.

Besides data base, model base, and method base, knowledge base is another spirit of culture DSS. To solve the structured demand, method base is used to store the fixed arithmetic without human factor. But for half-structured demand and nonstructured demand, there exists a certain rule or absolutely no rule to follow. Their determination is hold by the wisdom, instinct, sense, in sight, and so on of culture final user and business staff.

Figure 6 gives the knowledge base of culture DSS. The idea of cultural expert is stored to knowledge base by knowledge obtaining and then converted to

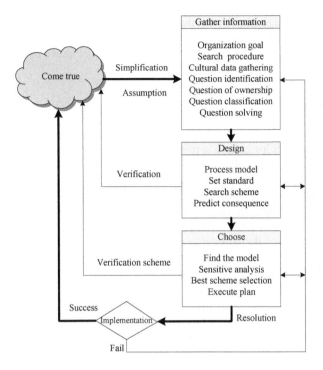

Figure 5: The data processing of data warehouse for culture DSS.

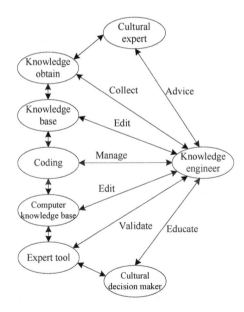

Figure 6: The knowledge base of culture DSS.

\computer knowledge base by coding. So, the computer knowledge could finally be used by cultural decision maker through expert tool. Besides, knowledge engineer is an important technical person for each step of above by advice, collect, edit, manage, validate, educate, and so on.

6 Conclusions

Under the background of emergent security demand and strategy institute requirement, a DSS for culture is proposed in this paper. Then, this paper designs the configuration of culture DSS and introduces each part of that. Its configuration is divided into consumer layer, business layer, application layer, and data layer. Especially, the data layer is composed of data base, model base, method base, and knowledge base. The proposed culture DSS combines the intelligence of people and the ability of computer to help the national culture macroscopic decision department.

Acknowledgments

Fulian Yin and Xi Jiang would like to thank the State Administration of Radio, Film, and Television and the Communication University of China. The views, opinions, and/or findings contained in this paper are those of the authors and should not be interpreted as representing the official views or policies, either expressed or implied.

References

[1] F. G. Zhou, B. R. Yang, L. N. Li, et al., Overview of the new types of intelligent decision support system. *2008 3rd International Conference on Innovative Computing Information and Control*, Dalian. Liaoning, pp. 267–270, 2008.
[2] A. H. Marion, Sustainable decision making: the role of decision support systems. *IEEE Transactions on Systems, Man, and Cybernetics, Part C: Applications and Reviews*, **29(3)**, pp. 395–408, 1999.
[3] A. Schuster, R. Sterritt, K. Adamson, et al., Towards a decision support system for automated testing of complex telecommunication networks. *2000 IEEE International Conference on Systems, Man, and Cybernetics*, Nashville, pp. 2002–2006, 2002.
[4] F. L. Yin, J. P. Chai, Research and design of broadcasting and television decision support system. *2011 International Conference on Management and Service Science*, Xian. Shanxi, pp. 1–4, 2011.
[5] J. R. Landry, Culture and the formalization of organizational decision support systems. *Proceedings of the Twenty-Eighth Hawaii International Conference on System Sciences*, pp. 913–916, 1995.
[6] D. L. Xu, D. Ruan, J. B. Yang, Supporting nuclear safety culture assessment using Intelligent Decision System software. *2011 IEEE Symposium on Computational Intelligence in Multicriteria Decision Making*, pp. 67–72, 2011.

Problems and solutions in the informatization construction of e-government in China

Zhiming Lin
Provincial Spatial Information Engineering Research Center, Fuzhou University, Fuzhou China; Zhicheng College, Fuzhou University, Fuzhou, China; School of Public Administration, Fuzhou University, Fuzhou, China

Abstract

The paper makes a summary of the achievements and core problems on the practice of the e-government project in China that has been implemented for more than a decade. For example, the starting point of e-government informatization construction, predominating direction, "digital divide" issue as well as its solutions. In the end, it points out the four basic contents of e-government construction and their correlations, which indicate the directions for the current construction of Chinese e-government.
Keywords: e-government, informatization, digital divide, solutions.

1 Introduction

E-government prefers to a process where the government departments achieve goals like the digitalization of administration information, publication of government affairs, and networking of government services with advanced electronic information technology. From the method point of view, it is also a process of optimization, integration, and reorganization of its internal managements and service functions for government. With the help of modern network communication technology and computer technology, the process should be realized on the Internet with high efficiency and break the restrictions of time and space, lightening the closure between departments and providing the public and itself with integrated managements and services that are of high efficiency, superior quality, and political honest [1].

WIT Transactions on Information and Communication Technologies, Vol. 61, © 2014 WIT Press
www.witpress.com, ISSN 1743-3517 (on-line)
doi:10.2495/MIIT130061

E-government usually consists of three parts. The first is the electronization and networking of office functions of government departments. The second is the instant and interconnected sharing of information between functional departments realized by computer network. The third is the bidirectional exchange of information and policies between government and enterprises and the public achieved by network. The last one is the outward manifestation of the success or failure of e-government, which is based on the efficiency of the former aspects and the effectiveness of information communication. Therefore, a high efficient e-government system should be an organic integration of the three parts above [2].

The practical experience of this project in over 10 years indicates that the most difficult and complicated problem is the achievement of government public platform and success of information exchange. In order to realize "one-stop" service that facilitates enterprises and residents, all the projects on government administration are working with all graded departments. It has become almost the toughest challenge for the projects to remove the varied hedges and obstacles that exist not only between departments but also between the central and local governments. At present, people have been aware of this problem, but still lack the solutions that can truly resolve it.

2 The achievements of informatization construction of Chinese government administration

2.1 The content of government websites have been increasingly rich and the interactive effectiveness has been more significant

In recent years, most of the government websites have offered specific services based on the hot political topics at home and abroad [3]. They have paid much attention and high sensitiveness to events such as WenChuan earthquake, 2012 Olympic, moon project, food safety, and financial crisis. It has become a trend for the online service website construction of governments at all levels to provide practical and customized services. The interactive contents have been more close to the public demands, and the communication effectiveness has been more significant. With more government collections of public opinion and help on the events and problems that win extensive public attention, more and more people now regard government websites as their first channels to communicate with governments. The popularizing rate of government websites has been further increased, services have been further deepened, and service quality has also been greatly improved [4].

2.2 The development, utilization, and sharing of information resources of government administration have increasingly gained new achievements

With available resources, local governments have set up several systems for local information exchange. They have also established sharing platform, catalog system, exchange system, and service system for information exchange of government administration.

2.3 The groundworks of e-government have been further enhanced

The management system of information and resources of government administration has been further improved, which has strengthened the managements of links such as collection, register, filing, storage, sharing, and security of government administration information, and ensured their authenticity, veracity, completeness, and promptness.

Generally speaking, the construction and application of e-government have entered from the starting-up phase to reintegration phase. The reintegration phase consists of three aspects. The first is the vertical integration of vertical industrial system. The second is the horizontal integration of local governments. The third is the integration of the vertical system and its subordinated department systems. With the three aspects, we can realize the communication between governments at all levels and achieve the organic combination of departments, organizations, and branches.

3 Important basic issues that should be solved in e-government construction

3.1 E-government should have public demands as their starting points

It is an issue of cognition whether to have management functions or public demands as the starting points of e-government. At present, the construction of comprehensive e-government is just in its preliminary stage. Many state leaders haven't fully understood its operating mechanisms, modes, and functions. From the angle of their managements, government departments just set about the construction of vertical industrial management system from the highest to the lowest and simply copy the former approved projects and put them on the Internet. As a result, all the systems are separated and enclosed to each other, forming an electronic framework of e-government that is centered on self-function and dominated by vertical industrial management system. It will give rise to new obstacles and deepen "digital divide" and put more emphasis on partial department interests. It will be difficult for local governments to manage harmoniously and is a burden for enterprises and people. Therefore, when developing e-government, government departments must be clear about its working thinking and modes and strengthen their cooperation and resource sharing.

With emphasis on its application and means of network, the essence of e-government should center on its users and serve for the convenience of people. Traditional working mode of government focuses on its departments and functions. Enterprise and people must totally rely on government departments. If they need to do some business, they must understand the functions and limitations of departments, go to them one by one, and repeatedly submit materials for approval. For the approval of an enterprise, dozens of materials will be needed. People must work around all the departments and spend at least several months to have dozens of seals. We can't imagine the efficiency.

Therefore, the new working mode of e-government must center on its users and base itself on public demands. Government must truly regard enterprises and people as its service and management objects. To the public, government must be a unified whole and window. When the public make a business request based on their own demands, they just need to fill in the materials and submit to the "virtual electronic government" on the Internet after inquiring and understanding the related laws and regulations. The virtual government should automatically hand out the materials to corresponding departments for graded and departmental approvals within the required time. The public don't need to know the settings and divisions of those departments, either the responsible departments or persons. However, they should be able to check anytime on the Internet the state and feedbacks of the approval. They don't need to go from department to department personally, so the time needed will be greatly lessened. In this way, we can not only increase efficiency and facilitate users, but also greatly help to alleviate corruptions.

3.2 The informatization construction of government affairs should be centered on horizontal regional management system

It is an issue of much dispute whether the informatization construction of government administration should be centered on horizontal regional management system or vertical industrial management system. In order to realize real e-government, government departments can't just start from their management functions, run websites, and simply focus on vertical industrial management system. Instead, they should base themselves on public demands, pay attention to the reorganization, optimization, and upgradation of their functions and realize "one-stop" networking services subordinated by horizontal regional management system [5].

E-government construction must be coordinated with reforms on government departments and personnel system. China's economic system has seen 20 years of reforms and openness, and has achieved a lot by the transformation from planned economy to market economy. As national base, economic development must call for reforms on administrative management system which is the superstructure. Because of that, reform direction of Chinese government must be changed from industrial management system to regional management system to adjust to the development of market economy. Similarly, e-government system must also be dominated by regional management system. That is to say, we must set up horizontal regional platforms for government administration that are open to users and connected between government units.

In terms of resource and data sharing and the reduction of repeated construction costs, if we center on industrial management system, there will be huge waste of resource caused by repeated constructions [6]. For example, a city has 70 ministries and commissions, and each unit is to establish its vertical industrial system in 5 regions, 8 counties, and 1 city (14 in total). That means, a city must set up over $940\times(70\times14)$ network information exchange platforms. As a result, overall network system will be as complicated as spider web. Huge resource wastes and new burdens for operation and maintenance will be caused, which will make it almost impossible to share and exchange data between different departments. On the contrary, if we adopt regional system and set up platforms for industrial sharing, we only need to establish 84×(70+14) information network systems, which count only 8.9% of the former one. Therefore, regional system can not only save considerable investments, but also help realize real e-government.

3.3 E-government construction must pay attention to the reduction and elimination of "digital divide"

According to World Bank, "digital divide" refers to the gap between the rich and the poor in different counties, different regions in the same country, or different social groups (on the basis of their different occupations, ages, sexes, education statuses, and income levels) in the following three aspects [2]:

(i) *input gap*: the gap between different action subjects on their utilization and bearing capacity of information and telecommunication infrastructure;

(ii) electronic preparation gap: the gap between different action subjects on their electronic preparations, electronic consciousness as well as their ability on electronic reading and writing;

(iii) application gap: the gap between different governments and enterprises on the validity of their usages of information and telecommunication technology.

With the deepening of e-government, it will become possible to further the "Matthew Effect" distributed by society, because people who are most in need of government services are usually socially vulnerable groups that have no access to the Internet and hi-tech means. The imbalance of economic development and differences on software and hardware environments will prevent the low-income families from using technological tools and share "public goods" provided by e-government. If the issue of "digital divide" can't be solved appropriately, the strong will get stronger while the weak will get weaker, and the gap on the possession of information and resources will be further deepened [7]. Therefore, how to narrow the "digital divide" in e-government construction is of profound theoretical significance and great practical meaning in the care about vulnerable groups and promotion of economic development in less developed areas.

The "digital divide" in our e-government construction is shown in both horizontal and vertical aspects. The former means the difference on regional levels of e-government constructions while the latter refers to the difference on e-government construction levels between different graded departments. Based on the data in the performance evaluation reports of Chinese government websites in recent years, this paper makes some analyses and refinements of "digital divide" in this two aspects. For local governments, their websites are the windows for them to serve enterprises and people. To a great extent, they also stand for their levels of e-government. Horizontally speaking, the performances

of eastern provincial websites are the best, then the middle ones, the west ones are the worst. The average website performance in eastern area is 1.4 times of that in western area. The development level of government website is related to the level of its local economy and social development. The more developed the region is, the more investments will be guaranteed. People's understanding toward
e-government will be more profound and enterprises and people's demands for government services will be stronger. Vertically speaking, performances of Chinese government websites are generally low and are all in their preliminary stage. There are huge gaps between provincial websites, municipal websites, and county websites. Provincial website performances rank first while the county ones rank last. Speaking of online business index, there are significant gaps between different graded government websites. From ministry and commission to province, city and county, performances are gradually getting poorer. All of these indicate that "digital divide" in e-government construction is real and obvious.

Eliminating "separations between different organizations and branches" and "digital island" in government informatization and realizing the coordinated informatization development of government departments are effective ways to narrow the "digital divide" in China. At the moment, government departments that performance well in informatization are all digitally strong. Those departments, with the opportunities to firstly establish vertical information systems take the lead in conducting digital explorations and have gained great achievements. But from the angle of government, no department is unimportant; they are all responsible for management and service. Any link going wrong can be a symbol of irresponsibility for people. With the deepening of informatization, the reorganization of government process and their connections and communications are becoming increasingly important. If we leave "digital divide" free between any departments, one day we will have to pay the price. In face with organization, organization and branch separation and "digital island" in government informatization, we must take measures to minimize the functions of vertical information system as fast as we can. We should strengthen the connections and communications between website information and keep pace with government informatization.

4 The four basic contents of e-government construction and their correlations must be based on our national conditions

The four basic contents of the construction of e-government system are network platform system, business application software system, data and information, and administrative management system [8]. With limited resource investments, the first one should consider how to construct a high-speed, efficient, secure, and manageable network platform system and how to make full use of varied resources. Because of the rapid development of hardware technology and the frequent upgrades of products, we can't expect to set up a platform that won't fall behind for long. We must make it clear that platform construction must firstly be able to meet the demands of the normal operation of business application software system and be based on some foresight in equipment purchases. The construction of business application software system is the core of the whole construction of e-government system, which is a process of long-term development and constant improvements. Therefore, as for development platforms and tools, we must adopt national standard techniques and mainstream tools to ensure that software applications can get constant upgrades and improvements with the development of technology, and joint development can be obtained with the latest and most advanced achievements of informatization development technology.

The key emphasis in the work of data and information lie in the research on the collection and input of basic data (initialized databases such as code and standards) in the application system. While problems such as what data are needed in the system operation, how to have prompt and accurate access to them, who is responsible for their collection and input, or who is in charge of the supervision, inspection and evaluation are the ones that should be solved by administrative management system.

The mutual relations between the four basic contents can be manifested by a vivid metaphor. The network is like a road, while application software is the car; databases are the goods in the car while administrative management system is the integration of traffic rules. The road can't play its role without the car, and goods are also indispensable even there has been road and car. Therefore, we should focus on the collection of basic information, specify the administrative management system, and ensure prompt, accurate, and correct input to the network of various information needed by application system. Only in this way, network information system can fully play its role. Moreover, without the cooperation of manpower, no system can play its part, no matter how well it is constructed. But the manpower in the system operation should be normalized by specific rules and regulations. Therefore, we must focus on institution construction.

5 Conclusion

In the current phase, government departments have generally paid too much attention to hardware, electronization, and reconstruction, and ignored software, government administration, integration in the informatization construction of government administration, and its application. Limited by institutional factors, informatization in each department is putting restrictions on the improvement of government public services, "information island" and "digital divide" that confront e-government are the witnesses. So the development of our e-government must be of systematic opinion and take the path of integration. From the content point of view, by obtainment, collection, processing, and application of information, e-government must effectively complete its business functions and office procedures, and consciously choose the construction orbit that has more emphasis on the combination of software and hardware and their coordinated development. That is to say, we must effect an overall design and a development and application system by means of business demands, data and information, software applications and their platforms, development tools, and network hardware platforms.

Acknowledgments

The research work was supported by National High Technology Research and Development Program of China (863 projects) under Grant No. SS2012AA120208 and Class A Foundation of Science and Technology in the education department in Fujian Province under Grant No. JA13358.

References

[1] Y. Wang, L. Xu, *E-government theory and practice*. Beijing: Tsinghua University Press, pp. 13–18, 2004.

[2] X.B. Li, *E-government and government management innovation*. Beijing: Science Press, pp. 36–40, 2004.

[3] S.Z. Tao, S.Y. Wang, Problems and solutions research in China's e-government legislation present. *China Information Guides*, **27(3)**, pp. 58–61, 2007.

[4] X.D. Yang, Z.X. Liu, Problems and suggestions of our country e-government gateway website construction. *E-Government*, **7(3)**, pp. 51–59, 2007.

[5] Z.C. Li, The latest development of e-government in Europe. *Beijing Archives*, **5(10)**, pp. 46–47, 2008.

[6] Y.K. Wang, The Chinese government informatization and e-government. *Public Administration Science*, **8(5)**, pp. 54–56, 2003.

[7] L. Jin, G.J. Shu, Our country e-government development situation and countermeasure research. *Mongolia Science and Technology and Economy*, **3(6)**, pp. 76–80, 2008.

[8] R.Y. Cai, J.W. Chu, Research and enlightenment about foreign government information resources construction. *Journal of Agricultural Information*, **9(1)**, pp. 34–36, 2009.

Confirmation and application of network communication layer theory

Pengyu Ding[1], Shujun Ye[1], Jiaji Hu[2]
School of Economics and Management, Beijing Jiaotong University, Beijing, China
School of Science, Beijing Jiaotong University, Beijing, China

Abstract

As a way of communication, network communication can also be stratified. Network communication layer theory defines four layers network communication, which are spread appealing layer, share appealing layer, emotion appealing layer, and value appealing layer. The paper confirmed the theory through direct visit and questionnaire survey. The study of the network communication layer theory has practical significance. The theory can be applied to assist companies and individuals use the network, to provide research ideas in related areas, and to guide the standardization of the Internet environment.

Keywords: network communication, the model of network communication layer, model validation, survey.

1 Introduction

With the development of network technology, network has a growing influence on human's lifestyle and communication behavior. Network communication refers to communicating on the Internet via text, audio, images, and other multimedia. The research for the network communication in foreign countries is earlier than China, and the famous network sociologists Howard Rheingold was among the pioneers to observe and investigate into online communication. Researches about the network communication focus mainly on network communication language itself and the compare with other communication language [1,2], network communication form [3], the influences on the organization communication behavior [4], the influences on people's lifestyle [5].

 WIT Transactions on Information and Communication Technologies, Vol. 61, © 2014 WIT Press
www.witpress.com, ISSN 1743-3517 (on-line)
doi:10.2495/MIIT130071

This paper argues that the network communication has all the general characteristics of communication. So the network communication has different levels, the same as normal communication. Based on this understanding, the paper puts forward the network communication layer theory and confirmed the theory through direct visit and questionnaire survey. In the end, the paper suggests the study of the network communication layer theory has practical significance. The theory can be applied to assist companies and individuals use the network, to provide research ideas in related areas, and to guide the standardization of the Internet environment.

2 The introduction of the network communication layer theory

The main ideas of the network communication layer theory are network communication has different levels, which are divided into spread appealing layer, share appealing layer, emotional appealing layer, and valve appealing layer. Network communication platform has five representative characteristics, namely, audience, share, communicate, alternative, and guidance. When these four network communication levels correspond to network communication platform, they display different characteristics. We will introduce the network communication layer theory in detail, the lower solution based on interpolation.

2.1 Spread appealing layer

Spread appealing layer is the lowest level of communication, which concerns mainly if the information can be delivered effectively. The information dissemination tends to be one-way and large scope. This layer has demonstrated outstanding performance in audience and guidance.

2.2 Share appealing layer

In share appealing layer, people not only exchange information, but also share personal ideas and judgment. This layer focuses on the interactivity of information, and it is strong in audience and communication.

2.3 Emotional appealing layer

In the emotional appealing layer, communicators share their feelings, emotions, and desires, thus affecting personal likes and dislikes. This layer is relatively outstanding in share and alternative.

2.4 Valve appealing layer

The valve appealing layer is the highest level of communication. It refers to the situation where the communicators reach a high degree of consensus which affect their personal judgment and understanding of things. It can be based on one-way or bidirectional communication. The layer is prominent in share, alternative, and guidance.

Table 1: Network Communication Layers and Network Communication Platform Features Relation Diagram.

Network Communication Platform / Network Communication Layers Features	Audience	Share	Communicative	Alternative	Guidance
Spread appealing layer	√				√
Share appealing layer	√		√		
Emotional appealing layer		√		√	
Valve appealing layer		√		√	√

3 Confirmation of network communication layer theory

This paper designed two methods to confirm the network communication layer theory. First, we visit professionals in related fields and collect dates according to the visit; second, we sample 1000 experiences for satisfaction survey and verify model according to public feedback results.

3.1 Targeted survey

The paper chooses four relative fields according to the four network communication layers, and interviews 254 professionals in these four fields. The requirement of the survey is getting the understanding of the professionals about the characteristics of network communication platforms, and score audience, share, communicative, alternative, guidance.

We collect data according to the result of visiting survey, and calculate mean, concentration, variance of the scores of selected 12 network communication platforms. Next, we compare the score with the data from the original model database. The computation formula is: deviation=(survey score − standard)/full range.

The result is given in Table 2.

From Table2 we find spread appealing layer is outstanding in audience and guidance; share appealing layer is strong in audience and communication; emotional appealing layer relatively outstanding in share and alternative; valve appealing layer is prominent in share, alternative, and guidance. All the variance is controlled in 0.25, which stand for a high data concentration in all levels .The above results agree with the original model basically.

3.2 Satisfaction survey

The survey, based on the previous one, is designed to identify the practicality of the network communication layer theory. The post-election survey sample size

Table 2: Scoring Statistics.

	Item	Audience Mean	Audience Dev.%	Share Mean	Share Dev.%	Communicative Mean	Communicative Dev.%	Alternative Mean	Alternative Dev.%	Guidance Mean	Guidance Dev.%
Spread appealing layer	126 mailbox	4.2	2.00	1.3	3.00	-2.7	3.00	1.3	3.00	-3.1	-1.00
	Sina	4.3	3.00	-2.85	1.50	-3.9	1.00	2.23	2.30	-1.94	0.60
	Sohu	3.4	4.00	-2.89	1.10	-3.79	2.10	1.19	1.90	-1.79	2.10
	Ganjicom	2.3	-7.00	-1.2	-2.00	-2.4	-4.00	1.9	-1.00	1.4	4.00
Share appealing layer	QQ	3.7	-3.00	1.22	2.20	4.12	1.20	-2.88	1.20	-2.92	0.80
	Tianya	3.4	4.00	-1.8	2.00	2.9	-1.00	-1.1	-1.00	-1.1	-1.00
	Mop	2.1	1.00	-0.9	1.00	2.19	1.90	-0.76	2.40	-0.78	2.20
	Zhixing	2.5	5.00	1.15	1.50	2.22	2.20	0.13	0.30	1.21	2.10
Emotional appealing layer	Q-Zone	-2.3	-3.00	2.17	1.70	1.07	0.70	1.1	1.00	3.09	0.90
	Renren	-0.8	2.00	2.23	2.30	2.18	1.80	1.09	0.90	4.21	2.10
	MicroBlog	0.6	0.30	3.16	1.60	2.21	2.10	1.23	2.30	4.25	2.50
	Douban	-2.1	-1.00	2.15	1.50	1.24	2.40	1.24	2.40	3.08	0.80
Valve appealing layer	QQ group	-2.5	-5.00	3.22	2.20	1.15	1.50	3.11	1.10	4.15	1.50
	Mtime	-2.8	2.00	3.22	2.20	-1.83	1.70	4.12	1.20	3.07	0.70
	Niubo nets	-3.7	3.00	4.17	1.70	-2.82	1.80	4.21	2.10	2.16	1.60
	FacebookPage	-2.4	-4.00	3.2	2.00	-0.82	1.80	4.2	2.00	3.14	1.40

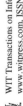WIT Transactions on Information and Communication Technologies, Vol. 61, © 2014 WIT Press
www.witpress.com, ISSN 1743-3517 (on-line)

was 1000. To ensure sampling of the survey, the survey sample included a large age span and a comprehensive income levels, and the social background of the survey was variable.

Table 3: Distribution of the Sample.

		Quantity	Proportion (%)
Sex	M	475	47.53
	F	525	52.47
Age	Under 10	54	5.37
	10–19	181	18.13
	21–25	285	28.53
	26–30	254	25.40
	31–40	108	10.77
	41–50	45	4.47
	50–59	42	4.23
	Older than 60	30	3.00
Monthly income	0	153	15.27
	Under 500	73	7.27
	501–1000	124	12.37
	1001–2000	172	17.23
	2001–3000	167	16.67
	3001–4000	98	9.77
	4001–5000	80	8.03
	5001–8000	75	7.47
	Older than 8000	59	5.87
Job occupation	Students	189	18.87
	Civil service	82	8.17
	Managers	34	3.40
	staff of a company	113	11.27
	Engineer	75	7.47
	Migrant workers	99	9.93
	Workers	123	12.30
	Freelance	86	8.57
	Farmers	59	5.90
	Retirees	46	4.60
	Unemployed	29	2.87
	Others	67	6.67
Education	Primary and below	64	6.40
	Junior school	95	9.47
	Senior school	164	16.37
	College	232	23.23
	Undergraduate	316	31.57
	Graduate and above	130	12.97

The survey consists of four phases:

(1) *Call for experiencers*: The first phase of the survey is to release the news of calling for experiencers by telephone, text messaging, e-mail, etc. to and aggregate the number of applicants.
(2) *Collect the demand information*: In this stage, information of experiencers called from different channels was collected sorted. The information collected includes the needs of experiencers (i.e., those who want to experience how the network platform for information exchange), the score given by the experiencers under the guidance of experience in the understanding of the five characteristics of elements (of the audience share of exchangeability, alternative, guidance).
(3) *Recommended platform*: Based on the information gathered in the stage before, the best match network communication platform determined by the network communication layer theory will be sent in time to the experiencers for a week long experience.
(4) *Feedback information collection and data analysis*: To grant the uniform experience of feedback comments, the evaluation of satisfaction will be analyzed to examine whether the platform recommended is met by the requirements of Internet users and to bring their constructive comments.

We can also see the users of the model also affirmed the constructive comments, showing that the network communication layer theory facilitates the Internet users to make constructive recommends on the use of the Internet, thus to verify the correctness of the theory. At the same time, they can still see several improvements to be made, which are summarized as follows:

(1) The model should be updated timely. Network communication platforms are growing very fast. In the two-month investigation of the model update process, we find that we need timely follow-up to become a more detailed split system required by the continued expansion of the platform functionality.
(2) Database and the corresponding software or network support will further optimize the model.

4 Application of the network communication layer theory

Network-level theory and the communication platform choice model allow individuals or groups to decompose their purposes and to find the most appropriate platform. This combination of theoretical ideas and models generally has the following four areas of application:

(1) To achieve maximum efficiency and cost minimization information dissemination within the organization
(2) With the accelerated pace of globalization, information communication within the organization often has widely varying, greatly changed trend.

With the emergence of new media such as micro-blogging, advertising and marketing are no longer limited to traditional media. In an era of information explosion, people are often more inclined to believe that "word of mouth" advertising effect brought about, and network development of the media to make this traditional way of marketing a new way. Through advertising audience, communication speed rate, and other conditions, you can select the appropriate model of the network platform to improve the effect of advertising and marketing.

(3) Psychological guidance

The application of psychological guidance is more focused on the personal initiative to solve their own problems. People will always believe that to accept new things and to communicate with others are two important ways to solve the psychological problems, and this is precisely the network platforms are good at; so, through the selection and scoring for the information content, you can find a suitable platform for emotional exchanges.

(4) Policy advocacy guide

In the Internet age, people's access to information increases significantly, and the government propaganda and public opinion for policy guidance are often in a passive position. Through communication platform with the network through the selection model, you can put a lot more humane policy of the spread, instead of rigidly preaching in the print media to raise public acceptance of information.

5 Conclusions and outlook

5.1 Conclusion

This paper first verified the network communication layer theory is correct by way of direct access to the Internet users. According to the results, this statistical average expert score and concentration, compared with the original model, show that the model is correct. Second, experience survey methods verify the practical of theoretical model. Survey, evaluation of the model that experience an average of "satisfactory," and affirmed level of theory in communication networks to facilitate the exchange of people's use of network through the Internet can be used on people to make constructive comments. Finally, the paper argues that the application of the network communication layer theory in four areas is quite well.

5.2 Outlook

The improvements make the model more complete. As an Internet-based theory, its application will also be a great start in the Internet field. The integration of software and the Internet will do lots of help in the application of the theory in the future. Internet time has come. The unparalleled Internet communications provide people with a broad communication platform. Efficient and reasonable use of it will enable people to meet the demand of the high-speed, fast-paced society. There are aspirations to achieve a reasonable and efficient integration of resources, and perhaps this will give us new direction of development of the Internet vision.

References

[1] Chunping Huang, Tiexiang Peng, Research review of computer-mediated interpersonal communication. *Journal of Liaodong University*, **6(2)**, pp. 42–45, 2005.
[2] Peng Lan, Interpersonal communication on Internet. *Journal of International Communication*, **3(1)**, pp. 47–53, 2001.
[3] D. Crystal, *Language and the internet*. Cambridge: Cambridge University Press, 2001.
[4] Zijiang Yang, The effect of network on the behaviors of organizational communication. *Journal of Henan University of Technology* (Social Science Edition), **9(2)**, pp. 37–38, 2006.
[5] Guilin Zhou, Huangen Xu, Way of network Communication and its impact on lifestyle. *Journal of Lishui Shifan University*, **26(6)**, pp. 16–18, 2004.

Social interaction and continuance intention toward online language learning

Rong Zhao, Jianlin Chen
Continuing Education College, Shanghai International Studies University, Shanghai, China
Research Center for Language Strategies in China, Shanghai International Studies University, Shanghai, China

Abstract

This study adopted sense of community (SOC), Technology-Acceptance Model, and Expectation-Confirmation Model to explore the effects of social interaction on learners' continuance intention toward online language learning. In this study, 356 students answered the survey questionnaire, of which 299 were available. With the results of hypothesis test that SOC is not positively related to learners' perceived ease of use or satisfaction, but to learners' perceived usefulness and continuance intention, the research proved that social interaction exerts influence on learners' continuance intention, but is not enough for learners' satisfaction or perceived ease of use.

Keywords: Sense of community, Technology-Acceptance Model, Expectation-Confirmation Model.

1 Introduction

Although online learning has been promoted to various levels of users, the intention to continue using learning information systems is still very low [1]; and it is true of online language learning. Thus, it is important to study how to construct the language learning system to maintain learners' continuance intention. Social interaction plays an important role in education; however, there are few concerning the impact of social interaction on learners' perceived ease of use, perceived usefulness, and continuance intention toward online language learning. Therefore, this paper will be committed to such an exploration by

WIT Transactions on Information and Communication Technologies, Vol. 61, © 2014 WIT Press
www.witpress.com, ISSN 1743-3517 (on-line)
doi:10.2495/MIIT130081

employing sense of community (SOC), Technology-Acceptance Model (TAM) and Expectation-Confirmation Model (ECM).

2 Concept definition

2.1 Technology-Acceptance Model

TAM model has been widely applied for the impact of different external variables on the intention toward e-learning [2,3]. In TAM, perceived usefulness (PU) is defined as the degree to which a person believes that using a particular information technology (IT) would enhance his or her job performance; perceived ease of use (PEOU) the degree to which a person believes that using a particular IT would be free of physical and mental effort [4]. TAM proposes that PU is responsible for the greatest influence on the behavior intention, PEOU is for small but significant effect on the intention, PU is positively influenced by PEOU, and external variables may exert influence on both PU and PEOU [5].

2.2 Expectation-Confirmation Model

Bhattacherjee [6] proposed ECM, in which there are five main statements: first, users' satisfaction with IT has a positive effect on their continuance intention; second, users' IT continuance intention is positively associated with their PU; third, users' satisfaction is determined by their confirmation of expectations; fourth, users' satisfaction is also dependent on their PU; fifth, users' confirmation of expectation is positively related to their PU.

In ECM, "continuance intention" is defined as "users' intention to continue using the IT"; "satisfaction" as "users' affect with prior IT use"; "perceived usefulness" as "users' perception of the expected benefits of IT use"; "confirmation" as "users' perception of the congruence between expectation of IT use and its actual performance" [6].

2.3 Sense of community

A strong SOC means that individuals in the community have strong feelings of community, have a motivated and responsible sense of belonging, and believe that active participation in the community will satisfy their needs [7]. Rovai [8] said that members of strong classroom communities should have feelings of connectedness, duties, and obligations to each other, and community can exist independently from geography, physical neighborhoods, and campuses, with a SOC nurtured through electronic media. The Classroom Community Scale is developed to conceptualize how SOC can be nurtured in distant learning environments [8]. Of the scale, while the learning items represent the degree to which members share values and beliefs concerning the extent to which their educational goals and expectations are being satisfied, the connectedness items typically represent the feelings regarding connectedness, spirit, trust, and interdependence [8].

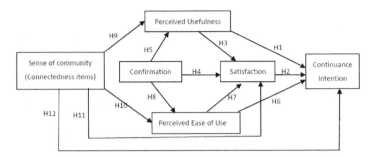

Figure 1: Research model.

3 Model and hypotheses

This study intends to explore the extent to which social interaction influences learners' continuance intention toward online language learning. According to ECM, this study posits (see Fig. 1):

H1. Learners' continuance intention toward online language learning is positively dependent on their PU.

H2. Learners' continuance intention is positively dependent on their satisfaction.

H3. Learners' satisfaction is positively related to their PU.

H4. Learners' satisfaction is positively related to their expectation confirmation.

H5. Learners' PU is positively related to their confirmation of expectation.

According to TAM, this study posits (see Fig. 1):

H6. Learners' continuance intention is positively dependent on their PEOU.

H7. Learners' satisfaction is positively related to their PEOU.

H8. Learners' PEOU is positively related to their confirmation of expectation.

This study intends to explore whether learners' SOC can contribute to their PU, PEOU, satisfaction, and continuance intention. This study posits:

H9. Learners' PU is related to their SOC.

H10. Learners' PEOU is closely related to their SOC.

H11. Learners' satisfaction is closely related to their SOC.

H12. Learners' continuance intention is closely related to their SOC.

4 Survey instrument

A paper-based survey was used for data collection. Valid existing scales were used, after adjusted to the context of online language learning. All the constructs were operationalized as reflective latent variables, in which "continuance intention," "satisfaction," and "confirmation" were measured with items adapted from Bhattacherjee [6], "PU" and "PEOU" with items adapted from Davis [4], and "SOC" with items adapted from Rovai [8].

Continuance intention:

1. I will frequently use the online language learning community in the future.
2. I will use the language learning community on a regular basis in the future.
3. I will strongly recommend others to use the language learning community.

Satisfaction:

1. I am satisfied with the performance of online language learning community.
2. I am pleased with the experience of using the language learning community.
3. My decision to use the online language learning community was a wise one.

Confirmation:

1. My experience with the online language learning was better than I expected.
2. The service of the online language learning was better than I expected.
3. The online language learning can meet the demands in excess of what I required for the service.

PU:

1. I feel that studying online can improve my learning better than studying offline.
2. Using the learning community is effective and my educational needs are met.
3. I find the learning community is useful and promotes my desire to learn.

PEOU:

1. Learning to operate the language learning system is easy for me.
2. It is easy for me to become skillful at using the language learning system.
3. Overall, the online language learning system is easy to use.

SOC:

1. I feel learners of online language learning community care about each other.
2. I feel, instead of alone, connected to others in the online language education.
3. I feel many learners of the online language learning community.
4. I feel that this online language learning community is like a family.
5. I do not feel isolated in this online language learning community.

6. I trust others in this online language learning community.
7. I feel that I can rely on others in this online language learning community.
8. I feel that members of online language learning community depend on me.
9. I feel certain about some of other learners in this online learning community.
10. I feel confident that others will support me in online language education.

5 Participants and procedure

For actual practicability, we picked the online learning modes (the Web Supplemented Mode, Web Dependent Mode, and Fully Online Mode) set by Australian Department of Education, Science, and Training [9], and three universities were selected. With 356 university students answering the survey questionnaire, this study received 299 available questionnaires. In data collection, this study sent out and collected the questionnaires in the second semester of an academic year to ensure that the students had used the language learning system offered by their university authorities for a substantial period.

6 Analysis and results

6.1 The measurement model

In our research, SmartPLS version 2.0 was chosen for data analysis. This study first examined factor loadings. The loadings of SOC item 3 and item 9 were 0.66 and 0.48, respectively, so they are deleted. Thus, all the loadings of SOC items are above 0.70, the AVE of SOC was 0.70, and the α of SOC was 0.94. Consequently, the lowest composite reliability was 0.89, all reliability coefficients were above 0.70, and all AVE scores over 0.50 (see Table1).

6.2 Hypothesis testing

Table 2 presents the estimates obtained from PLS analysis (Bootsrapping with 299 re-samples). An R^2 value of 0.6612 indicates that the model explains a

Table 1: Construct Reliabilities, AVE, and Correlations.

Construct (N=299)	α/AVE	ρ_c	(1)	(2)	(3)	(4)	(5)	(6)
(1) CONFIRM	0.85/0.78	0.91	0.88					
(2) SOC	0.94/0.70	0.95	0.61	0.84				
(3) CINT	0.86/0.78	0.91	0.73	0.64	0.88			
(4) PU	0.83/0.74	0.89	0.56	0.50	0.62	0.86		
(5) SATIS	0.91/0.84	0.94	0.75	0.52	0.73	0.63	0.92	
(6) PEOU	0.77/0.68	0.87	0.62	0.40	0.57	0.58	0.73	0.83

Note: ρ_c, Composite Reliability; CINT, Continuance Intention; CONFIRM, Confirmation; PU, Perceived Usefulness; SATIS, Satisfaction; SOC, Sense of Community.

Table 2: Test of Hypotheses.

No.	Hypothesis	T Statistics	P
H1	Perceived usefulness → intention	4.480564	***
H2	Satisfaction → intention	5.891801	***
H3	Perceived usefulness → satisfaction	2.754333	**
H4	Confirmation → satisfaction	5.538997	***
H5	Confirmation → perceived usefulness	6.814619	***
H6	Perceived ease of use → intention	0.559924	Not supported
H7	Perceived ease of use → satisfaction	7.331809	***
H8	Confirmation → perceived ease of use	9.074723	***
H9	Sense of community → perceived usefulness	8.829313	***
H10	Sense of community → perceived ease of use	0.559302	Not supported
H11	Sense of community → satisfaction	0.123231	Not supported
H12	Sense of community → intention	3.913086	***

*** $p < 0.001$; ** $p < 0.01$; * $p < 0.05$

substantial amount of variance in continuance intention. First, learners' continuance intention toward online language learning is dependent on their PU, satisfaction, and SOC. Second, learners' satisfaction is dependent on their confirmation, PEOU and PU. Third, learners' PU is dependent on their confirmation and SOC. Fourth, learners' PEOU is positively related to their confirmation.

7 Discussion

As is shown in the hypotheses test, SOC plays an important role in determining learners' PU and continuance intention toward online language learning. Learners need emotional support and social satisfaction to feel security in adventuring in the online learning to improve their learning performance; meanwhile, they tend to contend themselves with emotional maintenance and social satisfaction derived from online learning, which contributes to their continuance intention. Therefore, in developing language learning systems, it is essential to enhance learners' social interaction, to grant them more spirit, trust, and connectedness so as to facilitate their study and sustain their continuance intention; however, it is not enough just to enhance social interaction, especially learners' perceived ease of use and satisfaction are concerned.

Acknowledgment

The research work was supported by Educational Science Research Foundation of Shanghai under Grant No. KB1591104.

References

[1] C.-M. Chiu, S.-Y. Sun, P.-C. Sun, T.L. Ju, An empirical analysis of the antecedents of web-based learning continuance. *Computers & Education*, **49(4)**, pp. 1224–1245, 2007.

[2] K. A. Pituch, Y.-K. Lee, , The influence of system characteristics on e-learning use. *Computers & Education*, **47(2)**, pp. 222–244, 2006.

[3] I-Fan Liu, M.C. Chen, Y.S. Sun, et al., Extending the TAM model to explore the factors that affect Intention to Use an Online Learning Community. *Computers & Education*, **54**, pp. 600–610, 2010.

[4] F.D. Davis, Perceived usefulness, perceived ease of use, and user acceptance of information technology. *MIS Quarterly*, **13(3)**, pp. 319–340, 1989.

[5] F.D. Davis, R.P. Bagozzi, P.R. Warshaw, User acceptance of computer technology: a comparison of two theoretical models. *Management Science*, **35(8)**, pp. 982–1003, 1989.

[6] A. Bhattacherjee, Understanding information systems continuance an expectation–confirmation model. *MIS Quarterly*, **25(3)**, pp. 351–370, 2001.

[7] D. McAdam, *Political process and the development of black insurgency 1930–1970*. Chicago, IL: University of Chicago Press, 1982.

[8] A.P. Rovai, Development of an instrument to measure classroom community. *Internet and Higher Education*, **5**, pp. 197–211, 2002.

[9] M. Bell, D. Bush, P. Nicholson, et al., A survey of online education and services in Australia. Higher Educational Group, Commonwealth Department of Education, Science and Training, Report number: Occasional Paper Series 02-A, 2002.

Research status analysis of online thermometric for 10-35KV circuit breaker contacts

Degui Ji[1], Qing Ye[1,2], Cunguo Liu[1], Xinliang Bo[1], Mengnan Wang[1]
[1]Fuxin Power Supply Branch, Liaoning Electric Power Company Limitted of State Grid, Fuxin, China
[2]School of Electric Power, North China Electric Power University, Baoding, China

Abstract

To ensure the safe operation of the power system, fault diagnosis for thermal power system has attracted wide attention. When the high voltage busbar is in the overload operation or there are some breakpoints in the contacts of high voltage switch, the load current flows will produce heating phenomenon since the contact resistance increases. This phenomenon can cause insulation aging or breakdown and then a short circuit. Consequently, some major accidents and significant economic losses will take place. Based on the above cases, we analyze the reasons for the overheating of the circuit breaker contacts. Simultaneously, the status of online contact temperature monitoring device at home and abroad is analyzed. The precautions for use are presented as well.

Keywords: circuit breaker, contact, fault diagnosis.

1 Introduction

In order to ensure the safe operation of power system, people pay great attention to power system fault diagnosis [1]. When high voltage busbar in overload operation or bad contact of high-voltage switch, because the contact resistance becomes large, in the load the current flows will produce heat [2]. The heat caused by insulation aging and breakdown causes a short circuit, which results in major accidents and major economic losses [3].

In the power supply system of the transmission and distribution of power cable, more than 90% of the cable operation failure is caused by joint fault; contact resistance becomes large, and overload causing too high temperature are

WIT Transactions on Information and Communication Technologies, Vol. 61, © 2014 WIT Press
www.witpress.com, ISSN 1743-3517 (on-line)
doi:10.2495/MIIT130091

the main causes of fault. Beijing Electric Power Research Institute survey and statistics show that throughout the 1990s, Chinese power system voltage level switch accident temperature failure accounted for 8.9%; therefore, the detection and monitoring of high voltage switch contacts, busbar, and high-voltage cable joint temperature, early discover and eliminate the thermal fault have very important significance for safe and reliable operation of power system.

2   The main reasons for the overheating of contact

In the electricity tension, rapid load growth conditions,10–35 kV switchgear is often due to manufacture or use, resulting in the abnormal rise of the temperature of the contact. If not found in time or timely maintenance not done, it sometimes causes serious accidents. Malignant accidents caused by such reasons have occurred in China (see Figure 1). In order to prevent the contact temperature rise, switch explosion and malignant accident need to be prevented. Some domestic manufacturers and operating units are often used. Some technologies such as color film, infrared thermal imaging diagnosis to monitor the contact, busbar, and other parts temperature rise. But, because these methods exist in large deviation, there are not directly observation spots and other defects.

According to the requirements of power industry technology progress, switch cabinets are intelligent, maintenance free, the self-diagnostic function direction development. The development from the original regular maintenance to based maintenance technology. The aim of this paper is to develop a practical and economic on-line monitoring contact temperature rise device, under the premise of not reduce the original insulation performance, And to solve the problem of monitoring alarm of contact abnormal temperature. The device should be economical and practical, and should not substantially improve the switch cabinet cost, but should easy the installation of new equipment and old equipment renovation. And then we can improve the safety, reliability of switch equipment operation and reduce the occurrence of accidents.

Figure: 1 (a) The diagram of circuit breaker contact serious ablation.

Figure 1 (b): The diagram of circuit breaker contact serious ablation.

3   The main harm of the electrical overheating

(1)   Since the elastic variation, there is increase in contact resistance which causes the electrical heating, such as high voltage switchgear static and dynamic contact points.

(2)   The oxidation of drainage line connecting or loss caused by electrical heating.

(3)   Electric arc short circuit to ground.

(4)   Power cable insulation aging, even damage.

(5)   Electricity load increases resulting circuit overload.

(6)   Line harmonic current increase caused midline overload.

(7)   Construction quality come down, resulting in poor contact and insulation damage.

(8)   Power system transient conduction voltage along a line of PE lead to the breakdown of insulation.

(9)   Vicious spiral process of overheating, the accelerated insulation aging.

(10)   Vicious spiral of overheating lead to the contact resistance increasing.

(11)   The source of fire.

(12)   The source of explosive.

(13)   The source of power accident.

4   The research development of online thermometric for 10-35 kV circuit breaker contacts

According to the sensor and the measured object contact or not, it can be divided into contact measurement and non-contact measurement two kinds of methods. Noncontact temperature measurement uses thermal infrared detection technology, which is based on the existence of a certain relation between objects relative radiation intensity and temperature and made; it has the advantages of wide measuring range, high accuracy. But in the actual application, because of the limit of the instrument itself, distance coefficient and the angle have great limitations. The other disadvantage of infrared thermometer is the need for manual inspection. Sometimes it may be influenced by the weather and other factors, and it cannot check the cabinet in closed contact of high voltage switch. It is unable to realize the integration of high-voltage equipment and temperature on-line detection. Contact temperature measurement is more, and basically had the following kinds:

(1) Noncontact infrared sensor type

The use of infrared thermopile principle of optical sighting temperature has the following advantages. For example, advanced technology, simple methods of temperature measurement, insulate well. Meanwhile, the disadvantages are: it must be able to see each other between the probe and the measured points, only aligned busbar compartment and cable compartment fixed contacts connected to the busbar terminals, for indirect measurement the contact temperature. Installation of each point to mechanical tuning, sighting, lock, shock, or maintenance is easy to touch the sighting point displacement and failure. It can only be installed on the busbar chamber and a cable chamber. When installing the busbar must be cut, once the transmission, difficult to maintenance and repair.

(2) Fiber optic temperature measurement technology

Advantages: Advanced technology, wide measurement range, high accuracy. Disadvantages: The fiber bending radius is not too small, must ensure the surface of high voltage creepage distance, therefore, in the cabinet body distribution installation is complex, difficult maintenance, replacement. Each system must be equipped with an optical modem (about 30–40 million). When less monitoring points, there is higher cost. The more points installed, the price allocation will be lower. So it can only be installed in the busbar side, installation, repair the busbar must be cut.

(3) A fixed contact porcelain sleeve cavity embedded temperature measurement, infrared or wireless signal transmission mode

The thermal sensors and infrared or wireless transmitter head is mounted on the fixed contacts roots, the insulating magnetic kit of receiving head and contact assembling together. By constant contact, the primary current to take power, the temperature signal is sent to the receiving terminal. In this way must be installed, debugged in the switch cabinet before operation, when the switch cabinet once put into operation without of chance of repair and replacement, unless to wait for the transformer or into line outage overhaul. However, this opportunity is very little and normal maintenance of equipment online temperature measurement system is necessary.

5 Several problems of choose contact temperature online monitoring should be paid attention

When choosing on-line detection device installation, the factors such as convenient maintenance, reliable insulation should be considered. We must pay attention to the high potential terminal sensor and conversion device of power supply reliability problems.

In addition to optical fiber temperature sensor and other sensors and signal transmission device needs power; generally speaking, there are several ways of power supply of the following:

(1) Battery power supply

In the high potential sensor and signal transmission device with a lithium battery power supply, this way of power supply not only hard to do real-time detection in a row, normally 6 months to 2 years to replace the battery, also is not reliable. General battery, known as the available 5–10 years, refers to the application under ideal condition. When in practical application, the battery usually works under high temperature, in this environment the battery life even shortens to 1/10.

(2) There should be a special high voltage capacitor (and high voltage sensor mounted together) dividing power supply

Sensor and the sending circuit and high voltage side equipotential, power supply are possible in this way, but reliability is low. As pressure test or when the surge and the high harmonics in power grid, easy to damage the sensor and the sampling circuit. This way of power supply reliability is not high.

(3) Using small CT as a primary side current supply.

This is a more ideal way, its characteristics and application of technical difficulties in the above has been introduced.

6 The problems of on-line monitoring equipment installation and maintenance should be pay attention

High voltage switch cabinet must be planned outage maintenance. Device in the event of failure, within the prescribed power outage time must be repaired. On the other hand, old equipment modification and installing an on-line temperature monitoring system also must consider the fast and reliable installation. Otherwise, we cannot finish the installation task within the allotted time, and ring power outage plan, or just need special attention is that some products are installed online temperature measurement sensors and part of the circuit in busbar side. This way once installed on electricity, later have no chance to repair. Therefore, it is very important to choose the best product installation for future modification and maintenance.

7 Conclusion

On-line temperature measuring point and transmission circuit is installed in the area of high temperature may happen. The normal work of the commercially available wireless communication devices generally only about 85°C temperature indicators, when there is poor contact or high pressure contact under the condition of heavy load. The heating temperature tend to be more than 100°C, at this time, if the wireless temperature measuring sensor work is not normal, as you can imagine that it will bring a lot of trouble to users. Therefore, at high temperature, the work of the wireless sensor's own ability to resist high temperature must meet the requirements of military level (above 125°C). Otherwise, it will not target requirement of the online temperature measurement. It is a kind of very important indicator often overlooked by the user.

Acknowledgment

The research work was supported by National Natural Science Foundation of China under Grant No. 60942164.

References

[1] Y.P. Tian, *Infrared Detection and Diagnosis Technology*. Chemical Industry, Beijing, pp. 53–58, 2006.
[2] W.Q. Cao, B. Han, SMS using GSM remote monitoring. *Radio Engineering*, **32(1)**, pp. 23–26, 2002.
[3] D. Kong, A.Q. Hu, F. Zhang, Research and implementation of GPRS data terminal, *Micro Computer Information*, **23(9)**, pp. 38–42, 2007.

Application of 3D virtual technology in power system

Jian Zhang[1], Tingwu Yan[1], Hongliang Yuan[1], Qing Ye[2]
[1]*Fuxin Power Supply Branch, Liaoning Electric Power Company Limited of State Grid, Fuxin, China*
[2]*School of Electric Power, North China Electric Power University, Baoding, China*

Abstract

At present, IT people start thinking about how to use 3D virtual technology in other industries. The "Electricity 3D animation editing demonstration system" is a 3D virtual technology application in the power industry. The 3D virtual technology, including three elements (i.e., three-dimensional modeling), that is, the formation of virtual reality, video editing, and production of the organic combination of the power system together to achieve the self-guided, self-timer, real-time editing systems for electric power production.
Keywords: 3D virtual technology, dimensional model, power system, application.

1 Introduction

With the rapid development of the power system modernization process of its increasing scale, operation is also more frequent. The skill levels of staff and operational proficiency have put forward higher requirements [1]. Due to the particularity of the power system, it becomes difficult in the actual operation of the system of personnel training, which greatly increased the difficulty of practical training for the staff [2]. With the rapid development of computer technology, the staff of power system will be introduced into new areas by 3D virtual technology.

3D virtual computer technology as the core technology is based on high-tech means to generate realistic three-dimensional environments, three-dimensional figures, three-dimensional model of the scene, and is the most realistic simulation of live environment [3]. The "Electricity 3D animation editing demonstration system" is combined with this high-tech means with the actual situation of the power system to establish a 220, 66, and 10 kV, major equipment, industrial equipment, security facilities, and material library as the core power. To establish a virtual simulation scenario first of a first substation, secondary substation, the main control room, battery room, industrial equipment room, a technology reference library so that users can naturally interact with objects in the virtual environment and influence each other, producing hands-on feeling and experience [4]. The kind of interaction behavior and action is edited into a film; this is the 3D video production platform in power system. This article focuses on three major elements of 3D virtual technology application in power system.

2 3D electrical material library

In the "3D editing demonstration system," the material library model is used by three-dimensional production techniques: modeling, material production, manufacturing bones, skin, rendering, animation special processing, production of common equipment in first and secondary power system, the standard safety facilities, general industrial equipment, the necessary props in the production process. This vast material library basically meets the demand of filming.

(1) 3D modeling of primary equipment
    Model directly affects the strength of the film's realistic simulation results, so the skin of the model should be consistent with the color of the real equipment, overall dimensions of the model and the actual in line, model for the operation, acceptance. The key parts in special production, action parts make into a dynamic model in order to achieve control of the action when reflected.

(2) 3D modeling of secondary equipment
    The focus is reflected in the relay panel, automatic device screen, control panel, the screen DC system signal lights, plate, protection action signal, ambient temperature and humidity, alarm devices, equipment, and other joints.

(3) 3D modeling of tools and instruments
    Tools and instruments are important components of standardized operations, as an important form of action figures, so important tool shall be made for the corresponding model and its decomposition: insulation rod, electroscope, ground wire, etc. to ensure accuracy when people use instruments.

(4) 3D modeling of safety facilities
    Power is a kind of invisible object which is the biggest killer to human; therefore, in the process of electric power production, arrangement of safety facilities is a very important link. This must be done in the model making which is accurate and comprehensive to meet the highest requirements in safety facilities layout.

3   The formation of virtual reality

Virtual reality is the highest level of 3D virtual technology, which is applied to the scene. The construction of power system is a very complex and tedious work, to fully embody the representation of electric power production environment. The following principles are followed to set up scene in the "Power 3D editing demonstration system." (i) According to profession: transmission, transformation, distribution. (ii) According to the production environment: primary substation, secondary substation, the main control room, battery room, industrial equipment room, technical archives room, transformer station, distribution electrical tower. (iii) According to the weather: sunshine, greasy weather, thunderstorm or snowy day.

(1) Primary substation
Primary substation voltage rating: 220 kV/66 kV, mode of connection double-bus with transfer bus configuration, the main equipment: the main transformer, SF6 breaker, less oil breaker, disconnector, TA, TV, arresters, arc suppression coil, and other components of the overall three-dimensional virtual reality scenes interactive demonstration, roaming scenario any device area, and wire connection.

(2) Secondary substation
Secondary substation voltage rating: 66 kV/10 kV, sectionalized single bus with auxiliary bus configuration, the main equipment: transformer, SF6 circuit breaker, less oil circuit breaker, disconnector, TA, TV, arrester, SF6 breaker handcart, 10 kV vacuum breaker, 10 kV less oil breaker, and other components of the overall three-dimensional virtual reality scenes interactive demonstration, roaming scenario any device area, and wire connection.

(3) Main control room
The main control room reality scene is comprised of simulation set, control panel, protection screen, automated screen, metering screen, to which a substation control room is the prototype, to present a three-dimensional interactive demonstration.

(4) Battery room
Battery room reality scene is composed of the battery screen, the charging screen, feeder panel to present three-dimensional interactive demonstration.

4   3D video edit of the power system

After building 3D equipment, industrial equipment, safety facilities mode, etc., we can real-time drive in a virtual scene development environment. According to the character of the virtual platform of the power substation, the first step load for scene model and set the world converter to adjust the positional relationship between the models, meanwhile set the camera position angle, lighting, etc. We can move in three-dimensional space, operation, observe the range of 3600 virtual devices through the program engine load user, and virtual device to achieve the operation and control of the characters truly human–computer interaction.

(1) Human–machine interaction and recording system

To build up scene equipment, figures or mechanical equipment loaded, producer according to the requirements of the script, through the window interface function keys click the mouse to select the character to achieve, tool, equipment, control of movement to achieve human–computer interaction. Opening the recording system for each step operation can be real-time recording shooting and save the recorded video camera.

(2) Editing and production

The video camera will be saved by filtering, cutting, editing, and synthesis, and finally making it form a complete 3D film for everyone to training and learning. This system can also produce a variety of electrical incidents that occurred in the past, true reproduction process of the accident, to achieve the purpose of educating employees.

5   Conclusion

In conclusion, the "Electricity 3D animation editing demonstration system" is a 3D virtual technology in grid enterprise for the safety of production workers, "safety" training, and operating drills. The effective attempt accident has important practical significance. 3D virtual technology is the most imaginative and advanced video performance means at the present domestic and even in the world. This method is applied to electric power production, which will bring vitality to the future staff training, and play an important role in power system security production.

Acknowledgment

The research work was supported by National Natural Science Foundation of China under Grant No. 60804046.

References

[1] J. Ma, Virtual manufacturing technology: general review. *Mechanical Manufacturing Technology*, **23**(10), pp. 17–20, 2005.

[2] C. Meza, D. Biel, D. Jeltsema, Lyapunov-based control scheme for single-phase grid-connected PV central inverters. *IEEE Transactions on Control Systems Technology*, **20**(2), pp. 520–529, 2012.

[3] M.Q. Mao, L. Yu, B. Xu, Research of D-Q control and simulation for single phase current source inverters. *Journal of System Simulation*, **23**(12), pp. 2727–2731, 2011.

[4] T. Esram, P.L. Chapman, Comparison of photovoltaic array maximum power point tracking techniques. *IEEE Transactions on Energy Conversion*, **22**(2), pp. 439–449, 2007.

Safety role analysis of "3D simulation of power production safety system" for power production

Mingkai Yu, Hong Gang, Peng Qiu
[1]Jinzhou Power Supply Branch, Liaoning Electric Power Company Limited of State Grid, Jinzhou, China

Abstract

This paper focuses on the use of "3D simulation of power production safety system" produced by electrical accidents, standardized operation, standardized maintenance, professional electrical safety regulations, technical training, and other 3D animation videos played an important role in electricity production. To function, the system is expanding material library for all types of video editing providing a wealth of roles and elements that make editing. Editing the production process is simple and flexible, making films with high authenticity. The use of 3D videos for safety training is an innovation of the power system security management.

Keywords: Power 3D animation, editing demonstration system, electrical accident, standardization, safety procedure.

1 Introduction

In recent years, State Grid Company of China works on strengthening security decision, which is stressed as follows. We must unswervingly adhere to safety-first, prevention-oriented approach, and do a good safety education job, seriously implementing the "electrical safety regulations" [1]. This is sufficient to show the importance of safe production state. Therefore, the local electricity authorities spend great efforts to strengthen safety education each year [2]. This is one of the best approaches to education at all levels of authority. The "3D Simulation of Power Production Safety System" is used to the most current international popular 3D animation technology to achieve a variety of power system video production [3]. The use of video to the real, vivid, flexible forms for workers to carry out safety education and technical training is a pioneering power system, whose influence and role is profound.

2 An electrical accident movie for workers to have a profound reflection of the incident

As is well-known, power system including power generation, power transmission, power transmission and distribution with an alarming rate in the transformation of the expansion, strengthens the system every year. Safety management is not only involved in the industry itself, but also related to social stability and the security of electricity industry. Therefore, to reduce and avoid all kinds of electric accidents is staying beside the electricity worker accountability without responsibility. In the past, the power of the accident investigation is adopted after the accident, accident analysis, accident reporting, accident compilation series of measures to make the text file to be educated workers, but changed after a few months to make the same mistake again. If the accident had been made into a film, this analysis would be a permanent teaching material to the workers at any time. The education method is very advanced and effective. In Jinzhou power company, for example, the bleed of violation regulation accident assembly series had been edited at the 50th anniversary of the establishment of bureau where each employee was sent a book series. Some employees read the book, some lost, and some had thrown. Then "Power 3D simulation system for production safety" was used to produce blood of illegal series of incidents movie. The movie will be passed by the council since the 1960s. The typical accidents occurred are divided by their nature: a sense of personal power accident, high fall accidents, burn accidents, etc. The film was broadcast, which produced sensational effect by the following reasons.

(1) Workers the 3D film and not the written report. This visual change is unprecedented and the 3D simulation scenario is close to the real working process, which makes the worker feel kind and interesting.
(2) Employees see themselves or comrade, and even parents accident, whose heart must be shocked.
(3) The detailed and accurate reasons for the accident movie presentation impressed the staff, especially those who experienced immediate recovery of historical memory, and even the film did not describe the subtle plot can recall. This is no means of education and cannot achieve the intended effect.
(4) Video analysis of the causes of the accident fully adheres to the objective historical facts, while the staff is convinced.
(5) Flexible form of play to employees in the meeting, the team, who have a LAN in the home computer to watch on computer.
(6) Electricity accidents occurred on the current in the shortest possible time (24 hours) made and quickly released on the Internet, TV, and movies, which makes the worker in the first place by education and makes the leader for the first time through the video to watch the accident process.

Jinzhou electric power company has proved that the use of power accident videos to carry safety education for workers and the workers have had profound reflection on accidents is positive and effective way, which is to promote the safety of a major innovation in ideological education.

3 The profound impact of standardized movie

Standardized work is in strict accordance with safety laws and regulations, according to preset the only program operations, and meticulously implement safety measures, technology, organization. At the same time, it implements staff behavior and management normalization and standardization. Company is compiled and unified according to the SUW (Standard Unit of Work), and it regulates the behavior of on-site work over the years.

In-depth study and analysis of standardized implementation of relevant rules is an important part of standardization. The electrical power system had spent a lot of education funds for centralized training; the training methods have been stuck in paper, multimedia video phase every year. The birth of 3D video editing of the electrical power system had brought to a new ideas of the standardized training. Each basic unit according to different majors could produce standardized films by self-compile, self-conductance, and autodyne, with the continuous increase of material library expanding the scope of its production capacity unceasingly, such as substation operation professional can create substation switching operation, substation equipment inspection, substation equipment inspection, maintenance of substation DC-DC ground fault handling standardized video, etc. The new installing, replacement, major overhaul, minor repairs of those equipments, such as transformer, circuit breaker, isolating switch, current transformer, voltage transformer, arc suppression coil, could be made into standard operating films by substation maintenance profession. The distribution profession can produce standard operating films about 10 kV distribution line switching operation, new installation and replacement, pole set up newly and replacement, transformers' new intallation and replacement, cut down a tree, measurement, cable head production, insulator replacement, live working, etc. The standard work instruction as a script to shoot into a 3D film is a new measure for the domestic initiative. The popularization of this technology training method produces the profound influence, which will be reflected in the following aspects.

(1) Film production process can hold dangerous points and control counter measures to focus on filming. Film production process can hold dangerous points and control counter measures for the key, affectionately film effects instead of empty words, deeply impress on employees' heart after watching.

(2) The characters, equipment operation, the layout of safety facilities, the use of safety equipment such as electroscope, insulating rod, ground wire guide and so on in the film is shot completely by standard, specification of the actions and realistic simulation devices in film make staff being there.

(3) Flexible mode of training, playing the film is no restriction, only connected to the computer in bureau, and the staff can study in different forms, such as work area, team, profession.
(4) Save a lot of remote training funds.
(5) An investment in a lifetime.

The above shows that the overall work safety production standardization management, standardized operation, by means of 3D video training is currently one of the most advanced and effective measures.

4 Power 3D movie in safety training and assessment application

Electrical safety training and assessment procedures power system has been one of the important measures of the power system to ensure safety in production. Organizing to do a good job of compile a new "safety" makes it spread to the grass-roots units and the production line as soon as possible. For each basic unit we can take various measures to actively training and examination. Jinzhou power company uses the "power production safety 3D simulation system" produced by "Safety Knowledge Contest" 3D movie in the global safety regulations. A significant impact on competition, the reason is as follows. This evaluation method is novel and interesting, an illegal action of the character in place and accurate, produces accident consequences after illegal in reality and shock, and therefore has a very good effect.

How can we use the "3D Simulation of Power Production Safety System" (hereinafter referred to as the "System") to produce 3D movie applied to the safety training. First, we select the 'State Power Grid Corporation Safety Regulations' as a script. The terms were made by chapter, such as production of the basic requirements of high-voltage equipment. The first step to start the System window and set up a scene using the windows interface function to build the main control room, once changed, secondary variable 3D scene. The second start of the system settings window, add the necessary staff and vehicles. The third step is to start the system under the recording window. The basic requirements of high-voltage equipment regulations using of windows interface function action control and extract the material in the library to operate a variety of equipment such as bar, warning signs, working ticket, interphone, insulating rods, electroscope, ground simultaneously recording, etc. The fourth step starts the editing window using the interface functions for editing, special effects, editing, compositing, add text, sound recordings, thus completing the film production.

Application of 3D electrical safety training film's influence embodies the following points:

(1) The effect of the way of training of film and television with vivid, life-like is far more than the effect of reading the book files.
(2) "3D simulation of power production safety system" is a way of using animation and game video recording, simple and convenient operation.

The trainee will be with great interest to participate in the production of the film, thus improve the profound understanding of safety.

(3) Electricity 3D safety training film as permanent teaching materials, training for new recruits is very effective. Members do not need to live to a comprehensive understanding of the real system wiring, high-voltage electrical equipment layout, the use of safety equipment, to improve the students' perceptual knowledge quickly.

5 Conclusion

In summary, the "3D simulation of power production safety system," which is a 3D visualization technology was applied to safety of power grid enterprise safety in production training, drills, accident playback operation. This is an effective attempt, which has important practical significance. The system in advance material database, makes the editing process simple and flexible, improves production efficiency, and has higher practicability. Using animation to make game of 3D physics engine software architecture, realizing self-compile, self-conductance and autodyne, making all kinds of 3D films immediately, will play an important role in electric power production. There are vigorously promoting safety management innovations in power systems.

Acknowledgment

The research work was supported by National Natural Science Foundation of China under Grant No. 60904006.

References

[1] Y.G. Leu, T.T. Lee, W.Y. Wang, Observer-based adaptive fuzzy-neural control for unknown nonlinear dynamical systems. *IEEE Transactions on Systems, Man, and Cybernetics-Part B: Cybernetics*, **29(5)**, pp. 583–591, 1999.

[2] Y.S. Yang, Robust adaptive fuzzy tracking control for a class of perturbed strict-feedback nonlinear systems via small-gain approach. *Information Science*, **170(2)**, pp. 211–234, 2005.

[3] M.Q. Mao, L. Yu, B. Xu, Research of D-Q control and simulation for single phase current source inverters. *Journal of System Simulation*, **23(12)**, pp. 2727–2731, 2011.

Electronic music clothing

Dejun Li[1], Tian Xia[2]
[1]Office of Academic Affairs, Wuhan Textile University, Wuhan, China
[2]School of Electronic and Electrical Engineering, Wuhan Textile University, Wuhan, China

Abstract

This paper is based on flexible fabric connector electronic music clothing. It uses a new type of wire fabric, namely, the conductive yarn made by the method of weft yarn weaving fabric fittings, to replace the ordinary wire, improve the stability of player system, which is conducive to the appearance of the clothing design. The system uses LPC932A1 chip which as the core control of the music player. This player has simple design. It is only for the music clothing. It not only saves the cost, but also keeps the high performance.

Keyword: Functional clothing, fabric connection, conductive fabric, SD card, MP3 player.

1 Introduction

With the increasing development of science and technology and people's high living standards, the music has been integrated into our daily lives. People are fond of music, so you can see they walk on the streets with their headphones on. With the rapid development of electronic technology, especially microelectronics, technology advances. Electronic technology in the textile and clothing sector has been rapid development. In order to meet the demand for music, there has been associated music features special clothing on the market. However, there are some disadvantages of these garments; the connecting member between the electronic devices is mostly a metal wire, and the wire directly into the inner garment, which not only reduces the flexibility and wear comfort, but also the appearance of the garment has some impact. In the wear process, different parts of the fabric will be subjected to different mechanical actions; generally it will be affected by repeated tensile, shear, and compression force. Metal wires due to metal fatigue phenomenon will produce breakage, making music clothing reliability reduce greatly; the user must be careful to avoid the line loose or broken lines. In order to overcome these disadvantages of electronic music clothing, paper connections between electronic devices using a flexible fabric connection instead of the traditional metal wire, design new electronic music clothing.

2   The overall design of electronic music clothing

Electronic music clothing consists of the clothing, flexible fabric connector, and an MP3 player system. Playback system can be broadly divided into the following sections: control module, decoder, storage devices, controls, speaker, power supply, and so on. These electronic components by pasting, sewing, and other methods fixed on clothing, some of the sections can serve as decoration. The electronic music clothing's connections between components is flexible fabric connector, the flexible fabric connector is constituted by a core yarn and general yarn, the resulting electron clothing softness, washable, and comfortable are good. The electronic music clothing makes the electronics and the clothing together, making costumes and music players to form a whole, comfortable, easy to use good. The flexible fabric connections with the designs of clothing can play a decorative role.

2.1 The flexible fabric connections

The flexible fabric connections is composed of core yarn and general yarn. The core yarn for the warp, ordinary yarn is the weft. Core-spun yarn core is composed of a plurality of conductive metal wire; this selection is of 0.04 mm copper wire, paper yarn can choose natural fibers, or chemical fibers. Each conduction unit is composed of at least two corn yarn parallel. Fabric connections are shown in Figure 1. Figure 2 is a chart. And between each adjacent nonconductive covering yarn interaction, only one set of conducting work happens. If a core yarn fails, the system will immediately select another conductive core yarn, and it does not affect the role of the group conducting the conduction unit. Each guide-cell plays the role of a single wire, compared with the conventional single wire-cells, to improve stability of the connection between the electronic devices. And conducting means on the fabric of at least two or more groups. When one set of conductive unit completely lost conductive effect, you can separate the adjacent unit conducting wire to reconnect. This unit improves the stability, flexibility, and reliability of the overall circuit.

Further, according to different parts of the clothing, the number of conduction units is different. The number of conduction units is the same of that common metal wire. For the parts that will be repeated tensile, shear, compression, and friction, conduction left margin of 2-3margin. Treatment with connectors and components happens next. This paper uses soft cable slot for easy removal, which may also increase the life of the garment.

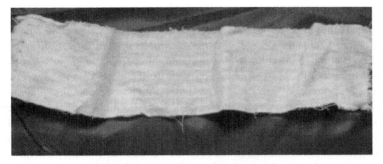

Figure 1: Fabric conduction unit.

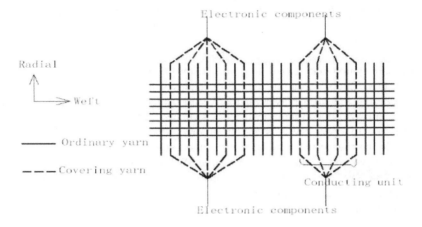

Figure 2: Structure diagram.

2.2 The overall design of the system of player

The overall design of the system includes hardware design and software design of the system. The hardware structure of the hardware design includes the device selection, the division of the module, the relationship between the modules and setting each particular function of each module, and the like. Software design includes various peripheral drivers and through the coordination of the C programming language to make each component.

3 The choice of hardware and integrated with clothing

3.1 Select components

As electronic music clothing itself not only should be comfortable and beautiful, and which can be washed, but also the play system should be compact and stable;

then, the components you selected need to consider the following factors: component miniaturization, waterproof, large memory capacity, processing speed, battery to maintain a long time, a simple system operation and so on. Based on the above conditions, this design choice NXP company's low-voltage and low-power LPC932A1 microcontroller as the core of the player control devices. Using memory capacity SD card as a high transfer rate fast songs storage medium, adopting audio decoding special VS1003B chip decoding and playback of music. 89LPC932A1 integrates many system-level functions, which can greatly reduce the number of elements as the core part of the system that controls the operation of the coordination between the various sub-module systems.

Owing to the large volume of ordinary batteries, the switch of power mounted on the power supply module directly, and because the button battery is too small, so lithium-ion batteries are used to power supply.

Since the membrane switch [1] has a good waterproof, dustproof, anti-oil, anti-erosion of harmful gases, stable and reliable performance, light weight, small size, long service life, convenient assemblies, panel can be washed and character is not damaged, rich colors, nice, etc., overcome the traditional keyboard switch that can't waterproof, dustproof and internal problems, such as electricity. Louis oxidation, therefore, chooses it as a player switch button. Considering the MP3 player interactive user interface should easy to operate and small size, this system designed 3 switches (SW1 ~ SW3), long press the SW1 key to open, SW2 is the front one, SW3 for the next one. Due to considering the switch may be the less the better, so using composite keys to adjust the volume of this player, press the SW1 and SW2 to turn the volume up, SW1 and SW3 is pressed on the same time to turn the volume down. For switching stabilization measures, the use of shunt capacitance method to eliminate buffeting is preferred.

3.2 Integrated electronic components and clothing

In order to make clothing and music players to form a whole, wearing comfortable, easy to use, we adopt the following design. There are a total of three parts of this music player control: memory modules, power modules, and key module. As the press button part is the core of its using, and need to be placed in an obvious place and easy to operate and finally choose stitched on the left inside sleeve. We use control and storage module in order to be able to garment wash, so for encapsulation of this part. However, this part will not often be used; we then put it in clothing decorations of the chest, use viscose glue hidden it invisible. Due to the use of lithium-ion battery for power supply and the lithium-ion battery's size is large and cannot be washed, a removable partial mode is to be designed, thus the batteries placed on lining the pockets of easy unpicking and washing. The design is shown in figure 3, figure block graphics placed components, such as control module can be placed, 2, 6, 4 can be put in the microphone. The fabric portion of the connection link is also shown.

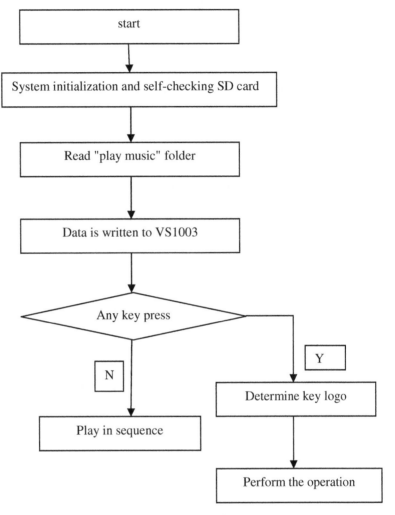

Figure 3: The flow chart of system software

4 System software [2]

System software has the following main functions: PlayMain () is a playback control module. Players master program key processing module that adds to jump to the ISP program area; VS1003. C is the player decode driver and controller and VS1003B using hardware SPI interface to communicate; New SD.e is the player SD card driver, which arranged a driver initialization and ditch with different sectors of the underlying hardware speed data read and write functions; FileSys.c for MP3 player file system can use a file name or order number of music files to find the file. Player software flow chart is shown in Figure 3.

The player currently supports FAT12 and FAT16 file system format an SD card; you can use 1M-2G SD card as the storage medium of songs. In order to facilitate storage of documents of different categories, Program agreed all music files stored in the SD card root directory "play music" subdirectory, other types of files or folders can be any place, be sure to select a time format FAT format on the PC, and the establishment of "play music" folder, and then copy the files can be played. After running the test, the system can normally smooth broadcast high quality MP3 music files [3,4].

5 Conclusion

Clothing is a basic need of the people. Clothing can express the wearer's personality; music embodies the passions of people. Design of electronic music clothing combine music and common clothing is clever, so that it is into people's daily life. The combination of high-tech and fashion will become a development direction of garment industry in the future. This paper introduces in detail the overall design of electronic music garment fabric connection based on. The garment itself is with electronic fabrics [5], conductive connection part acts as a hardware module, which overcomes the shortcomings of the traditional music of clothing does not wash fastness and discomfort, and flexible fabric connections with the garment pattern design, does not affect the appearance of clothing. Of course, this design also has many deficiencies. In future studies, we can consider to use fabric switch instead of membrane switch. The other is due to the continuous development of solar cell technology, where we can consider using solar cells instead of lithium ion battery. Then only need to put the clothes on his back, either to charge the battery, but also can be recycled.

References

[1] Zhengan Wang, The preliminary design principles of electronic membrane switch interface. *Popular Literature*, **22**, pp. 92–93, 2012.
[2] Yuyan Wang, Mingwei Li, Based on C51 MCU's MP3 player design. *Electronic Technology*, **10**, pp. 29–30, 2009.
[3] Jiaping Hong, Based on VS1003 decoder's MP3 player design. *Microcontrollers & Embedded Applications*, **11**, pp. 53–56, 2010.
[4] Qiyang Xiao, Yuan Fang, Design of SD card MP3 player based on LPC932A1. *Microcomputer and Application*, **31(5)**, pp. 92–94, 2013.
[5] Nenggang Zhen, Chaohui Wu, Advances in electronic fabric. *Journal of Computers*, **34(7)**, pp. 1172–1187, 2011.

Case study: e-government cloud computing platform design and implementation

Tiantian Liu[1], Qiang Yue[2], Jie Liu[3], Tongkai Ji[1], Nengzhan Xu[3]
[1]*Cloud Computing Center, Chinese Academy of Sciences, Dongguan, China*
[2]*Guangdong Electronics Industry Institute, Dongguan, China*
[3]*Dongguan E-government Office, Dongguan, China*

Abstract

In the field of e-government, cloud computing has good prospects because of its dramatically reduced cost and efficient and flexible working models. In this paper, a case study of Dongguan e-government cloud computing platform is introduced. Up to now, 189 e-government applications are migrated to this platform, and all run normally. By describing the design and implementation of this platform, we hope the experience will provide references for e-government cloud construction of other cities, so that this efficient, low-carbon, and low-cost construction model will be promoted in more and more places.
Keywords: e-government, cloud computing, G-Cloud, virtualization.

1 Introduction

In recent years, various government departments trustee more and more servers in the common machinery room of the e-government. The carrying capacity of the machinery room is almost full, while the utilization rate of machines is low, which brings challenges to the operation and maintenance of e-government management. Cloud computing is a new direction of computation, which ensures various applications and users to obtain computing capacity, storage space, and information services flexibly according to their needs. Currently, cloud computing is utilized in many industries and field, and also has good prospects in the field of e-government [1].

In this paper, a case study of e-government cloud computing platform, Dongguan City E-Government Cloud Computing Platform, is introduced.

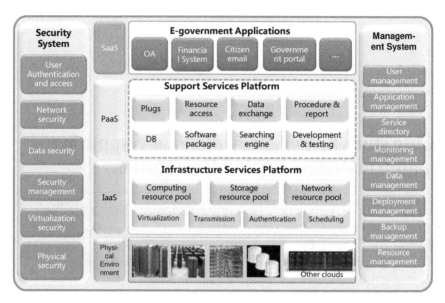

Figure 1: Framework of e-government cloud computing platform.

Dongguan e-government cloud project is a government procurement project. It utilizes G-Cloud as its core system, which is a secure and reliable cloud operating system product with independent intellectual property rights. Currently, the project has been completed, including two cloud centers, which are respectively in the internal zone and the demilitarized zone (DMZ). The benefits of the cloud platform are as follows: (1) the hardware value is maximized, (2) government resources can be shared, (3) maintenance costs are reduced substantially, (4) the system is more stable, reliable, and safe, and (5) a variety of service applications can be flexibly supported.

The paper is organized as follows. We first propose the framework and system software design of the e-government cloud computing platform in Section 2. Section 3 describes some implementation techniques. In Section 4, the test result is presented. Finally, we conclude our paper in Section 5.

2 Platform design and Cloud OS

2.1 Framework

The framework of the Dongguan e-government cloud computing platform is shown in Figure 1. It mainly includes several levels as discussed below.

(1) *Physical environment*: The existing and new added physical infrastructures, including servers, storage servers, network devices, various types of terminal equipment, host operating system kernel, and so on.

(2) *Infrastructure services platform*: Achieves the virtualization of infrastructures and offers infrastructure as a service (IaaS).

(3) *Support services platform*: Provides a variety of tools and functions to achieve the effective integration of e-government applications, thus providing Platform as a Service (PaaS).

(4) *Application level*: Deploys a variety of e-government applications. It uses the infrastructure services and support services from the below levels.

(5) *Security system*: Provides the security control and disaster recovery protection to all the levels of e-government cloud, from physical environment, infrastructure, virtualization, data, networks, applications, and users.

(6) *Cloud operating and management system*: Offers different types of resource managements: including physical resources, virtual resources, monitoring, data, applications, user, and identity.

2.2 Cloud operating system

The core part is the cloud infrastructure services platform, which implements IaaS. We use G-Cloud in this platform, which is a cloud operating system and supports the virtualization and unified management of large-scale computing resources, storage resources, and network resource.

The G-Cloud is built with a SOA architecture based on REST/SOAP web service technology. The system consists of a number of modules, as shown in Figure 2. All the modules can be deployed in a redundant configuration to avoid single point of failure and achieve load balance.

The functionalities of each module are described below.

1. *Front-end Proxy*: Distributes requests that are received from client servers to the most appropriate Portal according to a prior set-up load-balancing strategy.

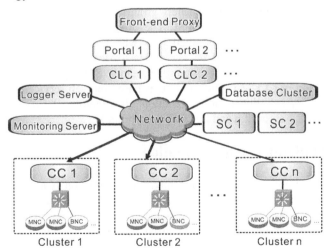

Figure 2: System architecture of G-Cloud.

2. *Portal*: Self-serviced. End users can manage their resources on Portal with no need to remember complicated commands.
3. *Cloud Controller (CLC)*: The dispatch center of G-Cloud system. It performs platform-level management, mainly for user authentication, request distribution and resource management and distribution.
4. *Cluster Controller (CC)*: To manage the access schedule of Node Controllers (NC) and resource adjustment of virtual machines (VMs) within a cluster.
5. *Master Node Controller (MNC)*: NC provides G-Cloud with computing resources and sets up the operating environment of VMs. There are two kinds of NCs, Master NCs (MNCs) and Backup NCs (BNCs). Each MNC can host different numbers of VMs.
6. *Backup Node Controller (BNC)*: BNC is the environmental infrastructure for implementing fault-tolerant technology in G-Cloud system.
7. *Storage Controller (SC)*: Virtualizes physical storage resources and stores them in the resource pool. It supports shared storage such as SAN, NAS, DAS, and distributed storage.
8. *Logger Server*: Basically for offline storage recovery. It will back up the metadata information in the storage system periodically.
9. *Monitoring Server*: To collect and summarize the real time resource utilization of all physical machines (PMs) and VMs on G-Cloud platform, and display information with charts and tables to users.
10. *Database clusters*: For providing high reliable database services and assuring the data consistence between clusters through transaction management.

It is important to minimize the impact of system crash, or treat faults as a special circumstance. G-Cloud system employs the no-destructive disaster recovery technology, which is applied to handle faults from CLC and NC.

G-Cloud can configure multiple safety groups with various authorities so as to control the access permission to VM. The image files are encrypted by ASE 128bit algorithm and stored as small files with a size of 10MB. Users send request to CLC suing the HMAC (keyed-Hash Message Authentication Code) authentication, 224 bit encryption key, and SSL protocol. The inter-communication of CLC, CC, NC, and SC is based on web service and with WS-security to expand the security function. It employs X.509 V3 security framework, RSA algorithm and 2048 bit encryption key.

3 Cloud platform implementation

In Dongguan e-government common machinery room, on blade server cabinet and 14 blade servers are added in respectively DMZ and intranet zone. A set of optical storage array is added, which is incorporated into the existing FC SAN Fibre Channel storage networks and provides service for both DMZ and the intranet zone.

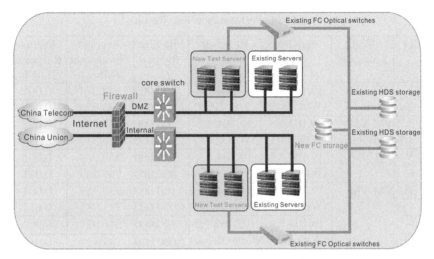

Figure 3: Physical deployment of e-government cloud computing platform.

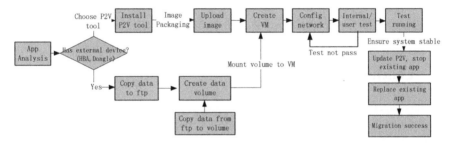

Figure 4: P2V migration process.

There are two ways of migration. One is using P2V migration; the other is to deploy applications directly to the cloud platform. There are several advantages of using the P2V migration. For example, the migration is semi-automated. The operating environment and data is consistent with the physical machine. We do not need to affect the original system. And P2V supports major operating systems (Windows XP, Win7, Win2003 or above, Linux, etc.). So P2V migration is used. Average packaging time for applications is about 3 hours. Figure 4 describes the P2V migration process. Up to now, 189 e-government applications are migrated to the cloud platform. All the applications run normally.

4 Evaluations

Before e-government cloud computing platform on-line using, we carry out tests for three weeks. Both functionality and performance are through the user acceptance. Performance test focuses on the network I/O performance and disk read-write performance. VMs disk read and write rate is a little bit slow than PM, but is reasonable and be able to meet the user needs. Network transmission

Table 1: Performance Test Results.

ID	Test Scenarios	Sender	Receiver	File Size (bytes)	Average Throughput (Mbps)	Average Response Time (s)
1	VM-VM (Same NC)	19.104.*.* (Win 2003)	19.104.*.* (Win 2003)	100,000	722.374	0.001
2				1,000,000	893.626	0.009
3	VM-VM (Diff NC)	19.104.*.* (Win 2003)	19.104.*.* (Win 2003)	100,000	414.796	0.002
4				1,000,000	569.533	0.014
5	PM-VM	19.104.*.* (Win 2003)	19.104.*.* (Win 2003)	100,000	550.909	0.001
6				1,000,000	709.265	0.011
7	VM-VM	19.104.*.* (Win 2003)	19.104.*.* (Win 2003)	100,000	630.359	0.001
8				1,000,000	731.985	0.011
9		19.104.*.* (Win 2003)	192.168.*.* (CentOS 5.0)	100,000	616.924	0.001
10				1,000,000	747.427	0.011
11	PM-PM	192.168.*.* (CentOS 5.0)	192.168.*.* (CentOS 5.0)	100,000	547.25	0.001
12				1,000,000	884.947	0.009

performance between VMs (on the same or different NCs) or between VMs and PMs achieves the desired requirements. The test results are shown below.

5 Conclusion

In this paper, Dongguan E-government Cloud Computing Platform is introduced. Using this platform, server utilization is improved from 10% to 60%. It shortens the construction cycle of e-government systems. We hope this efficient, low-carbon, and low-cost construction model will be promoted in more and more places.

Acknowledgments

The research work was supported by Guangdong-Hong Kong invited bidding special for Dongguan Grant (No. 201120510101), Province-Ministry Industry-University-Research Major Special Program 2012 (No.2012A090300001), and the introduction of innovative R&D team program of Guangdong Province (No. 201001D0104726115).

References

[1]   Kai Hwang, C. Geoffrey, Distributed and cloud computing. *Parallel Processing to the Internet of Things*, **3**, pp. 129–130, 2011.

Research on the e-commerce ecosystem - taking Beijing Unionpay Merchant Services Company Limited as an example

Kuoyi Shao[1], Yun Zhai[2], Haifeng Sui[1], Changsheng Zhang[3], Cui-Hua Li[4], Nan Ma[5]

[1]School of Computer and Communication Engineering, University of Science and Technology Beijing, Beijing, China
[2]E-Government Research Center, Chinese Academy of Governance, Beijing, China
[3]College of Physics & Electronic Information Engineering of Wenzhou University, Zhejiang, China
[4]The Military Office in Beijing, The GSH Information-based Department, Beijing, China
[5]College of Information Technology, Beijing Union University, Beijing, China

Abstract

With the business commerce coming into the internet era, it gradually becomes a trading platform, such that the e-commerce has become the new environment for the enterprise business activities. Compared with the traditional commerce business environment, the e-commerce exists under a more open environment. To better understand the e-commerce ecosystem for the researchers to make it develop more healthily and sustainably, we analyzed the meaning and goal of e-commerce ecosystem. Furthermore, we expatiated the financial payments ecosystem in the electric support link of Beijing Unionpay Merchant Services Company Limited. Finally, we analyzed the core tasks of the financial payment ecosystem in the business support link.

Keywords:e-commerce, ecosystem, data mining.

 WIT Transactions on Information and Communication Technologies, Vol. 61, © 2014 WIT Press
www.witpress.com, ISSN 1743-3517 (on-line)
doi:10.2495/MIIT130141

1 Introduction

In the e-commerce process, the electronic payment has developed with bank card. While the bank card has developed in China nearly 20 years, its rapid development is really in the twenty-first century. The number of bank cards in China rapidly increases, and it has been about 300 million to 400 million a year, and the bank card payment environment in China as well as the third party such as the Beijing Unionpay Merchant Services Company Limited are all in the process of continuous improvement. We can say that the development of bank card industry shows on a leapfrog growth. The bank card payment involves many links, and it has developed from traditional issuing, acquiring, transferring, professional services, and payment channels to the bank card chip research and making, machinery design and manufacturing, software development, system integration, key system, and safety certification bodies. All these issues are concerned with E-commerce ecosystem.

The e-commerce ecosystem comprises so many businesses and enterprises in the e-commerce systems that it experiences the birth, growth, maturity, and death process, and it has the same behavior as the biology in the nature, for example, competition, cooperation, continuation to evolve and adapt to the rapid environment change. At the same time, because of the development of Internet technology and demand driven by diversified customers, e-commerce ecosystem becomes increasingly large and complex, showing on co-competition and symbiosis characteristic in both internal and external sides.

2 Meaning and goal of e-commerce ecosystem

Because e-commerce [1–4] has adaptive, self-organization, multi-variables, strong-coupling, large scale, and multi-scale characteristics, we must adopt a research method named "systems engineering." Furthermore, we apply the ecosystem theory and commercial ecology theory to construct the e-commerce ecological model followed by the research on the core algorithm, for example, classification and clustering algorithm to analyze the relationship and main process between ecological system bodies.

Study on e-commerce ecology has great strategic significance. With the fierce competition in the world scope, the product life cycle shortening, trade barriers gradual collapsing, as well as customer demands becoming more and more diverse, such characteristics of the information society render the enterprise to face the fierce competition of the ecological environment. For survival and development, the enterprises must speed up to upgrade their products, continue to re-construct process and seek the collaboration with related enterprises, so that they can launch new products in the shortest time to adapt the new market. The reaction speeds to the ecological environment, and the enterprise flexibility has become the key to sustainable survival and development. At present, the ecology has formed a unique, mature theoretical system and methodology; however, the theory of business ecosystem theory still lacks exercised experience. The present research mainly uses the method of qualitative analysis, but the quantitative study by means of mathematical tools and computer technology remain to be strengthened.

There are two types of system competition. One is the interaction between system and its environment, when survival environment is adverse in contrast to the survival demand or it has a detrimental effect on the survival of system. The system will fight with the living environment, which is called the struggle for survival of the system. And the other is called system of survival competition, that is, in the same environment multiple systems compete for their own development on the living conditions. Study on e-commerce ecology is to use the ecology, system dynamics, and knowledge discovery theory to discuss the various competition and cooperation relationship, and to pull out their competitive strategies to achieve the optimal life. Through retrieving information in the massive data and complex systems, we need to research theory method and data mining technology for data extraction, refining, and navigation such that we can analyze the status, structure, function, behavior forecast, and analysis to provide theoretical basis and practical guidance for the e-commerce ecology with sustainable development.

3 E-commerce ecosystem—taking Beijing Unionpay Merchant Services Company Limited as an example

Next we analyze our own thinking about the e-commerce ecosystem in the field of financial payment in the business support link.

3.1 The financial payment history of Beijing Unionpay Merchant Services Company Limited

Beijing Unionpay Merchant Services Co., Ltd. was established in 2002 July; now it is the largest bank card collecting branch in Beijing. At the same time, it has built the most professional e-commerce service platform in Beijing which comprises nearly 100 civilian services fields such as the water, electricity, gas, heat, telecom operator payment, credit card payment, game card, insurance, fund purchase, and commodity purchase. These services are mainly through the self-service payment terminal, web, mobile phone, telephone, bank counter, to provide multidimensional services for the cardholders. Since its establishment, it has made rapid development of the payment service for the business support activities, and this company has formed an e-commerce ecosystem with multiple service contents, service channels, and payment channels.

3.2 Development stages from the ecological perspective of the e-commerce ecosystem

The first stage takes on natural growth characteristic. In this stage, we mainly deliver such products and services as water, coal, and gas related to the service to users according their needs, partly provide services for the people in the form of self-service payment channels.

The second stage takes on the ecological consciousness, that is, with the rapid growth of transaction volume, the terminal queue appears significantly increased and the users' demands become more diversified. We speeded up to rich business contents in the payment platform by adding more and more new contents for the payment terminal to meet the diversified needs of cardholders. At the same time, we opened more channels for the cardholder by introducing more partners, such as the Brothers Cooperation Chinapay. Furthermore, we provide more online service channels for the cardholders, for example, we cooperated with a multimedia terminal manufacturer to increase the number of service by self-service payment terminal, and cooperated with Beijing Unicom to launch phone service channels. In fact, we make full use of the co-existence and co-evolution principle to consciously construct the ecological circle of our business.

The third stage belongs to the ecological construction stage consciously. Of course, to make the ecological health develop in the long run, we need theoretical tools such that we can make every part of e-commerce ecosystem interact with each other. At the same time, they maintain their living status, and remain relative balance by the repulsion or attraction competitive process, in order to achieve the survival and best development.

For example, when we provide rich business for our partners by the self-service payment terminals, ideally, all profits distribution, the terminal layout, customer service, and the cardholder service are dealt according to established principles. On the other side, for example, when the pay fees adjust, all the factors should be rescheduled; otherwise, we will ultimately affect the ecological health. Therefore, it is necessary to build the ecological system where it involves regulatory policy, merchants, banks, China UnionPay, and the third party payment companies. Because the system industry links are complex, we should pay more attention to handling the ecological balance between them to the industry develop healthily.

4   Core tasks of the financial payment ecosystem

According to the actual business development experience, research on financial payments ecosystem in the electric support link should mainly include the following aspects:

(1) To construct the electronic payment industry ecosystem structure model, revealing the species status, function, relationship, and its relationship with the environment. And using the biology theory, to analyze the function structure of electronic payment industry ecological system, namely, the flow model of material, information as well as value, and analyzed the enterprise niche, "key factor," the system stability, diversity, and other characteristics.

(2) Based on the analysis above and the data mining technology, to build the user behavior model, mainly the user consumption behavior, risk control, risk control, strategy control.

(3) According to the ecology population growth theory, to establish the growth model of electronic payments business, which analyzed the survival strategies of different enterprises, and then to use the dynamics model to analyses the relationship between enterprises, including competition, mutualism, predation, etc. On these bases, to establish the way to mutually beneficial relationship within the electronic payment industry. Furthermore, to study the growth model and factors of the electronic payment population and user population followed by the analysis of the factors influencing the user population growth with simulation software.

(4) To research on the evolution of life cycle process by the mining algorithm for the complex systems, and on the dynamic mechanism for enterprise growth, and to summarize the characteristic of the birth, growth, development, and decline stages of e-commerce ecosystem.

5 Summary and suggestions

As future research lines, the following topics remain to be explored.

Firstly, the payment industry involves many links such that we should make care of interests of all parties, such that we can promote industry cooperative innovation. After all, any field cannot solve all the problems of the industry chain separately only with their own innovation.

Secondly, we should focus on the customer experience; here, we mainly stress the payment innovation work, so we must pay attention to the user experience and payment channels.

Last but not the least, we should apply the new technologies to analyze the risk control and the field analysis. The new payment methods, new experience channels, and the more rich application produce massive data which hinder to analyze the risk control and the field analysis by the traditional tools such that we necessarily establish the data mining system to control the risk and make the domain analysis.

Acknowledgments

The research work was supported by National Natural Science Foundation of China under Grant No. 61300078; by the Project of Chinese Academy of Governance under Grant No. 2012ZBKT016 and the Project of Zhejiang provincial Natural Science Foundation of China under Grant No. LY13F020024.

References

[1] E.P. Michai, Cluster and the new economics of competition. *Harvard Business Review*, **76(6)**, pp. 77–90, 1998.
[2] F.M. James, *The Death of Competition*. Harper Collins Publisher, USA, pp. 28–33, 1996.

[3] A. Cockbuin, *An Introduction to Evolutionary Approach.* Blackwell Science, Oxford, pp. 20–24, 1993.
[4] C.F. Joidan, Do ecosystem exist? *The American Naturalist*, **118**, pp. 284–287, 1981.

A novel customer knowledge management analysis model: with a case study in hospitality

Xuelian Liu[1,2], Nopasit Chakpitak[1], Pitipong Yodmongkol[1], Shuang Cang[3]
[1]College of Arts Media and Technology, Chiang Mai University, Huaykeaw Rd, Chiangmai, Thailand
[2]Faculty of Tourism & Culture Industry, Chengdu University, Shiling Rd, Chengdu, China
[3]School of Tourism, Bournemouth University, Poole, Dorset, UK

Abstract

Customer knowledge management process with models can help managers to find the real value chain in business. This paper proposes a novel two-dimension customer knowledge management analysis model, which make customer knowledge more understandable and manageable. A case study is illustrated and shows the application of the CKM model in customer processes can lead to increased process performance.

Keywords: knowledge management, customer knowledge, knowledge co-creation, process management.

1 Introduction

1.1 Challenges for understanding customers

In the age of information, the core competence of enterprises is differentiation rather than scale. To achieve differentiation, one good way for enterprises is better known of their customers. Unfortunately, customers are so elusive and unpredictable. Few firms are able to manage the dialogue with their customers effectively and use what they know to add more value for customers and ultimately improve firm performance [1]. Typically, they use Customer Relationship Management (CRM) system to capture, store, and discover the customer-related information, such as customer name and favorites. Many companies use tools that attempt to determine a customer's value to the organization [2]. With the database technology development, companies use data mining to understand their customers' demographic and behavioral patterns better and to segment customers into different types. The ideas, thoughts, and information the organization receives from its customers regarding the preferences, creativity, or consumption experience of specific products or services [3]. But most of companies just only have the information, and utilize surface value for improve customer loyalty and satisfaction [4]. As a result, they do not use what they know to understand their customers at a deeper level and develop differentiation against their competitors. One possible solution is to combine the Knowledge Management (KM) method to CRM system, so it is possible to develop a Customer Knowledge Management (CKM) process. The CKM process with models can help managers find the real value chain specifically in service-oriented business. This approach enables companies to improve knowledge support of their business processes, which aims to develop the differentiation of their products and services.

Some of the best examples of companies using their knowledge in this way are the big three e-business enterprises: Google, e-bay, and Amazon. Each uses knowledge to make their products and services more intuitive and user friendly. Using knowledge to support customers was found to be an important factor in retaining existing customers [3].

1.2 Research goals and structure

Our research focuses on how to understand CKM concepts and applied it within the area of service-oriented business. The method makes companies understand CKM in a deeper level, which aims at improving their service quality and making differentiation.

To achieve the research goals, firstly the theory of knowledge management and CK and CKM are reviewed. Base on that, a two-dimension analysis model for CKM is proposed, which makes the concept of CKM more clarity and more operational. An action research case is illustrated with the proposed analysis model. At last, this paper gives the conclusion and the future of the research.

2 Literature review

2.1 Knowledge management

The knowledge management literature provides some background theory of this research. Since massive research concern knowledge management, we only review the conception used in this research. The knowledge concept in business process was discussed in many papers. Hanvanich et al. [5] argues that the marketing knowledge resides in three key marketing processes: product development management, customer relationship management, and supply chain management. They also noticed that there is no consensus as to how marketing knowledge should be defined and measured.

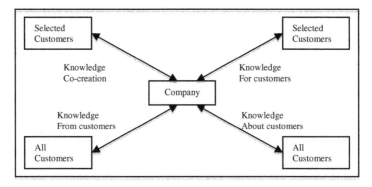

Figure 2: A concept framework for CKM [1].

One of the definitions of knowledge is from Davenport and Pruzak's [6] as a "fluid mix of framed experience, values, contextual information and expert insight that provide a framework for evaluation and incorporating new experiences and information" [7]. This research employs the definition as the base theory.

2.2 Customer knowledge and customer knowledge management

As a relatively new area of research, customer knowledge is varying from different background and research purpose. Rowley proposed two types of customer knowledge [8]:

Knowledge about customers, which may include knowledge about potential customers and customer segments as well as knowledge about individual customers.

Knowledge possessed by customers, about products ranges, such as compatibility between computer hardware components, and about the wider context and marketplace into which products and service are delivered.

Base on García's [9] results about distinction of customer knowledge, Gebert suggests that knowledge flows can be classified into three categories [10]:

Knowledge for customers is required in CRM processes to satisfy customers' knowledge needs. Examples include knowledge on products, markets and suppliers [9].

Knowledge about customers is accumulated to understand customer's motivations and to address them in a personalized way. It includes customer histories, connections, requirements, expectations, and their purchasing activity [11].

Knowledge from customers is customers' knowledge of products, suppliers and markets. Through interactions with customers this knowledge can be gathered to sustain continuous improvement, for example, service improvements or new product developments [9].

A later research illustrated a different customer knowledge categories framework [1] as follows:

As the graphic shown above, Smith proposed a four-dimension customer knowledge model.

Knowledge of customers

Knowledge of customers is the domain of traditional CRM systems and data mining. It not only includes basic tombstone data about a customer, but also includes a record of his/her transactions with the organization, products and services used, and certain personal preferences.

Knowledge for customers

A second type of customer knowledge includes everything an organization provides to its customers [10]. While traditionally, knowledge for customers focused on information and expertise about products and services developed by marketing or R&D, more recently, with the advent of e-business, customers are benefiting from a much broader range of company knowledge designed for them.

Knowledge from customers

Customers are a strategic opportunity for companies to learn [12]. This knowledge is often the domain of customer service or marketing. Understanding what customers know is an important but neglected part of an organization's knowledge [8]. Ideally, customers should be asked to share both their good and bad experiences with the firm. Studies show that when companies really listen to their customers and take their comments seriously, clients are impressed and feel more loyalty [13]. What is learned from customers provides economic value if the knowledge is used effectively [12]. However, this knowledge must be integrated into an organization's back-end processes to enable managers to act quickly and flexibly [10].

Knowledge co-creation

The final dimension of customer knowledge derives from a two-way relationship. As yet, little systematic attention is paid to customers as knowledge development partners. As many companies discovered, often what customers say they want is not what they really want. Therefore, true collaboration is important in this type of knowledge development [13]. Getting customers to cooperate more effectively and interactively in knowledge co-creation will be one of the biggest challenges facing knowledge managers in the future [6]. Companies involved in this type of CK should therefore consider the value this process generates for the customer as well as for their own organization. They should ensure that tangible benefits result for customers, for example, improved satisfaction, personalized products or services, or even monetary compensation [13].

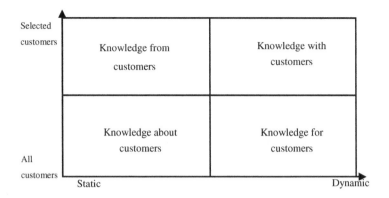

Figure 3: Two-dimension CKM analysis model.

3 A two-dimension analysis model for CKM

From the customer knowledge literature reviewed above, the previous researches mainly focus on the conceptual framework and process framework. As with other aspects of KM, the most significant challenges in implementing CKM effectively are organizational, not technical [1]. The main obstacle of most applications of CKM is absence of a simple and easy understanding model to analyze customer knowledge in practice.

We propose a novel analysis model for CKM to address this problem, which can improve CKM process design both in conception and practice aspects. The model illustrated in Figure 3. For keeping same preposition form, we use knowledge with customers instead of knowledge co-creation in former's models. So, the customer knowledge is assorted as: knowledge about customer, knowledge from customer, knowledge for customer, and knowledge with customer.

In this model, two dimensions are employed to construct the matrix. The first dimension is the customers' scope: from all customers to selected customers. This dimension identifies the different range of customers of customer knowledge. With known of that, the managers and front-line workers can use different strategy to collect, distribute, or create customer knowledge.

The second dimension is the variability of knowledge, from static to dynamic. From the knowledge definition of Davenport and Pruzak [6], the knowledge is a kind of mixed fluid. One characteristic of fluid is the variability, so the knowledge can be static or dynamic. With known of that, the managers and CKM system designer can use different methods to process customer knowledge.

The knowledge about customers is the base of all other types of knowledge, which locate in the lower left of the matrix. While most companies started out developing this type of customer knowledge by creating data warehouses or customer information files, few gained many true insights. "They may know more about their customers but they don't know the customers themselves or how to attract new ones" [6]. To create useful knowledge about customers, companies need more than transaction data. To be used, this knowledge must also be integrated across processes, information and technology. Few companies have yet achieved either goal [14]. The model tells that this kind of customer knowledge is from all customer and respectively static. The strategy to process this kind of CK is widely collected and stored. Then it needs statistics methods to get the whole picture of customers.

The knowledge for customers is the knowledge that makes customers to obtain maximum product or service value. It not only comes from company itself, but also from other customers and the third party. The position of it in matrix is lower right. That means this kind of knowledge is for all customers, and it is dynamic. It includes product manual, user experience, best practice, sometime even including the culture and history of product or brand, which become the highly attractive part of consumption experience. It requires managers to improve this part continually.

The knowledge from customers is a traditional and direct source of customer knowledge for companies. Typically, it comes from questionnaires and investigations in customers. This kind of knowledge helps company improve their products or services. It is located in higher left of the matrix, which means it is for selected customers and respectively static.

The knowledge with customers is also named knowledge co-creation. This is the newest and most complex knowledge in these four, and it shapes the future of business. The new business trend relates this kind of knowledge including prosumerism, mutual innovation, and communities of creation. The examples can be found in Google, Facebook, and IKEA. From the literature review, the knowledge is only for selected customers and dynamic. So, it is at higher right position in the matrix. This kind of knowledge is most valuable but difficult to obtain. Company employees and their customers create it with high degree of cooperation.

The strategy for manage customer knowledge depends on the different business type. For the common process, firms firstly need to build up CKM with about customer knowledge. That is the stage one. In stage two, there are two things to be done: the first thing is collecting knowledge from customers, and the second thing is disseminating knowledge for customers. The stage three will focus on the knowledge co-creation with customers. In this stage, a knowledge co-creation platform needs to be built.

4 Case study of CKM in hospitality

The following case study research of a five star luxury hotel shows the importance of deep understanding the knowledge characteristics in CKM practice. The case focuses on a major apartment within modern service management, VIP Reception Department (VRD), which serves government and business guests and common customers alike. It consists of 10 employees who offer support on two levels, depending on expertise and knowledge to resolve inquiries about a wide array of topics connected to hotel service and related business or tourism issues. They also collect customers' feedback and information from specific website, face-to-face talking and frontline workers.

4.1 CKM challenges

In order to address the needs of their customers and improve hotel service quality, VRD agents utilize different information channels collecting customers' knowledge and distribute to customers or other department. On one side, the content was disseminated via internal TV channel, booklet, and themed events. The selected knowledge passes to other departments through "Information liaison letter." Each VRD employee had to organize his or her content individually and new employees did not have access to older information. As the amount of content increased, the VRD agents tended to primarily use their computer documents folder for information retrieval. For customer knowledge processed in same method and same strategy without classification, the existing solution also caused significant costs for creating, formatting, and publishing content. The complicated process with only very basic support by internal hotel information management systems is critical to supporting the VRD agents.

4.2 Relevant knowledge aspects

The focus of the project was to provide the VRD employee with knowledge understanding and classification, thereby concentrating on customer knowledge flow that can be divided and processed by different strategy. This also applied to information support since the editors had no adequate tool to help them structure the knowledge and get an overview of existing documents. Up to the project, editors had to convert content manually with office software. To overcome the challenges, the customer knowledge management model is employed to make knowledge structured and accessible, also make the whole process clearly. The model for the editors enables them to collect new knowledge with purpose and provides an overview of existing knowledge. They can be processed and edited with proper methods. The knowledge about customer, collected by online booking system and reception, storage as static data, then produce statistic results about customers, for example, customer geographical distribution and age distribution. The knowledge for customers, as a dynamic content and for all of customers, updates regularly with VRD and distribute to other departments.

4.3 Results

Based on a detailed analysis of customer knowledge processes of VRD agents and editors, knowledge management performance was significantly improved. The new structure and improved timeliness of information available on the knowledge platform is an important factor in supporting VRD agents. It enables them to provide faster response with higher quality. For the information support department, the cost and time needed to maintain the new platform were greatly reduced by mostly eliminating efforts to convert existing content. The structure could now be maintained much more easily. The focus on fix range of information source makes it easier for agents to find what they need and reduces operational costs of publication for editors.

5 Conclusion

The understanding of customers can lead to differentiation for a company, which is the core competition ability. CKM process helps company communication with their customers. This paper proposes a CKM analysis model to reveal the properties of customer knowledge. The case study shows the application of the CKM model in customer processes can lead to increased process performance. The future research will focus on the knowledge with customers, which create strong connection between customers and company. That already and will continue create more compatible business models.

References

[1] H. Smith, Developments in practice XVIII-customer knowledge management: adding value for our customers. *Communications of the Association for Information Systems*, **16**, pp. 744–755, 2005.

[2] W. Reinartz, V. Kumar, The mismanagement of customer loyalty. *Harvard Business Review*, **80(7)**, pp. 86–94, 2002.

[3] K. Desouza, Y. Awazu, Gaining a competitive edge from your customers. *,M Review*, **7(3)**, pp. 12–15, 2004.

[4] M. Zanjani, R. Rouzbehani, H. Dabbagh, Proposing a conceptual model of customer knowledge management: a study of CKM tools in British dotcoms. *International Journal of Human and Social Sciences*, (136), 2008.

[5] S. Hanvanich, Reconceptualizing the meaning and domain of marketing knowledge. *Journal of knowledge*, **7(4)**, pp. 124–135, 2003.

[6] T. Davenport, L. Pruzak, Working Knowledge: How Organizations Manage What They Know. Harvard Business School Press, Boston, MA, pp. 35–36, 2000.

[7] T. Davenport, J. Harris, A. Kohli, How do they know their customers so well? *MIT Sloan Management Review*, **42(2)**, pp. 63–73, 2001.

[8] J. Rowley, Eight questions for customer knowledge management in e-business. *Journal of Knowledge Management*, **6(5)**, pp. 500–511, 2002.

[9] M. García-Murillo, H. Annabi, Customer knowledge management. *Journal of the Operational Research Society*, **53(8)**, pp. 875–884, 2002.

[10] H. Gebert, M. Geib, L. Kolbe, W. Brenner, Knowledge-enabled customer relationship management: integrating customer relationship management and knowledge management concepts. *Journal of Knowledge Management*, **7(5)**, pp. 107–123, 2003.

[11] G. Day, Capabilities for Forging Customer Relationships. Marketing Science Institute, Cambridge, pp. 89–90, 2000.

[12] M. Zack, Rethinking the knowledge based organization. *MIT Sloan Management Review*, **44(4)**, pp. 67–71, 2003.

[13] M. Gibbert, M. Leibold, G. Probst, Five styles of customer knowledge management, and how smart companies use them to create value. *European Management Journal*, **20(5)**, pp. 459–469, 2002.

[14] J. McKeen, H. Smith, *Making IT Happen: Critical Issues in IT Management*. John Wiley & Sons, Chichester, pp. 16–17, 2003.

Research and development of tourism information management system under the network background

Tao Li

Baotou Light Industry Professional Technology Institute, Baotou, China

Abstract

With the continuous development of tourism industry, tourism department for information is more and more big. This paper is based on the status of tourism industry, using modern unified computer network system to realize the network of the tourism management and store of all kinds of information in an orderly manner, and a variety of business systems to achieve data integration and information integration, all kinds of information resources of the travel agency, for collaborative centralized management. And the establishment of ASP dynamic web technology realizes the quick release and tourists to book online tourism information, saving manpower and improve work efficiency, to achieve a multiplier effect.

Keywords: network, information integration, synergy.

1 Introduction

Tourism has the laudatory name of "smokeless industry" and "eternal sunrise industry," and it has listed with the oil industry and automobile industry as the world's three largest industries. According to the statistics of WTTC, its output of US$4.7 trillion annual revenue, directly or indirectly providing employment for 27 million people, and supporting for the development of tens of thousands of enterprises[1-2].

Since the reform and opening up, China's tourism industry has developed very rapidly, but in comparison, the breadth and depth of domestic tourism development in our country is far cannot adapt to the needs of economic development and improve people's living standard. With the development of market economy and improve people's income level, people's demand for tourism consumption rise further, and the position and role of the domestic tourism industry in the national economy is more and more important in[3].

But the tourism industry in our country is still weak, and the management means are backward, low degree of information technology, so the enterprise benefit is poor. Now the tourism administrative department has such problems still that the management way is backward, and lack the measure of the information management, and the information communication channel not unobstructed. In the face of difficulties and challenges, China's tourism industry must change the idea, innovative thinking, to the informationization construction as the breakthrough point and a new method, integrate various resources, so as to realize new across the industry as a whole. To strengthen the construction of tourism informationization, we can improve the work efficiency of management departments at all levels and management levels, streamline procedures and work to reduce costs, increasing publicity, and speeding up the information communication to improve the information efficiency. On the other hand, we can conduct e-commerce, and meet the personalized needs of tourists to improve the quality of tourism services and change traditional tourism enterprise business model and reduce cost and increase benefit, so as to improve the quality of the whole tourism industry, tourism information, will further expand tourism pillar industry, to promote the overall information level of the tourism industry, optimize the industrial structure and resource allocation, perfect the industry chain, thus driving the development of many related industries, stimulating domestic demand, expanding employment, increasing the foreign exchange income, to play a positive role in promoting economic development[4-5].

2 The present situation of tourism information management system

At present, some of the tourism sectors in China in terms of information work and the investment is less, and play constraint role on their own development, so they can promote local customs and practices through the establishment of travel sites, network, information management of information, to improve their own competitive ability.

At present, there are many medium-sized tourism authorities still relying on manual used the original electronic document, spreadsheet (such as WORD, EXCEL, or simple ACCESS database) for the management of tourism information, and most travel agencies are still also without their tourism website, and are not in this network age accept customer online booking. As the business continues to expand, the travel agency business operations involve various fees, and the customers as well as tourism line is more and more complex, and the business operator if only by manual handling large amounts of data, is missing information phenomenon occurs more easily, but also likely to have a growth rate and the waste of resources and idle the problem. Therefore, only by strengthening the unified management, the integration of information resources for the tourism sector makes the industry more rational, efficient operation. The existed problems of the tourism information management mode are mainly embodied in the following aspects:

1. The query speed of all kinds of tourism information is slow, and is the intense work. Involved the visitor information, tour information, cost, line, attractions, hotels, and so on a large number of data of tourism information, with manual summary, speed is slow, tedious, error prone.
2. All kinds of resources allocation between are difficult. Due to the wide surface of information, large amount of information, so to some of the resources for unified management and deployment is need to spend a lot of artificial.
3. Quite a part of resource is lack of protection, in a state of insecurity, and a lot of information is easy disclosure.
4. The requirement reaction is slow for the customer service. Based on the above reasons, the customer service requirements will not make quick response.
5. Lacking quality feedback of the unified management service.

3 The demand analysis of tourism information management system under the background of network

3.1 Summary of overall demand

According to the demand of the tourism information management, our common problem of scenic spots, hotels, transportation, tourism, and the characteristics of holiday tourism related information management. It mainly includes the attractions information management, hotel management, traffic information management and tourism service information management, and the characteristics of holiday information management and so on several aspects of content. These aspects include the entry and query of information, and the updated information.

Administrator manage information for the change of information to ensure that the latest information and accuracy, and easy to daily operation and maintenance.

3.2 Specific analysis of demand

According to the overall functional requirements described the specific functional requirements are as follows:

1. Functional requirements
   When a query to the relevant content of the site, according to the route, interactive query can bus information on attractions, in the bus information module, can also according to the line via the spots on the spots information query.
   According to the scenic spot information update or bus information change, add, modify, and delete operations.

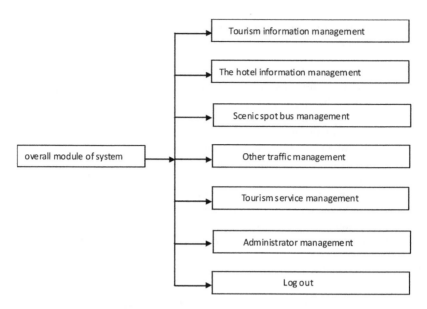

Figure 1: Overall module of system.

2. The hotel's functional requirements

   Hotel information, as an integral part of the tourism industry, in the system can do the corresponding query and management, and listed in the system level of the hotel, and hotel information, and can query the nearby attractions.

   According to the actual situation to update the hotel information to ensure the latest sex.

3. The functional demand of information service

   For the convenience of information query, this system provides the corresponding modules, such as traffic information and the characteristics of holiday for flight information, and long-distance passenger information and train information have made the concrete introduction, for the common problems and questions answer also solved in this function.

4 The overall design of the tourism information management system under the network

4.1 Module partition of the system

According to the analysis of system requirements, it divides the system into the system administrator module, tourism information module, the hotel information module, the scenic spot bus module, the other traffic management module, tourism service module, and exit the system module as shown in Figure 1.

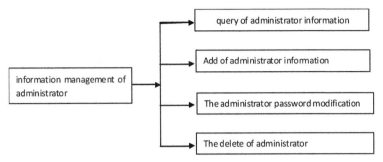

Figure 2: The module of the information management of administrator.

4.2 The design of each module function

1. The module of the system administrator
    The information system administrator module is mainly pointed to the system administrator for maintenance. It includes:

    Administrator information query: browse the administrator of the relevant information.
    Administrator information to add, add a new administrator to make the system administrator.
    Password change: the primary key and the user name cannot be modified, only you can change the password.
    Deleting the administrator: according to the user name to delete users of the system.

    System administrator module in the practical significance of each module is the traffic in the system increase, increasing the administrator can facilitate better management and maintenance of the system. This is shown in Figure 2.

2. Tourist information management module
    Tourist information management module including: Sightseeing information query module, add the module information on attractions, sights, and attractions information modification module remove modules. Specific functions are as follows:

    Attractions information inquiry: Tourist information attractions under the name of, or interest an appropriate query type. You can also directly check all information on attractions, and can query the corresponding points of the bus information.
    Attractions added: to input new attractions.
    Attractions information changes: changes to the attractions to make changes in a timely manner.
    Attractions information delete: to remove attractions.

    Tourism information management module of each submodule in the actual meaning is when the administrator in the management of tourism

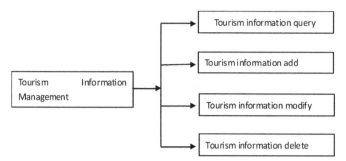

Figure 3: The module of the tourism information management.

information can quickly and easily add attractions information system, at the same time in the maintenance and management of information, and connected with the data in the database, not only convenient for visitors to browse, but also improve the accuracy of the information. Administrators can also to query of attractions, attractions to ensure that the information in the accuracy, timeliness, so as to ensure the accuracy and completeness of the system; this is shown in Figure 3.

3. The hotel information management module

The hotel information management module is mainly the information of hotel management and maintenance.

Hotel information module includes: adding hotel information query module, information module, information modify module, and hotel information delete module, specific function as follows:

Hotel information query: according to the name of the hotel or hotel belongs to the level of the corresponding query. It also can query all hotel information directly, and can also according to the hotel information query to nearby scenic spots.

Hotel information to add: add new hotel information.

Hotel information changes: for each change in the hotel related information to make changes in a timely manner.

Hotel information delete: delete the hotel information.

The actual meaning of each submodule in the hotel information management module is when the administrator in the management of the hotel information, you can quickly and easily add the hotel information system, at the same time in the maintenance and management of information, so when this hotel name or resettlement, also can timely modify the relevant information system and improve the accuracy of the information. Administrators can also directly do the hotel information query to ensure the accuracy of the hotel information, so as to ensure the accuracy and completeness of the system. Adding and modifying the information with dynamic background database connection; this is shown in Figure 4.

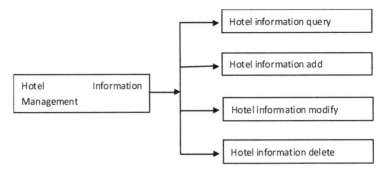

Figure 4: The module of the hotel information management.

4. Bus information management module of the scenic spot

The bus information management module mainly includes the scenic spot bus information management and the bus information management.

Resort bus information module includes: the bus information query module, resort bus information add module, bus information modify module and scenic spot bus information delete module, specific function as follows:

Scenic spot bus information query: according to the bus information query through the scenic spots or bus itself.

Scenic spot bus information to add, can be to enter the basic information of the bus into the database, can also according to the attractions of bus information input and perfect.

Scenic spot bus information change: according to the attractions to increase or delete or change bus lines itself to modify the basic information of the bus accordingly.

Scenic spot bus information delete: according to the scenic spots to delete or change or cancel the bus information deleted from the database.

Scenic spot bus information module of each submodule in the actual meaning is that when the administrator manages the system, they add the bus' own information of corresponding table in the database. At the same time information in the table according to the change of attractions information make a corresponding change, and the dynamic connection between table and table is completed. At the same times they also can accord the change to modify correspondingly, and delete, when information changes, the scenic spot bus information also can produce corresponding change.

5. Other traffic information management module

Other traffic information management module mainly includes: the train information management module, the aircraft information management module and long-distance passenger transport information management module, the specific function is as follows:

The train information management module includes:
The train information query: query of in and out of the train information;

The train information management: the information to add, delete and modify.
The plane information management module includes:
Flight information query: query for access to the flight information;
The plane information management: management for new routes, and the corresponding information.
Long-distance passenger transport information management module includes:
The long-distance passenger information query: the long-distance passenger vehicles in and out of information query;
Long-distance passenger transportation management: including information query, add, delete, and modify.

5 Conclusion

On the basis of the traditional tourism information system, the system use the WebGIS technology to build the tourism information system based on Internet and realize the network of tourism information query and management function, which can realize spatial analysis and at the same time the operating to provide rich and vivid images, voice, data, and electronic map. It with the local departments such as traffic, weather, travel service system, will provide more perfect function. Under the trend of the global digital, the tourism information system based on Internet will be a new generation of tourism information system development direction.

References

[1] J. Richter, *Applied Microsoft.NET Framework Programming*. Microsoft Press, New York, NY, pp. 12–16, 2003.
[2] E. Lamma, P. Mello, F. Riguzzi, A System for measuring function points from an ER-DFD specification. *The Computer Journal*,3(12), pp. 36–38, 2004.
[3] A. Tveit, *A Survey of Agent-Oriented Software Engineering*, 8(5), pp. 21–22, 2002.
[4] R. Rada, Levels of reuse in educational information systems. *Campus-Wide Information Systems*, 18(3), pp. 21–22, 2001.
[5] E. Lamma, P. Mello, F. Riguzzi, A system for measuring function points from an ER-DFD specification. *The Computer Journal*, 3(12), pp. 36–38, 2004.

Research on application of computer aided technology in art and design

Qiushi Li, Xin Meng
Shenyang Aerospace University; Liaoning Shenyang, China

Abstract

The computer has become an important part of the design field, and is widely used in the field of art design. This paper mainly discusses the most direct contribution of the computer aided technology on design—brought new modeling language and way of expression, and it has changed the design method and the design concept of people, caused the art design changes.

Keywords: art design, the computer aided technology, the most direct contribution.

1   Introduction

If a dozen years ago, people in the computer are still in the stage of cognition, and have no bottom, but today, computer has penetrated into every corner of social life. With the development of computer software and hardware technology continues to improve, computer graphics and user interactive methods, combined with art and design staff involved, the computer has become an important part of design. The plane advertisement design, construction of two-dimensional graphics, multimedia production, and publishing and printing, webpage design are not possible without computer. At the same time, the computer not only brings in new design tool, but also brings enormous change and impact on the ideas and methods of modern art design [1].

2   Application of computer in modern art design

2.1   Development and application of computer in modern art design

Design technology of art animation computer in the world has exceeded the scope for making simple. It is widely used in the field of film and television advertising,

Figure 1: Jurassic Park.   Figure 2: Lotus lantern.

television movie stunt, building simulation, industrial design, computer-aided education, because the computer is added, the past cannot be the technique to realize. For example: "Jurassic Park"(as shown in Figure 1) of the United States of America, breaking box office records, use special effects animation produced. With the "Jurassic Park," "Star Wars," "Predator," "Titanic" outstanding works, using computer animation design technology, and TV advertising art making is everywhere. Technology and reliable function of powerful software make the design personnel can swim in the infinite reverie and virtual space of thinking. Guangzhou Honda Automobile Co Ltd is a huge advertising for the new car has not been launched, in the ad, designers will be made by the computer of the car through the streets of the people are hurrying to and fro, crawling in the rugged mountain road, along the glittering on the surface of the water, all the back for the scene and real shooting, a perfect combination of two cars and real by computer simulation the people cannot identify the authenticity. Reflection on the body of the shadow and roadside trees in the street cars and real no difference, and the full performance of each part of performance of the car using animation unique function, the advertising effect can want to know.

Since before the 1990 domestic installed the first set of domestic animation software, computer is used as the dynamic design and plane advertising just by some very simple software. Later, with the workstation animation and graphic software are imported, domestic technical personnel and art designers to quickly will be widely applied in various fields of advertising, film, and art design. Today, we have been very frequent television in CCTV and the national each big city program, see a lot of the two-dimensional technology in the production of television advertising and TV drama, and also appeared company production with high production quality and creative, they in resource limited technology, with full technical, bold creativity, produced a batch of high quality computer animation, such as "journey to the west," "Lotus Lantern," "emergency landing," by domestic and foreign counterparts and the masses of praise in the production of technical and creative.

Because the domestic production technology continues to improve, so in the past many domestic large sums to foreign advertising production manufacturers and now have turned to find companies to make domestic cooperation. Now the new district planning and transformation of the old city more and more have used the computer technology to the two-dimensional design, and have not yet started

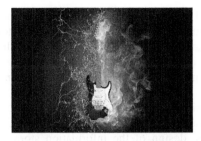

Figure 3: Fire and water compatible   Figure 4: Winter and summer. coexistence.

Figure 5: The two-dimensional virtual digital model.

building design, people can be very intuitive to the image, with a real sense of space and the two-dimensional graphics and the existing buildings and terrain are compared, thus providing technical guarantee for the planning and coordination.

In the print ad design, the computer also brought great changes, through the computer's graphics processing technology and image processing technology, can be a lot of different graphics images seamlessly combined to create a fantasy world unparalleled image. Such as the image of "fire and water compatible (as shown in Figure 3)," "winter and summer coexistence (as shown in Figure 4)" strange scene, by using this technology to produce advertising, its visual impact is not made face metaphor.

In the aspect of industrial product design (as shown in Figure 5), application of computer means to establish a two-dimensional virtual digital model, to the appearance processing, material analysis, structure analysis, mold analysis, simulation operation, and the later data conversion, mold processing. Intuitively, real-time miniaturized editing, operation is simple and convenient in particular, most directly reflect the designer's intention, has brought unprecedented ease of use, make the design more scientific, accuracy, reducing the design process of repetition work and mistakes, effectively reduces the product development costs, shorten product development cycle. The domestic design companies and designers can better meet the product promotion will, provide good service; therefore, computer art design industry in China are from young to mature, and gradually reduces with the latest international technology gap.

2.2 The innovation of computer of modern art design

The computer as a product of modern science and technology exists in today's culture; we cannot simply believe it is just a tool, but it is also the world's information and intermediary contacts, and is an interface of this culture. People learn and grasp the world with its communication, not only the computer communication of science and art, the more important is that it is to link the design tradition and future; it is integrated into the traditional design method and contains a unique language electronic world, in reality the development and changing reality.

The most direct contributions to the design is brought and expression of new modeling language. According to the characteristics of computer architecture, it is used to complete the rational analysis, design of the information storage, modeling performance for such tasks, which enable the designer to focus more on the concept of creative design, hand, when an idea is ripe can make the computer to modification, extension, strengthen the idea or practice, finally to determine the form of it. In the traditional design procedures, from creative design to the various stages of level of actual production, design personnel to participate in all stages of the work surface, into the computer, instead of the designer to do most of the complex production work. In another sense, it is the outstanding designers in the creative design of the ability, so that they can more work at a higher level, which makes the modern art design is more systematic and hierarchy.

The computer screen mode opens a new field to design communication, and the computer can make the design process visualization, and image generation process can be effectively controlled, and the direct feedback control effect, from the surface to eliminate the defects of the traditional design process. In the design of just storage change results, it can return to any work creation process, the design process is no longer a one-way development; face is multidirectional repeated. In addition, the calculation speed of computers is too quick that the human brain cannot match; it will soon be the designer's creation intention into visual graphics, and change the color, material, light, body, and the point of observation is also very convenient. It brought new problems; designers sometimes need to face many design options, in the many nonrational method to solve the problem. It is very difficult to achieve the optimal choice, because the optimization is endless; therefore, the design principle of harmonious and moderate it conforms to the development of modern society.

The two-dimensional modeling and rendering technology enables the design personnel in the observation of objects, and the viewpoint is mobile, and it can show various aspects and details of objects, to build and modify the form, but also in the space point of view, such as reflection and evaluation, problems can start from the two-dimensional space close to reality. In addition, due to the global and local performance, objects from the angle of reality do not exist, so you can create exaggerated deformation, and the effect is remarkable. In the two-dimensional space of computer, a plurality of body can be connected or scattered, creating a complex form therefore face. Linked objects can be set into a group, preserving the spatial relationships in the same change, so in the analysis of object more levels and relevance. The computer simulation technology in space to complete the authenticity of the same time, due to the introduction of animation technology, the motion of objects, or through the object, in order to understand the relationship between various parts. The combination of computer multimedia and virtual reality technology, even the sound effect, designers can design results show more vivid and intuitive.

Due to the complexity and variety of social life, the designer must meet multi-level, multi-field cooperation; therefore, are words _ exchange in modern art and design work is very important, the development of computer network and remote transmission technology, make the communication without the limitation of time and space. For example, research and design personnel can be in different places at the same time, to do the same work design. The traditional design room limitation has been broken; the true meaning of the "nonwall design room" will be established, and the designer will emphasize more on cooperation and exchanges.

Computer which is a new design tool has been widely used in more and more fields, and has brought the huge change for these fields, and has changed the design method and the design concept of people, causing the art design changes. But the essence of design will remain unchanged, and the design will always commit to the creation of human life.

3   Research on method of applying computer technology in art design

The development of the arts is inevitably influenced by the society and science and technology. With the development of computer technology, computer technology is widely used in people's life and work, and art design and computer technology combined with computer art design is the application of computer technology to form the new development, and it also promotes the innovation and development of traditional art skill. Recently the application of computer technology in art designing is mainly manifested in the following aspects:

3.1 Application in the creation of the basic pattern

In the basic design pattern, we need make basic graphics, different or the same, build a new visual image in two-dimensional space. This design has very strong flexibility, which use the same basic graphics and the picture in the skeletal framework and are placed in different ways. With different permutations and combinations, they will produce multiple and totally different picture effects, which have high requirements on the designer's way of thinking. But the computer AutoCAD drawing software can solve this problem, as shown in Figure 6, and it has the powerful drawing function, and the two-dimensional graphics can not only draw the general, but also for modeling of three-dimensional entity. Using the computer technology can not only make flat pattern design quickly and accurately, but also can be repeatedly sought to change and combination by copy, mirror, rotate the command; then the surface rendering is difficult to get out of hand drawn graphic, greatly reducing the designers work.

Figure 6: Pattern drawn by AutoCAD.

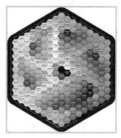

Figure 7: The color harmony.

3.2 The application of color blending

Color is an important aspect of a piece of design work, different color combinations can give a person different feelings of the visual and psychological form. Before using the computer technology, the designer of the deployment of color is a lot of abstract imagination in your mind, thus mastery of color is not clear, and easy to cause imagine away from the actual and inevitably needs to be repeated debug to designers. The software, Adobe Photoshop (as shown in Figure 7), has a strong advantage in the use of color, and has fast and flexible way of color change, so designer can apply real color performance, get the feeling of color; color is tie-in, and easily reduced color collocation errors.

3.3 The application of three-dimensional design

In the three-dimensional design, designers need space imagination; the designers of spatial imagination ability requirements are relatively high, but only to imagine, the designer to work feeling more fuzzy, three-dimensional design is difficult. While the computer 3D modeling and rendering technology can show various aspects and details of objects, so that in designers point of view in the observation object, flow, then can the body build and modify. At present, the use of computer 3DS MAX software in the three-dimensional design is seen widely (as shown in Figure 8). 3DS MAX software system provides a command panel standard aggregates, makes the establishment of standard assembly is convenient. At the same time, in the design also facilitates the collection of materials. 3DS MAX software system to provide a powerful material library, can simulate the

Figure 8: The color harmony.

convenient art designer of material, greatly reducing the manual operation more difficult.

3.4 Issues to be considered in the design

First of all, beautiful external form and the deep cultural connotation is the basic requirement of two people a successful design works. We believe that as a contemporary designer must first have the art foundation; it can help us to instinctively grasp the composition, shape, brightness, color picture form elements; without a professional art training people is impossible to become a qualified designer, because there is no basic painting ability, also there can be no professional skill experience, no professional skill experience, there can be no good art feeling. This is the first factor to achieve outstanding design works. A basic art people in general, only could be the general designer, an art foundation outstanding person, will it be possible to become a good designer.

Second, we must have a design idea of open. This is the key difference between design works, an outstanding design works and a mediocre. This design idea we said is not just to think; it is the accumulation of mountain deep cultural literacy, advanced information resources, and rich life results. If the art basic solution is the external form, design works well, the design concept is to solve the deep meaning of the works. The culture and design of analogy "the relations between the roots and the plants" or "compared to the foundation and high-rise" relationship or, in short, is to explain the close degree. If we just stay in the fine arts study, in the face of history, literature, philosophy, little technology, cultural knowledge, design, and development at home and abroad, the lack of an overall understanding, it will seriously restrict our imagination and creativity, greatly limiting the thinking of horizontal and vertical extension, produce works must be narrow-minded, pale, lack of depth, so that designers can't be called a designer, the surface is only a craftsman. We have a lot of people who do not know the simple truth, which really confuses them that so many colorful cultural phenomenon today do not know where to start, why? It is very simple, we fell into a surface where we cannot find the source; therefore, the precipitation of culture must start from the source. This requests us not only to lay a solid foundation of art, must also lay a solid cultural foundation, a solid cultural foundation is get through long period of hard study . If we master the culture source, we will soon know each branch of the sequence of events, we know what we need, which is need to be discarded, which branch is our own need to develop, in such a clear cultural ideas before, our designs is the extensive and profound.

In twenty-first century, the information has become the powerful productivity, information stream varies from minute to minute; a designer if not timely to have this information, so in this era will be far behind. The advantages of modern designer is the largest in the first time, enjoy the same information resources and the world's top designers. A variety of media, magazines, Internet, forum, seminars, exhibitions, we must prompt attention and participation, which not only can bring skills and creative nutrition infinite for a designer, more important is to ensure that you are always the most advanced.

4 Conclusion

To sum up, we need to establish a new system of art: art and design concept (literacy, information resources, the accumulation of life) and computer technology. In this system, we will make art as design basis, the concept as the soul of the design, the computer as a design tool. We must correctly understand the relationship between them, and will not have the order reversed. I believe that through our continuous efforts and exploration, there will be one batch of outstanding design works.

References

[1] M. Nanni, D. Pedreschi. Time-focused clustering of trajectories of moving objects. *Journal of Intelligent Information Systems*, **27(3)**, pp. 267–289, 2009.

Design and implementation of mobile social networking communication platform based on Wi-Fi and Android

Zeng Wei
Network Center, China West Normal University, Nanchong Sichuan, China

Abstract

In recent years, Internet is heading toward the development of mobility, wireless, and personalization. With the rapid development pace of Mobile Internet, smart handheld devices have been widely popularized. They can provide Wi-Fi, Bluetooth, EDGE, 3G, and some other wireless access to meet the demand of the hardware of mobile social communications applications. While operating systems like Android and IOS provide a better development platform. But, without access by fixed infrastructure such as base station or city hotspot support, it lacks web application technologies to provide effective protection of communication between handheld terminals. This paper briefly introduces the technology of mobile Wi-Fi hotspot, P2P network technology, and the recent development of the operating system of smart handheld device. Then, by analyzing social network applications, this paper designs and implements a mobile social networking communication application on the Android platform, which provides a new way for the mode of social network application.
Keywords: Wi-Fi, social application communication framework, Android.

1 Introduction

With the development of mobile networks and popularity of social networking service, demand wherever and whenever we can establish or maintain social relationship with relatives, friends and even strangers become more and more urgent. Social apps on intelligent terminals commonly use the client/server (c/s) structure [1]. However, if the users do not want to access the Internet through the infrastructure network, these social apps cannot meet the user' social contact needs for the lack of server's support. On the other hand, existing social applications based on intelligent handheld terminals can

WIT Transactions on Information and Communication Technologies, Vol. 61, © 2014 WIT Press
www.witpress.com, ISSN 1743-3517 (on-line)
doi:10.2495/MIIT130181

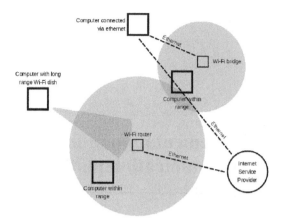

Figure 1: A diagram shows a Wi-Fi network.

provide good support on the application mode based on the relationship between the friendships of network members. But Application Mode based on relationship between the locations of network members just develops at an early stage. This paper focuses on how the users of smart handheld device can make social communication with each other without access to network server through infrastructure network. By using the Android application software based on MPCF designed in this paper, we can achieve dynamic maintenance member list and make a broadcast or unicast communication between the terminals on the list. By installing this social communication software on Android handset, we can use chart room function, instant message function based on Wi-Fi connection established by mobile hotspot.

2   Wi-Fi hotspot, ad hoc network, and Android

2.1 Introduction of Wi-Fi hotspot

An increase in the adoption of Wi-Fi technology is expected with rapidly falling prices and ever improving performance. Wi-Fi has become the technology of choice for home and office networks as it has claimed its place as the wireless replacement of Ethernet. Wi-Fi is an attractive feature that offers enhanced data connectivity and also offers the potential of making voice calls over a Wi-Fi network expanding the mobile network into home or enterprise. It is predicted that more than 450 million Wi-Fi enabled units will be shipped by 2010 to take the mobile phone and home entertainment markets.

A hotspot is a site that offers Internet access over a wireless local area network (WLAN) through the use of a router connected to a link to an Internet service provider. It typically uses Wi-Fi technology.

It can be divided into four types: Free Wi-Fi hotspots, commercial hotspots, software hotspots, HS2, and Wi-Fi Certified Passpoint.

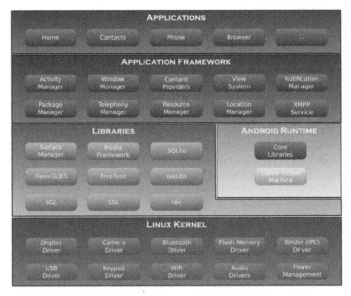

Figure 2: Architecture of Android.

2.2 Introduction of ad hoc network

A wireless ad hoc network is a decentralized type of wireless network. The network is ad hoc because it does not rely on a pre-existing infrastructure, such as routers in wired networks or access points in managed (infrastructure) wireless networks. Instead, each node participates in routing by forwarding data for other nodes, so the determination of which nodes forward data is made dynamically on the basis of network connectivity. In addition to the classic routing, ad hoc networks can use flooding for forwarding the data. Ad hoc network often refers to a mode of operation of IEEE 802.11 wireless networks. Wireless ad hoc networks can be further classified by their application: mobile ad hoc networks (MANET). A MANET is a self-configuring infrastructureless network of mobile devices connected by wireless. MANET can be divided into two types: Vehicular Ad hoc Networks (VANETs) and Internet-based mobile ad hoc networks (iMANET).

2.3 Introduction of Android

Android is a Linux-based operating system designed primarily for touchscreen mobile devices such as smart phones and tablet computers. It is initially developed by Android, Inc., which Google backed financially and later bought in 2005. Android is open source and Google releases the code under the Apache License. Android consists of a kernel based on Linux kernel version 3.x (version 2.6 prior to Android 4.0 Ice Cream Sandwich). The main hardware platform for Android is the ARM architecture.

Android is a customized operating system to suit Mobile Devices including software stack and key applications. Figure 2 shows architecture of Android.

3 Design and implementation of mobile social networking communication platform

3.1 Design and implementation of mobile peer-to-peer network communication components

There are two ways to build Wi-Fi hotspot: central portable access point mode or non-central portable access point mode. Before implementing mobile peer-to-peer network communication components, we need to build Wi-Fi hotspot in Android operating system first to support social communication function on physical layer and data link layer. As we can see from Figure2, Wi-Fi driver is in Linux kernel. So, we can use JNI to call interface implemented by C\C++ library to run the binary command program to build Wi-Fi hotspot. In this process, it needs to declare the definition of local function's interface in advance. The related code of java program is below:

```
Public class NativeTask{
    ...
    static{
      try{
        //load local function library libnativetask.so
        System.loadLibrary("nativetask");
      }catch(UnsatisfiedLinkError e){
        ...
        e.printStackTrace();
      }
    }
    public static native String getProp(String name);
    public static native int runCommand(String command);
}
```

The name of this class is NativeTask. Its function is to load local function library. In the end of this code, we use the keyword "native" to declare getProp() and runCommand() to achieve configuration information and to run native command line program.

In order to establish a basic ad hoc network in the Android platform, we need to use commands based on Linux system including iwconfig, ifconfig, and echo. The detailed procedures to build Wi-Fi hotspot in ad-hoc model are as below:

1. declare this Wi-Fi hotspot's external ESSID as CoolSocial;
2. set the working pattern of hardware module wlan() as ad-hoc;
3. start wlan();
4. configure IP for wlan();
5. enable IP packet forward

The relevant script is as below:

```
WLAN_INTERFACE=WLAN()
iwconfig $WLAN_INTERFACE essid "CoolSocial"
iwconfig $WLAN_INTERFACE mode ad-hoc
iwconfig $WLAN_INTERFACE up
#take 192.168.2.254 as an example
iwconfig $WLAN_INTERFACE 192.168.2.254
echo 1>/proc/sys/net/ipv4/ip_forward
```

3.2 Design and implementation of mobile social networking communication platform on Android platform

Based on the introductions earlier, this paper mainly talks about the social apps called CoolSocial with the function of chat room, instant message, and so on.

The function of chat room involves class UnicastSendMsgByUdpAsyncTask and UnicastSendMsgByUdpService. After the user writes down group message, he can click the "send" button on the top. Code about title bar's onclick event listener is as below:

```
@Override
public void onClick(View v){
  mSpeakTabContent.makHeaderShakeAni();
  ......
  // send chat room messages
  mNeighborManager.doSendMulticastMsg(editTextContent);
  // add messages that have been sent in chat room message list
  TalkMessage taklMsg= new TalkMessage();
  talkMsg.setContent(editTextContent);
  talkMsg.setName(mNeighbormanager.getHost().getName());
  mSpeakMsgs.add(talkMsg);
  //notify adapter that chat room message data has been changed
  mSpeakMsgAdpter.notifyDataSetChanged();
  //navigate to the newest message
  mySpeakTabContent.setSelection(mSpeakMsgs.size());
  //clear message input box
  mSpeakTabContent.clearEditTextContent();

}
```

4 File transfer rate test

Speed of file transfer includes use Wi-Fi and Bluetooth between CoolSocial to transfer file. Choose three different size and types of files as showed in Table 1 to transfer and test.

Table1: Selection of Testing Files.

Tap of File	Name	Size
A	IMG_20130801.jpg	1.59M
B	Ubuntu.Sever.pdf	54.29M
C	Madonnashow.mp4	110M

Table 2: The Record and Statistics of Transmission Time of File A.

File information	Name: IMG_20130801.jpg	Size:1.59M
Transmission mode	Wi-Fi(CoolSocial)	Bluetooth
Test data (second)	1.02	36.12
	1.34	35.22
	1.52	35.07
	1.2	36.21
	1.02	35.34
Average value (second)	1.22	35.59
Average rate	1.3MB/s	0.045MB/s

Table 3: The Record and Statistics of Transmission Time of File B.

File information	Name: Ubuntu.Sever.pdf	Size: 54.29M
Transmission mode	Wi-Fi(CoolSocial)	Bluetooth
Test data (second)	29.54	1275.1
	28.92	1239.5
	30.3	1240.7
	29.02	1260.3
	30.66	1248.5
Average value (second)	29.69	1252.8
Average rate	1.83MB/s	0.043MB/s

Table 4: The Record and Statistics of Transmission Time of File C.

File information	Name: Madonnashow.mp4	Size: 110M
Transmission mode	Wi-Fi(CoolSocial)	Bluetooth
Test Data(second)	48.5	2585.8
	56.86	2596.1
	65.62	2585.1
	53.22	2600.9
	58.9	2576.2
average value(second)	56.62	2588.82
Average rate	1.94MB/s	0.042MB/s

When testing, we use Wi-Fi and Bluetooth to send the same file for 5 times, test data and transmission time are as shown in Figures 2–4.

As we can see in the test data, it is faster to use Wi-Fi than Bluetooth to transfer file.

Summary

Mobile social networking communication platform based on Wi-Fi can avoid users relying on large base stations. This paper implements a Mobile Social Networking Communication Platform based on Wi-Fi hotspot and ad hoc network. And it also tries a new application mode based on relationship between the locations of network members. It can solve the problem of communication and data transmission without Internet service. This paper concludes about technology of Wi-Fi hotspot, ad hoc network, and social service application. Then it describes method to set mobile Wi-Fi hotspot. Last but not the least, it designs CoolSocial—a social application based on Wi-Fi and Android. By testing the rate of file transmission, this implementation can really provide a good choice for Wi-Fi technology.

References

[1] D. Boyd, N. Ellison, Social network sites: definition, history, and scholarship. *Journal of Computer-Mediated Communication*, **13(1)**, pp. 36–36, 2007.

Research of WSN localization algorithm based on RSSI classification

G. Yang, X.F. Wang, J.L. Huang, J.P. Ma
Key Laboratory of High-Speed Circuit Design and EMC, Department of Electronic Engineering, Xidian University, Xi'an, China

Abstract

With the rapid development of wireless sensor networks, wireless sensor positioning technology becomes a research hot spot. RSSI localization algorithm and DV-Hop localization algorithm are typical representatives of the range-based and range-free localization algorithms of wireless sensor networks, respectively. DV-Hop localization algorithm is simple, but the localization error is relatively large. In this paper, we propose a new localization algorithm, which incorporates the advantages of RSSI location method and DV-Hop location method and make some improvement. The simulation results show that the new localization algorithm outperforms the DV-Hop algorithm in localization accuracy and uses less anchor nodes than the DV-Hop algorithm, reducing the cost of network hardware.

Keywords: wireless sensor networks, RSSI technology, DV-Hop, positioning technology, range-based, range-free, localization algorithms.

1 Introduction

With the development of information and communication technology (ICT), the microelectronic mechanical system, and automatic control, the wireless sensor networks has emerged from military needs and found its way into civil applications [1]. This technology has been widely used in many fields such as military, video monitoring, environmental monitoring, and building monitoring. The data collected will not be useful unless the location information can be discerned from it. In such scenarios, localization and position estimation play a major role in wireless sensor networks.

The existing work on localization falls into two main categories: range-based and range-free localization [2]. The range-free approaches are mainly based on

 WIT Transactions on Information and Communication Technologies, Vol. 61, © 2014 WIT Press
www.witpress.com, ISSN 1743-3517 (on-line)
doi:10.2495/MIIT130191

the topology of the network to estimate the approximate location of nodes, the most common form of which is DV-Hop (short Vector Hop) algorithm. The DV-Hop algorithm is easy to implement and has less demanding on the hardware conditions, but its location error is relatively large being greatly influenced by the uneven distribution of nodes. This type of algorithm includes centroid method [3], Amorphous algorithm, and APIT algorithm. Tian He and APIT's APIT algorithm has built up thoughts of using received signal strength indicator (RSSI) as a positioning reference; they can estimate the distance between two nodes using the signal intensity attenuation model. This type of positioning method has higher precision than simply using topology to determine the positioning, but the RSSI is not stable which is not taken into consideration. The range-based location algorithms can be implemented by measuring the RSSI, angle of arriving signal (AOA), time of arriving signal (TOA), time difference of arriving signals (TDOA) [4], etc. Range-based algorithm for its high requirement of time synchronization or expensive receiving equipment is not fit for sensor node which is sensitive to power consumption and cost.

2 Related works

RSSI is based on the characteristics that in actual environment signal attenuation with the increase of distance to calculate the distance. Paper by Benkic et al. [5] mentioned the commonly used signal attenuation model, namely, the ideal signal transmission model and irregular signal propagation model, and the latter can be divided into Logarithmic Attenuation model, DOI Attenuation model, and RIM Attenuation model. Signal propagation model can be expressed by Eq. (1)

$$PL(d) = PL(d_0) - 10n \log\left(\frac{d_0}{d}\right) \tag{1}$$

$PL(d)$ is the received signal strength where the distance to the sending node is d. While, $PL(d_0)$ is the received signal strength at reference distance d_0, n is the path loss factor, ranging from 2.0 to 5.0.

DV-hop [1] is proposed by D. Niculescu and B. Nath. In the first stage, each anchor node generates packets including their ID no., position information, and a hop-count parameter initialized as 0. These packets are flooded in WSN. When they are transmitted by the relay nodes, the hop number is increased by 1. Each receiving node maintains the minimum hop count value to the particular anchor node i. Anchors with higher hop count values to a particular anchor are defined as the useless information and ignored. In this way, any node can determine the hop number from it to a certain anchor node.

In the second stage, anchor node i gets the average hop distance using Eq. (2), which is then flooded to the entire network.

Unknown nodes receive hop-size information, and save the first one. At the same time, they transmit the hop-size to their neighbor nodes. When an unknown node accepts the information from one anchor node, it computes the distance between itself and the anchor nodes (hop distance*hop count).

$$\text{HopSize}_i = \frac{\sum\limits_{j \neq i} \sqrt{(x_i - x_j)^2 + (y_i - y_j)^2}}{\sum\limits_{j \neq i} h_{ij}} \tag{2}$$

where (x_i, y_i), (x_j, y_j) are coordinates of anchor i and anchor j, h_{ij} is the hops between anchor i and anchor j.

In the third stage, each unknown node computes its location coordinate. After it obtains three or more estimated values from anchor nodes, its location can be figured out.

To improve the DV-Hop positioning accuracy of algorithm, many scholars improved the DV-Hop algorithm from all aspects. Zhang fixed the anchor nodes at the border land of the network [6]. Papers by Yang et al. [7] and Yin et al. [8] proposed improved method to compute each jump count to reduce localization error. In paper by Yu and Li [3], the RSSI ranging technology is introduced into the literature of positioning algorithm, mainly for positioning accuracy one jump scope within the anchor node. As is known to all, the resources of the wireless nodes is very precious, both Refs. [6] and [7] have increased the complexity of the algorithm and data storage.

3 The improved localization algorithm

The key to improve the DV-Hop localization accuracy is to improve the accuracy of the average hop distance.

An experiment on the relationship between RSSI and the distance is made and the relationship curve graph is shown in Figure 1. At the same time, its fitting curve is shown to make a comparison.

We can see from the curve of actual measurement in Figure 1 that in the process of the distance increasing, measured value trend has appeared repeatability at 20 m, and RSSI value at the distance of less than 20 m is bigger than that of greater than 20 m. In DV-Hop algorithm, uneven distribution of nodes leads to the actual distance vary greatly with each jump. In this paper, the improved scheme is to use the RSSI value in the fitted curve at 20 m as the threshold to refine a jump and we called this value RSSI0. If RSSI technology is applied to positioning area, the RSSI values greater than 87 dBm has a better effect [9], so this paper we select 40 m as communication radius. If RSSI value is greater than the RSSI0 is graded as 0.5 jump, when less than this value is considered to be 1 jump. The proposed algorithm is described as a RCDV-Hop algorithm.

Step 1: Determine the RSSI classification threshold value RSSI0 corresponding to half the distance of communication radius using Eq. (1).

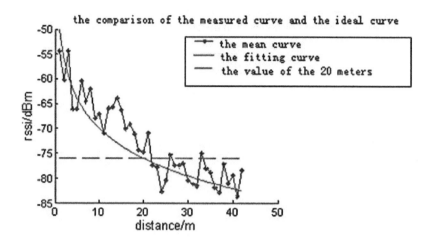

Figure 1: Actual curve and the fitting curve of the contrast.

Step 2: (Calculate the minimum hop) If the received signal strength of RSSI is greater than RSSI0, the hop count is 0.5. Receiving nodes store beacon with minimum hop of an anchor node and discard beacons with larger hop count of the same anchor.

Step 3: (Calculate the average hop distance) Each anchor node calculates the average hop distance by getting the location and corresponding hop count of other anchor nodes and broadcasts it as a correction to the wireless network.

Step 4: (Average hop distance correction) Receiving nodes store correction corresponding to the smallest hop count as per hop distance.

Step 5: Calculate the distance of receiving node to an anchor node by the multiplication of the average hop distance with the hop count of the receiving node to the anchor node, and after getting at least three of the anchor node distance we calculate the receiving node position with Least Square Method.

From the above steps, we can infer that this algorithm complexity is lower than other improved DV-Hop algorithm, and compared with DV-Hop algorithm only increase the calculation of Eq. (1) when initialization.

4 Performance simulations

$$\mathrm{MSE}_n = E\left[\left(x_n - \hat{x}_n\right)^2 + (y_n - \hat{y}_n)^2\right] \tag{3}$$

$$\mathrm{RMSE}_n = \sqrt{E\left[\left(x_n - \hat{x}_n\right)^2 + (y_n - \hat{y}_n)^2\right]} \tag{4}$$

Table 1: Location Error of Two Algorithms in Regular Model.

	Average Neighbor Anchor Nodes Number	$RMSE_n$
DV-Hop	8.1	0.31192
RCDV-Hop	8.1	0.20501

Table 2: Location Error of Two Algorithms in Rim Model.

	Average Neighbor Anchor Nodes Number	$RMSE_n$
DV-Hop	7.5	0.61837
RCDV-Hop	7.5	0.52289

In order to prove the high performance of the new algorithm, we use Matlab to simulate the DV-Hop algorithm and the improved algorithm to compare their performance. Equations (3) and (4), (x_n, y_n) denote the real coordinates of node n, and $(\hat{x}_n, \hat{y}_n)$ denote the estimated coordinate, MSE_n mean square error and $RMSE_n$ the root mean square error of node n.

RIM model is more in line with our environment, so we choose the RIM irregular transmission model, signal transmission loss parameter $n=2$, and the attenuation $PL(d_0)$ =50 dBm at 1 m in, irregular DOI=0.02, the transmitted power is set to 0 dBm, variance parameter $\delta = 0.5$ [5].

Assuming that all the 500 nodes are distributed randomly in the region of 300 m × 300 m, and the ratio of anchor nodes is set by 30%. The communication radius R of each node is 40 m. The simulation results are given in Tables 1 and 2.

Each algorithm simulates 500 times and their average value will be chosen. The test results are shown in Figures 2 and 3.

From the figure we can see that the improved positioning algorithm reduces the average location error by about 13% in regular transmission model and by 12% in RIM transmission model.

In order to better compare the DV-Hop and RCDV-Hop in the difference of the positioning accuracy in RIM model, the positioning accuracy in situations with different anchor nodes density and different total number of nodes are respectively simulated.

Total number of nodes is 500; the ratio of anchor nodes is set from 10% to 30%, increased by 5% at a time, and 1000 times repeated. The simulation results are shown in Figure 4. With anchor node taking a proportion of 25%, the total number of nodes increases from 200 to 500 and increases 50 at a time. Repeat the simulation 1000 times and the average accuracy of nodes corresponding to that is shown in Figure 5.

As can be seen from the Figure 4, in the case of a total number of 500 nodes, the anchor node density does not significantly improve positioning accuracy, while anchor node density is set to 16%, an increase of the number of nodes has evident effect on the improvement of location accuracy. But as the anchor density increases to 22%, the upward trend would become slow, finally become stable.

 WIT Transactions on Information and Communication Technologies, Vol. 61, © 2014 WIT Press
www.witpress.com, ISSN 1743-3517 (on-line)

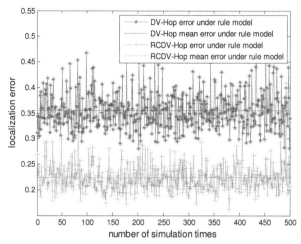

Figure 2: Location error of DV-Hop algorithm and improved algorithm in regular mode.

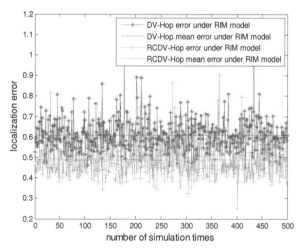

Figure 3: Location error of DV-Hop algorithm and improved algorithm in RIM model.

In Figure 5, with the increasing of anchor nodes, there is a quick downward trend on the error of DV-Hop positioning algorithm. As the number of anchor nodes reaches 300, the error would never decrease according to the increasing of number of nodes, but would be stabilized at 0.58. The average positioning error of improved DV-Hop algorithm is lower than DV-Hop, and the positioning error is decreasing significantly with the increasing of number of nodes. The downward trend becomes slow and when the number of nodes increased to 450, there still a slow trend.

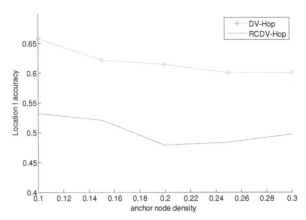

Figure 4: The relation of positioning error and number of anchor nodes.

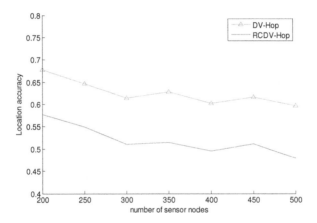

Figure 5: The relation between position error and number of nodes.

5 Summary

In both regular propagation model and irregular propagation model which is close to the actual environment, the localization accuracy of RCDV-Hop algorithm is significantly improved compared with that of DV-Hop algorithm. To achieve the same precision, RCDV-Hop algorithm requires less anchor nodes than DV-Hop algorithm and does not need to increase the hardware cost at the same time and almost does not increase the algorithm complexity.

References

[1] J. Yick, B. Mukherjee, D. Ghosal, Wireless sensor network survey. Computer Networks, **52(12)**, pp. 2292–2330, 2008.

[2]   G. Han, H. Xu, T.Q. Duong, Localization algorithms of wireless sensor networks: a survey. Telecommunication Systems, **52(4)**, pp 2419–2436, 2013.

[3]   W.Q. Yu, H. Li, An improved DV-Hop localization method in wireless sensor networks. Computer Science and Automation Engineering (CSAE), 2012 IEEE International Conference on (Volume 3), Zhangjiajie, pp. 199–202, 2012.

[4]   Y.C. Li, O. Oh, J.H. Kim, et al., A novel subspace-based joint TDOA and FDOA estimation using chirp signals for mobile multipath environment. 2012 IX International Symposium on Telecommunications, Saraje-vo, pp. 1–5, 2012.

[5]   K. Benkic, M. Malajner, P. Planinic, et al., Using RSSI value for distance estimation in wireless sensor networks based on ZigBee. 15th International Conference on Systems, Signals and Image Processing, Institute of Electrical and Electronics Engineers, Bratislava, pp. 303–306, 2008.

[6]   D.Y. Zhang, G.D. Cui, A union node localization algorithm based on RSSI and DV-Hop for WSNs. Second International Conference on Instrumentation & Measurement, Computer, Communication and Control, Harbin, pp. 1094–1098, 2012.

[7]   Q.H. Yang, H.C. Shi, An improved dv-hop algorithm for anisotropic wireless sensor network. IET International Communication Conference on Wireless Mobile and Computing (CCWMC 2011), Shanghai, pp. 517–521, 2011.

[8]   J.Z. Lin, H.B. Liu, G.J. Li, et al., Study for improved DV-Hop localization algorithm in WSN. Application Research of Computers, **26(4)**, pp. 1272–1275, 2009.

[9]   Y. Chen, A. Terzis, On the mechanisms and effects of calibrating RSSI measurements for 802.15.4 Radios. Wireless Sensor Networks, **5970**, pp. 256–271, 2010.

Unicode-based zero-watermarking algorithm for Chinese documents

Shiru Zhang, Shi Yan
College of Communications and Information Engineering, Xi'an University of Science and Technology, Xi'an, Shaanxi, China

Abstract

Digital watermarking techniques have been used in the copyright protection of electronic documents, but there are still some problems in this area. A zero-watermarking algorithm is proposed based on Unicode and SHA512 transformation for Chinese document in this paper. Simulation results indicate that this algorithm is completely robust against attacks irrelevant to document contents, such as deleting, substitution, and other editing.

Keywords: zero-watermarking, Unicode, SHA512.

1 Introduction

With the development of the computers and Internet, traditional paper documents have been gradually replaced by electronic documents. But, if used improperly, the advantages of electronic document in turn raise a severe problem: copyright infringement. Obviously research on the copyright protection for electronic documents is urgent.

Document watermarking technique introduces a new concept to protect digital copyright. Generally, watermarking schemes, which are developed for electronic documents, can be divided into two categories: HVS-based [1] and semantic-based. The first kind is fragile to format and edit attacks, and has limited watermarking capacity. The second kind is also vulnerable to the variation and destruction of the original text [2]. Zero-watermarking algorithm [3] does not change the original data and also can solve the above problems.

In this paper, a zero-watermarking algorithm based on Unicode and SHA512 transformation is proposed. This algorithm is robust against attacks such as

WIT Transactions on Information and Communication Technologies, Vol. 61, © 2014 WIT Press
www.witpress.com, ISSN 1743-3517 (on-line)
doi:10.2495/MIIT130201

deleting, tampering, and inserting. Moreover, this watermarking algorithm will not damage the structure of the document.

2 Watermark embedding location selection

Unicode is a computing industry standard for the consistent encoding, representation and handling of text expressed in most of the world's writing systems. In other words, Unicode allows us to process a text message to certain extent in mathematical ways without considering the character of the font size, typography design, and shape etc. Unicode provides a good basis for processing Chinese document and embedding watermarks [2].

Considering the mutual restriction relationship between the robustness and capacity of the document watermarking, the choice of watermark embedding location and the number of watermarks must be selected carefully.

The Chinese character in Unicode is coded from 19970 to 40869. There are 902 rarely used Chinese characters from 19970 to 19999 and 40000 to 40869, accounting for 4.3 percent of the Chinese character. In the proposed algorithm, watermark is embedded in the segment from 20000 to 39999. This is a huge range and contains a lot of characters, so the range of proper embedding location needs to be narrowed down.

Suppose a document contains x characters (excluding space), and y watermarks need to be embedded in this document. Equation (1) is an empirical formula. We have tested it in a lot of documents. The empirical results show that deletion of 30% of the text will seriously damage the readability of a Chinese document. Thus, the number of watermarks is

$$\frac{C_{x-y}^{x \cdot t - y}}{C_x^{x \cdot t}} < 0.0001 \qquad t = 0.1,\, 0.2,\, 0.3 \qquad (1)$$

where C is a permutation and combination operation, t is the character deletion ratio. Equation (1) indicates that if 30 percent characters are deleted randomly in a document, the probability of all the embedded locations can be deleted will be less than 0.0001. It is such a small probability that once this relationship is reached, the embedded watermarks are difficult to be completely removed.

Another requirement to improve the error correction ability of watermarks is that the embedded watermarks need to be spread uniformly over the entire document. Let a set of watermark embedding locations be $\vec{X} = \{x_1, x_2, ..., x_n\}$, the variance of $\vec{X}$'s first order difference is w as in Eq. (2).

$$w = D(\Delta y(k)) \qquad (2)$$

The extent of uniform distribution will be increasing as w is decreasing.

Based on the analysis above, the watermark embedding locations are selected by the three steps as in the following.

Step 1: Read the code values of the characters in the document in Unicode, and quantize them with an appropriate step size, which will be described later.
Step 2: Analyze the statistics of the quantized Unicode values and select some desire groups of data satisfying Eq. (1).
Step 3: Using Eq. (2) select the most uniformly distributed group of data as the ultimate watermark embedding locations k. Save the corresponding quantized value q.

In step 1, quantization makes it convenient to find the statistics feature of Unicode values. A bigger quantization interval implies more evident statistics feature and less selectivity of embedding locations. Different quantization parameter will correspond to a different length document. In this paper, the quantum step size of 1000 is used.

3   Watermarking algorithm

SHA512 hash operation can transform any input sequence of the length less than 2^{128} to an output sequence of the length 512. Once a bit is changed, approximate 50 percent of the output sequence will subsequently be changed. The probability of different sequence comes out identical results is very low, and this is an unbreakable problem during an acceptable time. Because of the security and its fixed length of 512 bits output, SHA512 algorithm can improve the security and increase the watermark capacity [4].

3.1 Watermarking embeding algorithm

According to the analysis results about the embedded number and their locations, the proposed zero-watermarking embedding algorithm based on SHA512 transform is as the following steps.

Step 1: Transform the original watermark into a vector.
Step 2: Read the embedding location k and the quantized value q, and calculate the maximum distance D between adjacent embedding locations.
Step 3: Perform SHA512-transform to the D-bit Unicode value at every embedding location (including initial location). Especially perform SHA512-transform separately to the two kinds of data, one is from the first character of the document to the first embedding location, the other is from the last character to the last embedding location. Write all the results into a binary matrix.
Step 4: Perform XOR operation to the binary watermark vector and the binary matrix line by line, the key matrix M is obtained.
Step 5: Send q, D, and M to the third party as all the secret keys of the watermark information.

Figure 1: Original watermark.

3.2 Watermarking extracting algorithm

Step 1: Download the secret key from the third party.
Step2: Search for the characters whose quantized value equals q and mark the locations to be detected.
Step3: Calculate SHA512-transform value of the D bits at every candidate locations. Especially perform SHA512-transform separately to two areas, one is from the first character of the document to the first candidate location, the other is from the last character to the last candidate location. Integrate all the results into a binary matrix.
Step 4: Perform XOR operation between the binary matrix obtained in step 3 and the secret key line by line.

The operation in step 4 is to detect the unmodified parts of the attacked document, and to enable this algorithm to detect errors.

In step 4, a result matrix is generated. Each clear watermark image in the matrix means the corresponding part in the original text and the revised text. For example, if there is a clear watermark image (the same image with the original watermark) in location $(1, 2)$, this means the first row of M and the second row of M is the same. A same value in M and M indicates the same content in the original text and the revised text.

In the proposed algorithm, the bit number of the original watermark will affect the error detecting capability and the computation complexity. The large the original watermark bit number is, the better the error detection effect is, and the more robustness the algorithm will have. Smaller embedding watermark bit number will result in the decreasing error detection effect, but the computation cost becomes less. Therefore, the bit number of the original watermark should be set according to the requirements of the protected document.

4 Simulation results

Many experiments are conducted in Matlab environment. Simulation results indicate that the proposed algorithm has a very good performance. Two group experimental results are listed below.

4.1 Format attacks

Modifications were performed on the character font, color, size, line space, and word space. Simulation results show that our algorithm is completely robust against the various format attacks. Figure 1 is the original watermark of binary image. Figure 2 is an arbitrarily selected part of the attacked document of 1246 words in all. Figure 3 is the extracted watermarks.

这是一部渭河平原 50 年变迁的雄奇史诗，一轴中国农村斑斓多彩，触目惊心的长幅画卷。主人公白嘉轩六娶，神秘的序曲预示着不祥。一个家庭两代子孙，为争夺白鹿原的统治代代争斗不已，上演了一幕幕惊心动魄的话剧；巧取风水地，恶施美人计，牵子为匪，亲娘杀媳，兄弟相煎，情人反目……大革命，日寇入侵，三年内战，白鹿原翻云覆雨，王旗变幻，家仇国恨，交错缠结，冤冤相报代代不已……古老的土地在新生的阵痛中颤栗。

白嘉轩后来，引以豪壮的是一生里娶过七房女人。第六房女人胡氏死去以后，母亲白赵氏仍然坚持胡氏不过也是一张破旧了的糊窗纸，撕了就应该尽快重新糊上一张完好的。

他在去请阴阳先生的路上，无意间发现了传说中的白鹿。白嘉轩用先退後进的韬略，借助冷先生的撮合，谋到了是鹿家的那块风水宝地。随即给父亲迁坟。

Figure 2: Part of document after format modification.

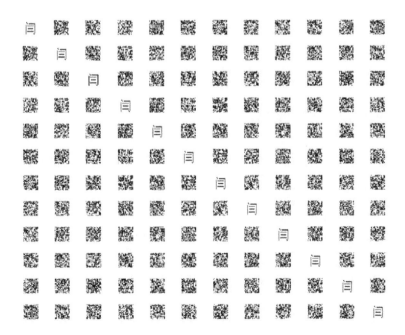

Figure 3: Extracted watermarks.

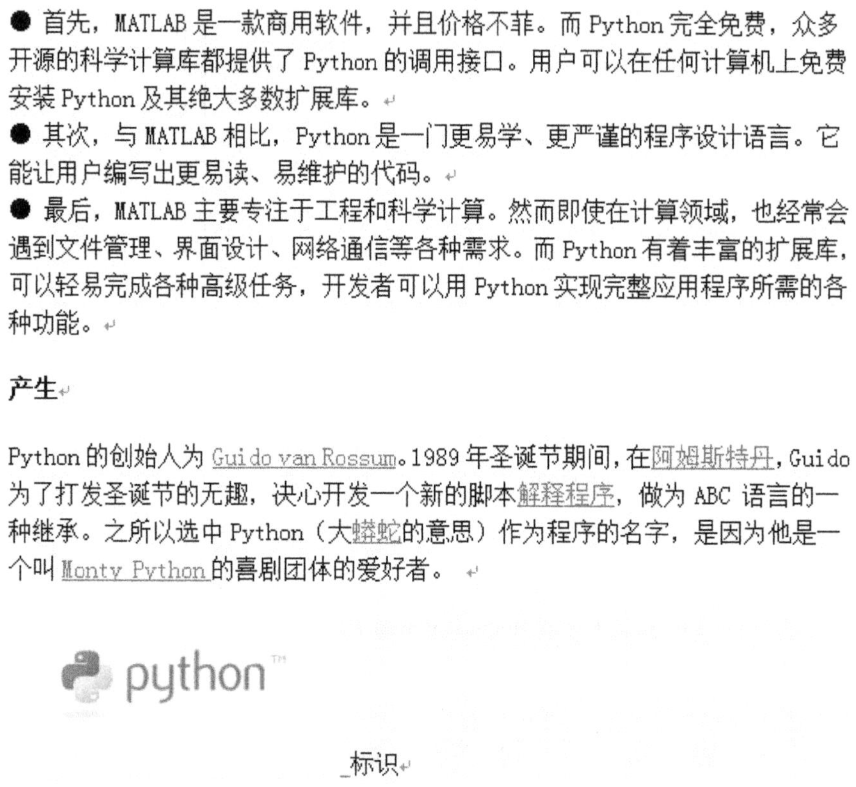

● 首先，MATLAB 是一款商用软件，并且价格不菲。而 Python 完全免费，众多开源的科学计算库都提供了 Python 的调用接口。用户可以在任何计算机上免费安装 Python 及其绝大多数扩展库。

● 其次，与 MATLAB 相比，Python 是一门更易学、更严谨的程序设计语言。它能让用户编写出更易读、易维护的代码。

● 最后，MATLAB 主要专注于工程和科学计算。然而即使在计算领域，也经常会遇到文件管理、界面设计、网络通信等各种需求。而 Python 有着丰富的扩展库，可以轻易完成各种高级任务，开发者可以用 Python 实现完整应用程序所需的各种功能。

产生

Python 的创始人为 Guido van Rossum。1989 年圣诞节期间，在阿姆斯特丹，Guido 为了打发圣诞节的无趣，决心开发一个新的脚本解释程序，做为 ABC 语言的一种继承。之所以选中 Python（大蟒蛇的意思）作为程序的名字，是因为他是一个叫 Monty Python 的喜剧团体的爱好者。

_标识

Figure 4: Original document.

4.2 Adding and deleting attacks

Figure 4 is an arbitrarily selected part of the original document. Figure 5 is the attacked document. This document suffers various kinds of attacks including adding a table, deleting some special characters and texts, and substituting a picture. Figure 6 shows the extracted watermarks. After 148 characters were deleted from 818 characters, which accounts for 18 percent characters of the whole document, 5 intact watermarks still can be extracted. Meanwhile, the corresponding locations to the five intact watermarks can be confirmed to be untouched. Other locations must have undergone some attacks. Adding a table and substituting an image in the document have no influence on watermark extraction. It is a very surprising good result.

● 首先，MATLAB 是一款商用软件，并且价格不菲。而 Python 完全免费，众多开源的科学计算库都提供了 Python 的调用接口。用户可以在任何计算机上免费安装 Python 及其绝大多数扩展库。

产生

Python 的创始人为 Guido van Rossum。1989 年圣诞节期间，在阿姆斯特丹，Guido 为了打发圣诞节的无趣，决心开发一个新的脚本解释程序，做为 ABC 语言的一种继承。之所以选中 Python（大蟒蛇的意思）作为程序的名字，是因为他是一个叫 Monty Python 的喜剧团体的爱好者。

Figure 5: Format attacked document.

Figure 6: Extracted watermarks.

5 Conclusion

A zero-watermarking algorithm based on Unicode for electronic documents is proposed in this paper. The algorithm is robust against attacks such as deleting, inserting, and substitution. This algorithm will not damage the document content, because it is independent to the character features and the text format. Another significant advantage is that this algorithm has a very high robustness against attacks irrelevant to document content. By the way, the size of the secret key will increase with the increasing of the document size. There are still some empirical results need to be proved theoretically. These problems will be studied in-depth in our future work.

References

[1] L. Yee, K. Wong, K.O. Chee, UniSpaCh: a text-based data hiding method using Unicode space characters. *Journal of Systems and Software*, **85(5)**, pp. 1075–1082, 2008.
[2] Z. Jalil, A.M. Mirza, T. Iqbal, A zero-watermarking algorithm for text documents based on structural components. In *Information and Emerging Technologies (ICIET)*, 2010 International Conference Karachi, pp. 1–5, 2010.
[3] Q. Wen, T.F. Sun, S.X. Wang, Concept and application of zero-watermark. *Acta Electronica Sinica*, **31(2)**, pp. 214–216, 2010. (in Chinese)
[4] X.H. Zhang, Y.T. Yang, Image authentication scheme research based on fragile watermarking. *Acta Electronica Sinica*, **35(1)**, pp. 34–39, 2006. (in Chinese)

Computer software in the application of descriptive geometry course

Xiaoqiu Ma
JiLin JianZhu University, Changchun, China

Abstract

In view of the descriptive geometry course teaching, present situation and problems are put forward adjusting the teaching contents, using blackboard writing combined with multimedia, using a variety of the teaching methods of computer software, pointing out the development direction of the course, inspiring and mobilizing students' thinking, actively participating in, making the descriptive geometry course simple and interesting.

Keywords: descriptive geometry course, multimedia, computer software.

1 Introduction

Descriptive geometry course is the basis of the engineering drawing course, is the national standard, according to the mapping based on projection theory to express the course of the form. This is the basic requirement of the engineering and technical personnel, not knowledge chart; you can't understand others' design intent; not drawing, also cannot express your ideas. For engineering drawing course is a professional basic course in colleges of engineering. Different professionals have different engineering drawing, such as mechanical engineering drawing, bridge and road engineering drawing, and engineering drawing. Engineering drawing course by learning is to cultivate the students mapping and map reading ability and to enhance students' space imagination ability.

2 Discussed problems the current situation of the descriptive geometry course teaching methods

2.1 The traditional teaching methods

The traditional teaching means is the teacher on the blackboard with chalk, ruler gauge drawing, drawing large workload, slow speed of teaching. Efficiency is low, abstract concept of unimaginable, can only through the model and charts, single method, the teaching effect is poor, the backward teaching means restricted the teachers' teaching and students' learning, with the deepening of informationization, teachers' teaching means to keep pace with time.

Also, most of descriptive geometry teaching process is the teacher as the center, teaching content as the breakthrough point, it is hard to abstract, astringent, strange knowledge visualization, visualization, three-dimensional formation process is difficult to see real graphics. This can't stimulate students' interest in learning, cannot mobilize the enthusiasm and initiative of student learning, and is not conducive to cultivate students' creative thinking [1]. These are the shortages of the traditional teaching method.

2.2 Multimedia courseware

Using multimedia courseware teaching is better than the traditional teaching method, can make the classroom teaching effect and teaching quality been improved significantly, and can also make the principal role of students gets a greater degree of play, but relying too much on multimedia courseware teaching; there are some problems that cannot be ignored.

1. **Bad for students to understand imitation**
    Multimedia courseware teaching is through modern teaching equipment, use of multimedia technology serves for the teaching process. Multimedia courseware is a production, fixed, closed before class, the plot to finalize the design of software, classroom teaching, relying too much on use. Teachers easily become projectionist and commentator of courseware, drawing process is screened out, fast, short staying time in students' mind, demonstration effect is poorer, students find this difficult to understand and assimilate. It's very hard to imitate. Time grows, can appear the classroom teacher is busy, the classroom students do exercise is difficult. So you can't play to the advantages of multimedia.
2. **Unfavorable to the teacher**
    Multimedia courseware in narrow, difficult to meet the different levels, different needs of students. It is difficult to play to teachers' subjective initiative, it is difficult to show the teachers' teaching style, the time cannot adapt to changes in the actual classroom teaching, cannot achieve the teaching goal of presupposition, and the ideal teaching effect.
    Teachers' explanation and inspiration is difficult to control at anytime, anywhere, follow one's inclinations of teaching media, nor the teaching

contents, way, adjust speed, is not conducive to play to the readjustment of teachers ability, is not conducive to teaching and extension, is not conducive to the emotional communication between teachers and students.

3   The combination of traditional teaching and multimedia teaching

Rich teaching method can promote students' mastery of descriptive geometry course knowledge. To make the modern teaching means in the teaching of engineering drawing is applied proper, must adhere to the principle of "timeliness and appropriateness." In the classroom teaching environment, the comprehensive use of various media, such as the blackboard, chalk, materials, models, slide show, video, computers, and projectors, with the help of the media of different characteristics and advantages, creating a variety of scenarios, motivate students' active learning. This offers a variety of sensory participation in learning atmosphere, and lets the students' eyes, ears, brain, hand senses move, experience, perceiving, understanding concepts, which greatly improve the students' learning.

3.1   The arrangement of the targeted blackboard writing

Years of experience, according to the key part in the outline, as examples, the problem, the arrangement of the targeted blackboard writing teaching effect is very good. Teachers on the blackboard, the interpretation of this process, let the students to form the concept understanding, their thinking, drawing process. There are more intuitive perception and imitate, interaction between teachers and students in the process of blackboard writing, will attract students' attention, arouse the interest in learning, active classroom atmosphere. By asking questions, and getting answers, teachers can understand students on the degree of master of knowledge, timely adjust the interpretation of the way and speed, in order to achieve good teaching effect. Students can also from the teacher's action in tone and display of teaching aids, teaching content, master key, drawing skills, etc. This is the kind of communication between teachers and students which the man–machine can't replace. Including geometric drawing parts, unarmed axonometric drawing and SanShiTu, traditional methods ruler gauge drawing effect is very good.

3.2   The reasonable use of multimedia courseware

Multimedia technology to the teaching process the required text, graphics, images, animation, and sound information through a variety of software together, making multimedia courseware, finally implemented in the form of PowerPiont or Flash demo and play. Using multimedia computer software in-class presentations of these processes, both vivid and intuitive, and increased the amount of information, improve the teaching efficiency, the key is to cultivate the students' interest in learning and spatial thinking ability, for subsequent professional design course to lay a certain foundation [2].

But beware, the teaching content is the main body, the multimedia technology is auxiliary, cannot rely too much on multimedia courseware, teaching should attach great importance to the exemplary role of teachers and students understand the copying process. In the process of practice teaching, the multimedia technology and the combination of teaching content, reasonable use of multimedia courseware, attaches great importance to the teachers in the teaching activities leading and exemplary role.

4 Uses a variety of computer software

4.1 Make full use of AutoCAD software

Descriptive geometry is based on the projection feature, according to the order of point, line, plane, and three-dimensional (3-d) space form expressed by the two-dimensional (2-d) projection, and watch the two-dimensional projection design process of space form. Object is the relationship between 2-d and 3-d conversion is difficult to learn engineering drawing, understand or to express the relationship, is often very important, and the spatial ability is in "2-d" and "3-d" relationship transformation of cultivated gradually. Along with the continuously upgrade AutoCAD version, you can now use AutoCAD to establish 3-d entity model, image, vivid, intuitive representation of an object's 3-d entity and the relationship between the 2-d views.

In engineering, drawing teaching model was established based on AutoCAD 3-d modeling technology, internal and external structure, expression from the geometry model and feature concept into traditional teaching, strengthen the imagination of three-dimensional shape, molding analysis, the power of expression, the 3-d and 2-d graphics conversion ability is much more than traditional teaching.

The dynamic observer using AutoCAD environment inside and outside modeling show form from any angle, can transform a variety of position according to different requirements, make all directions projection and axonometric drawing. This can make students form from different angles, with the view repeated comparison, development train of thought, thus improve the space of imagination.

Also AutoCAD can be used on problem sets operation, draw the solutions under a lesson for a class where students can explain in detail the solutions quickly; AutoCAD can also be used drawing while in class, using graphics screen instead of the blackboard, drawing tool instead of feet, graphic various lines, line width to clear and accurate, and obtain good teaching effect.

4.2 Choose appropriate Catierr software

In the construction drawings, using AutoCAD software rendering 2-d plane figure is particularly convenient, widely due to the design and construction units, but 3-d rendering has used 3 or POTOshop on3-dmax software, such as one of the main reason is the use of AutoCAD software to create 3-d graphics, size is not convenient to modify. And applied in the construction drawings Catierr mechanical design software, to create 3-d arbitrary size, and then through the size after the definition, modify the size and shape of the form, can be convenient to 3-d form. Catierr software is widely used in mechanical design, achieve no drawings processing, can also play a big role in the construction design and production.

4.3   Pointpower courseware drawing function into full play

Multimedia courseware is fixed, aired by pointpower software, draw pointpower software tool provides a way of teachers can be free play, different teachers in different knowledge has different ways of understanding and interpretation of the flexible use of pointpower software drawing function, can follow the drawing in the courseware content, as well as emphasis, correct mistakes, can play the teacher's personal charisma, creative, and mobilize the students' interest in learning. Drawing graphics on the original courseware has no effect. Using the "drawing" tools to implement the free play of teaching.

4.4   Experience Revit series software

With the development of science and technology, the construction industry to gradually no drawings and visual direction. The Revit series software plays an important role in it. Revit series software (http://baike.baidu.com/view/1788980.htm) is designed for building information model (BIM) to build, can help architects to design, build, and maintain better quality, more energy-efficient buildings.

By using a specially designed for workflow and build tools support building information model, concept can be captured and analyzed, and through the design, documentation, and construction keep your vision. It has strong architectural design tools that can help you capture and analyze the concept, and maintain the consistency of all stages from design to construction. Revit is design information data integration software, color print effect is accomplished, automatic generation of 3-d rendering, can freely roaming animation, its design objective, accuracy, and efficiency greatly improve the design quality and design efficiency of the whole [3].

Revit series software modeling and mapping is an important content. To create a good building model, we can automatically generate the flat vertical section drawings and details, details, and they are interrelated; this will be the development direction of construction drawings.

5   Conclusion

Follow the time development, meet the demand of teaching reform, choose appropriate teaching material, arrange teaching contents rationally, give full play to the advantages of a variety of computer software, adopt scientific teaching methods, arouse the enthusiasm of students, and teachers play personality, make descriptive geometry as a simple and interesting courses, improve teaching quality and teaching effect.

References

[1] You, Engineering cartography curriculum reform of classroom teaching exploration. *All Big Division Skill*, **5**, pp. 45–48, 2011.
[2] Aiwen Xue, The application of multimedia technology in engineering drawing teaching. *Mechanical Engineering & Automation*, **3**, pp. 12–13, 2004.
[3] Kai Zou, Xiaodong Huang, *Revit Application Examples and Techniques*. China Building Industry Press, pp. 21–25, 2006.

The subspace approaches on deterministic CRB of array processing

Chao Shao, Yu-Ming Liu, Xin Shi
*Department of Telecommunication and Information Engineering,
Xi'an University of post and Telecommunications, Xi'an, China*

Abstract

The Deterministic Cramér–Rao bound (CRB) for direction estimation in array processing applications was derived by employing the subspace projection approach. The subspace decomposition as well as subspace projection method were utilized, and the inversion of partition matrix formulation was adopted in a simple proof of the Deterministic CRB for direction parameters estimation in array processing circumstance. The main factor of the CRB matrix is analyzed and demonstrated by the simulation result.

Keywords: Cramér–Rao bound, array signal processing, subspace decomposition and projection.

1 Introduction

The Deterministic Cramér–Rao Bound (CRB) is a comprehensive useful tool for signal parameters estimating error analysis in various application cases, such as the signal strength estimation in wireless communication [1], the moving target parameters estimation by MIMO radar system [2], and the channel parameters estimation for quantize-and-forward cooperative systems [3]. Here, we presented a simple proof on the deterministic case of CRB by employing the subspace projection methods, though the problem had been dealt in Refs. [4,5], but some key step of the proof is not given in the literature as yet. Finally, we displayed the computer simulation results shown that in array processing case, the diagonal element of the CRB matrix carries more information than its cross-term even if the signals are strongly correlated in spatial. The result reveals the fact that even in multiple signal case, the diagonal element of the CRB is the main concern to our study.

2 Signal model

Let an array of M sensors receive D $(D < M)$ narrowband signals impinging from the sources with unknown DOA parameters vector $\boldsymbol{\theta} = [\theta_1, \cdots, \theta_D]^T$. The t-th snapshot vector of sensor array outputs can be modeled as [4–6],

$$x(t) = As(t) + n(t), \quad t = 1, 2, \ldots, N \tag{1}$$

where $A = A(\boldsymbol{\theta}) = [a(\theta_1), \cdots, a(\theta_D)]$ is the $M \times D$ matrix composed of the signal direction vectors $a(\theta_i)$ $(i = 1, \ldots, D)$, $s(t)$ is the $D \times 1$ vector of the source waveforms. It is assumed to be deterministic but unknown, $n(t)$ is the $M \times 1$ vector of white sensor noise, which is assumed to be a zero-mean spatially and temporally white Gaussian process with the unknown diagonal covariance matrix,

$$\boldsymbol{Q} = E\{n(t)n^H(t)\} = \mathrm{diag}\{\sigma_1^2, \sigma_2^2, \ldots, \sigma_D^2\} \tag{2}$$

And the signal waveforms will be assumed to be deterministic unknown processes [1]. In particular, the signal snapshots are assumed to satisfy the following models:

$$x(t) \, \square \, \mathcal{CN}(As(t), \boldsymbol{Q}) \tag{3}$$

where $\mathcal{CN}(\cdot, \cdot)$ denotes the complex Gaussian distribution. Here the snapshots data covariance matrix $\boldsymbol{R}$ has the structure of,

$$\boldsymbol{R} = E\{x(t)x^H(t)\} = APA^H + \boldsymbol{Q} \tag{4}$$

with $\boldsymbol{P} = E\{s(t)s^H(t)\}$ is the source waveform covariance matrix.

3 The establishment of CRB on deterministic data model

Based on the data model of Eq. (3), the unknown parameters could be decomposed as follows [7]:

$$\text{Let } \boldsymbol{\alpha} = [\boldsymbol{\theta}^T, \boldsymbol{\rho}^T, \boldsymbol{\sigma}]^T = \left[\boldsymbol{\theta}^T, \boldsymbol{\rho} = [\mathrm{Re}(s^T(t)), \mathrm{Im}(s^T(t))]^T, \boldsymbol{\sigma} \right]^T \tag{5}$$

where $\boldsymbol{\theta} = (\theta_1, \cdots, \theta_{N_s})^T$, and $\boldsymbol{\rho}$ is the $2ND \times 1$—vector made from the signal waveform of $s(t)$, $\boldsymbol{\sigma} = [\sigma_1, \ldots, \sigma_{N_R}]$, the Fisher information matrix (FIM) for the parameter vector $\boldsymbol{\alpha}$ is given by [4],

$$\mathrm{FIM}_{n,m} = N \cdot \mathrm{tr}\left\{ \frac{\partial \boldsymbol{Q}}{\partial \alpha_n} \boldsymbol{Q}^{-1} \frac{\partial \boldsymbol{Q}}{\partial \alpha_m} \boldsymbol{Q}^{-1} \right\} + 2 \cdot \mathrm{Re}\left\{ \frac{\partial b^H}{\partial \alpha_n} (\boldsymbol{I} \otimes \boldsymbol{Q}^{-1}) \frac{\partial b}{\partial \alpha_m} \right\}$$

$$\text{for } n, m = 1, \ldots, N_s^2 + N_s + N_R \tag{6}$$

where $b = \left[[As(t)]^T, [As(2)]^T, \ldots, [As(N)]^T \right]^T$. As in most applications, both $\boldsymbol{\rho}$ and $\boldsymbol{\sigma}$ are nuisance parameters. We are often interested only in the $\boldsymbol{\theta}$-block of

CRB = FIM^{-1}, which we denote by CRB(θ). We know that the information of signal $x(t)$ contains is determined only by its covariance matrix and mean values [8], so the expression of FIM matrix (Eq. (6)) is rational.

4 Derivation of the CRB(θ)

We will make relatively frequent use of the following readily-checked facts [6]:

$$\text{tr}(XY) = \text{vec}(X^H)^H \text{vec}(Y); \ \text{vec}(XYZ) = (Z^T \otimes X)\text{vec}(Y) \qquad (7)$$

which hold for any conformable matrices X, Y, and Z. Using the partition of

$$(I \otimes Q^{-1/2}) \left[\frac{\partial b}{\partial \theta^T} \ \middle| \ \frac{\partial b}{\partial \rho^T} \ \frac{\partial b}{\partial \sigma^T} \right] = \left[\frac{\partial \tilde{b}}{\partial \theta^T} \ \middle| \ \frac{\partial \tilde{b}}{\partial \rho^T} \ \frac{\partial \tilde{b}}{\partial \sigma^T} \right] \ [G \mid \Delta] \qquad (8)$$

where $\tilde{b} = Q^{-1/2}b$, $\rho = [\text{Re}(s(1)), \text{Im}(s(1)), \dots, \text{Re}(s(N)), \text{Im}(s(N))]^T$, $\sigma = [\sigma_1,$ $\sigma_2, \dots, \sigma_M]^T$, we can write Eq. (6) as

$$\frac{1}{N}\text{FIM} = \begin{bmatrix} G^H \\ \Delta^H \end{bmatrix} [G \ \Delta] \qquad (9)$$

that is, we decompose the FIM into tangent subspace of $\tilde{b}$ about component θ and $[\rho, \sigma]$. By a standard result on the inversion of partitioned matrices (see, e.g., Ref. [1]), formula (9) gives CRB on component θ as

$$\frac{1}{N}\text{CRB}^{-1}(\theta) = G^H G - (G^H \Delta)(\Delta^H \Delta)^{-1}(\Delta^H G) = G^H P_\Delta^\perp G \qquad (10)$$

that is, the CRB on θ is the G projected onto the orthogonal complement space of Δ. Since b is independent of σ, therefore, Δ contains the component $\partial \tilde{b} / \partial \rho^T$ only, that is, Δ being the tangent subspace of vector $\tilde{b}$ on the signal waveform components. Another fact is the existence of $(\Delta^H \Delta)^{-1}$ is guaranteed by the existence of FIM. After some straightforward manipulations, we have

$$\frac{\partial b^H}{\partial \theta} = [H^H(1)D^H, H^H(2)D^H, \dots, H^H(N)D^H] \in \ ^{D \times M \cdot N} \qquad (11)$$

$$\frac{\partial b}{\partial \text{Re}(s(t))} = \left[\frac{\partial b}{\partial \text{Re}(s_1(t))}, \frac{\partial b}{\partial \text{Re}(s_2(t))}, \cdots, \frac{\partial b}{\partial \partial \text{Re}(s_D(t))} \right] = (e_t \otimes A) \in \ ^{M \cdot N \times D}$$

$$\frac{\partial b^H}{\partial \text{Re}\{s(t)\}} = (e_t \otimes A)^H \in \ ^{D \times NM}, \ \frac{\partial b}{\partial \text{Re}\{s(t)\}} = (e_t \otimes A) \in \ ^{M \cdot N \times D} \qquad (12)$$

$$\frac{\partial b^H}{\partial \text{Im}\{s(t)\}} = -j(e_t \otimes A)^H, \ \frac{\partial b}{\partial \text{Im}\{s(t)\}} = j(e_t \otimes A) \in \ ^{M \cdot N \times D} \qquad (13)$$

where D is defined by $D = D(\theta) = [d(\theta_1),\ldots,d(\theta_D)]$ and $d(\theta_i) = \partial a(\theta)/\partial\theta\big|_{\theta=\theta_i}$, $H(t) = \mathrm{diag}\{s_1(t), s_1(t),\ldots, s_D(t)\}$, and e_t is the t-th $N \times N$ dimensional unit vector. Using Eqs. (10) and (12)–(13), we obtain that the sub-matrices of the FIM matrix are given by,

$$F(\theta,\theta) = 2\cdot\left(\mathrm{Re}\left\{\frac{\partial b^H}{\partial\theta_k}(I\otimes Q^{-1})\frac{\partial b}{\partial\theta_\ell}\right\}\right) = 2\sum_{t=1}^{N}\mathrm{Re}\left\{H^H(t)\tilde{D}^H\tilde{D}H(t)\right\} \quad (14)$$

$$F(\theta,\mathrm{Re}(s(t))) = 2\,\mathrm{Re}\left\{(H^H(1)D^H,\ldots,H^H(N)D^H)(I\otimes Q^{-1})(e_t\otimes A)\right\}$$
$$= 2\,\mathrm{Re}\left\{H^H(t)(Q^{-1/2}D)^H(Q^{-1/2}A)\right\} = 2\,\mathrm{Re}\left\{H^H(t)\tilde{D}^H\tilde{A}\right\} \quad (15)$$

$$F(\mathrm{Re}(s(t)),\theta) = 2\,\mathrm{Re}\left\{(e_t\otimes A)^H(I\otimes Q^{-1})\frac{\partial b}{\partial\theta}\right\}$$
$$= 2\,\mathrm{Re}\left\{(Q^{-1/2}A)^H(Q^{-1/2}D)H(t)\right\} = 2\,\mathrm{Re}\left\{\tilde{A}^H\tilde{D}H(t)\right\} \quad (16)$$

$$F(\theta,\mathrm{Im}\{s(t)\}) = 2\,\mathrm{Re}\left\{j\left[\frac{\partial b^H}{\partial\theta}(I\otimes Q^{-1})(e_t\otimes A)\right]\right\}$$
$$= -2\,\mathrm{Im}\left\{H^H(t)D^H Q^{-1}A\right\} = F^H(\mathrm{Im}\{s(t)\},\theta) \quad (17)$$

$$F(\mathrm{Re}(s(k)),\mathrm{Re}(s(\ell))) = 2\cdot\mathrm{Re}\left\{\frac{\partial b^H}{\partial\mathrm{Re}(s(k))}(I\otimes Q^{-1})\frac{\partial b}{\partial\mathrm{Re}(s(\ell))}\right\}$$
$$= F(\mathrm{Im}(s(k)),\mathrm{Im}(s(\ell))) = 2\,\mathrm{Re}\left\{\tilde{A}^H\tilde{A}\right\}\delta_{k,\ell} \quad (18)$$

$$F(\mathrm{Re}(s(k)),\mathrm{Im}(s(\ell))) = 2\cdot\left(\mathrm{Re}\left\{\frac{\partial b^H}{\partial\mathrm{Re}(s(k))}(I\otimes Q^{-1})\frac{\partial b}{\partial\mathrm{Im}(s(\ell))}\right\}\right)$$
$$= -2\cdot\mathrm{Im}\left\{\tilde{A}^H\tilde{A}\right\}\delta_{k,\ell} = -F(\mathrm{Im}(s(\ell)),\mathrm{Re}(s(k))) \quad (19)$$

All FIM cross-terms involving both signal and noise parameters are identically zero. Let us introduce the block-diagonal matrix

$$F(s,s) = \mathrm{Bdiag}\left\{F(s(t),s(t))\right\} \quad (20)$$

where the matrices $F(s(t),s(t))$, $t = 1,\ldots,N$ are defined as

$$F(s(t),s(t)) = \begin{bmatrix} F(\mathrm{Re}(s(t)),\mathrm{Re}(s(t))) & F(\mathrm{Re}(s(t)),\mathrm{Im}(s(t))) \\ F(\mathrm{Im}(s(t)),\mathrm{Re}(s(t))) & F(\mathrm{Im}(s(t)),\mathrm{Im}(s(t))) \end{bmatrix}$$
$$= 2\begin{bmatrix} \mathrm{Re}\left\{\tilde{A}^H\tilde{A}\right\} & -\mathrm{Im}\left\{\tilde{A}^H\tilde{A}\right\} \\ \mathrm{Im}\left\{\tilde{A}^H\tilde{A}\right\} & \mathrm{Re}\left\{\tilde{A}^H\tilde{A}\right\} \end{bmatrix} \quad (21)$$

Furthermore, we introduce the matrices

$$F(\theta, s) = [F(\theta, s(1)), F(\theta, s(2)), \ldots, F(\theta, s(N))] \tag{22}$$

$$F(s, \theta) = [F(s(1), \theta), F(s(2), \theta), \ldots, F(s(N), \theta)]^T \tag{23}$$

where the matrices $F(\theta, s(t))$ and $F(s(t), \theta)$ are defined as

$$F(\theta, s(t)) = [F(\theta, \mathrm{Re}[s(t)]), F(\theta, \mathrm{Im}[s(t)])] \tag{24}$$

$$F(s(t), \theta) = [F(\mathrm{Re}[s(t)], \theta), F(\mathrm{Im}[s(t)], \theta)] \tag{25}$$

Using these notations, the FIM can be written as

$$F = \begin{bmatrix} F_{\theta,\theta} & F_{\theta,s} & 0 \\ F_{s,\theta} & F_{s,s} & 0 \\ 0 & 0 & F_{\sigma,\sigma} \end{bmatrix} \tag{26}$$

Applying the partitioned matrix inversion formula (1), we obtain

$$\mathrm{CRB}_{\mathrm{DET}}^{-1}(\theta) = F_{\theta,\theta} - F_{s,\theta} F_{s,s}^{-1} F_{\theta,s} = F_{\theta,\theta} - \sum_{t=1}^{N} F_{s(t),\theta} F_{s(t),s(t)}^{-1} F_{\theta,s(t)} \tag{27}$$

Using Eqs. (14)–(19), we obtain

$$F_{s(k),s(k)} = 2 \begin{bmatrix} \mathrm{Re}\{\tilde{A}^H \tilde{A}\} & -\mathrm{Im}\{\tilde{A}^H \tilde{A}\} \\ \mathrm{Im}\{\tilde{A}^H \tilde{A}\} & \mathrm{Re}\{\tilde{A}^H \tilde{A}\} \end{bmatrix} \in \mathfrak{R}^{2D \times 2D} \tag{28}$$

$$F_{\theta,s(t)} = 2 \left[\mathrm{Re}\{H^H(t)\tilde{D}^H \tilde{A}\}, \mathrm{Im}\{H^H(t)\tilde{D}^H \tilde{A}\} \right] \in \mathfrak{R}^{D \times 2D} \tag{29}$$

$$F_{s(t),\theta} = 2 \begin{bmatrix} \mathrm{Re}\{H^H(t)\tilde{D}^H \tilde{A}\}^T \\ -\mathrm{Im}\{H^H(t)\tilde{D}^H \tilde{A}\}^T \end{bmatrix} \in \mathfrak{R}^{2D \times D} \tag{30}$$

Let $\bar{F} = \mathrm{Re}(F)$, $\tilde{F} = \mathrm{Im}(F)$ and the same definition is applied for matrix G, we get $\bar{G}$ and $\tilde{G}$. If let $G = F^{-1}$, then there is the relationship of $\bar{F}\bar{G} + \tilde{F}\tilde{G} = I$ and $\tilde{F}\bar{G} - \bar{F}\tilde{G} = 0$, here G satisfies the relations is unique. With the holding of the relationships, and using the equality of $\mathrm{Re}(X)\mathrm{Re}(Y^T) + \mathrm{Im}(X)\mathrm{Im}(Y^T) = \mathrm{Re}(XY^H)$, when we assume that

$$\begin{bmatrix} \mathrm{Re}\{\tilde{A}^H \tilde{A}\} & -\mathrm{Im}\{\tilde{A}^H \tilde{A}\} \\ \mathrm{Im}\{\tilde{A}^H \tilde{A}\} & \mathrm{Re}\{\tilde{A}^H \tilde{A}\} \end{bmatrix}^{-1} = \begin{bmatrix} \mathrm{Re}\{B\} & -\mathrm{Im}\{B\} \\ -\mathrm{Im}\{B\} & \mathrm{Re}\{B\} \end{bmatrix}$$

Then there is the result of $B = (\tilde{A}^T \tilde{A}^*)$. By using the equality of $\mathrm{Re}(X)\mathrm{Re}(Y^T) + \mathrm{Im}(X)\mathrm{Im}(Y^T) = \mathrm{Re}(XY^H)$ repeatedly, we have the main result of

$$\mathrm{CRB}_{\mathrm{DET}}^{-1}(\theta) = F_{\theta,\theta} - 2\sum_{t=1}^{N}\left[\mathrm{Re}\{H^H(t)\tilde{D}^H\tilde{A}\}, -\mathrm{Im}\{H^H(t)\tilde{D}^H\tilde{A}\}\right] \cdot$$

$$\begin{bmatrix} \mathrm{Re}\{\tilde{A}^H\tilde{A}\} & -\mathrm{Im}\{\tilde{A}^H\tilde{A}\} \\ \mathrm{Im}\{\tilde{A}^H\tilde{A}\} & \mathrm{Re}\{\tilde{A}^H\tilde{A}\} \end{bmatrix}^{-1} \begin{bmatrix} \mathrm{Re}\{\tilde{A}^H\tilde{D}H(t)\} \\ \mathrm{Im}\{\tilde{A}^H\tilde{D}H(t)\} \end{bmatrix}$$

$$= F_{\theta,\theta} - 2\sum_{t=1}^{N}\left[\mathrm{Re}\{H^H(t)\tilde{D}^H\tilde{A}\}, -\mathrm{Im}\{H^H(t)\tilde{D}^H\tilde{A}\}\right] \cdot$$

$$\begin{bmatrix} \mathrm{Re}\{B\} & \mathrm{Im}\{B\} \\ -\mathrm{Im}\{B\} & \mathrm{Re}\{B\} \end{bmatrix} \begin{bmatrix} \mathrm{Re}\{\tilde{A}^H\tilde{D}H(t)\} \\ \mathrm{Im}\{\tilde{A}^H\tilde{D}H(t)\} \end{bmatrix}$$

$$= F_{\theta,\theta} - 2\sum_{t=1}^{N}\mathrm{Re}\{H^H(t)\tilde{D}^H\tilde{A}B^*\tilde{A}^H\tilde{D}H(t)\}$$

$$= 2\sum_{t=1}^{N}\left[\mathrm{Re}\{H^H(t)\tilde{D}^H\tilde{D}H(t) - H^H(t)\tilde{D}^H\tilde{A}(\tilde{A}^H\tilde{A})^{-1}\tilde{A}^H\tilde{D}H(t)\}\right] \quad (31)$$

It is straightforward to show that

$$\mathrm{CRB}(\theta) = \frac{1}{2N}\mathrm{Re}\left\{\left[(\tilde{D}^H P_{\tilde{A}}^{\perp}\tilde{D})\Box\ \hat{P}^T\right]^{-1}\right\} \quad (32)$$

Where $\hat{P} = \frac{1}{N}\sum_{t=1}^{N} s(t)s^H(t)$. When the signal number $D = 1$, the corresponding $\mathrm{CRB}(\theta)$ has the form of

$$\mathrm{CRB}^{-1}(\theta) = 2N\sigma_s\,\mathrm{Re}\left\{\left(d^H(\theta)(I - a(\theta)a^H(\theta))d(\theta)\right)\right\}$$

Here we assumed that $a(\theta)$ is a unit vector.

5   The simulation results and conclusion

In the computer simulations, we assume that the array is a uniform linear array with 10 elements, the elements distance is 0.5 wavelength, and the two signals with azimuth interval $\Delta\theta$ or the power of $\mathcal{P} = [10,10]$ impinging on the array. And the additive noise power is always assumed to be 1, and the snapshots number $N = 100$. The diagonal element of matrix Q is randomly produced subject to uniform distribution of interval $(0,1)$.

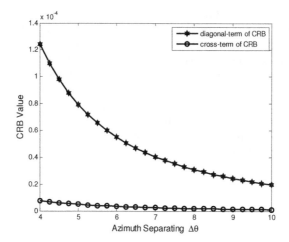

Figure 1: The variation of main- and cross-term of CRB (θ).

In Figure 1, we present the variation of first diagonal element and a cross-term of matrix CRB(θ) with the separation of the angle of arrival of the signals. The variation of the main-component and cross-term of CRB(θ) shows that the estimating accuracy of the azimuth parameter becoming better as the azimuth separation increasing.

Acknowledgment

The research was partly supported by Industrial Research plan of Science and technology department of Shaanxi Provincial Government under Grant 2012K06-27.

References

[1] N. Salman, M. Ghogho, A.H. Kemp, On the Joint Estimation of the RSS-Based Location and Path-loss Exponent. *IEEE Wireless Communication Letters*, **1(1)**, pp. 34–37, 2012.

[2] A. Hassanien, S.A. Vorobyov, A.B. Gershman, Moving Target Parameters Estimation in Noncoherent MIMO Radar Systems. *IEEE Transactions on Signal Processing*, **60(5)**, pp. 2354–2361, 2012.

[3] I. Avram, M. Moeneclaey, The modified Cramer-Rao bound for channel estimation in quantize-and-forward cooperative systems. *2013 IEEE WCNC*, pp. 2862–2867, 2013.

[4] P. Stoica, A. Nehorai, Performance study of conditional and unconditional direction-of-arrival estimation. *IEEE Transactions on Acoustics, Speech, and Signal Processing*, **38**, pp. 1783–1795, 1990.

[5] M. Pesavento, A.B. Gershman, Maximum-likelihood direction-of-arrival estimation in the presence of unknown non-uniform noise. *IEEE Transactions on Signal Processing*, **49(7)**, pp. 1310–1325, 2001.

[6] P. Stoica, A. Nehorai, Music, maximum likelihood and Cramér-Rao bound. *IEEE Transactions on Acoustics Speech and Signal Processing*, **37**, pp. 720–741, 1989.

[7] J.F. Böhme, Estimation of spectral parameters of correlated signals in wavefields. Signal Processing, **10**, pp. 329–337, 1986.

[8] Shao Chao, *MIMO System and STBC*. Publishing House of Electronics Industry, Beijing, 2013.

Study on aquaculture monitoring system design method based on CC2530 and WSN

A-Long Yu, Jinqiao Dai, Xinhui Li
School of Physics and Electronic Electrical Engineering,
Huaiyin Normal University, Huaian, China

Abstract

CC2530 is applied to ZigBee product radio frequency transceiver. Combined with CC2530 performance and operational principle, a low power wireless sensor network is designed by CC2530 in this paper for aquaculture monitoring system. With the small modifications of protocol stack, the system implements each breeding pool as a cluster with artificial setting, and automatically selects the cluster head work into artificial fixed cluster head node itself by using suitable modification routing protocol. The principle of aquaculture monitoring system design and algorithms are introduced. The results show that the amount of calculation can be greatly reduced, and the new aquaculture monitoring system structure is simple, high-precision, and low power consumption.

Key words: aquaculture, CC2530, wireless sensor network.

1 Introduction

With the increasing demands of fishery products, aquaculture has become one of the main projects of livestock breeding. In aquaculture, it is very important to real-time monitoring of key environmental factors such as fishponds water's dissolved oxygen, pH, and temperature, and so on [1].

Wireless sensor network (WSN) is a network formed by sensor nodes, which could monitor, sense, and collect real-time all kinds of information of perception targets in node deployment area (such as light, temperature, humidity, noise, and harmful gas concentration and other physical phenomena). With the help of wireless network, people can get the information which is processed by WSN and then sent out wirelessly. WSN is a new cross research field, which combines

 WIT Transactions on Information and Communication Technologies, Vol. 61, © 2014 WIT Press
www.witpress.com, ISSN 1743-3517 (on-line)
doi:10.2495/MIIT130231

the modern sensor technology, microelectronic technology, communication technology, embedded computing technology, distributed information processing technology, and other subjects. It has attracted worldwide attention, and was known as the most influential technologies in twenty-first century [2]. Therefore, the implementation of the wireless sensor network technology into aquiculture monitoring, which is integrated with the existing monitoring system organically to construct intelligent monitoring system of collecting aquaculture water quality parameter wirelessly and controlling remotely, is the trend of aquaculture development in the future [3].

Because of a large amount of consumption of energy in communication of wireless sensor network, a low power consumption device is applied based on CC2530.

2 CC2530 operational principle

RF transceiver CC2530 is a real system on chip which compatible with IEEE802.15.4, and supports the standards of proprietary 802.15.4 market as well as the ZigBee, ZigBee PRO, and ZigBeeRF4CE. CC2530 provides a link with quality of 101 dB, excellent sensitivity of receiver, and robust immunity of interference, four kinds modes of power supply, multiple flash memory size, as well as a broad set of peripherals which includes five Direct Memory Access (DMA) channels, battery monitors, 2 Universal Synchronous/Asynchronous Receivers/Transmitters (USART), 8 channels with 12 bits converter of Analog to Digital (ADC) and 21 Input/Output (I/O) pins, etc. In addition to the excellent performance of RF, selectivity and industry standard enhanced 8051 Microprocessor Control Unit (MCU) kernel which can support the general low power wireless communication, CC2530 made some improvements on the basis of CC2430 according to the practical applications. The cache in CC2530 is much bigger and the storage capacity can maximum support to the 256K, so no limits of the code for the small storage capacity, and the communication distance can reach 400 m, so not to plus amplifier to extend distance. The application of CC2530 includes remote control, consumer electronics, home control, measurement and intelligent energy, building automation, medical as well as more areas [4].

3 System structure

This system consists of two parts, real-time monitoring unit and wireless sensor networks unit. The structure diagram is shown in Figure 1.

Real-time monitoring unit is composed by computers distributed in the on-site monitoring center and the remote monitoring center. On-site monitoring center computer is mainly used to receive and process data uploaded by the wireless sensor network, then send out the control signal to drive control node according to the result in order to achieve closed-loop control, and eventually achieve the control. Remote monitoring center computers located on the top of the on-site

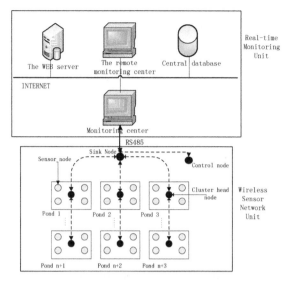

Figure 1: System structure.

monitoring center which is to mainly display all kinds of information by monitoring software, such as historical data query, dynamic data display, and so on.

The wireless sensor network unit, which is field-oriented, is composed by necessary hardware to be ZigBee Wireless Sensor Network such as control nodes, sensor nodes, sink nodes, and cluster head nodes [5]. With consideration of pond's size and independence of each other, it is appropriate to set wireless sensor network as cluster tree structure. Certain sensor nodes in each pond are set to form a cluster including cluster head by interface functions provided by equipment manufacturers. Sensor nodes can only communicate with the corresponding cluster head nodes, while the exchange of data between nodes is not allowed. Each cluster head which can communicate with another one to transmit information finally completes data communications with the sink node by means of single-hop or multi-hop. The sink nodes communicate with on-site monitoring computer through the bus RS232/485 including data communication and uploading the signal acquisition. Then monitoring computer eventually forms a control signal, and starts the control node through the sink node by the mean of wireless to achieve closed-loop control of environment factors.

4 Control node design

The control node includes control module and execution module. The structure diagram is shown in Figure 2. The control node is actuator-oriented and is suitable to control one or more ponds. But in order to simplify the program and peripheral interface circuit design of the processor, experience has shown that it is appropriate to control less than six fish ponds at once with one control node [6]. A CC2530 chip is the processing center of the node, which is responsible for

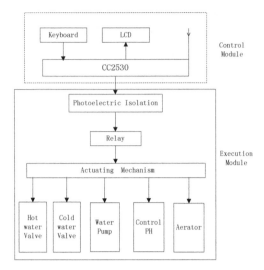

Figure 2: Control node structure.

receiving the control signal form the monitoring computer which is sent by the integrated wireless communication function of the CC2530 chip inside and, then making implementation module act to regulate environment factors of ponds to achieve the most adapted environment for fish growth.

5 Sensor node design

The sensor nodes are the basic elements of the wireless sensor network. The sensor node structure of the system diagram is shown in Figure 3. All kinds of sensors, such as temperature sensors, dissolved oxygen sensors, and pH sensors, are responsible for the collected analog data through the conditioning circuit to interference immunity and voltage tuning. Then, the digital signal can be obtained by putting the data through the CC2530 chip general-purpose I/O port into the A/D converter which is integrated within the chip, which will be processed by the enhanced 8051 microcontroller. At last, the final data is transferred into ZigBee network unit in CC2530 chip which has the function of sending and receiving data within the ZigBee network. The wireless units transmit data to the cluster head within the same cluster by the RF signal. In this place, the cluster head is equivalent to the router, with the function of the path searching. It sends data to the sink node by means of single-hop or multi-hop.

6 Cluster head node design

The structure of cluster head node is similar to the sensor node, but it has no sensors and conditioning circuits. As the cluster head node act as router for data exchange, it is particularly important to use appropriate routing protocol. LEACH

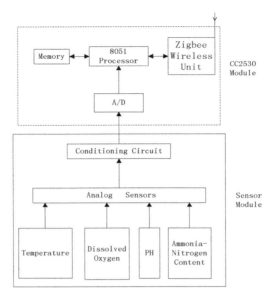

Figure 3: Sensor node structure.

(low energy the adaptive Clustering hierarchy) routing protocol, a hierarchical protocol, has been widely used in clustering wireless network. It selects a cluster circularly randomly which can make the energy load evenly distribute to each node equally, thus reduce energy consumption and achieve extending the lifecycle of network. LEACH routing protocol still uses the dynamic calculated to select cluster head, resulting in a large energy overhead which is not propitious to energy conservation. In this system, we set each fish pond as a cluster and set the fixed cluster head manually, which will save the overhead of dynamic cluster head selecting and reduce a considerable number of energy consumption. The optimization of the routing algorithm can be obtained only by modifying dynamic cluster head in the LEACH routing protocol as the fixed head. So, using the optimized LEACH routing protocol as routing algorithm for system is an appropriate choice.

7 Sink node design

Playing a connecting role in the entire monitoring wireless network, the sink node is composed by a CC2530 chip module and connects to computer via RS232/485 bus. The wireless unit of the sink node collects and demodulates wireless data signal from scattered cluster heads, and then sends the result to the computers in monitoring center.

Another important function of the sink node is transmitting the control signal based on the algorithm down to each control node. Then, control nodes drive relays or D/A converter with the control signal to make control actuator act.

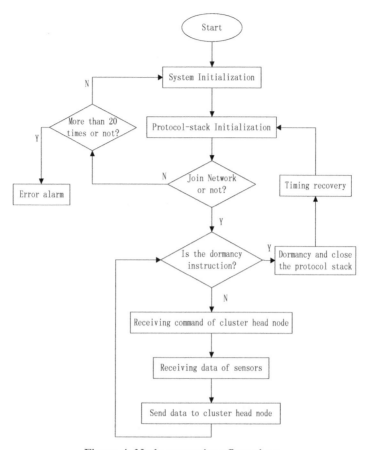

Figure 4: Node transceiver flow chart.

In this way, the closed-loop control for the water-environment factors of ponds can be achieved.

8 Software design

Sensor node is responsible for collecting field data and sending the data to the cluster head. The software of nodes is written by C language. The flow diagram is shown in Figure 4.

Software processes of cluster head nodes are similar with control nodes and sensor nodes. The cluster head node has no function of receive sensor data and increase function of computing routing, while the control node increases the function of controlling actuator.

The data transfer from sensor nodes to the sink node and finally to the cluster head is composed by frame control, destination address, source address, payload, and another six parts in network layer.

9 Conclusion

Aimed at adverse factors caused by wide application of wired monitoring system in the field at present and characteristics of aquaculture field of scale, a new method is applied for aquiculture monitoring system based on CC2530 and WSN. From the experimental results, we learn that the new aquaculture monitoring system structure is simple, high-precision, and low power consumption. The new aquaculture monitoring system has a potential future in the field of measurement and control.

Acknowledgments

The research work was supported by the Learning with Research and Production Foundation of Jiangsu Province, China and by the Learning with Research and Production Foundation of the Higher Education Institutions of Jiangsu Province, China. Grant No: SBY201220211 and JHB2012-55).

References

[1] T. Pan, D. Zhao, Control system on many environmental factors of aquaculture. *Industrial Control Computer*, **14(12)**, pp. 35–37, 2001.
[2] H.F. Rashvand, W. Yi, L. Cui, Wireless sensor networks (WSN) 2011. *IET Wireless Sensor Systems*, **1(4)**, pp. 179–180, 2011.
[3] Jing Ke, Shifeng Yang, Hailing Hou, Wireless monitoring system for aquiculture environment. *Journal of Tianjin University*, **22(4)**, pp. 56–58, 2007.
[4] B. Radin, S. Dušan, N. Teslic, One solution of the light source based on LED with radio-control provided with Zigbee-compatible microcontroller CC2530. *Proceedings of the 19th Telecommunications Forum. IEEE Computer Society*, Belgrade, Serbia, pp. 932–935, 2011.
[5] Wei Yang, Minzan Li, Lihua Zheng, A remote monitoring system of automatic soil sampler based on ZigBee WSN. *American Society of Agricultural and Biological Engineers Annual International Meeting.* Kansas City, MO, pp. 4023–4028, 2013.
[6] Bing Shi, Dean Zhao, Xingqiao Liu, et al., Intelligent monitoring system of aquiculture on a large scale based on WSN. *Journal of Agricultural Engineering*, **27(9)**, pp. 136–140, 2011.

Double Cox risk model of reinsurance with portfolio

Yinju Niu[1], Yongli Luo[2], Yafeng Xia[2]
[1]College of Computer, Dongguan University of Technology, Dongguan, China
[2]School of Sciences, Lanzhou University of Science and Technology, Lanzhou, China

Abstract

As a result of some random factors that will not regularly appear in the process of insurance business, it is entirely possible that customers choose reinsurance business. For the condition that the insurance company policy arrival process and claims process are Cox process, considering the insurance company investment combination and reinsurance to evade bankruptcy, a double Cox risk model of reinsurance with portfolio is established. Using the knowledge of martingale theory, the upper bounds of ruin probability and Lundberg-index of this model are obtained. The analysis shows that the results of the model are feasible and can provide some good ideas for insurance company to prevent and control some risks.

Keywords: risk model, Cox process, Lundberg inequality, martingale, ruin probability.

1 Introduction

The Cox risk model was made a further research by Grandell [1] and had got many conclusions such as Lundberg inequality of ruin probability and other conclusions. What had been studied in literature [2–5] was a class of two types of insurance in which the numbers of claims submit to the Cox process model. The ruin probability to satisfy the promotion of Lundberg inequality and the explicit expression of ruin probability in exceptional circum stances were studied. With the expansion of business scale, business insurance needs diversification. Besides, due to the impacts of many other factors such as inflation, climate, interest rate, and so on, the insurance company may face risk of bankruptcy in practical course of operation. To this end, we can guarantee risk diversification through reinsurance and portfolio. In literature [6–9], the reinsurance Cox risk models to study the explicit expression of ruin probability and Lundberg inequality are established. In the paper, the reinsurance dual Cox risk model with portfolio is established, and the upper bound of the ruin probability and Lundberg-index are obtained.

2 Model building

Definition 1
When the probability of stochastic process $\{\Lambda(t), t \geq 0\}$ equals to 1, it satisfies:

(i) $\Lambda(0) = 0$;
(ii) For any $t \to +\infty$, $\Lambda(t) \to +\infty$;
(iii) Its sample track is a monotone nondecreasing continues function of time t and when $t \to +\infty$, $\Lambda(t) \to +\infty$, $p - a.s.$, then it is a diffused random measure.

Definition 2
Assume $\Lambda(t)$ to be random measure, $\{\tilde{N}(t), t \geq 0\}$ is a standard Poisson process, and $\Lambda(t)$ and $\tilde{N}(t)$ are independent of each other, then point process $N(t) = \tilde{N} \cdot \Lambda(t) = \tilde{N}(\Lambda(t))$ is called Cox process, in which $\Lambda(t)$ is cumulative intensity process.

Definition 3
Assume that $\Lambda(t)$ is random measure, $\{N(t), t \geq 0\}$ is a Cox process whose Cumulative intensity is $\Lambda(t)$. Besides $\{Z_i, i \geq 1\}$ is independent and identically distributed non-negative random sequence that its distribution function is $F(\cdot)$ and the mean is μ. Moreover, we supposed that they are mutually independent, then we get $h(z_i) = \begin{cases} 0, & z_i \leq m \\ z_i - m, & z_i > m \end{cases}$ $(i = 1, 2, 3, \cdots)$.

Before led into the model of this paper, we also need to make these five following assumptions:

(i) The model hypothesized that the insurance business with a portfolio has reached a certain scale. And u_1 means the initial fund of the insurance company and u_2 stands for the fund from investing in the project which can bring stable profit which meanly invests in government bounds, mortgage, and others. r_1 is said to be portfolio yield of u_2 after the deduction of tax and investment management costs. u_3 is the funding of project which has large investment risk and the profit is uncertain. Furthermore, it mainly invests in stokes and futures and hypothesized that its portfolio income is a random variable $u_3[r_2t + aW(t)]$. Especially $r_2t + aW(t)$ is a Brownian motion with drift parameter, r_2 stands for the drift parameter, a is interference factor, and $W(t)$ is normative Brownian movement.

(ii) The number of premiums to be received $\{N_1(t), t \geq 0\}$ during $[0,t]$ is a Cox process whose strength is $\{\Lambda_1(t), t \geq 0\}$.

(iii) During $[0,t]$ the number of claims $\{N_2(t), t \geq 0\}$ is Cox process whose strength is $\{\Lambda_2(t), t \geq 0\}$. And each claim amounts $\{Y_k, k \geq 0\}$ is independent random variables and is independent from $\{N_2(t), t \geq 0\}$.

(iv) When settling a claim, $h(z_k)$ is said to be the claim amount which is from reinsurance companies and give it to the insurance company which has been separated. While if $0 \leq h(z_k) \leq z_k$, m is the maximum upper limit of the insurance company.

(v) $\{N_2(t), t \geq 0\}$, $\{X_k, k \geq 1\}$; $\{N_2(t), t \geq 0\}$, $\{Y_k, k \geq 1\}$; $\{N_3(t), t \geq 0\}$, $\{z_k - h(z_k), k \geq 0\}$ are independent from each other.

Suppose that the assumptions (i)–(v) hold and we established reinsurance dual Cox risk model with portfolio, then

$$U(t) = u_1 + u_2(1 + r_1 t) + u_3(1 + r_2 t + aW(t))$$
$$+ \sum_{k=1}^{N_1(t)} (1 + \rho)X_k - \sum_{k=1}^{N_2(t)} Y_k - \sum_{k=1}^{N_3(t)} (z_k - h(z_k)) \tag{1}$$

where $u_1 > 0$, $u_2 > 0$, $u_3 > 0$, $r_1 > 0$, $r_2 > 0$, $a > 0$.

Let

$$u = u_1 + u_2 + u_3,$$

$$b = r_1 u_2 + r_2 u_3,$$

$$S(t) = bt + \sum_{k=1}^{N_1(t)} (1 + \rho)X_k - \sum_{k=1}^{N_2(t)} Y_k - \sum_{k=1}^{N_3(t)} (z_k - h(z_k)) + au_3 W(t).$$

Then

$$U(t) = u + S(t).$$

Let

$$\psi(u) = p(u + S(t) < 0, \exists t \geq 0),$$
$$\varphi(u) = 1 - \psi(u),$$
$$T_u = \inf \{t \geq 0, u + S(t) < 0\}.$$

then $\psi(u)$ is to be said as the ruin probability and T_u is the time of ruin.

3 Upper bound of the ruin probability

Definition 4

Setting up an arbitrary process $\{X(t), t \geq 0\}$, and the filter $F_t^X = \sigma(X(s), 0 \leq s \leq t)$ is σ— algebra generated by $X(t)$.

Lemma 1

Assume that $\Lambda(t)$ is random measure and $E[\Lambda(t)] < \infty$, $F_\infty^\Lambda = \sigma(\Lambda(t), t \geq 0)$.
Then $N(t)$ is the Corresponding Cox process and only if it satisfies the following conditions:

(i) $N(t)$ has conditionally independent increments of F_∞^Λ;

(ii) $N(t) - N(s)$ must obey Poisson distribution with the mean of $\Lambda(t) - \Lambda(s)$. That means, for any $0 \leq s \leq t$ and non-negative integer k, according to the probability, we know

$$p\left(N(t) - N(s) = k \big| F_\infty^\Lambda\right) = \exp\left\{-[\Lambda(t) - \Lambda(s)]\right\} \frac{\left[\Lambda(t) - \Lambda(s)\right]^k}{k!}.$$

The proof of Lemma is in [1].

Theorem 1

Let $M_u(t) = \dfrac{\exp\left[-r(u + S(t))\right]}{E^{F_\infty^\Lambda}\left[\exp(-rS(t))\right]}$, then $M_u(t)$ is a martingale of F_t.

Proof

Let

$$\begin{cases} F_\infty^{\Lambda_i} = \sigma(\Lambda_i(t), t \geq 0), i = 1, 2, 3 \\ F_t^{N_i} = \sigma\left(N_i(s), s \leq t\right), i = 1, 2, 3 \\ F_t^W = \sigma\left(W(s), s \leq t\right) \end{cases} \quad \text{and} \quad \begin{cases} F_\infty^\Lambda = F_\infty^{\Lambda_1} \vee F_\infty^{\Lambda_2} \vee F_\infty^{\Lambda_3} \\ F_t^N = F_t^{N_1} \vee F_t^{N_2} \vee F_t^{N_3} \\ F_t = F_\infty^\Lambda \vee F_t^N \vee F_t^W \end{cases},$$

Then

$$\begin{cases} g_1(r) = \int_0^\infty e^{-r(1+\rho)x}\, dF(x) - 1 \\ g_2(r) = \int_0^\infty e^{ry}\, dG(y) - 1 \\ g_3(r) = \int_0^\infty e^{r(z-h(z))}\, dF(z) - 1 \end{cases} \tag{2}$$

where $F(x)$, $G(y)$, $F(z)$ are the distribution functions of random variables X, Y, Z, respectively.

From Lemma 1 and re-expectation formula (2), we have

$$E^{F_\infty^{\Lambda_1}}\left[\exp(-r\sum_{k=1}^{N_1(t)}(1+\rho)X_k)\right] = \sum_{k=0}^{\yen} \frac{[\Lambda_1(t)]^k}{k!}e^{-\Lambda_1(t)}(g_1(r)+1)^k$$

$$= e^{-\Lambda_1(t)}e^{\Lambda_1(t)(g_1(r)+1)} = e^{\Lambda_1(t)g_1(r)},$$

$$E^{F_\infty^{\Lambda_2}}\left[\exp(r\sum_{k=1}^{N_2(t)} Y_k)\right] = \sum_{k=0}^{\infty} \frac{[\Lambda_2(t)]^k}{k!}e^{-\Lambda_2(t)}(g_2(r)+1)^k$$

$$= e^{-\Lambda_2(t)}e^{\Lambda_2(t)(g_2(r)+1)} = e^{\Lambda_2(t)g_2(r)},$$

$$E^{F_\infty^{\Lambda_3}}\left[\exp[r\sum_{k=1}^{N_3(t)} (Z_K - h(Z_K))]\right] = \sum_{k=0}^{\infty} \frac{[\Lambda_3(t)]^k}{k!}e^{-\Lambda_3(t)}(g_3(r)+1)^k$$

$$= e^{-\Lambda_3(t)}e^{\Lambda_3(t)(g_3(r)+1)} = e^{\Lambda_3(t)g_3(r)}.$$

Hence,

$$E^{F_\infty^{\Lambda}}\left[\exp\left(-rS(t)\right)\right] = E^{F_\infty^{\Lambda}}\exp\left[-r\begin{pmatrix} bt + \sum_{k=1}^{N_1(t)}(1+\rho)X_k - \sum_{k=1}^{N_2(t)} Y_k \\ -\sum_{k=1}^{N_3(t)}(z_k - h(z_k)) + au_3W(t) \end{pmatrix}\right]$$

$$= E^{F_\infty^{\Lambda}}\left[\exp(-rbt)\right] E^{F_\infty^{\Lambda}}\left[\exp\left(-r\sum_{k=1}^{N_1(t)}(1+\rho)X_k\right)\right] E^{F_\infty^{\Lambda}}\left[\exp\sum_{k=1}^{N_2(t)} Y_k\right] \qquad (3)$$

$$E^{F_\infty^{\Lambda}}\left[\exp\sum_{k=1}^{N_3(t)}(z_k - h(z_k))\right] E^{F_\infty^{\Lambda}}\left[\exp(-rau_3W(t))\right]$$

$$= \exp\left[-rbt + \sum_{k=1}^{3}\Lambda_k(t)g_k(r) + \frac{1}{2}a^2u_3^2r^2t\right]$$

Besides,

$$E^{F_s}(\exp[-r(S(t)) - S(s)])$$

$$= E^{F_s}\{\exp[-r[b(t-s) + (1+\rho)((\sum_{k=1}^{N_1(t)} X_k - \sum_{k=1}^{N_1(s)} X_k) - (\sum_{k=1}^{N_2(t)} Y_k - \sum_{k=1}^{N_2(s)} Y_k))$$

$$-(\sum_{k=1}^{N_3(t)}(z_k - h(z_k)) - \sum_{k=1}^{N(s)}(z_k - h(z_k))) + au_3(W(t) - W(s))]]\}$$

$$= \exp\{-rb(t-s) + \sum_{k=1}^{3}[\Lambda_k(t) - \Lambda_k(s)]g_k(r) + \frac{1}{2}a^2u_3^2r^2(t-s)\}.$$

Therefore, from Eq. (3) we have

$$E^{F_s}\left[M_u(t)\right] = E^{F_s}\left[\frac{\exp\left[-r\left(u + S(t)\right)\right]}{\exp\left[-rbt + \sum_{k=1}^{3}\Lambda_k(t)g_k(r) + \frac{1}{2}a^2u_3^2r^2t\right]}\right]$$

$$= M_u(s) \cdot E^{F_s}\left[\frac{\exp\left[-r\left(S(t) - S(s)\right)\right]}{\exp\left[\begin{array}{c}-rb(t - s) + \sum_{k=1}^{3}\left[\Lambda_k(t) - \Lambda_k(s)\right]g_k(r) \\ + \frac{1}{2}a^2u_3^2r^2(t - s)\end{array}\right]}\right]$$

$$= M_u(s).$$

So $M_u(t)$ is one martingale of F_t.

Theorem 2

$$\psi(u) \le e^{-ru} \cdot G(r) \tag{4}$$

Furthermore,

$$G(r) = E\left[\sup_{t \ge 0}\exp\left(-rbt + \sum_{k=1}^{3}\Lambda_k(t)g_k(r) + \frac{1}{2}a^2u_3^2r^2t\right)\right].$$

Proof

Assume that T_u is the time of ruin. We can easily know that T_u is stopping. In addition, we assumed that $t_0 < \infty$, and it is constant, then $t_0 \wedge T_u \ge 0$ and it is unbounded stopping. Therefore, by the optional martingale stopping theorem, we obtain

$$\exp(-ru) = M_u(0) = E^{F_0}\left[M_u(t_0 \wedge T_u)\right]$$
$$\ge E^{F_0}\left[M_u(t_0 \wedge T_u)\middle|T_u \le t_0\right]P^{F_0}(T_u \le t_0)$$
$$= E^{F_0}\left[M_u(T_u)\middle|T_u \le t_0\right]P^{F_0}(T_u \le t_0).$$

Therefore,

$$P^{F_0}(T_u \le t_0) \le \frac{e^{-ru}}{E^{F_0}\left[M_u(T_u)\middle|T_u \le t_0\right]} \tag{5}$$

Because that when the time is T_u, the insurance company will announce to bankrupt, then $-r(u + S(T_u)) \geq 0, \exp\left[-r(u + S(T_u))\right] \geq 1$. So

$$
E^{F_0}\left[M_u(T_u)|T_u \leq t_0\right]
$$

$$
\geq E^{F_0}\left[\exp\left\{-\left[-rbT_u + \sum_{k=1}^{3}\Lambda_k(T_u)g_k(r) + \frac{1}{2}a^2u_3^2r^2T_u\right]\right\}\right]
$$

$$
\geq \inf_{0 \leq t \leq t_0}\exp\left\{-\left[-rbT_u + \sum_{k=1}^{3}\Lambda_k(T_u)g_k(r) + \frac{1}{2}a^2u_3^2r^2T_u\right]\right\}.
$$

Equation (5) can be rewritten as

$$
P^{F_0}(T_u \leq t_0) \leq e^{-ru} \cdot \sup_{0 \leq t \leq t_0}\exp\left(-rbt + \sum_{k=1}^{3}\Lambda_k(t)g_k(r) + \frac{1}{2}a^2u_3^2r^2t\right)
$$
$$
\leq e^{-ru} \cdot \sup_{0 \leq t \leq t_0}\exp\left(-rbt + \sum_{k=1}^{3}\Lambda_k(t)g_k(r) + \frac{1}{2}a^2u_3^2r^2t\right) \tag{6}
$$

Taking expectations on both sides of Eq. (6)

$$
P(T_u \leq t_0) \leq e^{-ru} \cdot E\left[\sup_{0 \leq t \leq t_0}\exp\left(-rbt + \sum_{k=1}^{3}\Lambda_k(t)g_k(r) + \frac{1}{2}a^2u_3^2r^2t\right)\right].
$$

where, when $t_0 \to +\infty$,

$$
\psi(u) \leq e^{-ru} \cdot E\left[\sup_{t \geq 0}\exp\left(-rbt + \sum_{k=1}^{3}\Lambda_k(t)g_k(r) + \frac{1}{2}a^2u_3^2r^2t\right)\right] \tag{7}
$$

Let

$$
G(r) = E\left[\sup_{t \geq 0}\exp\left(-rbt + \sum_{k=1}^{3}\Lambda_k(t)g_k(r) + \frac{1}{2}a^2u_3^2r^2t\right)\right] \tag{8}
$$

Conjoining Eqs. (7) and (8), we obtained (4). Let $R = \sup_{r > 0}\{r|G(r) < +\infty\}$; then R is the Lundberg upper bound of this model.

4 Conclusion

The customers may choose reinsurance business because of some random factors that will not regularly appear in the process of insurance business. The double Cox risk model of portfolio and reinsurance is set up to study the problems of the ultimate ruin probability and Lundberg inequality. The upper bounds of ruin probability and Lundberg-index of this model can reflect more truly and accurately the actual operational situation of insurance companies. Therefore, the paper is helpful for the insurance companies to make the overall plan arrangement in insurance business.

Acknowledgments

The authors appreciate the financial supports by Science and technology Program for Guangdong Province (Grant No. 2012B010100044) and Science and Technological Program for Dongguan's Higher Education, and Science and Research Institutions (Grant No. 2012108102031).

References

[1] J. Grandell, *Aspects of Risk Theory*. Springer-Verlag, Berlin and New York, pp. 117–128, 1991.
[2] A.L. Zeng, X. Lin, H.J. Zhang, Double Cox risk model. *Mathematical Theory and Applications*, **23(1)**, pp. 107–112, 2003. (in Chinese)
[3] S.H. He, X.F. Xu, Double Cox risk model. *Journal of Yunnan University*, **26(4)**, pp. 275–278, 2004. (in Chinese)
[4] L.N. He, Z.M. Liu, Ruin probability of a Cox risk model. *Journal of Guangxi University for Nationalities*, **12(2)**, pp. 80–82, 2006. (in Chinese)
[5] S.J. Yang, X.K. Li, W.L. Li, The upper bounds for ruin probability in Double Cox ruin model. *Acta Scientiarum Naturalium Universitatis Nankaiensis*, **42(1)**, pp. 34–43, 2009. (in Chinese)
[6] S.G. Hong, X.Q. Zhao, A Cox risk model of reinsurance. *Journal of Changchun Institute of Technology*, **9(2)**, pp. 86–88, 2008. (in Chinese)
[7] Q. Tang, G. Wang, K.C. Yuen, Uniform tail asymptotics for the stochastic present value of aggregate claims in the renewal risk model. *Insurance: Mathematics and Economics*, **46(2)**, pp. 362–370, 2010.
[8] M. Song, R. Wu, G.J. Wang, On the joint distribution for a kind of Cox risk process. *Chinese Journal of Applied Probability and Statistics*, **26(6)**, pp. 597–604, 2010.
[9] F. Guo, D. Wang, Ruin probability with investment returns and dependent structures. *Mathematica Aeterna*, **2(3)**, pp. 263–271, 2012.

Network traffic application type identification based on gravitational clustering

Dengyin Zhang[1], Xiuyun Li[1], Jianfei Liao[1], Mingxiang Wang[1]
[1]Key Lab of Broadband Wireless Communication and Sensor Network Technology, Nanjing University of Posts and Telecommunications, China

Abstract

The application identification, which aims at classifying traffic accurately, is the basic of the analysis network traffic. Various improved clustering methods which based on *k*-means are widely used in the application identification of the network traffic. However, these algorithms are highly complex, and difficult to meet the real-time and high accuracy of the application requirements in traffic identification. By taking the *k*-means as the prototype and merging distance and density together, this paper proposes a gravitational clustering method to identify network traffic type which has resolved the localized solutions problem of the original clustering algorithm. The experiment result and analysis show that, traffic identification method based on this paper has higher recognition rate, faster convergence, and better clustering effect.
Keywords: network traffic, application identification, gravitational clustering.

1 Introduction

Network traffic is the important carrier of recording and reflecting the network, application type identification is the basis of network traffic analysis technology. Correct and effective identification of application contribute to traffic QoS management, grade of service (SLA) guarantee, bandwidth estimation, and other network source planning.

Currently, the main identification method of network traffic are: (1) Port-based identification method; (2) deep-packet-based identification method (DPI); (3) depth-flow-based identification method (DFI); (4) identification method based on network traffic communication behavior; (5) identification method based on machine learning. Because the static characteristic flow is hidden and cannot easily got, the simple DPI-based method and port-mapping-based method to

 WIT Transactions on Information and Communication Technologies, Vol. 61, © 2014 WIT Press
www.witpress.com, ISSN 1743-3517 (on-line)
doi:10.2495/MIIT130251

identify the type of application will be increasingly undesirable in the future; the traffic identification method, which is based on the connect characteristic of transport layer and application layer, in a particular application type been able to meet the needs, but this method has no universal adaptability and strong robustness. Therefore, this paper takes K-means algorithm as the prototype, adds clustering quality factor and proposes a gravitational clustering method to identify the network traffic application type.

2   Relate work

The application type identification is an important topic in network traffic analysis techniques. In recent years, the machine learning method has become a new research direction of processing network traffic classification [1–3]. But their application scope is very limited. At present, the K-means clustering algorithms [4,5] are widely used to classify the network traffic. However, these algorithms are very sensitive to set cluster's original center. In order to make the clustering results close to the global optimal solution, new feedback mechanism [6] is added, to dynamically adjust the speed of convergence based on the current quality of clustering, but these improvements are at the cost of function E' convergence speed; in order to make the algorithm get better optimization, the particle swarm [7] is applied to the K-means semi-supervised algorithm, which called PSOSC classify learning method. The improved algorithm can get the global optimal solution, effectively identify the P2P complex traffic but has high complexity.

In order to meet the real-time traffic identification need, this paper takes K-means algorithm as the prototype, adds clustering quality factor and proposes a gravitational clustering method to identify the network traffic's application type. This method incorporates division (distance) and density (mass) thought, but relatively simple and fast. By processing the isolated stream and setting initial cluster centroid, the improved algorithm can avoid falling into local optimum and make the traffic classification ability more accurate.

3   Gravity clustering

3.1 Traffic gravity

Definition 1 (Traffic cluster plasmid)
The network traffic cluster plasmid referred to as "traffic cluster," is the traffic cluster unit with "traffic cluster mass" in traffic data space.

Definition 2 (Traffic cluster mass)
The traffic cluster mass refers to the number of objects in network traffic clusters plasmid.

Definition 3 (Traffic cluster centroid)
Assuming $X_1,...,X_n$ ($X_i \leq x_{i,1}, x_{i,2},..., x_{i,d} >$, $1 \leq i \leq n$) are network traffic sequences in d-dimensional traffic space S, if C_j is a traffic cluster plasmid which composed of

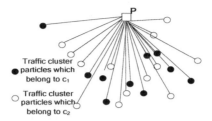

Figure 1: Gravity-based network traffic classifications.

$X_1, X_2, \ldots, X_e$ ($j \leq n, e \leq n$), the C_j traffic cluster centroid, $O_j \leq x_{0,1}, x_{0,2}, \ldots, x_{0,d}$, is the geometric center of $X_1, X_2, \ldots, X_e$ in traffic data space.

Definition 4 (Atomic traffic cluster plasmid)
Atomic traffic cluster plasmid is the traffic cluster plasmid which contains only one network traffic, whose mass is 1.

Definition 5 (Traffic gravity)
The traffic gravity is defined as the matching degree among traffic application type. The gravity between traffic cluster C_1 and C_2 is defined as follows:

$$F(C_1, C_2) = G \frac{M_1 \bullet M_2}{(\text{dist}(O_1, O_2)^2)} \qquad (1)$$

Lemma 1 (The Superposition Principle)
Assuming $p_1, p_2, \ldots, p_m$ are m traffic cluster particles which belong to the same application type in the network traffic space, the traffic gravity $F_1, F_2, \ldots, F_m$ are respectively formed by $p_1, p_2, \ldots, p_m$ and another network traffic, so the gravitational superposition is defined as follows:

$$F = \sum_{i=1}^{m} F_i \qquad (2)$$

Lemma 2 (The Classification Principle)
Assuming C_1 and C_2 are two class clusters which composed of two different traffic cluster particle. The class cluster property of P is to be known, given that the traffic gravity between P and C_1 is F_1, the traffic gravity between P and C_2 is F_2. If $F_1/F_2 > 1$, p is more likely to be type C_1 than type C_2.

4 Gravity-based clustering traffic identification

4.1 Characteristic attribute selection

The first step of traffic application identification is to select the attribute set of network traffic, which directly affects the identification efficiency. In order to

Table 1: Network Traffic Characteristic Attributes and Description.

Attribute	Characteristic	Characterization
x_1	T_{alive}	Network traffic duration
x_2	E_{packet}	The average size of transmitted data packets
x_3	$N_{inpacket}$	The number of received packets
x_4	$N_{outpacket}$	The number of sent packets
x_5	N_{inbyte}	The amount of received data
x_6	$N_{outbyte}$	The amount of sent data
x_7	M_{packet}	the maximum packet size in traffic
x_8	D	Inflows or outflows
x_9	$T_{maxpacket}$	The maximum packet interval
x_{10}	E_{pinter}	The mean of packet interval
x_{11}	P_{inout}	The ratio of sent data and received data

maintain the portability of the algorithmic process, 37 kinds of attributes are used to describe the different application type. Expressed as x_1, x_2,..., x_{37}, where, X_{ij} represents the normalized value of the i-th network traffic in the j-th attribute, n represents the number of network traffic.

The variance contribution rate ϑ is used to measure the importance that different eigenvalues and eigenvectors determine the network traffic belongs to which type. The dataset are quoted, by experiment, d is 11 when $\vartheta \geq 80\%$, the 11 kinds of characteristic attributes are given in Table 1.

4.2 Isolated stream processing

The isolated stream (noise stream) in network traffic set refers to the network traffic which is not consistent with the general behavior model of traffic set. The isolated stream affects traffic clustering, need to be isolated firstly.

To isolate the isolated stream, it is must be identified firstly. The traffic whose absolute value of Z-score above 2 is defined as isolated stream. $s[i][k]$ denotes the k-dimensional value of the i-th traffic, whose field intensity is written for:

$$F[i] = \ln(m_i + 1) \sum_{j=1 \cap j \neq i}^{n} \frac{\ln(m_j + 1)}{\sum_{k=1}^{d} (s[i][k] - s[j][k])^2} \tag{3}$$

d is the dimension of traffic sample point, n is the number of network traffic. Then, the Z-score of sample traffic i is defined:

$$Z[i] = \frac{1}{\sigma}(F[i] - \varpi) \tag{4}$$

where, $\varpi = \bar{s} = \frac{1}{n}\sum_{i=1}^{n} F[i], \sigma = \sqrt{\frac{1}{n}\sum_{i=1}^{n} (F[i] - \varpi)^2}$.

4.3 The initial cluster centroid setting

This paper isolates the isolated stream firstly, then classifies the traffic which distribute intensively in traffic set as a class roughly, sets the initial cluster centroid. The algorithm of setting initial cluster centroid is as follows:

Input: the number of traffic clusters is K, the traffic set Ω contains N sample streams (assuming isolate isolated stream).
Output: The initial cluster centroids are $O_1, O_2, \ldots O_k$.

For $i = 1: K - 1$

(1) Calculate the gravitational field of sample traffic in Ω, the minimum field intensity of network traffic, denoted as O_{i1}.
(2) Calculate the network traffic in $\Omega - O_{i1}$ traffic set which has the minimum traffic gravity, denoted as O_{i2}.
(3) Calculate former $N - 1/K$ sample traffic in $\Omega - O_{i1} - O_{i2}$ traffic set which has the greatest traffic gravity with O_i2 (the calculated sample traffic are closer to O_{i2} than others), and classify these calculated sample traffic as C_i.
(4) Calculate the cluster centroid of C_i, take it as the initial cluster centroid O_i.
(5) The rest of sample set, $\Omega = \Omega - C_i$, contains $N = N - \dfrac{N-1}{K} - 1$ sample traffic.

The rest network traffic in Ω set is classified as C_k, its cluster centroid O_k is calculated yet. The steps of the algorithm only involve correlate gravitational calculation; do not include other additional complex operation.

4.4 Traffic classification recognition

The network traffic gravity classification method is proposed, based on the theory of gravitation, its main steps are as follows:

A. The training phase
   (1) Obtain the network traffic; form network traffic sequence, based on the merge principle of network traffic.
   (2) Select the network traffic attributes, calculate the value of network traffic in the relevant attributes and do the normalization process, form the network traffic training set.
   (3) Calculate the traffic field intensity of each sample stream in training set, select the isolated stream by the Z-scores, and isolate then from other sample stream.
   (4) Use the algorithm of setting initial cluster centroid, select the traffic set initial cluster centroid in the all non-isolated stream set.
   (5) Use the Semi-supervised learning gravitational clustering principles and methods to iterate learning each traffic in training set, and simultaneously update traffic cluster centroid.
   (6) Finally, complete the classification of isolated stream.

B. Identification phase

(1) Form a network traffic sequence, based on the merge principle of network traffic.

(2) Compute the value of network traffic in the relevant attribute, do the normalization process.

(3) According to the classification model obtained from training phase, use gravitational clustering principle, classify the to be identified network traffic for each network stream, and simultaneously update traffic cluster centroid.

(4) The clusters map to specific application types, complete the network traffic identification.

5 Experiment and result analysis

This paper uses the Moore_Set from Professor Moore provided in Cambridge laboratory, it contains 10 kinds of application types of 377526 network stream samples. Select the five former proportion traffic in traffic application set (namely, *WWW, MAIL, BULK, P2P, DATABASE*), get out of 2000 traffic from each traffic type to as experimental traffic set, these traffic are equalized and mixed for 10 traffic set. This paper adopts 10-fold cross method to experiment, takes *Set1* set as a test set, and the remaining nine *Set2,...,Set10* set as training set.

5.1 The formation of traffic clusters

In the original training set, the gravitational clustering method is used, the isolated stream and the initial clustering centroid are processed, the setting of the initial clustering centroid map to x_1 (network traffic duration), x_2 (the average size of transmitted data packets), the result is shown in Figure 2.

From x_1, x_2 attributes, it can be found that traffic identify classification based on gravitational clustering in the selection of the initial cluster centroid are more scientific and rational than the *K*-Means and *PSOS*.

After trained by the *Set2,...,Set10* traffic set, the traffic clusters projected on x_1, x_2 attributes, its clustering results is shown in Figure 3. From the result seen, the cluster clustering effect is clear, error class is not obvious.

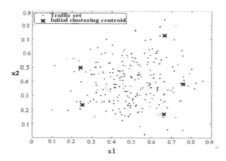

Figure 2: Original traffic set and the initial cluster centroid.

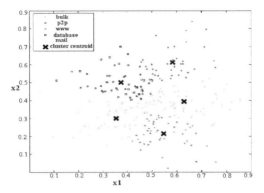

Figure 3: The traffic clusters results after training clustering.

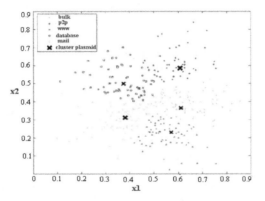

Figure 4: The traffic cluster result of test set after clustering.

Table 2: Comparison of Algorithms Recognition Rate.

Experiment Method	Recognition Accuracy
K-means	73%
PSOSC	86%
Gravity-based method	91%

Figure 4 is added the test flow set, the clustered traffic cluster project in x_1, x_2 attributes, after the training of nine traffic training set, gravity-based traffic clustering algorithm basically achieve convergence, and has strong algorithm stability.

5.2   Recognition rate comparison

We take the three methods iteration number as 40 times, repeat the experiment 5 times, and take the mean to calculate the correct rate. As presented in Table 2, the correct traffic clustering number and the correct cluster recognition rate of this paper algorithm are larger than the other two methods.

6 Conclusion

This paper introduces the "space" and "distance" concept, proposes a gravitational clustering method to identify the network traffic's application type,besides, processes the selection of network traffic characteristics attributes, isolated stream and the setting of initial cluster centroid. Compare with the original two algorithms, experimental results show that the gravitational clustering method not only resolves the localized solutions problem but also has higher recognition rate, and better clustering effect.

Acknowledgments

This research work is supported by the National Natural Science Foundations of P.R. China (NSFC) under Grant No. 61071093, National 863 Program No.2010AA701202, Sweden-Asian International Cooperation Project No.348-2008-6212, Returned Overseas Project, Jiangsu Province Major Technology Support Program No. BE2012849, Jiangsu Province Scientific and Technological Innovation Projects No. CXLX12_0481.

References

[1] Ma Yongli, Chien Jue, Machine learning for network traffic identification. *Journal of Beijing University of Posts and Telecommunications (Natural Science)*, **32(1)**, pp. 65–68, 2009.

[2] A.W. Moore, D. Zuer, Internet traffic classification using Bayesian analysis techniques. *Proceedings of the ACM SIGMETRICS*, pp. 50–60, 2005.

[3] T. Auld, A.W. Moore, Bayesian neural networks for Internet traffic classification. *IEEE Transactions on Neural Networks*, **18(1)**, pp. 223–239, 2007.

[4] Xu Peng, Liu Qiong, Internet traffic classification based on supporting vector machine. *Computer Research and Development*, **46(3)**, pp. 407–414, 2009.

[5] J. Erman, A. Mahanti, et al., Semi supervised network traffic classification. *Proceedings of the 2007 ACM SIGMETRICS International Conference on Measurement and Modeling of Computer Systems*, pp. 369–371, 2007.

[6] S. Jigui, Research on clustering algorithm. *Journal of Software*, **19(1)**, pp. 48–61, 2008.

[7] Z. Jian, Online clustering network traffic identification. *Journal of Beijing University of Posts and Telecommunications*, **34(1)**, pp. 104, 2011.

A measure of discrimination of attributes based on Fuzzy Gini Index

Zhenyu Liu[1,2], Ruiqing Yan[2], Zhihui Song[2]
[1]School of Traffic and Transport, Beijing Jiaotong University, Beijing, China
[2]Department of Transportation engineering, University of Inner Mongolia, Hohhot, China

Abstract

In the building process of decision tree, the choice of splitting attributes is critical to the power of the decision tree. In this paper, we propose a new method to choose splitting attributes, Fuzzy Gini Index, which is the extension of Gini Index in fuzzy context, and represent the application in detail with a data set. The result shows the method can increase prediction accuracy and comprehensibility to a certain degree.
Key words: decision tree, fuzzy partition, splitting attributes, Fuzzy Gini Index.

1 Introduction

Nowadays, in almost every real-life field, one is confronted with growing amounts of data, and it would be a waste not to take advantage of these data. In this context, data mining is a modern concept beginning to be widely used. The general purpose of data mining is to process the information embedded in data so as to develop better ways to handle data and support future decision making. Machine learning, association rules, clustering methods, artificial neural networks, statistical and visualization tools are common techniques used in data mining, while decision trees are more widely used because it is more simple, interpretable, and efficient.

Most algorithms to construct decision trees proceed in the same way: the so-called top-down induction of decision tree method. They build a tree from the root to the leaves, by successive partitioning of the training set into subsets. Each partition is done by means of a test on an attribute and leads to the definition of a

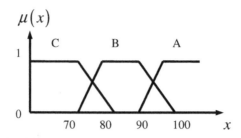

Figure 1: Fuzzy partition of study grade.

node of the tree. An attribute is selected, thanks to a measure of discrimination H. Such a measure enables us to order the attributes according to an increasing accuracy when splitting the training set. The discriminating power of each attribute in A is valued with regard to the classes. The attribute with the highest discriminating power is selected to constructing decision trees, whether crisp or fuzzy, differ mainly in their choice of H [1]. Different decision tree techniques use different measure of discrimination that enables the ranking of attributes during the construction step; one popular approach is information gain, that is, ID3, Fuzzy-ID3, which were proposed by Quinlan in 1986 [2], and further studied by many researchers [3]. Many heuristic decision tree algorithms are listed in work [4], and their difference compared. This paper presents a measure of discrimination-Fuzzy Gini Index, when building a fuzzy decision tree in fuzzy events.

2 Fuzzy Gini Index

Gini Index algorithm is an impure splitting method, which is first proposed by Breiman et al. in "Classification and Regression Trees" [5]. Fuzzy Gini Index presented in this paper is extension of the Gini Index on fuzzy events. So, we need to introduce fuzzy set theory first, which is foundation of fuzzy partition.

2.1 Attribute value space fuzzy partition

When attribute discretization is done by means of partitions, in order to avoid the artificial preciseness arising from sharp interval boundaries, we suggest using fuzzy partition to solve this problem.

We denote the attribute A with $(A_1, A_2, \cdots, A_n)$ n fuzzy attribute value; every fuzzy subset has its own membership function $\mu_{A_i}(x)$. To each specific value x of A, we can get membership degree $\mu'_{A_i}(x)$ through $\mu_{A_i}(x)$, $i = 1, 2, \cdots, n$, and fuzzy distribution of x is $\{\mu_{A_1}, \mu_{A_2}, \cdots \mu_{A_n}\}$. The above fuzzy predicates are more natural and accurate than classic theory [6].

For example, to attribute "study grade," we can use $A =$ "excellent," $B =$ "good," $C =$ "bad," three fuzzy subsets to describe. We use the trapezoid-shaped functions to represent these membership functions (see Figure 1).

After fuzzy partition, any value x of "study grade" is represented by three parts $\{\mu_A(x), \mu_B(x), \mu_C(x)\}$, which represent membership degree of x to fuzzy sets "A", "B", "C".

2.2 Selection of branching attribute

In order to describe a phenomenon, a specific concept or a fuzzy concept can be used. If a fuzzy concept was used, the fuzzy concept can be further partitioned into some fuzzy subsets in general, which will be contributed to comprehend the phenomena in detail. Based on fuzzy partition mentioned above, I propose "Fuzzy Gini Index" attribute partitioning for selection of branching attribute to built decision tree.

Given a set of examples, which contain m fuzzy attribute, during building fuzzy decision tree, node N contain L examples, after splitting it creates k children of node N. Before we define the Fuzzy Gini Index, let us introduce subsequently used notations: $|T_i|$ denotes the amount of examples leading to child node T_i;

$\mu_{l,j}$ is membership degree of example l to fuzzy subset j, $l \in T_i$; $u_{i,j} = \sum_{l=1}^{T_i} \mu_{l,j}$

denotes the sum membership degree of fuzzy subset j at T_i; , the sum membership degree of fuzzy concept β at child node i; then define:

$$\text{gini}(i) = 1 - \sum_{j=1}^{n} \left(\frac{u_{i,j}}{U} \right)^2 \tag{1}$$

And $U = \sum_{j=1}^{n} u_{i,j}$

denote the Gini Index of child node i, n is the amount of child node;

$$\text{gini}_{\text{split}}(T) = \sum_{i=1}^{k} \frac{|T_i|}{|T|} \text{gini}(i) \tag{2}$$

denote the Gini Index of node T, $|T|$ is the amount of example at child T.

Attribute, which has the minimum $\text{gini}_{\text{split}}$, will be selected as splitting attribute at the node.

3 The experimental results

Table 1 presents 16 experimental instances; a sample is represented by a set of features, which are outlook, temperature, humidity, and a fuzzy classification, which is easement. We aim at analyzing which of these factors is most closed to human feeling about the weather—easement. There are four symbolic attributes: outlook, temperature, humidity, windy, and one fuzzy concept: easement.

Table1: Data Set.

Number	Outlook	Tem	Humidity	Windy	Class		
					Good	Average	Bad
1	Sunny	Hot	High	False	0.0	0.8	0.2
2	Sunny	Hot	Normal	False	1.0	0.6	0.0
3	Sunny	Hot	High	True	0.2	0.8	0.0
4	Sunny	Mild	Normal	False	0.8	0.6	0.0
5	Sunny	Mild	Normal	True	0.0	0.0	1.0
6	Sunny	Cold	Normal	True	0.0	0.3	0.7
7	Cloudy	Cold	Normal	False	0.7	0.0	0.3
8	Cloudy	Mild	Normal	False	0.9	0.1	0.0
9	Cloudy	Hot	High	False	0.3	0.7	0.6
10	Cloudy	Mild	Normal	False	0.7	0.2	0.1
11	Cloudy	Mild	Normal	True	0.0	0.0	1.0
12	Rainy	Cold	High	False	0.2	0.0	0.8
13	Rainy	Hot	Normal	True	0.0	0.0	1.0
14	Rainy	Cold	Normal	False	0.0	0.0	1.0
15	Rainy	Hot	Normal	False	0.3	0.6	0.1
16	Rainy	Cold	High	True	0.0	0.0	1.0

Table 2: "Sunny" Child Node Table.

	Sunny	
	Good	2.0
Class	Average	3.1
	Bad	1.9

which is easement. We aim at analyzing which of these factors is most closed to human feeling about the weather—easement. There are four symbolic attributes: outlook, temperature, humidity, windy, and one fuzzy concept: easement. Attribute outlook has three values: sunny, cloudy, rainy; temperature also has three values: hot, mild, cold; humidity can be high or normal; windy can be false or true. Fuzzy concept easement has three fuzzy subsets: good, average, and bad. The classification for a given instance can give a membership. The figures below the fuzzy subset represent membership degree the instance belongs to the fuzzy subset (see Table 1).

The procedure of building the decision tree starts with all the examples in the root node. At any node still to be expanded, we have to find the best partition. Here, we use fuzzy Gini Index algorithm. Set outlook as example, first get the child node table—Tables 2–4—from Table 1.

Then according to Eq. (1) we get:

$$gini(sunny) = 1 - \left(\frac{2}{7}\right)^2 - \left(\frac{3.1}{7}\right)^2 - \left(\frac{1.9}{7}\right)^2 = 0.65$$

Table 3: "Cloudy" Child Node Table.

		Cloudy
	Good	2.6
Class	Average	1.0
	Bad	1.4

Table 4: "Rainy" Child Node Table.

		Rainy
	Good	0.5
Class	Average	0.6
	Bad	3.9

$$\text{gini(cloudy)} = 1 - \left(\frac{2.6}{5}\right)^2 - \left(\frac{1.0}{5}\right)^2 - \left(\frac{1.4}{5}\right)^2 = 0.61$$

$$\text{gini(rainy)} = 1 - \left(\frac{0.5}{5}\right)^2 - \left(\frac{0.6}{5}\right)^2 - \left(\frac{3.9}{5}\right)^2 = 0.37$$

Then according to Eq. (2) we get:

$$\text{gini}_{\text{split}}(\text{outlook}) = \frac{6}{16} \times 0.65 + \frac{5}{16} \times 0.37 + \frac{5}{16} \times 0.61 = 0.550$$

The same as outlook, using temperature, humidity and windy attribute, we can get:

$$\text{gini}_{\text{split}}(\text{temperature}) = \frac{6}{16} \times 0.61 + \frac{5}{16} \times 0.62 + \frac{5}{16} \times 0.61 = 0.610$$

$$\text{gini}_{\text{split}}(\text{humidity}) = \frac{5}{16} \times 0.61 + \frac{11}{16} \times 0.64 = 0.631$$

$$\text{gini}_{\text{split}}(\text{windy}) = \frac{6}{16} \times 0.35 + \frac{10}{16} \times 0.46 = 0.424$$

According to the above results, we can get the first attribute splitting result based fuzzy Gini Index (see Table 5).

Based on the Table 5, obviously we will choose "windy" as the splitting attribute which has the smallest $\text{gini}_{\text{split}}$ at the root node. As we know, decision tree pruning is indispensable for making the overfitting trees more accurate in classifying unseen data.

Here we use pre-pruning algorithm which stop growing the tree earlier to prune the tree with threshold $\alpha = 0.3$. If the truth level of classifying into one class is above the given threshold, return as a leaf. For example, after root node expanded the datasets with "windy = true" 79% belong to class "bad," 3% belong to class

Table 5: The Result of the First Attribute Splitting with Fuzzy Gini Index.

Attribute	Feature	Good	Average	Bad	GINI(i)	GINI
	Sunny	2.0	3.1	1.9	0.65	
Outlook	Rainy	0.5	0.6	3.9	0.37	0.550
	Cloudy	2.6	1.0	1.4	0.61	
	Hot	1.8	3.5	1.3	0.61	
temper	Mild	2.4	0.9	2.1	0.62	0.610
	Cold	0.9	0.3	3.8	0.61	
	High	0.7	2.3	2.0	0.61	
Humidity	Normal	4.4	2.4	5.2	0.64	0.631
	True	0.2	1.1	4.7	0.35	
Windy	False	4.9	3.6	2.5	0.46	0.424

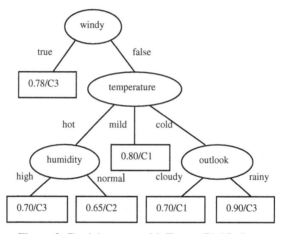

Figure 2: Decision tree with Fuzzy Gini Index.

"good," and 18% belong to "average." The latter two degrees is less than a given threshold, so return a leaf node 0.78/C3; if all attributes have been used, return as a leaf.

Repeating this further for each of the child nodes, we arrive at the decision tree shown in Figure 2. From the decision tree, we can get easily that the "windy" is most closed to human feeling about the weather, second will be "temperature,", so if it is "windy = true" much people will feel "bad."

4 Conclusion

During the procedure to build a decision tree, there are many ways to select the splitting attribute. To a given dataset, it is hard to say which is better. This paper presents a new method—Fuzzy Gini Index method, and addresses the procedure in detail through an example, then gets a simple decision tree. The experiment results prove this method can improve the prediction capability and interpretability to a certain degree. The main contribution of our work is the combination of fuzzy set theory with Gini Index, but first we need to partitioning fuzzy concept than build membership function of fuzzy set, which are not described in detail in this paper, so we have to continue the study in future.

Acknowledgment

The research work was supported by Natural Science Foundation of Inner Mongolia Autonomous Region under Grant No. 2010MS0705.

References

[1] C. Marsala, B. Bouchon-Meunier, Choice of a method for the construction of fuzzy decision trees. *Proceedings of the 12st International Conference on Fuzzy Systems*, St Louis, USA, pp. 584–589, 2003.
[2] J.R. Quinlan, *Machine Learning, Induction of Decision Trees*. Kluwer Academic Publishers, Hingham, USA, pp. 81–106, 1986.
[3] C. Olaru, L. Wehenkel. A complete fuzzy decision tree technica. *Fuzzy Sets and Systems*, **138(2)**, pp. 221–254, 2003.
[4] X.Z Wang, D.S. Yeung, E.C.C. Tsang, A comparative study on heuristic algorithms for generating fuzzy decision trees. *IEEE Transactions on Systems, Man, and Cybemetics, Part B: Cybemetics*, **31(2)**, pp. 215–226, 2001.
[5] L. Breiman, J.H. Friedman, R.A. Olshen, *Classification and Regression Trees*. Chapman and Hall/CRCMontery, New York, NY, pp. 189–196, 1984.
[6] Yang Jie, Ye Chen-zhou, Hang Xin, Decision tree based on fuzzy discretization. *Computer Emulation*, **17(6)**, pp. 35–39, 2000.

3D model family design and development based on ontology: a knowledge support approach

Jihua Wang[1], Huayu Wang[2]
1.College of Information Science and Engineering, Shandong Normal University,
2.Shandong Provincial Key Laboratory for Distributed Computer Software Novel Technology,

Abstract

The design of 3D model family in knowledge support framework has been recognized as an efficient means to realize sufficient 3D model variety to satisfy a range of customer demands. This paper proposed 3D model family modeling and design process based on FBS (function-behavior-structure) and API ontology, built the knowledge support design platform and framework, and described the knowledge-intensive design process. Finally, the prototype was developed for the actual design.
Key word: 3D model family, 3D model variant, FBS, geometry API, design ontology, design framework, knowledge support design.

1 Introduction

3D model as a virtual product in the environment of computer aided design and collaborative design is in fact the geometry structure of a real product. 3D model family is a group of related geometry models sharing common features and components to meet the similar design requirements. Design platform is a set of features, rules, interfaces, and manufacturing processes among a set of 3D models [1]. Design framework is the design platform for a particular purpose or specific application. 3D model family can be derived from a design framework according to some design goals.

Contemporary design processes have become increasingly knowledge-intensive and collaborative [2–4]. Knowledge support becomes more critical in the design process and has been recognized as a key solution toward future competitive advantages in product development, so it is imperative to provide knowledge support and to share design knowledge among distributed designers [5]. The design framework is a kind of knowledge support approach or intelligent methodology in which ontology is the best way.

The aim of this paper is to discuss knowledge support methodologies and technologies for 3D model family design. The design processes with ontology representation including customer requirements, functions-behaviors-geometry structures of 3D models, model family generation, evolution, and evaluation are explored in order to provide more series or variants to meet design innovation and diverse needs. The organization of this paper is as follows. Section 2 reviews the background and current research status related to 3D models or products development and their family design. Sections 3 and 4 outline the 3D model family modeling based on function-behavior-structure (FBS) and geometry API ontology, as well as the iterative design process and the methodology for model family design. Section 5 discusses the knowledge support platform and framework for a specific domain. Section 6 addresses the relevant issues and technologies for implementing a prototype. Section 7 summarizes the paper and points out the future work.

2   Background

There are various approaches and strategies for designing families of products and mass customized goods reported in varied disciplines such as computer science [6], marketing and management science [7–9], and engineering design [10,11]. The most important characteristics that have been stressed in these researches for designing product families are modularity, commonality, reusability, and standardization, and product modeling, product family modeling, design processes, and design platforms or bases are mainly discussed.

Product models are mostly based on the FBS models and recently stress the semantic transfer and the detailed configuration of every function, behavior and structure. The knowledge representation schema for design called design prototypes was introduced in the FBS models of design as a process, and the design prototypes are shown to provide a suitable framework to distinguish routine, innovative and creative design [12]. Design prototypes FBS are used to represent the 3D model architecture from both the functional and the structural perspectives [13]. A uniform behavior modeling approach is proposed based on SysML to express their various behavioral requirements in which a set of new constructs is proposed to compose the uniform behavior modeling profile, and the hybrid behavior can be uniformly represented in a multi-view and hierarchical way based on the profile [14].

The model is built to transfer the construction history, parameters, constraints, features, and other elements of "design intent" for CAD data exchange [15]. A system called the "Shape Annotator" is described to annotate the detected parts through concepts expressed by ontology, and each part is connected to an instance that can be stored in a knowledge base to ease the retrieval process based on semantics for product design in e-manufacturing.

Design knowledge representation is based on two aspects of product models and design processes, and it should be put in design repositories to share and reuse. Design repositories of heterogeneous information to support knowledge-based design are built to enable representation, capture, sharing, and reuse of design knowledge, which present a language for the modeling of engineering design artifacts and implement intelligent web-based interfaces that allow distributed users to create, edit, and browse design knowledge. The data schema as a complete description of fundamental design knowledge to support design reuse is built to specify the design information which can be divided into seven main categories of artifact-, function-, failure-, physical-, performance-, sensory- and media-related information types.

On the basis of product models, the family modeling can be completed. An information model is presented in a product family, in which the product structure architecture is selected as a template for product variants, maximizing data sharing between them and the mapping from the logical systems design to the geometric design is achieved.

3 3D model family modeling

3.1 3D model based on FBS and API ontology

3D model is the specific form of a product in the virtual computer environment, which is not just a simple geometric model and also carries other semantics with the development of knowledge-based design. FBS models to describe a product from customer requirements, working principles, and implementation structures is popularly accepted. 3D model as product geometry structures implies the product functions and behaviors. The functions and structures can separately be decomposed into hierarchical tree modes, and the behaviors link each other as a graph pattern.

The function system and structure system of a 3D model can be regarded as a concept tree in ontology; every node represents a function concept or structure concept, every edge represents a kind of parent-child relation. The behavior system of a 3D model can be regarded as a concept graph in ontology, every node is an action or a state, every edge is a kind of interaction relationship.

1. *Function ontology*

    Functions are the abstract vocabulary usually represented with verb–noun pairs, verb means function semantics, noun means the objects of the verb. The functions can be standardized to achieve the function knowledge sharing with the function vocabulary, which are a lexical symbol and an artificial convention or abstraction.

    The function ontology is represented by the concepts of verb-noun pairs, the high-level functions involve the multiple whole_part attributes for subordinate ones whose values are the corresponding low-level function instances, and the lowest-level functions involve a series of behavior attributes. The core function has multiple _supported or whole_part attributes whose values are the auxiliary function instances.

2. *Structure ontology*

The structure of 3D model is hierarchically decomposed into a variety of geometry elements such as features, geometry APIs (application programming interfaces for geometry modeling), and surfaces or loops as the basic geometrical units. Geometry APIs as mathematical expression in the geometric disciplines sense and as micros are the basic geometric particles according with designers' intuitive thinking in the design process, and API ontology is easier to reach connotation unity in the cross-CAD systems and interdisciplinary.

Thus structure ontology can be represented with the concepts of features, geometry APIs, even surfaces in the corresponding level, and it has the attributes about functions which maybe practical or symbolic ones: _function; the attributes about shape or performance parameters: _parameter; the attributes about structure decomposition: whole_part to illustrate instances from top to down in a tree mode. The lowest-level elements such as surfaces are related to actions or behaviors.

3. *Behavior ontology*

Functions and structure features are artificial convention relations. To describe functions formally, the concept of behavior is introduced to decompose and quantify functions, behaviors need complete how the functions work and how the structures interact with themselves. Functions as the abstract description of design intent and customer requirements are specifically expressed and implemented with series of behaviors in accordance with certain principles or rules. Functions are also the subjective abstraction of behaviors with static characteristics and behaviors are the concrete realization of functions with dynamic characteristics.

Only on the surface of certain structures can the static behaviors complete the appropriate action that manifest by a physical force, tension. Actions show by forces, curvature on surfaces in mechanical product, and a behavior is in fact an action-surface pair. Many behaviors of 3D model are formalized through physical forces.

Definition 1: A surface-behavior (action-surface pair) is the action bearing on the surface of 3D model, manifested as a physical force or curvature on a surface. All surfaces and their actions together constitute the outline structure and functions of 3D model. Let a behavior be B, a surface be S, an action be A, a force be F, curvature be C, then B=<A, S>, A=F|C|, S as an independent surface entity which is generated only by calling geometric modeling APIs, and A is a vector force, a curvature scalar or a resource identifier.

4. *Geometry API ontology*

Though surfaces are the standardized elements to represent and render 3D model in STEP, they cannot alone generate except by calling geometry APIs. Geometry APIs and action-surface pairs are the critical elements of the above FBS ontology. There are two kinds of geometry modeling APIs: geometric topology APIs and geometric body APIs. The APIs or the different modeling macros for the same geometry body in heterogeneous CAD systems can be unified by defining the geometry API ontology, and it is easier for design data interchange.

3D model is consisted of geometry features, and a feature is generated by calling the geometric topology APIs and geometric body APIs. The common body API entities include sphere, cone, sweep and so on. Body APIs are combined into a feature through topology APIs such as Boolean operating, which reflect the spatial topological relationships.

So geometry API ontology links 3D models and their design processes together, it is the _generating attribute value of a behavior surface.

In general, 3D model is built with FBS and geometry APIs; however, it is eventually constituted of geometry APIs with the attributes related structure, function, and behavior, so variants of a 3D model can be achieved by the addition and subtraction of geometry APIs or by alteration of API's attributes, FBS-API-ontology-based 3D model is shown in Figure 1.

3.2   3D model variants and family architecture modeling

Without consideration of the relationship of attributes of APIs, 3D model is decomposed into a pure API tree, and its nodes are body API instances or topology API instances, its edges represent parent-child or whole-part relation. 3D model is divided into geometry APIs that can be swapped by others with different sizes or types to create variants. 3D model is a graph mode when the surface-behavior attributes is considered on perspective of the combination of behaviors.

Through the combination and standardization of APIs, many series of 3D models or 3D model families can be produced. A model family architecture represents structural elements and their logical organization. A well-developed model family architecture can provide a generic framework to capture and utilize commonality and to instantiate the cases for differentiate market niches and law restrictions.

The modeling and representation scheme used in this research by hierarchically decomposing model families into features, geometry APIs, and attributes. Under this hierarchical representation scheme, 3D model variety is implemented at different levels (function level, feature level, behavior level, API level) within the model family architecture.

The commonality of a 3D model family is the maximum sub-tree with the same root or sub-graph among the family members. Every member is produced by inserting API blocks to the common sub-tree or sub-graph in any node.

4   3D model family design process based on FBS and API ontology

The 3D model customization stage aims at obtaining a feasible architecture of the 3D model family member through reasoning over FBS and API space according to design requirements and principles. Design requirements such as function, performance, manufacturability, and cost need to be converted to design constraints, and then the reasoning is performed at API levels and attributes levels which are related with design process to determine feasible 3D model architecture.

The family design process should be a parallel, collaborative, and iterative process in the geographically distributed environment and design teams. The detail design steps and stages are the following:

(1) Customer requirement analysis and function are modeled using design function deployment. The voice of customers and market trends are captured for generating design specifications, and a function tree is generated.
(2) The lowest-level functions are represented by a series of surface-behaviors which are derived from a principle or a workflow. A function-behavior interaction matrix is generated.
(3) Every surface and its action in a behavior node are confirmed. The action is a resource identifier or data type, and the surface is produced by calling API blocks consisted of some body APIs and topology APIs.
(4) Heuristic algorithms is used to find the function and its structure features consisted of API blocks, and a feature-API block matrix is constructed, and all structure features are mapped to functions through the feature-API block matrix.
(5) The functional suites are mapped to structural suites using the function-structure interaction matrix.
(6) Other design objectives such as cost and profit are transformed into constraints to configure and optimize model family architecture by adjusting the spatial positions, types and parameters of API blocks.
(7) The model family architecture is rebuilt to form a hierarchical architecture by using the optimized features from the functional and structural perspectives.
(8) The space of features and their API blocks form the 3D model platform, the 3D model family portfolio is derived from the platform.
(9) The interfaces are developed to facilitate designers to operate the addition, removal and substitution of features and their APIs.
(10) The 3D model family can be generated by feature and API configuration or reconfiguration.
(11) 3D model variants are evaluated and selected to meet the customer's satisfaction.

5   Knowledge support design platform and framework for 3D model family design

How to deploy the functions of 3D model to lower level elements; How to select the solutions among features or surface-behaviors; after being selected, all solutions are configured to be an end model; these problems can efficiently and effectively be solved with the help of knowledge support platforms and frameworks.

A 3D model family usually originates in a differentiation process of a basic model or in an aggregation process of distinct models. The 3D model family design process is linked to product functions, geometry features, and manufacturability. An effective platform for a model family can provide a variety of derivative models rapidly and easily according to some basic features to meet design requirements.

Modern design process is knowledge-intensive, and design knowledge refers to the collection of knowledge to support the design activities including 3D models and the process of designing them. Successfully capturing design knowledge, effectively representing it and easily accessing it are crucial in building the frameworks.

The fundamental issues underlying knowledge frameworks include capturing, representing, and accessing the knowledge about model and family architecture information modeling, family generation and derivation, family evolution and assessment. The knowledge support assists the designer to capture the voice of customers and market trends, and to embed them into the design objective for generating 3D model design specifications, then to realize sufficient model variety in the subsequent design process.

As discussed above, the whole design process on the knowledge support framework is knowledge-intensive, and designers are in the environment inspired by knowledge, at least don't have to rack their brains to look for cases and seek rules, the design knowledge repository helps designers quickly get and utilize the most relevant knowledge to solve problems in design processes.

In applying the above knowledge support scheme, the following points should be noted: Development of a 3D model family is a complex task; A systematic and structured approach is a mandatory; Functional analysis is best suited for developing a new family, rather than modifying existing ones.

6   Summary and future work

This paper presented a knowledge support methodology and framework for 3D model family design and development. An integrated family design scheme is proposed with knowledge support for customer requirements' modeling, 3D model architecture modeling based on FBS-API ontology, family generation, and variant assessment.

The developed methodology and framework can be used for capturing, representing, and managing family design knowledge and offer support in the design process. When fully developed, the system can support 3D model family design effectively and efficiently and improve customer satisfaction.

Future work is required to further develop the knowledge modeling in all design stages, and effectively to integrate the various design and calculation components.

Acknowledgment

This work was supported by Shandong Provincial Science and Technology Development Plan (2010G0020807).

References

[1] M.H. Meyer, A.P. Lehnerd, *The Power of Product Platforms*, The Free Press, New York, NY, 1997.

[2] C. Tong, D. Sriram, (Eds.), *Artificial Intelligence in Engineering Design: Volume I—Representation: Structure, Function and Constraints; Routine Design*. Academic Press, USA, 1991.

[3] C. Tong, D. Sriram, D. (Eds.), *Artificial Intelligence in Engineering Design: Volume III—Knowledge Acquisition, Commercial Systems; Integrated Environments*. Academic Press, USA, 1991.

[4] R.D. Sriram, *Distributed and Integrated Collaborative Engineering Design*. Sarven Publishers, Glenwood, MD, 2002.

[5] Xuan F. Zha, Ram D. Sriram, *Platform-Based Product Design and Development: A Knowledge Intensive Support Approach, Knowledge-Based Systems* (Vol. 19). Gaithersburg, MD, pp. 524–543, 2006.

[6] G.J. Nutt, *Open Systems*, Prentice Hall, Englewood Cliffs, NJ, 1992.

[7] P. Kotler, From mass marketing to mass customization. *Planning Review*, **17(5)**, pp. 10–15, 1989.

[8] M.H. Meyer, J.H. Utterback, The product family and the dynamics of core capability. *Sloan Management Review*, **34**, pp. 29–47, 1993.

[9] B.J. Pine, *Mass Customization—The New Frontier in Business Competition*. Harvard Business School Press, Boston, MA, 1993.

[10] T.W. Simpson, A Concept Exploration Method for Product Family Design', Ph.D. Dissertation, System Realization Laboratory, Woodruff School of Mechanical Engineering, Georgia Institute of Technology, Atlanta,1998.

[11] T.W. Simpson, J.R.A. Maier, F. Mistree, Product platform design: method and application. *Research in Engineering Design*, **13**, pp. 2–22, 2001.

[12] J.S. Gero, Design prototypes: a knowledge representation schema for design. *AI Magazine*, **11(4)**, pp. 26–36, 1990.

[13] X.F. Zha, H. Du, Mechanical systems and assemblies modeling using knowledge intensive Petri Net formalisms. *Artificial Intelligence for Engineering Design, Analysis and Manufacturing*, **15(2)**, pp. 145–171, 2001.

[14] Yue Cao, Yusheng Liu, Hongri Fan, et al., SysML-based uniform behavior modeling and automated mapping of design and simulation model for complex mechatronics. *Computer-Aided Design*, **45(3)**, pp. 764–776, 2013.

[15] J. Kim, M.J. Pratt, R.G. Iyer, et al., Standardized data exchange of CAD models with design intent. *Computer-Aided Design*, **40(7)**, pp. 760–777, 2008.

Research on the model of network survivability monitoring and control for traffic flow

Jun Deng[1], Bailong Ye[2], Hao Chen[1]
[1]*Hunan Vocational College of Science and Technology, Changsha, Hunan, China*
[2]*Central South University, Changsha, Hunan China*

Abstract

In order to improve the survivability of the network, it adopts the monitoring collaboration, cooperation collaboration, and monitoring & controlling collaboration for business, which combine the network monitoring with the network control to establish a survivability model based on the collaborative network. Firstly, the current network survivability problems were analyzed; secondly, the model architecture was put forward; finally, it carried out the detailed design and implementation. Through the change of state and the association between the service flow, the system model analyzes the business classification and correlation of flow characteristics and solves the single link network traffic monitoring and network flow control technology which cannot meet the needs of business development

Keywords: network survivability, network monitoring, network control, collaboration, business flow.

1 Introduction

Network survivability [1] is a kind of ability that it can still accomplish its task in time when the network system is attacked and broken down occasionally. In the basic attributes of network security, network survivability focuses more on availability of network system. From the current situation and development of information security, one of the best ways is to enhance the network survivability in order to cope with all the attacks, invasion and destruction. Security network survivability is the key technology of network monitoring and network control technology. The former is the foundation to ensure the network survivability; the latter is an important method to guarantee the survival of the network. Since the beginning of 1950s, the academic circles home and abroad have started extensive monitoring of [2] on the internet. At present, this research on network monitoring has got a lot of achievements in the aspects of the network flow model, the data packet filtering, the sampling technology, the traffic monitoring network traffic information compression storage, and each data packet timestamps. But there still exist many problems.

2   Existing problems of network survivability

According to the monitoring granularity, the present traffic monitoring methods are divided into: the link level monitoring, the packet level monitoring and the service level monitoring. But there exist many shortcomings from the flow monitoring link level monitoring, such as unable to obtain the flow index of the upper layer protocols; even unable to obtain the flow level and the detailed and related flow characteristics of the specific business, and unable to direct the traffic flow control.

The packet level monitoring based on the packet classification is always the core of the network traffic monitoring and the core of the routing that checks out problems. This technology is not only used in distinguishing the quality of service, but also widely used in a variety of network security devices. However it still cannot meet the higher and faster demands of the flow monitoring.

In recent years, the network monitoring based on business flow was an important direction of network traffic monitoring. The traffic monitoring level was a higher flow monitoring method, which can access behavior characteristics of business conversation and is one of the methods that can analyze business characteristics of the network application layer. However, the existing traffic flow monitoring foundation still adopts the packet classification without considering the business flow classification of the higher level which directly faces the business. This method does not consider the business classification through the state changes of the business flow and related relationships; meanwhile it does not consider the flow characteristics related business, even more does not take into account the relationship of connections and the relationship of flows. For example, the VoIP service [3] based on H.323 is jointly completed by many protocols. According to the current traffic monitoring method, in a complete VoIP session there will be 8 independent business flows, which split the relationship among lots of flows generated by the specific business. It will influence the analysis method of the flow models so greatly that it is unable to effectively guide the implementation of real-time traffic control.

Based on analysis above, this paper puts forward a survival monitoring and controlling system model based on the collaborative network facing the business flow. Adopting the monitoring, cooperative and supervisory collaboration [4], we can make monitoring analysis from the backbone network. We can obtain running information from the terminal large network in the access layer convergence monitoring and will directly allocate the unreasonable flows. We can meet the needs of business development through the link network traffic monitoring and network flow control technology.

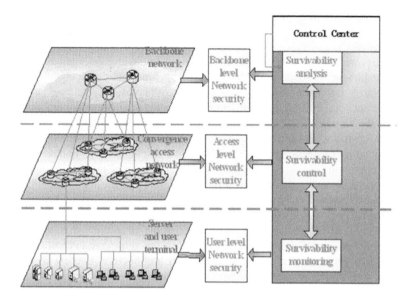

Figure 1: Model technology architecture.

3   Analysis of system architecture modeling

Network survivability is a comprehensive problem. For example, in the backbone layer, convergence layer, the access layer there are different kinds of work. Each level has different representations, which can produce different kinds of work between the layers. They are mutually independent and mutually cooperative and they constitute a multileveled and collaborative integrated solutions. As shown in Figure 1.

It can be seen from Figure 1, the security detection and control is implemented in different network layers. In each layer, the control management center implements configuration management, task scheduling and cooperative communication. Their functions and relationships of the completion can be divided into three levels:

(i)   *Survivability analysis*: It is located at the backbone level. Understand the macroscopic flow state and perceptual evaluation of the network security situation through the survivability analysis; adjust dynamically the whole network traffic distribution based on the relevant business information; be responsible for service identification, generation mechanism, protocols of evolution and the link of protocols; analyze the protocol characteristics of open and unopened new business (such as the application layer load character string) by using the method of reverse engineering; learn to extract new business flow characteristics automatically. On this basis, the port dynamic recognition and the payload analysis combined with neural network, support vector machine and other artificial intelligence methods, we can achieve an artificial and extended new business recognition engine.

(ii) *Survivability control*: It is located at the access layer convergence. It is a core component of modeling. There are many functions, such as, survivability control, using the network flow control collaboration, selecting key link of the network traffic control scientifically, evaluating the collaborative control of the network flow control multiple distributed nodes and the spread effect on business, designing comprehensive control effect evaluation function orienting business service, and using multiple control nodes to control cooperation algorithm to reduce the control cost of multiple control tasks. According to the demand of business monitoring, the use of adaptive flow control method can feedback and control the information of flow obtained from the network.

For network monitoring and coordination structure, it is worth using feedback control theory and technology in the automatic control, evaluation of the hierarchical architecture and direct architecture, making the network flow monitoring collaborative structure based on distributed network monitoring.

When the network monitoring collaboration makes cooperative synchronization, adopting the monitoring collaboration, the synchronization technology and the network time protocol (NTP) of the controlling collaboration, time synchronization and the method to reduce the time synchronization error can realize the need for network monitoring, control and coordination of comprehensive cooperation.

(iii) *Survivability monitoring*: It is used to monitor the user terminal and server and is responsible for network survivability monitoring scheduling and coordination. In the face of the complexity of the network topology coverage, it can combine with business monitoring demands and business logic topology characteristics and can make use of the scheduling algorithm and collaborative algorithm of the network optimization or redundant coverage flow monitoring and for network coverage optimization or redundant coverage to find the best links and nodes; then according to the node and the link of the network topology, according to the importance of evaluation and analysis, according to comprehensive node and link merge, we can make use of the optimization or redundant flow monitoring nodes arrangement algorithm to prey the best monitoring point. When the network topology has some dynamic change, we can dynamically realize it through the moving mechanism and moving technology of the flow monitoring nodes.

As can be seen from above, in the three levels, each has its respective functions, but each must cooperate and rely on each other. The purpose is to collaborate mutually and make the controlled network can complete its main task efficiently in time when the network system is attacked and broken down occasionally according to the current network flow.

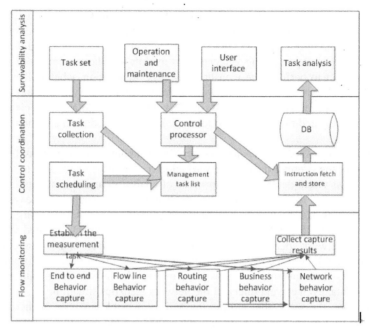

Figure 2: Flow monitoring and analysis of survivability of system structure diagram.

4   Designs and realizations of the model

4.1   Survivable network monitoring and subsystem design of survivability analysis

According to the designs and requirements of the technical architecture of the model, in order to effectively realize a variety of network behavior measurement and the support of survivability analysis needs, there are three-layer structure in the design of monitoring system, namely, the flow monitoring module, the control module, and the collaborative survivability analysis module. They are responsible for the business data from the network to collect, cooperative control, and network survivability analysis respectively in order to provide more excellent service for the user. This is shown in Figure 2.

Flow Monitoring Module: The controlled network has special probes in each measuring point. Each probe deposits all kinds of network behavior data-collecting tools, including a routing simulator, end-to-end measurement tools, the traffic capture device, the SNMP agent and the business simulation tools. During performing measurements, it is responsible for the import and measurement of various business data; then the measuring results after specific algorithm is sent to the survivability control subsystem; the measurement which has not been successfully sent is stored in the local probe.

Control Coordination Module: Main functions include business data collection, task scheduling, sending measurement commands and data collection from monitoring module; under the control coordination module, task scheduling, task collection, control processing, data analysis module and data visualization need to work together to perform the measurement task; in addition, when collecting the capture results, the data of the network behavior monitoring is very large. After the control processing units and the obtaining-depositing units clean data collaboratively and then store them into the database to reduce the amount of data storage.

Survivability Analysis Module: Generally speaking, it is a process from the business of the original data to the formation of complete index data to the final formation of visual data. This is a process of analyzing and abstracting data. The main function is to remove the large number of original data and measurement data which is not related to the network behavior in order to construct the behavior index data collection. Through the routine analysis, applied behavior analysis, network performance analysis, fault analysis and comprehensive analysis according to the task, it is responsible for an overall analysis of all kinds of business data and all kinds of data query, alarm and visualization of all kinds of data, even current query of the network statistics situation.

Therefore, the survivable monitoring and the feasible analysis of the network are composed by the network monitoring probe and the monitoring management analysis system. According to the monitoring management task deployment and testing deployment algorithm, the monitoring management and analysis subsystem can load monitoring and management tasks to the information collecting probe. And how to control the management task scheduling is one of the core technologies of this design (see the 3.2 survivable network control subsystem). This system adopts the mode of centralized control and the distributed measurements, the analysis tools are inserted with the way of adding flexibly measurement tools to the probe and using the plug-in module. Thus we can realize flexible monitoring analysis of various network behaviors. It has good openness and scalability and it is very suitable for large-scale deployment. In addition, the feasibility analysis module through the comprehensive analysis of various data can be very convenient to achieve a comprehensive evaluation on the overall performance of the network. When the data are captured, the flow monitoring module can flexibly lead into the network management data and business data of other controlled system monitoring by way of the plug-in.

4.2 Survivable network control system design

The survivable network control system is responsible for the daily business management scheduling and the structure design shown in figure 3. From the chart, the system design has two parts: service control prototyping and user management. The former is the controlled system, and the later is operated by users. The user management is responsible for initiating, configuring information of the service control prototype, and automatically generating of logs. Service control prototype is mainly responsible for the data packet capture, identification,

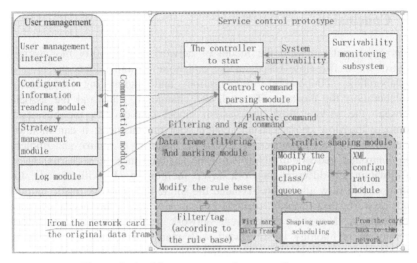

Figure 3: Architecture control system diagram.

labeling and traffic shaping and powering the survivable flow monitoring subsystem.

The service control prototype mainly includes the data frame filtering, marking module, traffic shaping module and control command parsing module. According to the management strategy and the configuration information from the user management, the system in the form of instructions transfer the frame filtering, marking module and traffic shaping modules to packet filtering, label and shaping traffic. First, the original data frame from the network card access the control systems and separate into data packets and capture then in the form of data packets. The capture of the network data packets is the basis for traffic control. Only getting the data packets can process the next step. After obtaining the data packets, we also need to distinguish, filter, mark labels and form different classifications. Different types have different bandwidth limitation, and then it will enter the traffic shaping module scheduling and shaping of different queue. Shaping different algorithms have advantages and disadvantages. Compared the network traffic controller scheduling appropriate algorithm comprehensively, the final shaping algorithm is ensured. The large number of the network flow control commands make up of the control rules. Realization of control rules will affect the response time and the processing time of network traffic. The control rule configuration module based on XML is responsible for completing the work. Therefore, it can facilitate recording, track and modify.

When users operate the network traffic controllers, user management and flow controller prototype must exist interactive data and command transmission, so the communications between them can increase their security through the communication module with encryption. In the software of users, the strategy management module will merge with the flow control strategy, which may conflict with the merger. On the flow control prototype, a heartbeat detection method will control the state of the flow process.

5   Conclusion

This paper puts forward the model of network survivability monitoring and control for traffic flow based on the collaboration and adopts the monitoring collaboration, cooperation collaboration and monitoring & controlling collaboration for business. Through the change of state and the association between the service flow, the system model can classify the business and compare the flow characteristics related with the business; it can monitor the relationship between connections and flows in order to realize and implements the controlled network to obtain from the terminal in a network running status information of different network layer monitoring. It will directly to the unreasonable flow allocation. Avoided the single link network traffic monitoring and network flow control technology can not meet the needs of business development. However, the current network traffic monitoring and network monitoring technology is still faced with many challenges. How both better synchronous collaborative, detection and control, we needs further study.

Acknowledgment

The research work was supported by Foundation Project of Hunan Science and Technology Department under Grant No. 2013FJ6066 and Youth Foundation Project of Hunan Vocational College of Science and Technology under Grant No. KJ13205.

References

[1]   Yuan Dan, Zhang Yuqing, Research on definition of network survivability. *Journal of Computer Research and Development*, **43(1)**, pp. 525–529, 2006.
[2]   C. Hakki, Cankaya, Improved survivability analysis for SONET SHRs. *Computer Networks*, **11(23)**, pp. 21–23, 9995.
[3]   Bi Xiaan, Zhang Dafang, Flow of speech recognition VoIP based on H.323 protocol. *Computer Application*, **9**, pp. 23–25, 2008.
[4]   Jun Deng, A distributed web site security protection system. *Application of Computer System*, **21(3)**, pp. 42–45, 2012.

Research on improved model-free adaptive control algorithm to suppress the influence of disturbances

Dakuo He, Haoran Chen, Bingbing Zhang
Key Laboratory of Process Industry Automation, Ministry of Education, Northeastern University, Shenyang, China

Abstract

The model-free adaptive control (MFAC) algorithm is the key point in the control. It is significance to deeply study on MFAC. Aiming to suppress the influence of disturbances, an improved hybrid model-free adaptive control algorithms is proposed based on the MFAC with a decreasing gain and MFAC with a filter. Considering the advantages and disadvantages of two MFAC algorithms, the algorithms proposed are combined two methods and introduced threshold switching. Simulation results verify the effectiveness of the algorithms proposed.

Keywords: model-free adaptive control, disturbances, decreasing gain, filter, threshold switching.

1 Introduction

MFAC was proposed by professor Zhongsheng Hou. The design of this controller is only involved with the I/O data, without any information about the model of the controlled object. The basic idea is the application of a pseudo-gradient vector and pseudo-order, using a series of dynamical linear time-variable model around the rail lines, the guiding ideology of MFAC is to develop a controller, which can be easily gained without any professional knowledge, without establishing models. MFAC has a great advantage, as to the completely unknown knowledge of mathematical model, as well as the model uncertainty, but also the changeable structure during the controlled process. Under some assumptions, the method has been proved convergence and stability, which is based on the tight format linearization and partial format linearization [1,2].

WIT Transactions on Information and Communication Technologies, Vol. 61, © 2014 WIT Press
www.witpress.com, ISSN 1743-3517 (on-line)
doi:10.2495/MIIT130291

Since the feedback control is driven by the deviation, the deviation is determined by the measured output, during this process, the external disturbance is being the measured disturbance. The measured deviation is the common external disturbance faced by the control system. As a feedback control system, measurement disturbance has a great impact on the control performance of the MFAC system [3]. As the existence of the measured deviation the detecting link will not detect the real output of the system which will do harm to the control system. When the deviation exists, the system can still maintain and consolidate its convergence, but its original control performance will be reduced. To solve this question, many researches were conducted and obtained the expected results, such as the introduction of the attenuation factor, filter links and dead links and other methods [4–6]. The measurement deviation is mostly high frequency noise signals in our actual industrial systems which are drawn into through the sensor from the measured output signals. Before it was applied in the controller the signals applied are updated, the influence of the measurement disturbance can be effectively suppressed [7–10]. Considering the advantages and disadvantages, an improved hybrid MFAC algorithm is proposed in this paper.

2 Two MFAC algorithms

2.1 The MFAC algorithms with a decreasing gain

The basic idea is to add attenuation Factor in the updating algorithm, to achieve the goal that: with the time going on, the algorithm's updating is gradually reducing. The attenuation factor can suppress the measurement deviation effectively, when the system configuration or the given changes, some problem occurs. So, to solve this problem, the common method is the improved algorithm.

According to MFAC algorithm of the SISO discrete-time system, the algorithm with the attenuation factor $\dfrac{1}{k - k_m + 1}$ can be expressed as follows.

$$u(k) = \begin{cases} u(k-1) + \dfrac{\rho \hat{\phi}(k)}{\lambda + \left|\hat{\phi}(k)\right|^2} e_m(k) & \left|e_m(k)\right| \geq e_s \\[4mm] u(k-1) + \dfrac{\rho \hat{\phi}(k)}{\lambda + \left|\hat{\phi}(k)\right|^2} \dfrac{e_m(k)}{k - k_m + 1} & \left|e_m(k)\right| < e_s \end{cases} \tag{1}$$

Among which e_s is a positive constant, k_m is the switch moment ranging from $\left|e_m(k)\right| \geq e_s$ to $\left|e_m(k)\right| < e_s$.

The function of the decreasing factor is, under the condition of the rising k, the impact of $e_m(k)$ is being weaker and weaker. Cause that the measurement disturbance is largely due to the system's output error. So, with the time k

increasing, the attenuation factor will weaken the measurement deviation's effect on the system.

2.2 The MFAC algorithm with a filter

Since most of the measurement deviations are high frequency signals, so the introducing of filter can reduce the impact of measurement deviation.

According to MFAC algorithm of the SISO discrete-time system, the algorithm with a filter may be written as follows:

$$u(k) = u(k-1) + \frac{\rho \hat{\phi}(k)}{\lambda + \left|\hat{\phi}(k)\right|^2} z(k) \tag{2}$$

$$z(k) = L(s)e_m(k) \tag{3}$$

Among which: $L(s)$ is an n-order linear filter links, and can be expressed by

$$L(s) = \frac{1}{\alpha_0 + \alpha_1 s^{-1} + \cdots + \alpha_n s^{-n}} \tag{4}$$

where α_0, α_1, ..., α_n are the parameters of the filter, $z(k)$ is the output signal through the filter and the initial value is zero. When $n = 1$, $L(s)$ is a first-order linear filter.

In practical applications, the system structure changes, and the time-variable parameters, as well as the measurement deviation, are all high frequency signals. Therefore, $L(s)$ should be set as low-pass filter, the purpose is to eliminate high-frequency signals and get a sufficient control.

3 An improved hybrid MFAC algorithm

With the joining of the attenuation factor for the system, the impact of the measurement deviation is suppressed gradually, and the output signal is being more accurate, the response speed being faster. However, due to the introducing of the attenuation factor, the controlled parameters will stop updating after a certain time and be un-sensitive to the changes of the system when the controlled system is changed. The volatility of the instantaneous output value and the overshoot is relatively large. The filter is used to impact the measurement deviation, the effect of the measurement deviation is suppressed. while, with the drawing of the filter link, the output is delayed for a certain time, what's more, the response time is also slowed.

Considering the advantages and disadvantages, an improved hybrid MFAC algorithm is proposed based on combining two methods. When the deviation is large, the algorithm with attenuation factor is used, the response time can be improved. When the deviation is small, the algorithm with a filter is used, the response to the system's changes can be sensitive, the performance of control can be improved.

According to MFAC algorithm of the SISO discrete-time system, the improved hybrid algorithm can be expressed by

$$
u(k) =
\begin{cases}
u(k-1) + \dfrac{\rho\hat{\phi}(k)}{\lambda + \left|\hat{\phi}(k)\right|^2} \dfrac{e_m(k)}{k - k_m + 1} & \left|e_m(k)\right| \geq e_s \\[4ex]
u(k-1) + \dfrac{\rho\hat{\phi}(k)}{\lambda + \left|\hat{\phi}(k)\right|^2} z(k) & \left|e_m(k)\right| < e_s
\end{cases}
\tag{5}
$$

4 Simulation

Considering the nonlinear SISO system:

$$
\begin{cases}
y(k+1) = \dfrac{y(k)}{1 + y^2(k)} + u^3(k), & k \leq 500 \\[3ex]
y(k+1) = \dfrac{y(k)y(k-1)y(k-2)u(k-1)(y(k-2)-1) + a(k)u(k)}{1 + y^2(k-1) + y^2(k-2)}, & \\
\qquad\qquad 500 < k \leq 1000
\end{cases}
\tag{6}
$$

where: $a(k) = 1 + round\left(\dfrac{k}{300}\right)$ is time-variable parameter, the object function can be given by

$$
\begin{cases}
y^*(k+1) = 1 & 1 \leq k \leq 500 \\
y^*(k+1) = -1 & 500 < k \leq 1000
\end{cases}
\tag{7}
$$

When $k = 500$, the system structure changes, moreover, the expected output of the system has also changed, the system's initial values are $u(1{:}2) = 0$, $y(1) = -1$, $y(2) = 1$, the initial value of Pseudo-partial derivative are $\phi^*(1) = 0.5$, $\varepsilon = 1 \times 10^{-5}$, the initial value of the controller is set as $\mu = 1$, $\lambda = 2$, $\eta = 0.5$, $\rho = 1$, $e_s = 0.28$, $L(s) = \dfrac{1}{-0.1s^2 - 0.5s + 1}$. The system has a measurement disturbance $w(k) = 0.1 rand(1,1000)$. Using the algorithm mentioned above the simulation result is given in Figure 1.

Figure 1 shows that the hybrid improved MFAC algorithm proposed in this paper can suppress the measurement deviation to some extent, moreover, making the output signal more accurate and stable. The method inherits the advantage of the single method that mentioned in the early part of the paper, and it overcomes

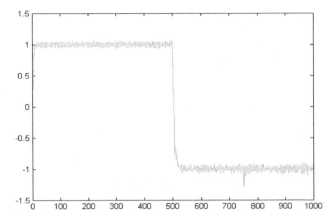

Figure 1: Responses of the system using the hybrid improved MFAC proposed.

the disadvantages and improves the control performance effectively. It should be noted that by adjusting the value of e_s, the algorithm can simply adjust the speed of both control performance and the response to the systems changes.

5   Conclusion

For a class of single-input single-output (SISO) systems, the measurement disturbance impacts to a model-free adaptive control are considered. An improved hybrid model-free adaptive control immunity algorithm proposed combines the MFAC with a decreasing gain with MFAC with a filter to improve the performance of the algorithm. The improved model-free adaptive control algorithm proposed suppresses the measurement disturbance effectively. The analysis is supported by simulations.

Acknowledgment

This work is supported by the National Nature Science Foundation of China under Grant 61004083 and 61374147 and 973 Project No. 2009CB320601 and 863 Project No. 2011AA060204 and the Fundamental Research Funds for the Central Universities N120404014.

References

[1]   R.H. Chi, Z.S. Hou, Optimal higher order learning adaptive control approach for a class of SISO nonlinear systems. *Journal of Control Theory and Applications*, **3(3)**, pp. 247–251, 2005.
[2]   Z.S. Hou, On model-free adaptive control: the state of the art and perspective. *Control theory and Application*, **23(4)**, pp. 586–592, 2006.

[3] W.H. Wang, Z.S. Hou, New adaptive quasi-sliding mode control for nonlinear discrete-time systems. *Journal of Systems Engineering and Electronics*, **19(1)**, pp. 154–160, 2008.

[4] T.J. Jang, C.H. Choi, H.S. Ahn, Iterative learning control in feedback system. *Automatica*, **31(2)**, pp. 243–248, 1995.

[5] B.B. Peterson, K.S. Narendra, Bounded error adaptive control. *IEEE Trans on Automatic Control*, **27(6)**, pp. 161–1168, 1982.

[6] D.F. Chichka, J.L. Speyer, Adaptive control based on disturbance attention. *IEEE Transactions on Automatic Control*, **40(7)**, pp. 1220–1223, 1995.

[7] Y.H. Huang, W. Messner, A novel disturbance observer design for magnetic hard drive servo system with rotary actuator. *IEEE Transactions on Magnetics*, **4(7)**, pp. 1892–1894, 1998.

[8] W.H. Chen, Disturbance observer based control for nonlinear systems. *IEEE/ASME Transactions on Mechatronics*, **9(4)**, pp. 706–710, 2004.

[9] V. Levin, E. Kreindler, Use of disturbance estimator for disturbance suppression. *IEEE Transactions on Automatic Control*, **21(5)**, pp. 776–778, 1976.

[10] J.Y. Yao, Z.X. Jiao, Friction compensation for low velocity control of hydraulic flight motion simulator: A simple adaptive robust approach. *Chinese Journal of Aeronautics*, **26(3)**, pp. 814–822, 2013.

A study on factors of retention rate for mobile games user

Heyong Wang, Zejin Huang, Kaiting Lin
College of E-Business, South China University of Technology, Guangzhou, China

Abstract

Current researches on mobile games are more reflected in product design and development trends. However, researches on retention rate for mobile games user are less. Based on mobile games in China, this paper analyses the 28 factors of retention rate for mobile games user. These factors are based on the product properties of mobile games and operating characteristics that are relayed on by mobile game company how to promote users play the mobile games. The result shows that it is the important factors that the mobile game type, the level of pictures, game themes, emotional factors and the impact of word of mouth that effect retention rate for mobile game user.

Keywords: mobile games, user retention rate, influencing factors.

1 Introduction

Mobile Internet is a new industry, mobile gaming as an important pillar of its business is gradually recognized and accepted by society, gradually showing its great potential for development. Current researches on mobile games are more reflected in product design and trends forecasting. However, research on retention rate of mobile games is less, which cannot provide sufficient support and guidance for the rapid development of mobile games, and it is difficult to keep up with the pace of development of the mobile Internet industry. Based on mobile games in China, this paper analyses the retention rate using 28 factors for mobile games. From the basis of questionnaire survey, this paper combines features of product properties of mobile games and operating experience that are relayed on by mobile game company how to promote users play the mobile games, and analyses how the mobile game product factor and operating factor affect the retention rate of games for mobile users. The result shows that it is the important factors that the mobile game type, the level of pictures, game themes, emotional factors and the impact of word of mouth that effect retention rate for mobile game user.

2 Factor analysis of the user's retention rate

User retention rate is most intuitive reflected in the user's satisfaction for mobile games and a return visit game is based on a certain level of demand and recognition. It is the user preferences for the various aspects of the mobile game that affect their attitude of the mobile game. This paper mainly studies on the user's retention rate from the following aspects (given in Table 1).

A. *Factor analysis of user preferences*
    It is inevitably that users have personal preferences in playing the mobile games, which will directly affect the retention rate.
B. *Factor analysis of Service guarantee*
    In addition to product characteristics, stability and security of the server that mobile game is loaded on determine the user long-term impression of the product and affect the future of users.
C. *Factor analysis of Experience cost*
    Users will have cost when they play mobile games, including the cost of learning, restrictions of skill level and material cost, etc.
D. *Factor analysis of immersion on mobile game*
    For self-actualization needs, the users of mobile game are easily led to gaming addiction. Thus, it must allow users to pursue varied objectives such as power, capacity, shape, interest and the opposite sex attraction and so on.
E. *Factor analysis of deeper demand*
    Pursuing of differentiation and being product innovation of mobile game can truly meet the needs of users in order to establish market brand and achieve the industry's healthy development.

This study extract the 28 factors of user retention rate from the present problems of the mobile game and build questionnaire part of the factors affecting the problem.

3 Principal component analysis

Principal component analysis (PCA) [19] is one of the important multivariate statistical analysis method. Its idea is to use the original dimensionality reduction or multivariate indicators that is reassembled into a new set of a few unrelated variables or indicators integrated, according to the actual need to select from as few variables or indicators integrated as much as possible to reflect the original variables or indicators of information, while the new index to determine the

Table 1: The Index System of the Mobile Game Retention Rate.

First Level Indicators	Secondary Indicators	Factors Explanation	Reference
User preferences	Word of mouth	For mobile games recommended by Friends, it will be a greater interest in playing	Guo Guoqing [1]
	Game type	Have their own preference for game type	Zhao Dandan [2]
	Game themes	Familiar with the story of the plot and cultural background can attract more	Hakan Ustunel [3]
	The picture level	Exquisite picture of the game will attract more	Luo Min [4]
	Emotional factors	Exciting and memorable of mobile game story	Jesper Juul [5]
	Interactivity	Like to cooperate or compete with other players	Han Shuai [6]
	System complexity	Easy game has limited appeal	Lin Luolong [7]
Service Guarantee	Server Stability	It feels unbearable when games appear disconnected and correction, etc	Totoidc [8]
	Convenient and secure on payment	Can't accept that money can't credited into account and top-up delay problems	Yue Che [9]
	Fault	Loses confidence when games often have fault.	Lu Jinliang [10]
	Compatibility and suitability	Give up the game that has poor adaptation of equipment.	
	Balance	Hope to get a fair gaming environment.	Lin Luolong [7]
	Homogeneity	Obvious signs of plagiarism that are lack of recognition.	Ma Yingying [11]
	Innovative elements	Games with new gameplay	
	Level of product completeness	No confidence of the game with imperfect version.	
	Operating activities	Pay attention and participate in related	Xia Yongfeng [12]

		activities of the game.	
	Localization	Can't accept the game without localization.	Cui Qiliang [13]
	Tutorial guide	Lack of guidance and help, it is difficult to familiar with a new game.	Yan Ruihua [14]
Experience cost	Operational complexity	The game of simple operation is more suitable.	Gavriel Salvendy [15]
	Difficulty settings	Give up too difficult games.	
	The cost of network flow	The games cost too much and network flow is unbearable.	Chen Liang [16]
	User hardware affordability	The configuration of mobile devices (mobile phones, tablet computers, etc.)	Jie Fang [17]
Immersion	Reward and incentive	Getting awards in the mobile game can stimulate me to continue playing	Zheng Zhuoqi [18]
	Conventional mechanics of mobile game	Willing to take the trouble to reach some goals for a high-value items	
	Popularity	Not willing to stay in the ghost zone (the mobile game has a few game player)	Han Shuai [6]
	Self-actualization	Always strive to become a master of the mobile game	Zheng Zhuoqi [18]
Deeper demand	Content updates	Want to play the game that can often bring freshness.	Ma Yingying [11]
	The impact of competitive products	Finding a better game, it could not help to try.	

variable weights and create a new evaluation model. The following is its main implementation process:

Step1: Standardization processing on the original data
According to the formula (1) obtained arithmetic mean of the variable

$$\overline{x}_j = \frac{1}{n} \sum_{i=1}^{n} x_{ij} \tag{1}$$

The data are arranged as a set of n data vectors $x_1 \cdots x_n$ with each x_i representing a single grouped observation of the p variables.

According to the formula (2) obtained the sample standard deviation

$$\sigma_j = \left[\frac{1}{n-1} \sum_{i=1}^{n} (x_{ij} - \overline{x}_j)^2 \right]^{\frac{1}{2}} \tag{2}$$

According to the formula (3) find the standardized data

$$z_{ij} = \frac{x_{ij} - \overline{x}_j}{\sigma_j} \tag{3}$$

Step 2: Calculate the correlation coefficient between the two indicators and get the correlation matrix

$$R = (r_{ij})_{p \times p} : r_{ij} = \frac{s_{ij}}{\sqrt{s_{ii} \bullet s_{jj}}} \tag{4}$$

$$s_{ij} = \frac{1}{n-1} \sum_{k=1}^{n} (z_{ki} - \overline{z}_i)(z_{kj} - \overline{z}_j) \tag{5}$$

$$\overline{z}_i = \frac{\sum_{k=1}^{n} z_{ki}}{n} ; \overline{z}_j = \frac{\sum_{k=1}^{n} z_{kj}}{n} \tag{6}$$

Step 3: Calculate the eigenvalues of the correlation matrix R, eigenvectors and cumulative contribution rate

Compute the matrix R of eigenvectors T

$$|\lambda E - R| = 0 \tag{7}$$

$$(\lambda E - R)X = 0 \tag{8}$$

Step 4: According to cumulative contribution rate the principal components are determined

Table 2: Result of Reliability Analysis.

Cronbach's Alpha	Number of factors
0.864	28

Table 3: The Validity Analysis Results.

Sampling sufficient degree of Kaiser-Meyer-Olkin measure		0.858
Bartlett's test of sphericity	approximate chi-square	2023.259
	df	378
	Sig.	0.000

4 Experiments

4.1 Data sources

The data of the empirical analysis is from the questionnaire. The form is online surveys questionnaires. The questionnaire is shown in the major mobile gaming forums, communities and gaming group of internet users with communicate instructions and questionnaires links and is received a total of 203 copies of questionnaires. Due to set required strictly, valid questionnaires were 203. Likert is adopted on data quantization methods.

4.2 Reliability analysis

Using SPSS19.0 to implement reliability analysis with influencing factors in the questionnaire, results was shown in table2 and Cronbach's Alpha value[20] was 0.864, greater than 0.8, it proved that the influencing factors have good reliability.

4.3 Validity analysis

The results about factor analysis of affecting user retention rate are got by SPSS19.0 software, as shown in Table 3. In order to prove the suitability, validity analysis is carried out. In Kaiser-Meyer-Olkin(KMO) and Bartlett's test of sphericity, the KMO test value is 0.858, close to 0.9, the number of samples is more fully to meet the basic needs of validity analysis. Approximate chi-square is 2023.259, degree of freedom is 378, the value of Sig. is 0.000, the original assumption of independent variables is not established, and it indicates that there is a certain correlation between variables. Therefore, the sample is suitable for factor analysis.

4.4 The results of experiment

After using PCA method, the original 28 measured variables are extracted 5 factors. As the scree plot show (shown in Figure 1), when the fraction is 5, the

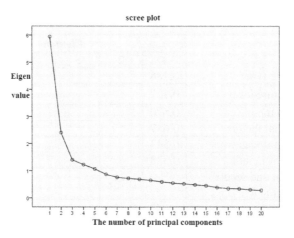

Figure 1: Screen plot.

eigenvalue curves gradually tends to be gentle. should be 5 that the scree plot can roughly be identified in the factor analysis. It is consistent with the number of principal components gained by the cumulative contribution rate. The number of principal components

From the rotating component matrix (shown in Table IV), game type, level of pictures, game theme, emotional factors and word of mouth are mainly explained by the first principal component, payment convenience and security, faults, balance and reward and motivation are mainly explained by the second principal component, tutorial guide, operational complexity, difficulty settings, and user hardware capacity are explained by the third principal component, self-realization, conventional game mechanics, The impact of competitive products is explained by the fourth principal components, level of product completeness, the homogeneity and innovative elements are explained by the fifth principal component.

5 Conclusion

This paper analyses the 28 factors of retention rate for mobile games user based on mobile games in China. These factors are based on the product properties of mobile games and operating characteristics. The result shows that it is the important factors that the mobile game type, the level of pictures, game themes, emotional factors and the impact of word of mouth that effect retention rate for mobile game user.

Acknowledgment

This research was supported by Project of National Social Sciences Foundation, Grant No. 13BTJ005, the Fundamental Research Funds for the Central

Table 4: Rotation Matrix Components.

	Element				
	1	2	3	4	5
Game type	0.786				
The picture level	0.727				
Game themes	0.670				
Emotional factors	0.637				
Content updates	0.543				
Word of mouth	0.538				
Convenient and secure payment		0.758			
fault		0.717			
Balance		0.654			
Reward and incentive		0.580			
Tutorial guide			0.815		
Operational complexity			0.782		
Difficulty settings			0.693		
User hardware affordability			0.579		
self-actualization				0.783	
Conventional game mechanics				0.632	
The impact of competitive products				0.555	
level of product completeness					0.715
homogeneity					0.648
Innovative elements					0.623
Extraction Method: Principal Component. Rotation method: [a]Kaiser standardized orthogonal rotation method.					
[a]Rotating in after 6 times of iteration converge.					

Universities, Grant No. 2013XZD01, supported by the Guangdong Province Science and Technology Fund, Grant No. 2012B091100309, and 2012B040500010, and supported by the Foshan Science and Technology Fund, Grant No. 2012HC100043.

References

[1] Guo Guoqing, Niu Haipeng, Hu Jingjing, et al., Research on relationship among consumer experience, experiencing value and customer loyalty— taking the large and medium-sized casual online games as an example. *Journal of Wuhan University of Technology (Social Science Edition)*, **14(1)**, pp. 81–87, 2012.

[2]   Zhao Dandan, The personality characteristics of online game players. *Journal of Mianyang Normal University*, **26(1)**, pp. 126–131, 2007.

[3]   Hakan Ustunel, Mustafa Meral, Erdem Ucar, et al., The factors effecting students' PC game types preferences. *Procedia-Social and Behavioral Sciences*, **47**, pp. 943–949, 2012.

[4]   Luo Min, Computer game screen effect evaluation. *Software Guide*, **17(9)**, pp. 22–23, 2007.

[5]   Jesper Juul, Guan Pingping, Game story?—Research on game and narrative. *Studies in Culture & Art*, **3(1)**, pp. 218-225, 2010.

[6]   Han Shuai, Interaction, immersion and aesthetic of electronic games. *Industry and Technology Forum*, **10(5)**, pp. 140–141, 2011.

[7]   Lin Luolong, Balance strategy of computer game design. *Computer Knowledge and Technology*, **5(21)**, pp. 5733–5734, 2009.

[8]   Totoidc, Seven issues should be noted to ensure server stability. *Network and Information*, **(12)**, p. 23, 2009.

[9]   Yue Che, Third-party payment & online games boosting joint. *Electronic Commerce*, **7(10)**, pp. 34–35, 2008.

[10] Lu Jinliang, Quality control of mobile software development. *China Science and Technology Information*, **74(12)**, pp. 133–134, 2009.

[11] Ma Yingying, For the online gaming industry homogenization analysis. *Science Technology and Industry*, **12(8)**, pp. 1513–1533, 2012.

[12] Xia Yongfeng, The online game, operation is king. *World of IT Managers*, **1(2)**, pp. 43–45, 2009.

[13] Cui Qiliang, Face software localization gap. *Computer World*, **48(8)**, pp. 1–2, 2003.

[14] Yan Ruihua, Chen Hongmei, Computer application software learning practice research. *Journal of Social Science of Jiamusi University*, **27(3)**, pp. 116–117, 2009.

[15] Qin Hua, Rao Peilun, Gavriel Salvendy. The effect on the game's results with game players experience and the difficulty of the game. *Industrial Engineering*, **(5)**, pp. 104–106, 2009.

[16] Chen Liang, 3G Competition: adjust cost of net flow really guarantee to cure all diseases. *Communications World*, **(44)**, pp. 24–25, 2009.

[17] Jie Fang, Online games portal. Family of technology, (9), pp. 39-40,2002.

[18] Zheng Zhuoqi. *Factors Affecting Online Game Addiction Research*. Xiamen University, 2007. DOI: 10.7666/d.y1343578.

[19] Wang Heyong, Yao Zhengan, Li Lei, The application of feature extraction on using kernel principal component analysis based on cluster. *Journal of Computer Science*, **(4)**, pp. 64–66, 2005.

[20] L. Cronbach, Coefficient alpha and the internal structure of tests. *Psychomerika*, **16(3)**, pp. 297–334, 1951.

Allocation of urban logistics park based on improved BP neural network algorithm

Rongzu Qiu, Lanyi Zhang
Transportation and Civil Engineering Institute, Fujian Agriculture and Forestry University, Fuzhou, China

Abstract

As the major gathering place for enterprises, Logistics Park can achieve rational distribution for logistics system resources, which will have a long-term impact on regional economic coordination and scale benefit of the Logistics Park. At present, the site selection of Logistics Park has some problems such as various subjective factors, model solely, and so on. Back Propagation Neural Network (BP Neural Network) was applied to select site of Logistics Park. The parameter of BP Neural Network was improved and MATLAB toolbox was used to solve the model with a set of real data from case study. Result shows that the improvement is feasible and the method has a theoretical significance in site selection of Logistics Park.

Keywords: logistics park, back propagation neural network, allocation, evaluation.

1 Introduction

Logistics Park integrates various logistic functions such as delivery, transportation, storage, distribution processing, and information processing into a logistic enterprise concentration. It can promote the economic development in a city or regional area. Logistics Park centralizes logistics enterprises, freight yards, and freight depots distracted in a city into a park, which improves the city landscape, relieves traffic pressure, and decreases the environmental pollutions. Reasonable allocation of Logistics Park (ALP) has far-reaching effect on the scale merit and regional economic coordination. The ALP problem is a complex dynamic selection process and it is affected by natural environment, operation environment, infrastructure, etc. The natural environment contains climate

WIT Transactions on Information and Communication Technologies, Vol. 61, © 2014 WIT Press
www.witpress.com, ISSN 1743-3517 (on-line)
doi:10.2495/MIIT130311

condition, geological condition, hydrologic condition, and topographic condition. The operating environment contains commodity characteristic, logistics cost, service level, and client distribution. And infrastructure contains traffic condition, public facilities as well as land resources, etc. The ALP should accommodate with city overall planning and is consistent with the functional orientation and stage goal of cities. Therefore, it belongs to the logistics planning strategy problems and is of primary importance in logistics system.

The concept of Logistics Park was introduced into China originally in 1999. Researches on the theory of Logistics Park started in 2000. Over the past decade, ALP mainly depended on subjective qualitative analysis, while the quantitative analysis was used little. Qualitative analysis methods include AHP method [1, 2], improved AHP method [3, 4], etc. Quantitative analysis methods include optimal mathematical model [5], principal component analysis [6], factor analysis [7], multiobjective programming approach [8], etc. However, these methods usually simply the problem and take a few constraints into account. As a result, developed models and algorithm for solving them are too simple even to lead to low accuracy. It is necessary to introduce some new-type artificial intelligence algorithm to allocate Logistics Park to reduce subjectivity and increase accuracy. Among them, Back Propagation Neural Network (BP Neural Network) is a better choice. BP Neural Network can conduct both multilevel forward propagation and error back propagation. The function is useful when the internal law of a matter can be hardly described with mathematical models. In fact, ALP is restricted by multifactors with variety, randomness, and interference. Neural network can establish this kind of model to acquire reliable prediction result.

2   The model and algorithm of ALP based on BP neural network

2.1 Development of the evaluation index system

Numbers of input node of BP Neural Network and relative evaluation index need to be established to develop the evaluation index system of ALP. The factors influencing ALP are numerous. It is not scientific and realistic to take all factors into account. It is crucial to select some of them. Ten of them such as climate condition, geological condition, hydrologic condition, operating environment, logistics expenses, client distribution, traffic condition, public facilities, land resources as well as road facility were selected to develop evaluation index system in the case study. Thus, 10 input nodes in input layer of BP Neural Network were established [9]. The evaluation index system was divided into three layers: object layer O, criterion layer P, and subcriterion layer Q. The solute of ALP is in object layer O; criterion layer contains environmental benefit, economic benefit, facility benefit. Subcriterion layer contains above-mentioned 10 parameters. According to the evaluation index system, data of case study was collected and processed. Using comprehensive evaluation method to ensure the precision of neural network training, N data samples were considered serving as the training set and M alternative programs were selected as the evaluation set [10].

1. Development of factors set

   The criterion layer P was determined as follows, $P=\{P1, P2, P3\}=\{$environmental benefit, economic benefit, facility benefit$\}$. The subcriterion layer Q was determined as follows, $Q1=\{Q11, Q12, Q13\}=\{$climate condition, geological condition, hydrologic condition$\}$, $Q2=\{Q21, Q22, Q23, Q24\}=\{$operating environment, logistics expenses, client distribution, land resources$\}$, $Q3=\{Q31, Q32, Q33\}=\{$traffic condition, public facilities, road facility$\}$.

2. Development of evaluation result set

   The evaluation result set refers to value of evaluation index. The values in the set is in [0, 1] interval. The higher the value is the better the evaluation index is.

3. Single-index fuzzy evaluation

   In order to evaluate the subjection degree of solutes toward every index in the system, one of indices was taken as an example for evaluating. Assumption that r_{mn} stands subjection degree of solute n in object layer O toward factor m, the single-index evaluation vector R_m is described as follows:

$$R_m = (r_{m1}, r_{m2}, \cdots, r_{mn})$$

Similarly, total m single-index evaluation vectors were obtained as follow:

$$R_1 = (r_{11}, r_{12}, \cdots, r_{1n})$$
$$R_2 = (r_{21}, r_{22}, \cdots, r_{2n})$$
$$\vdots$$
$$R_m = (r_{m1}, r_{m2}, \cdots, r_{mn})$$

where m is the number of factors in evaluation set, $m=10$.

The subjection degree of every single-index evaluation set is arranged by matrix, and fuzzy evaluation matrix R was obtained as follows:

$$R = \begin{bmatrix} r_{11} & r_{12} & \cdots & r_{1n} \\ r_{21} & r_{22} & \cdots & r_{2n} \\ \vdots & \vdots & & \vdots \\ r_{m1} & r_{m2} & \cdots & r_{mn} \end{bmatrix}$$

2.2 Description of BP Neural Network algorithm

1. Fundamental formula

   The output of hidden layer: $B = f(\sum_n UA - \theta_i)$

   where θ_i—Node threshold.

   The output of output layer: $C = f(\sum_n VB - \theta_j)$.

2. The correction formula of output layer node to hidden layer node
   (1) The total error of all the sample data:

$$X = \sum_{a=1}^{b} x_a < \xi$$

   where ξ—One of the sample error;

   a—sample number. $x_a = \sum_{1}^{n} |D^{(a)} - C^{(a)}|$

   (2) Error formula: $\zeta = (D - C) \times C \times (1 - C)$
   (3) Weight correction: $V(b + 1) = V(b) + \eta \zeta B$
      where b—iterations;
      η—learning rate.
   (4) Threshold correction: $\theta_j(b + 1) = \theta_j(b) + \eta' \zeta'$

3. The correction formula of hidden layer node to output layer node
   (1) error formula: $\zeta' = B(1-B)\Sigma\zeta V$

   (2) weight correction: $U(b + 1) = U(b) + \eta' \zeta' A$

   (3) threshold correction: $\theta_i(b + 1) = \theta_i(b) + \eta' \zeta'$.

2.2.1 Improvements of BP Neural Network algorithm

The threshold correction of BP Neural Network algorithm is down along section of error curved surface. Error curved surface with a large sample may distribute local minimum points. In the adaptive training of BP Neural Network, it is easy to fall into local minimum points and lead to error predicting results. Concerned with this defect, the BP Neural Network was improved. A momentum was added to the parameter of threshold and weight correction to avoid mutations of threshold and weight.

The original change of weight: $\Delta U(k) = \eta' \zeta' A$

The change of improved weight: $\Delta U(k + 1) = \Delta U(k) + d_k \times \Delta U(k)$

The original change of threshold: $\Delta\theta(k) = \eta' \zeta'$

The change of improved threshold: $\Delta\theta(k + 1) = \Delta\theta(k) + d_k \times \Delta\theta(k)$

where

d_k—momentum factor, value range: $0 < d_k < 1$;

k— training number.

The improved BP Neural Network could avoid local minimum points effectively in the adaptive training, which can enable the rate of convergence of neural network in training decrease as smooth gradient and the pattern change of weight and threshold without mutations.

3 Application analysis

3.1 Overview of case study

3.1.1 Overview of case Logistics Park

The 2009–2020 over Planning of Fuzhou City proposed explicitly that spatial structure of Fuzhou city was planned to be "One district with two wings, biaxial and multieconomic growth poles." The advantage of port in south wing should be taken to construct grand harbor and develop port Logistics Park. The south wing contains Fuqing urban area, Longtian mountain, Jingyangdongzhang, Pingtan Island, Jiangyinyuxi, and Haikouchengtou, etc. One region of the south wing will be selected as planning lands for logistic park with the advantages of convenient sea transportation. This paper researched ALP based on the planning lands.

3.1.2 Data source for Neural Network training

When carrying out learning with BP Neural Network, known learning samples should be prepared and input. Then, weight and threshold values were modified through iteration step by step until the convergence precision was reached. Thus, sufficient data are required for training so as to reach higher precision. Research result before showed that at least 80 sets of data were needed to make the satisfying precision. Therefore, this paper adopted $N=100$ data samples for training and marks the above-mentioned 10 indices. Then, they were equalized and input into the BP network for training, in the hope that the result of BP network training can be close to expert's evaluation. The results can provide basis for evaluating ALP.

3.1.3 Solutes source

In planning lands Fuqing urban area is restricted by land resources and was excluded. Thus, other five alternative solutes, including Longtian mountain, Jingyangdongzhang, Pingtan Island, Jiangyinyuxi, Haikouchengtou were selected to develop object layer O.

3.2 Results and analysis

3.2.1 Data processing

Through fuzzy comprehensive evaluation method, the fuzzy evaluation matrix representing 100 plans of ALP was obtained (omitted here). The 100 plans were marked by eight experts. The eight questionnaires were equalized to obtain evaluation matrix t, as below after transposition.

$$
\begin{array}{ccccccccccc}
[0.79 & 0.74 & 0.99 & 0.81 & 0.96 & 0.83 & 0.69 & 0.75 & 0.58 & 0.51 \\
0.75 & 0.74 & 0.28 & 0.19 & 0.61 & 0.46 & 0.33 & 0.76 & 0.67 & 0.52 \\
0.80 & 0.75 & 1.00 & 0.82 & 0.97 & 0.84 & 0.70 & 0.76 & 0.59 & 0.52 \\
0.76 & 0.75 & 0.29 & 0.20 & 0.62 & 0.47 & 0.34 & 0.77 & 0.68 & 0.53 \\
0.78 & 0.73 & 0.98 & 0.80 & 0.95 & 0.82 & 0.68 & 0.74 & 0.57 & 0.50 \\
0.74 & 0.73 & 0.27 & 0.18 & 0.60 & 0.45 & 0.32 & 0.75 & 0.66 & 0.51 \\
0.81 & 0.76 & 1.00 & 0.83 & 0.98 & 0.85 & 0.71 & 0.77 & 0.60 & 0.53 \\
0.77 & 0.76 & 0.30 & 0.21 & 0.63 & 0.48 & 0.35 & 0.78 & 0.69 & 0.54 \\
0.77 & 0.72 & 0.97 & 0.79 & 0.94 & 0.81 & 0.67 & 0.73 & 0.56 & 0.49 \\
0.73 & 0.72 & 0.26 & 0.17 & 0.59 & 0.44 & 0.31 & 0.74 & 0.65 & 0.50]
\end{array}
$$

3.2.2 BP Neural Network training

Firstly, relevant parameters were initialized. Let error equal to 0, the precision of output result equal to 10^{-3}, both of sample counter and learning frequency device equal to 1. Weight matrix U, V are random number, node number of input layer β equals 10, output layer γ equals 1. 1–5 levels were used for grading. Due to the large number of samples, calculating would be time-consuming. Hidden layer was designed as 2 for better prediction precision. Neural network toolbox in MATLAB 7.0 was used for neural network learning. A *newff* function of toolbox was created, and *S-type logsig* function was selected as the transfer function of hidden later and linear function *purelin* as the transfer function of output layer. The basis of ALP in the paper is making use of BP Neural Network algorithm by letting the training value closer to experts' value. ALP prediction with the trained model means reaching the purpose of function fitting, so the method of numerical optimization is selected. The amount of calculation of BFGS algorithm function *trainbfg* is directly proportional to the scale of network. Despite large space occupied, it is of fast constringency, so this function was adopted. Run neural network toolbox in MATLAB for systematically self-adaptive cyclic learning. Figure 1 shows the running chart which means adopting two hidden layer for neural network calculation of the alternative address of Logistics Park.

After 1000 times of training, when the error reaches $10^{-4.8}(<10^{-3.0})$, stop training; and when the training error is close to 10^{-5}, it indicates that the prediction is very close to experts' value, and expected effect is obtained from the training result. The BP Neural Network training result is shown in Figure 2.

Figure 1: BP Neural Network running chart in MATLAB.

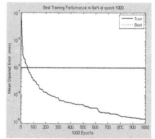

Figure 2: The BP Neural Network training result.

Table 1: The Matrix of Alternative Solutes.

5 Alternative Solutes	Climate Condition	Geological Condition	Hydrologic Condition	Operating Environment	Logistics Cost
101	0.45	0.35	0.38	0.28	0.38
102	0.32	0.28	0.38	0.19	0.27
103	0.25	0.65	0.27	0.92	0.16
104	0.12	0.02	0.56	0.52	0.94
105	0.13	0.88	0.61	0.87	0.94
5 Alternative Solutes	Client Distribution	Traffic Condition	Public Facilities	Land Resources	Road Facility
101	0.37	0.37	0.44	0.78	0.66
102	0.17	0.26	0.19	0.74	0.65
103	0.17	0.17	0.15	0.19	0.26
104	0.79	0.88	0.09	0.20	0.21
105	0.57	0.74	0.55	0.72	0.51

Table 2: The Evaluation Result of BP Neural Network.

Evaluation Solutes	101	102	103	104	105
Grading	2	1	4	5	1

3.2.3 BP Neural Network evaluation

The matrix of 101–105 evaluation set (Table 1) was input into established BP Neural Network. Five alternative solutes for ALP were evaluated with the program.

The command o0=sim(net,d1) was used for simulating, and the evaluation result of five evaluation sets were obtained after BP Neural Network training, as shown in Table 2. The result shows that solute 104 is optimal, solute 103 suboptimal, and program 102 and 105 are the worst. The result also shows that the index values of logistics expense and traffic condition are 0.94 and 0.88, respectively. A developed transportation network is the most critical for delivery with low cost and high efficiency.

4 Conclusion and discussion

Applying BP Neural Network for ALP can obtain the output value quickly and efficiently. It is much more applicable than the traditional mathematical modeling and algorithm. BP Neural Network learn and training repeatedly to find the internal law of sample data and finally obtain the prediction value by using the provided samples [11, 12]. Result shows that BP Neural Network has the advantages of good convergence effect and small error. However, BP Neural Network simulates the expert evaluation for the prediction value. If the numbers of training sample is not large enough, it is difficult to find the regular pattern of expert evaluation. Generally, training times need to be at lest 600 times. BP Neural Network obtained the result after 1000 times' training using 100 groups of sample data in the case study. As result, the prediction value had high reliability.

It should be noted, however, that the two hidden layers of BP Neural Network applied in this research is actually a simplified one. It is suggested that the further researches should focus on using multineural network to learn respectively at the same time for improving training precision. On the other hand, larger samples could increase practicability of model and reliability of ALP. In addition, fuzzy comprehensive evaluation to develop fuzzy evaluation matrix has the disadvantage of subjectivity. How to improve the objectivity needs further research also.

Acknowledgment

The research work was supported by Nature Science Foundation of Fujian Province of China under Grant No. 2012J01071.

References

[1] Liu Fang, Gao Bo, The application of hierarchy process in the site selection of the Logistics Park. *Group Technology & Production Modernization*, **21**, pp. 37–39, 2004.

[2] Xu Xiaomei, Liu Yingying, Chen Lingling, et al., Fuzzy comprehensive evaluation in the site selection of Logistics Park based on AHP method take the example of Wuhu City. *Chinese Agricultural Science Bulletin*, **14**, pp. 275–279, 2009.

[3] Zhang Dezhi, Xie Ruhe, Li Shuangyan, Application of combined evaluation method to situate Logistics Park. *Journal of Wuhan University of Technology (Transportation Science & Engineering)*, **10**, pp. 762–765, 2005.

[4] Ling Chunyu, Zhang Dezhi, Li Shuangjiao, Application of improved grey conjunction analysis method in choosing the location of logistics zone. *Railway Transport and Economy*, **27**, pp. 20–23, 2005.

[5] Xia Hui, Hu Jiping, Xu Zheng, Site-selection of the Logistics Park based on a combination determining weights method. *Science Technology and Industry*, **9**, pp. 28–30, 2009.

[6] Wang Wenling, Chen Dapeng, Application of principle component analysis in choosing the location of logistics zone. *Logistics Sci-Tech*, **32**, pp. 35–37, 67, 2009.

[7] Zou Xiaoping, Guan Dongmei, Zhou Haiying, Application of factor analysis in the location allocation of zhuhai logistics park. *Logistics Technology*, **3**, pp. 124–126, 2010.

[8] Zhu Ziping, Zhao Guojie, Research on logistics park site of agricultural products. *Chinese Agricultural Mechanization*, **1**, pp. 127–129, 2011.

[9] Zhang Liming, *Models and Applications of Artificial Neural Networks*. Fudan University Publishing House, Shanghai, 1998.

[10]   Eiichi Taniguchi, Michihiko Noritake, Tadashi Yamada, Optimal size and location planning of public logistics terminal. *Transportation Research Part E*, **35**, pp. 207–222, 1999.

[11]   Chen-Tung Chen, A fuzzy approach to select the location of the distribution center. *Fuzzy Sets and Systems*, **118**, pp. 65–73, 2001.

[12]   Andreas Klose, Andreas Drexl, Facility location models for distribution system design. *European Journal of Operational Research*, **162**, pp. 4–29, 2005.

Our country ordinary university sports network education platform design and development

Kun Liu, Na Liu
PE Department of Jiangxi University of Traditional Chinese Medicine, Nanchang City, China

Abstract

By the methods of literature material, expert consultation method, the methods of investigation and study, to our country universities sports current situation of network education research. The result shows that: Our country university sports network education development is slow, it cannot satisfy the need of the contemporary education development and the students. Sports network curriculum development mode of research to promote sports network education research progressed, to deepen the reform of physical education teaching, to promote the sports teaching mode and method of change and even physical education thought and the theory of change has important significance.

Keywords: sports, network education, design.

1 Introduction

With the development of electronic technology and computer technology, network education will become an important link of modern education system. Sports teaching is propaganda and carry out the national fitness program, the key to the implementation of quality education, supplement of traditional physical education and sports network courses, with openness, its overlapping, sharing, collaborative and autonomy, etc. Sports teaching in colleges and universities should follow the steps of era, make full use of information technology, development of integrating text, images, animation, and audio and video network sports curriculum, gradually form the physical network teaching system based on campus network, accelerate the reform of physical education teaching and promote the innovation of teaching mode [1, 2].

2 Discussed problems

After the enrolment expansion in colleges and universities sports education resources serious shortage, although national investment to improve the conditions for offering education of colleges and universities, but the per capita possession of sports venues and the product is less than one of the original. Stadium facilities shortage, make part of the school was forced to stop driving his graduate students of physical education curriculum. This will seriously affect the overall quality of high-level talents in our country, also faces the challenge of higher education in the new period [3].

3 Sports network teaching

Sports network learning can achieve the following:

1. To carry out network teaching is a necessary complement to traditional teaching methods and develop sports teaching tend to leave the venue, equipment, equipment, etc, some also adopted in teaching closed-circuit television, satellite television, computer aided teaching, and sports network teaching. For individual teaching, and do according to their aptitude. As an extension of the physical education, sports network teaching can carry out health care, special technical theory, sport competition enjoy and exercise prescription teaching. It provides learners with a variety of learning style, students can according to their own needs, abilities, the freedom to choose learning content and way.
2. To carry out network teaching is helpful to expand the scale of teaching physical network teaching form will break through the limit of space and time, combined with the traditional sports teaching, increased the learning opportunities, expanding the size of the person in the teaching, to reduce the teaching cost. Students of physical education, can through the network and multimedia teaching in your convenient time, right place, according to the speed and the way that suits his, using online resources to learn to guide their extracurricular physical exercise, can say, expanded learning in network education, also provided the condition for the lifelong physical education.
3. To carry out the sports network teaching to promote the study and communication network teaching both in content and the way is open, one party and by campus network internally open on the other side and through the Internet opening to the outside world. One party and collecting the feedback information of the school students' physical education learning, the other party and promote study and communication between teachers. Convenience of standardized teaching management, also can

timely study and draw lessons from the advanced experience of foreign teachers and successful practices, so never leave school can broad and deep communication with other schools. With the development of digital technology, the application of network technology, to carry out the physical network teaching is the inevitable choice of modern sports teaching organization form.

4. To carry out the physical network teaching is the need of quality education, school sports implements the education for all-around development the important carrier. Demand of modern society to person with the change of the people, in addition to a solid basic knowledge and profound professional knowledge, also requires strong and have good psychological factors, good professional ethics, competition consciousness, and cooperation spirit. Survey shows that sports to students forms the correct outlook on life, values, good communication skills and team spirit plays an important role. Sports in the modern education is more and more important position. Can use of network education in physical education in colleges and universities, health, education, training students' lifelong sports view, makes it become physical and mental health.

4 The sports network curriculum design and development

4.1 Sports remote network education platform design criteria

Most in sports remote network education platform, the application of education technology more biased, in general, physical distance education platform should follow extensibility, practicability, unity, the principle of safety and reliability, etc.

1. Sports a focal point of study design is not only a remote network platform in order to meet the needs of the sports teaching work in colleges and universities, but also lay a good foundation for the platform for future expansion.

2. Includes both the practical function is practical, including the development process the practicability of the platform itself. The development of the sports remote network education platform aims to promote the reform of college sports teaching work and innovation.

3. Sports remote network teaching platform must firmly grasp the development and construction process is one of the principles of system guarantee each function module run smoothly, it is an important premise of platform function.

4.2 The overall model design of sports remote network education platform

1. Sports remote network education platform design aim is to provide users with a work based on the Internet online learning environment. Platform to

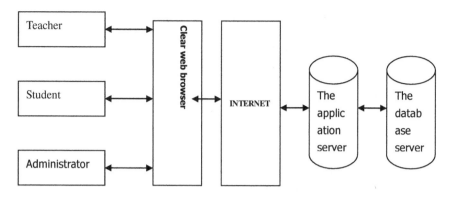

Figure 1: Sports remote network education teaching mode based on Internet.

realize the functions through the interaction between the application server and the user's browser. The sports simple schematic diagram of the remote network education platform application mode is shown in Figure 1.

Through hardware and software platform connecting between various levels, to complete the interaction between the user and platforms, it is essentially a realization of client and server interaction. Sports remote network education platform is divided into client and server side. So as to realize including browsing, learn, practice, discussion, exchange, corresponding functions such as test and other extensions. While the server through the MY SQL database platform and Tomcat exchange and transfer between a Web server, complete the request and send information.

2. Diagram reflects the work mode is, first of all to participate in sports teaching network users (students, teachers, administrators) must connect Internet network, by their own browser sends a request to the application server application server based on the user's request to make corresponding responses, and if necessary to retrieve data from the database server, the response or retrieval services such as the result feedback to the user via a browser. Set up the deployment of the sports remote network education platform is divided into the following five levels, namely, My SQL database server, Tomcat Web server, campus network and its accessory facilities, education management system platform, professor client and learning system. Sports remote network education platform development research project system deployment diagram are shown in Figure 2.

Through hardware and software platform connecting between various levels, to complete the interaction between the user and platforms. Sports remote network education platform is divided into client and server side, the client application through interface and access to the server resources, complete the information request and receive. So as to realize including browsing, learn, practice, discussion, exchange, corresponding functions such as test and other extensions. While the server through the MY SQL

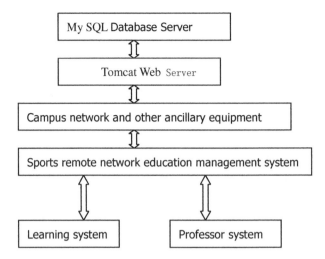

Figure 2: System server structure.

database platform and Tomcat exchange and transfer between a Web server, complete the request and send information.

3. The overall application architecture of remote education platform. The system structure are shown in Figure 3. Sports remote network education platform for different user access channel, realize the corresponding administrator data maintenance function, students learning access functions.

The establishment of sports remote network education platform is based on hierarchical structure, to solve the isolation between various departments interconnected between business application system, to build basic general software platform between participants, to provide a unified platform for the business operation environment.

5   Conclusions and recommendations

The sports in the main function of the remote network education advantage, better reflects the teachers' leading and students' main body status, the classroom and complementary role play to the largest outside the classroom, to the cultivation of the students' independent consciousness and innovation ability has a lot of help, at the same time is able to promote the sports education resources saving and efficient utilization of resource in the whole teaching and learning-related learning mode has prominent effect. This sports remote network teaching platform adopts the object-oriented programming technology, from the overall to the detailed design with object as the core, has good openness and extensibility, is a good further development platform, I believe after put into use the platform will achieve good economic and social benefits. At the same time also can have certain reference for other related systems and practical values.

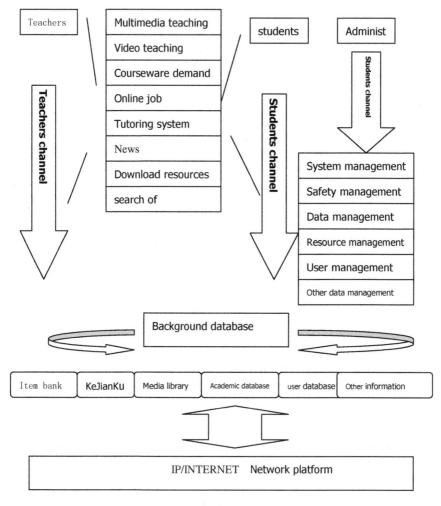

Figure 3: Sports network education platform system structure.

References

[1] Jiang Gufu, The characteristics of network curriculum, the principle of building and its construction model, audio-visual education research is discussed in this paper, **(3)**, p. 45, 2004.

[2] Yang Kaesong, The design principle of constructivism learning environment. *Journal of Chinese Audio-visual Education*, **(4)**, p. 17, 2004.

[3] Gong Zhengwei, *The Sports Teaching Theory*. Beijing Sports Study Press, Beijing, p. 346, 2004.

Optimal design of an arch girder based on neural networks and genetic algorithms

Minghai Yuan, Shuo Cheng, Zhiyong Dai, Aimin Ji
College of Mechanical and Electrical Engineering, Hohai University, Changzhou, China

Abstract

The arch girders are a kind of usual structure, applied in building and bridge, etc. The object of optimal design of the arch girder is that it has the lightest weight based on meeting the distortion request. Aiming at this problem, uniform design is used to collect the sample and train BP network. Using BP network instead of finite element analysis, the fitness of genetic algorithm was calculated in order to optimize the structure of the arch girders. Using the methods in this paper, the precision and the speed of the optimization is improved.

Keywords: optimal design, genetic algorithm, BP Neural Networks, uniform design.

1 Introduction

Because of the good appearance and the clear force, arch structure is widely used in building, bridge engineering practice [1]. The mentioned arch girders are welded by profiles, and are used to support the astronomical observational equipment in astronomical observations [2]. Its structure and the force maintain constant. This structure is suitable for parametric design, namely according to the section size of arch girders' radius and deformed requirements, the design only need to change the span and sectional dimensions [3]. The traditional method is based on the experiences of analogy to meet the design requirements of the case, so it is difficult to achieve the best results [4].

According to design features of this arch girder in this paper, we can obtain the sample with the method of uniform test, to train the BP neural network with a single hidden layer, using BP neural networks instead of the finite element to judge the constraints and determine the fitness of GA. GA is used to obtain the

 WIT Transactions on Information and Communication Technologies, Vol. 61, © 2014 WIT Press
www.witpress.com, ISSN 1743-3517 (on-line)
doi:10.2495/MIIT130331

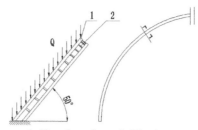

1. Equal angle   2. Flat iron

Figure 1: Force model of the arch girder.

global optimal solution and optimize the structure of arch girders to get the minimum weight under meeting its deformed condition. Due to the fast running speed and the high precision, this method has achieved good results in practice.

2 Establishment of the optimization model

The force model of the arch girder is more special, which has an angle of 50° between the girder and the plane. A plurality of wide-angle telescopes and the auxiliary observing apparatus are evenly distributed in the girder. The girder has a vertical downward gravity. The simple force model of distributing vertical downward stress in the girder is shown in Figure 1.

The optimization requirement of the arch girder is that the weight is lightest under keeping the span and the load constant, and meeting the stiffness and the strength. The optimized mathematical model can be expressed as:

$$\begin{cases} X = \left[B_1, B_2, t_1, t_2 \right]^T \\ \min W(X) \\ \sigma_{\max} \leq [\sigma] \\ d_{\max} \leq [d] \\ X_{\min} \leq X \leq X_{\max} \end{cases} \tag{1}$$

where B_1—the side-length of the equal angle, B_2—the width of the flat iron, t_1—the thickness of the equal angle, t_2—the thickness of the flat iron, $\sigma_{\max}$—the maximum stress, $[\sigma]$—the allowable stress, $d_{\max}$—the maximum displacement in the vertical direction of the deformation of the arch girder, $[d]$ —the allowable displacement in the vertical direction of the deformation of the arch girder, $X_{\min}$—the upper limit of the design variables, $X_{\max}$—the lower limit of the design variables.

As seen from the above mathematical model, this optimization is a single objective multiconstraint optimization. The constraint problem that optimized by GA needs to design the penalty function. Penalty function is designed for:

$$P(X) = W(X) + r\sum_{i=1}^{2} \left(\max[0, g_i(x)]^2 \right) \tag{2}$$

where W(X) is the weight value of BP networks. $g_1(x) = \dfrac{\sigma_{max}}{[\sigma]} - 1$,

$g_2(x) = \dfrac{d_{max}}{[d]} - 1$. r is a positive coefficient.

Fitness function as follows: $f(X) = C_0 - P(X)$. C_0 is a constant to ensure that $f(X)$ is positive. $f(x)$ is a function about $W(X)$, σ_{max} and d_{max}, namely $f(X) = f(W(X), \sigma_{max}, d_{max})$. This fitness of the structure can be obtained as long as the results of $f(X)$, σ_{max} and d_{max} are successfully calculated. Finally, using the fitness optimizes the structure.

3 The optimization process of arch girders

3.1 The obtainment of sample points

Training BP neural network must have a certain number of sample points. The selection of the sample points directly affects the quality of the BP network [5]. The test method for sample points is obviously not desirable [6]. Because the profile section of the girder is constantly changing, it is impossible to produce a lot of the finished products to do test in practice. Therefore, we use the finite element software to analyze different sizes of arch girders and obtain the sample points. However, due to the wide variety of sections and the huge workload analysis of combining each case, the comprehensive calculation loses significance of this work. Using the uniform design method determines the sample point and does the finite element analysis in this article. This greatly reduces the number of sample points and meets the training requirements in BP networks. The optimizing model is affected by four factors of B_1, t_1, B_2, and t_2. According to GB, the equal angle in the different side-length has different thickness range, while the flat iron with different width thickness range changed little. Therefore, B_1(36–90 mm), B_2(35–80 mm) and t_2(3–12 mm) are divided into 10 levels when we design the uniform form. t_1(4–8 mm) is divided into 10 levels by GB. The above size takes the table $U_{10}(10^3 \times 5)$ (Fang, 2011) of a mixed level uniform design by GB and selects 10 training samples (1–10 from Table 1,) and the sample points of the two tests (11–12 form Table 1).

3.2 The design of BP networks

Optimization model of the arch girder can determine four input nodes, namely B_1, t_1, B_2, t_2, and three output nodes, namely W, σ, d. A single hidden layer of 16 nodes are used in the above optimization problem. Using samples of Table 1 to train BP networks, when the total error is less than 0.0001, or learning numbers are more than 10,000 times after finishing training, weights and thresholds of BP networks are saved. Table 2 is test results of the sample 11–12 in Table 1. The error rate is shown in the brackets.

Table 1: The Sample with Mixed Level Uniform Design.

No.	B1 (mm)	B2 (mm)	t2 (mm)	t1 (mm)	σ (10^8 N/m^2)	d (cm)	W (kg)
1	36	45	10	4	2.5730	2.6803	50.596
2	40	60	7	5	2.1820	2.1540	61.203
3	45	75	4	6	1.8473	1.5120	71.306
4	50	35	12	7	1.5342	0.8087	94.150
5	56	50	9	8	1.3180	0.5517	116.39
6	63	65	6	4	1.7522	1.1080	73.943
7	70	80	3	5	1.5470	0.7213	89.615
8	75	40	11	6	1.2974	0.4260	120.71
9	80	55	8	7	1.2309	0.3140	144.76
10	90	70	5	8	1.1722	0.2077	176.89
11	70	50	12	8	1.2205	0.3183	149.07
12	50	80	4	6	1.6345	1.1890	79.049

Table 2: Network Test Results.

No.	B1 (mm)	B2 (mm)	t2 (mm)	t1 (mm)	σ (10^8 N/m^2)	d (cm)	W (kg)
1	70	50	12	8	1.2102 (1.03%)	0.2962 (6.9%)	151.746 (1.8%)
2	50	80	4	6	1.6681 (2.06%)	1.1382 (4.3%)	77.860 (1.5%)

Table 3: Parameters of GA.

Crossing-Over Rate	Aberration Rate	Population Size	Genetic Algebra	Variables Number	Constraints Number
0.1	0.8	20	10000	4	2

From Table 2, the test results, the network training results are satisfactory and can replace basically the fitness of GA by using the finite element calculation.

3.3 The optimization process of GA

Optimizing genetic algorithm (GA) after training the network, the fitness selects the maximum weight of 176.89 in the sample subtracting the calculated weight of the network (Fitness=176.89-$W(X)$). Other initial parameters of GA are shown in Table 3.

GA optimization steps: (1) To create the initial population; (2) To calculate the fitness and constraint value by using BP neural networks, when it satisfies the optimization criteria and constraints, the results output, or turn to (3); (3) To select the high fitness individuals to generate a new individual by performing genetic operations and turn to (2). The specific process is shown in Figure 2.

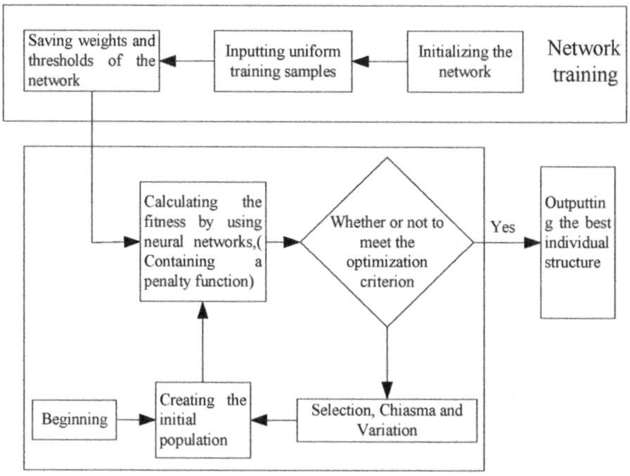

Figure 2: The flowchart of GA optimization.

Table 4: Contrasting Optimization Results.

	$B1$	$B2$	$t2$	$t1$	$\sigma(10^8 \text{ N/m}^2)$	d (cm)	W (kg)
Finite element optimization results	80.59	80.2	3	4	1.4782	0.6483	85.93
The optimization results in this paper	80.46	58.55	4.05	4	1.4810	0.6492	85.62

4 Application

The diameter of the above arch girder is 5 m. Ten groups of devices are uniformly distributed in the arch beam, each group heavy 20 kg. The arch girder is fixed at both ends, a dip angle of 50°, [d] = 0.65 cm, [σ] = 300 MPa.

Because the sizes of the equal angle and the flat iron must meet the national standard, according to Table 4, it is able to meet the basic requirements that the material occurs the deformation of 0.6506 cm and the weight of 84.634 kg when the equal angle is used the side length of 80 mm, the thickness of 4 mm, and the flat iron is used the width of 60 mm, the thickness of 4 mm.

From Table 4, it can be seen that the optimization results in this paper and finite element optimization results about minimum weight of the arch girder are basically same. It takes approximately 40 min to iterate 30 times for using finite element optimization. While it only consumes approximately a few minutes for using the above sample in this article, as the BP network parameters and GA parameters, so the optimized speed is greatly increased.

5 Conclusion

Based on uniform sample, calculating the degree of adaptation and constraint conditions by using BP neural networks, obtaining the global optimal solution of arch girders' weight by using GA, this method which has the fast speed of the optimization and high precision is suitable for practical application of Engineering. At the same time, it is difficult to obtain the sample, so this method and the mean need to be further improved.

Acknowledgment

This work was supported by the Fundamental Research Funds for the Central Universities under Grant No. 2012B14014 and the national natural science foundation of China under Grant No. 51175146.

References

[1] X.P. Wang, L.M. Cao, *Genetic Algorithm—Theory, Application and Software Implementation*. Xi'an Jiaotong University Press, Xi'an , pp. 25–34, 2008.
[2] H.D. Guo, Z.F. Lu, Structure optimization design based on BP neural networks and genetic algorithms. *Journal of Aerospace Power*, **18(2)**, pp. 216–220, 2010.
[3] Q.S. Xie, J. Yin, Y.K. Luo, *Neural Network Method in Mechanical Engineering*. Mechanical Industry Press, Beijing, pp. 29–35, 2011.
[4] X.S. Lai, Neural network combined with the genetic algorithm to optimize the application. *Guizhou University (Natural Science)*, **21(2)**, pp. 179–184, 2004.
[5] S.Z. Han, C.S. Mei, Research on CGA algorithm for optimization design of engineering structures. *Journal of Basic Science and Engineering*, **12(2)**, pp. 197–205, 2009.
[6] D.E. Goldberg, Genetic algorithms in search, optimization and machine learning. *MA: Addison-Wesley Publishing Company*, **3(2)**, pp. 54–58, 2009.

An algorithm for detecting overlapping and multilayer communities in complex networks

Cheng Jing, Ling Chen, Sheng-Rong Zou

Department of Computer Science, Yangzhou University, China
State Key Laboratory of Novel Software Tech, Nanjing University, China

Abstract

In this paper, we define the modularity for multilayer communities, and present a new algorithm which can detect both the overlapping and multilayer communities in the networks simultaneously. The method first selects some nodes as cores, and then extends them to form communities. Experimental results on several networks demonstrate that our algorithm can achieve higher quality results than other methods.

Keywords: complex network, community detecting, overlapping communities, multilayer communities.

1 Introduction

Community structure is a nature characteristic in many real networks such as social networks [1], biological networks, and technological networks. In the past decade, many methods have been proposed and applied for specific complex networks [2]. In real world networks, some nodes naturally belong to several communities. Therefore, many algorithms have been designed to detect such overlapping communities.

One way to detect overlapping communities is the module penetration method. Rosvall [3] presented a sequential clique percolation (SCP) algorithm to perform fast community detection in networks. This method sequentially inserts the constituent links to the network and simultaneously keeps track of the emerging community structure. Fuzzy clustering is a useful approach for detecting overlapping community.

Communities in the network usually are organized in a hierarchical structure. Moreover, nodes in each layer can be shared by different communities, and those

 WIT Transactions on Information and Communication Technologies, Vol. 61, © 2014 WIT Press
www.witpress.com, ISSN 1743-3517 (on-line)
doi:10.2495/MIIT130341

communities are overlapped. In this paper, we present an algorithm that can concurrently find overlapping communities and the hierarchical structure. Experimental results on several networks demonstrate that the algorithm can achieve higher quality results than other methods.

2 Modularity of the multilayer communities

To evaluate the quality of a particular communities partitioning scheme, modularity is broadly applied as a measurement. Therefore, we first define a modularity measure for multilayer community detection. Our modularity measure for multilayer community structure can be quantified using the difference of the number of links between the vertexes within a community and the number of links between nodes in different communities.

In the hierarchical structure of a network $G=(V,E)$, a community in the ith layer of the network is given as a subgraph $G_i = (V_i, E_i)$. We denote $In(V_i) = \{e \mid e = (v_j, v_k) \in E_i\}$ as the set of edges inside G_i, and $Out(V_i) = \{e \mid e = (v_j, v_k) \in E, v_j \in V_i, v_k \notin V_i\}$ as the set of the edges connecting the nodes inside and outside G_i. We define the modularity of G_i as

$$M(G_i) = \frac{|In(V_i)| - |Out(V_i)|}{\alpha_i . d_i (d_i + 1)} \tag{1}$$

Here, $d_i = |V_i|$ is the number of vertices in G_i. Suppose the network is portioned into k communities in the ith layer, the modularity of this partition scheme is:

$$M(G_i, P, \alpha_i) = \sum_{i=1}^{k} M(G_i) = \sum_{i=1}^{k} \frac{|In(V_i)| - |Out(V_i)|}{\alpha_i . d_i (d_i + 1)} \tag{2}$$

Here, α_i is a parameter to adjust the size of the communities detected. Let r be the maximum number of layers considered, we set $\alpha_1 \leq \alpha_2 \leq \dots \leq \alpha_r$ for r layers. Using lager value of α_i, we can detect communities of small sizes. By using different values of α, we can detect the communities in the layers from the bottom to top.

In our algorithm for multilayer community detecting, some communities in the higher layer should be divided to form smaller communities in the lower layer, and some communities in the lower layer should be merged to form larger communities in the higher layer. To divide or merge the communities, we need to measure the closeness of each node with its neighbours. Therefore, we define the clustering coefficient for each node. For a node v_i, let $N_i = \{v \mid (v, v_i) \in E\}$ be the set of neighbour nodes of v_i, namely, the set of nodes which directly link with v_i. Let k_i be the degree of v_i. Define the set of all edges connecting the nodes in set N_i as $S_i = \{(v, v') \mid (v, v') \in E, v \in N_i, v' \in N_i\}$. Then the clustering coefficient of node v_i is defined as:

$$C(v_i) = \frac{2 \mid S_i \mid}{k_i(k_i + 1)} \tag{3}$$

A node with larger clustering coefficient has closer connections with its neighbours, and is more likely to be the core of a cluster.

3 Framework of the algorithm

In large scale hierarchical networks, huge number of nodes may greatly increase the computational complexity of the community detecting algorithm. To reduce the computational complexity, we adopt the sampling method in our algorithm for detecting overlapping and multilayer communities. The algorithm detects the multilayer communities' recursively. At layer i, a parameter α_i is used in calculating the modularity using (2). Suppose G is a community detected in the $(i-1)$th layer, the recursive algorithm Community_detecting(G, α_i) detects the communities in G at layers i, $i+1$, ..., r. The algorithm consists of two major steps. In the first step, the algorithm selects some proper nodes in the network to see if they could extend into communities. In the second step, the nodes selected are extended to form larger groups, which represent the communities in different layers. The algorithm repeats such procedures of selecting and expanding until all the nodes are covered.

Framework of the algorithm Community_detecting(G, α_i) is as follows:

Algorithm Community_detecting(G, α_i)
input: $G=(V,E)$: a community in the $(i-1)$th layer;
         r: maximum number of the layers;
         $\alpha_1 \leq \alpha_2 \leq ... \leq \alpha_r$: parameters for r layers;
Output: communities in G at layers i, $i+1$, ..., r;
Begin
1 **If** $i<r+1$ **then**
2 Select $k(\alpha_i)$ nodes with the largest clustering coefficients: $v_1, v_2,..., v_{k(\alpha i)}$;
3 Using $v_1, v_2,..., v_{k(\alpha i)}$ as cores to form l-cliques ($l>4$);
4 Those cliques are denoted as $G_{i1}, G_{i2},$ ..., $G_{i,k(\alpha i)}$, and are used as the initial communities;
5 **Repeat**
6 Choose the community G_{ij} which has the maximal extensible degree $X(G_{ij})$;
7 Choose the node v from $N(G_{ij})$ which has the maximal $Pr(v)$;
8 $G_{ij} = G_{ij} \cup \{v\}$;
9 Make split, merge and transfer operations on G_{ij} at a certain probability;
10 **until** modularity $M(G,P,\alpha_i)$ cannot be improved;
11 **output** the communities detected in G at layer i;
12 Select $k(\alpha_i)$ communities with the largest modularities: $G_{i1},G_{i2},...,G_{i,k(\alpha i)}$;
13 **For** $j=1$ **to** $k(\alpha_i)$ **do**
14 Community_detecting(G_{ij}, α_{i+1})

15 **End for** *j*
16 **End if**
End

In the algorithm, line 6 selects the communities with lager extensible degree, and extends them to form larger communities. The extensible degree of a community G_i is defined as:

$$X(G_i) = \frac{|N(G_i)|}{|V_i|} \tag{4}$$

Here, V_i is the set of nodes in community G_i, and $N(G_i)$ is the nodes set neighbor nodes of G_i. Line 7 in the algorithm selects a node v from $N(G_i)$ with the largest contribution degree $Pr(G_i, v)$ to join the community G_i. The contribution degree $Pr(G_i, v)$ is defined as:

$$\Pr(G_i, v) = \begin{cases} \dfrac{[M(V_i \cup \{v\}) - M(V_i)]^\beta}{M(V_i)} & if \quad M(V_i \cup \{v\}) > M(V_i) \\ 0 & otherwise \end{cases} \tag{5}$$

Here, β is a parameter to adjust the influence of the modularity on the contribution degree. Lines 13–15 detects the communities in G_{i1}, G_{i2}, ..., $G_{i,k(\alpha i)}$ at the layers $i+1$ to r by recursively calling the algorithm Community_detecting. For a given network G, we can detect its communities in all layers by executing algorithm Community_detecting(G, α_1). Since the nodes could be selected by a number of different communities, the communities detected by the algorithm may overlap at each layer. Therefore, the algorithm can discover overlapping communities at different layers.

4 Experimental results

In this section, we empirically demonstrate the effectiveness of our proposed algorithm on benchmark datasets of real world networks "Karate club" and "dolphin social network." All experiments have been run on Pentium IV, Windows XP, P1.7G. The algorithms are coded using Java, and the results are visualized by the graph analysis and visualization tool Pajek.

4.1 Test on Karate club network

The network of "Karate Club" illustrates the pattern of friendships between 34 members of a Karate club at a US university in 1970s. As shown in Figure 1, this network contains 34 nodes and 78 edges. As shown in Figure 1, our algorithm can find two communities in the network, which is very close to the optimal solution. When extending the communities, a node is selected and added to a

Figure 1: Karate club network.

Figure 2: Dolphin social network.

community only when its contribution degree is larger than 0.2. The modality of each community we found is 0.078, which is very close to the results of the actually separation of the club.

4.2 Test on dolphin social network

We also test our algorithm on the dolphin social network. This network was constructed from observations of a community of 62 bottlenose dolphins living in Doubtful Sound, New Zealand, over a period of 7 years from 1994 to 2001. Vertexes in the network represent 62 dolphins, while the edges reflect the ties between dolphin pairs. It is believed that dolphins with statistically significant frequent ties form an association.

We test our algorithm on this data set and compare the results with that of the previously proposed algorithm based on betweenness score. When extending the communities, a node is selected and added to a community only when its contribution degree is larger than 0.18. The operations of merging and splitting communities can be performed only when the increment of modularity is greater than 0.03. Four communities can be obtained by the betweenness-based algorithm, and the modalities of the communities are -0.017, 0.045, 0.051, 0.088. Our algorithm also identifies four communities as shown in Figure 2, where the purple, blue, orange, and dark grey nodes represents four communities. From the figure, we can see that the three green points are overlapped by part of the purple and blue communities. The modularity of the four communities are 0.051, 0.051, 0.072, and 0.0875 respectively, which are better than that of the betweenness-based algorithm.

5   Conclusions

A new algorithm for detecting both the overlapping and multilayer communities is advanced. The algorithm is based on the modularity we defined for multilayer communities. Operations of community splitting, merging and node transferring are also proposed to improve the quality of the results. Experimental results on several networks demonstrate that the algorithm is can detect the overlapping and multilayer communities accurately and effectively.

Acknowledgments

This research was supported in part by the Chinese National Natural Science Foundation under Grant Nos. 61379066, 61070047, 61379064, State Key Fundamentals Research (973) Project under contract 2012CB316003, Natural Science Foundation of Jiangsu Province under contracts BK20130452, BK2012672, and Natural Science Foundation of Education Department of Jiangsu Province under contracts 12KJB520019, 13KJB520026.

References

[1] R.J.H. Albert, A.-L. Barabasi, Diameter of the World-Wide Web. *Nature*, **401**, pp. 130–131, 1999.

[2] G. Agarwal, D. Kempe, Modularity maximizing graph communities via mathematical programming. *The European Physical Journal B, Condensed Matter and Complex Systems*, **66(3)**, pp. 409–418, 2008.

[3] M. Rosvall, C.T. Bergstrom, An information theoretic framework for resolving community structure in complex networks. *Proceedings of the National Academy of Sciences USA*, **104(18)**, pp. 7327–7331, 2007.

Wavelet collocation methods for viscosity solutions to swing options

Hua Li[1], Antony Ware[2], Li Guo[1], Wei Na Chen[1]
[1]School of Mathematics and Statistics, Zhengzhou University, China
[2]Department of Mathematics and Statistics, University of Calgary, China

Abstract

This paper presents wavelet collocation methods for the numerical approximation of viscosity solutions of Hamilton–Jacobi–Bellman (HJB) equations, which arise in pricing swing options in a mean reverting market. The differential operator is formulated exactly and efficiently. The convergence and stability is studied in the framework of viscosity solution theory.

Keywords: swing option, viscosity solution, wavelet, collocation.

1 Introduction

Models of swing options are an extension of the Black–Scholes model. Due to the uncertainty of future consumption and the limited fungibility of many commodities, some commodity markets have introduced swing options which give the consumer flexibility with respect to both the timing and the amount of commodity delivered. For descriptions of swing options, we refer to [1, 2] and the references therein. Swing options are very common in energy markets, because they provide consumers with flexibility to vary their rate of consumption without being exposed to price fluctuations, which can be extreme, especially in the case of electricity. For swing options on coal, see Ref. [3], for example.

Due to their importance in the energy markets, the pricing of swing options has gained more and more attention over the last decade, and much effort has been expanded in designing algorithms for pricing swing options. The discrete valuation of swing options has been studied by several authors. In Ref. [1], a discrete forest methodology is developed, in Ref. [2], a binomial/trinomial forest is built. In Refs. [4, 5], Monte Carlo techniques are employed. Continuous time models allow the use of powerful mathematical tools to analyze the properties of solutions and have

WIT Transactions on Information and Communication Technologies, Vol. 61, © 2014 WIT Press
www.witpress.com, ISSN 1743-3517 (on-line)
doi:10.2495/MIIT130351

recently appeared in the literature. A continuous time model for the price of the general commodity-based swing option is presented in Ref. [6], where the price function is the solution of a system of quasi-variational inequalities. In this paper, we study the numerical solution of swing option models in an HJB equation.

2   Second generation interpolating wavelets

2.1 Scaling functions on an interval

Consider the interval $\Omega = [0,1]$. For each level j, we place a grid

$$G^j = \left\{ x_{j,k} \mid x_{j,k} = \frac{k}{2^j}, k = 0, 1, \cdots, 2^j \right\}$$

on Ω. A set of interpolating scaling functions $\{ \phi_{j,k}, k = 0, 1, \cdots, 2^j \}$ can be constructed using the interpolating subdivision scheme and they satisfy the two-scale relationship

$$\phi_{j,k} = \sum_{l=0}^{2^{j+1}} h_{j,k,l} \phi_{j+1,l} \tag{1}$$

The scaling function space

$$V_j := \text{span}\{ \phi_{j,k}(x), k = 0, 1, \cdots, 2^j \}$$

satisfies a second-generation multiresolution analysis.

2.2 Projections and wavelet transforms

For convenience, we denote $\phi_j = [\phi_{j,0}, \phi_{j,1}, \cdots, \phi_{j,2^j}]'$. Similarly, ψ_j, $\tilde{\phi}_j$ and $\tilde{\psi}_j$ denote the vectors of wavelet functions, dual scaling functions and dual wavelets respectively, and the corresponding spaces are denoted by W_j, $\tilde{V}_j$, and $\tilde{W}_j$, respectively.   Define the projections of $f \in L_2(\Omega)$ onto V_j and W_j respectively by

$$P_j f(x) := \sum_{k=0}^{2^j} v_{j,k} \phi_{j,k}(x) \quad \text{and} \quad Q_j f(x) := \sum_{k=0}^{2^j-1} w_{j,k} \psi_{j,k}(x)$$

Similarly, we have the dual projections $\tilde{P}_j$ and $\tilde{Q}_j$ and

$$P_j = P_{j-1} + Q_{j-1}, \quad \tilde{P}_j = \tilde{P}_{j-1} + \tilde{Q}_{j-1}. \tag{2}$$

2.3 Wavelet collocation representations of operators

Let $\hat{\phi}(x) := \delta(x)$, where $\delta(x)$ is the Dirac distribution function. Define

$$\hat{\phi}_{j,k}(x) := \hat{\phi}(2^j x - k) \quad \text{and} \quad \hat{\psi}_{j,k}(x) := \hat{\phi}(2^{j+1} x - 2k + 1).$$

Let $\hat{P}_j$ and $\hat{Q}_j$ be "collocation" operators defined as

$$\hat{P}_j f := \sum_{m=0}^{2^j} \left\langle f, \hat{\phi}_{j,m} \right\rangle \phi_{j,m} \quad \text{and} \quad \hat{Q}_j f := \sum_{m=0}^{2^j - 1} \left\langle f, \hat{\psi}_{j,m} \right\rangle \psi_{j,m}$$

Therefore, if we take G^j as the collocation points,

$$LP_j f(G^j) = \hat{P}_j LP_j f. \tag{3}$$

The nonstandard form by expanding $\hat{P}_J LP_J$ in a telescopic series:

$$\hat{P}_J LP_J = \sum_{j=j_0}^{J-1} (\hat{Q}_j LQ_j + \hat{Q}_j LP_j + \hat{P}_j LQ_j) + \hat{P}_{j_0} LP_{j_0}. \tag{4}$$

The advantage of the representation is that it only involves "interaction" on one scale j and the formulation only results in an order of N computation.

3 Models of swing options

A swing option price is a function V^k which depends on a strategy k and satisfies

$$V_t^k - rV^k + \frac{\sigma^2}{2} V_{SS}^k + \mu^* V_S^k + \max_{k \in I(q)} \left[k(V_q^k - S) - \chi_{st} - \chi_{iw}(k) \right] = 0, \tag{5}$$

$$V^k(S, T; q) = \lambda qS,$$

The hedge ratio is

$$\Delta = \frac{V_S + \lambda q}{F_S}. \tag{6}$$

where $F(S,t)$ is the forward contract we hedge with, and $F_S = \frac{\partial F}{\partial S}$. Eq. (5) is called an HJB equation. Due to possible degeneration, the classical solutions may not exist. Therefore, we study the viscosity solutions.

4 Wavelet collocation scheme

We employ a hybrid wavelet/finite difference semi-Lagrangian numerical scheme to solve Eq. (6). Throughout this section, we consider the case where $-\mu^*(S,t) = (\ddot{b} \ln S + \ddot{a})S$, $\ddot{a}$ and $\ddot{b}$ are constants, and $\sigma(S) = \sigma_0 S$.

We first apply time reverse and logarithm transform to Eq. (6) by (Maximization will be dealt with later)

$$\tau = T - t, \quad x = \ln S, \quad \text{and} \quad e^{-r\tau}u(x,\tau;q) = V^k(S,t;q).$$

This results in

$$u_\tau + (bx + a + \frac{\sigma_0^2}{2})u_x - ku_q - \frac{\sigma_0^2}{2}u_{xx} = e^{r\tau}\left[-\chi_{iw}(k) - ke^x - \chi_{st}\right], \tag{7}$$
$$u(x,0;q) = \lambda qe^x.$$

We then introduce a change of variables to remove the drift term in x: u_x term by

$$y = e^{-b\tau}\left(x + \frac{a + \frac{\sigma_0^2}{2}}{b}\right), \quad \text{and} \quad w(y,\tau;q) = u(x,\tau;q).$$

Eq. (7) is reduced to

$$w_\tau - kw_q - \frac{\sigma_0^2}{2}e^{-2b\tau}w_{yy} = e^{r\tau}\left[-\chi_{iw}(k) - ke^x - \chi_{st}\right], \tag{8}$$
$$w(x,0;q) = \lambda qe^x.$$

Since there is no diffusion term and only drift term in q, we employ a semi-Lagrangian method to deal with the drift term in q: i.e., $w_\tau - kw_q$ is expressed as a single directional derivative in the direction of the curve $(Q(\tau;q,\tau_0),\tau)_\tau$ passing through the point (y,τ), where, given q and τ_0, $Q(\tau)$ satisfies

$$\frac{dQ}{d\tau} = -k, \quad Q(\tau) = q. \tag{9}$$

Solving the above ordinary differential equation,

$$Q(\tau_0) = q + k(\tau - \tau_0). \tag{10}$$

Thus, we obtain

$$\frac{d}{d\tau} w - \frac{\sigma_0^2}{2} e^{-2b\tau} w_{yy} = e^{r\tau}\left[-\chi_{iw}(k) - kS(y) - \chi_{st} \right], \tag{11}$$

$$w(y, 0; q) = \lambda qS(y).$$

The maximization problem is as follows.

Problem 4.1 *Find w such that*

$$\frac{\sigma_0^2}{2} e^{-2b\tau} w_{yy} = \max_{k \in l(q)} \left\{ \frac{d}{d\tau} w - e^{r\tau}\left[-\chi_{iw}(k) - kS(y) - \chi_{st} \right] \right\} \tag{12}$$

$$w(y, 0; q) = \lambda qS(y).$$

For the numerical approximation, we take an implicit finite difference method in τ, and a wavelet collocation method in y. Then the approximation problem to Problem 4.1 is written as follows.

Problem 4.2 *Give* $\tau_n = n\Delta\tau, n = 0, \cdots, N$, *find a map* $U : \{ \tau_0, \tau_1, \cdots, \tau_N \} \to V_j$ *such that, for any* $y \in G^j$, *the following equation holds for each m.*

$$U_m^{n+1} - \frac{\sigma_0^2}{2} \Delta\tau e^{-2b\tau^{n+1}} A U_m^{n+1} = \max_{k \in l(q)}\left[U_m^n(y; Q_m^n) + f(y, \tau^{n+1}; k) \right], \tag{13}$$

$$U^0(y; q_m) = \lambda q_m S(y),$$

where $U_m^n(y) = U(y, \tau^n; q_m)$, $m = 0, 1, \cdots, M$, $Q_m^n := q_m + k\Delta\tau$, A is the wavelet collocation representation of the operator $\frac{d^2}{dx^2}$, and

$$f(y, \tau; k) = e^{r\tau}\left[-\Delta\tau\chi_{iw}(k) - k\Delta\tau S(y) - \Delta\tau\chi_{st} \right].$$

Please note that the "max" function is realized as follows. For each m, find a set

$$K = \{k \mid \{q_m + k\Delta\tau\}_{k \in l(q)} \bigcap \{q_i \mid i = 0, 1, \cdots, M\} \neq 0\},$$

then

$$\max_{k \in I(q)} \left[U_m^n(y; Q_m^n) + f(y, \tau^{n+1}; k) \right] = \max_{k \in K} \left[U_m^n(y; Q_m^n) + f(y, \tau^{n+1}; k) \right].$$

And also we use a free boundary condition in the space domain y.

5   Convergence rate of the scheme

The approximation of viscosity solutions to HJB equations has been intensively studied by Barles and Jakobsen [7] in 2005. The theory of viscosity solutions provides a means of analysis in this setting. We can demonstrate the monotonicity and prove the regularity and consistency of this numerical scheme. For convenience, we rewrite the numerical scheme as

$$Q(h, \tau, y_s, U_s^{n+1}, [U^{n+1}])$$
$$= \frac{1}{\Delta \tau} \left\{ U_m^{n+1}(y; q_m) - M^{-1} \max_{k \in I(q)} \left[U^n(y, Q_m^n) + f(y, \tau^{n+1}; k) \right] \right\}_s \quad (14)$$

where $M = (I - \frac{\sigma_0^2}{2} \Delta \tau e^{-2b\tau^{n+1}} A)$. We assume that $M^{-1} \leq 0$ which is true and can be numerically shown.

1. *Monotonicity*

   For any $v \geq 0$, $h_0 > 0$ such that if $|h| \leq h_0$, $u \leq v$ are functions in $V_j(G^j)$, and $\phi(\tau) = e^{v\tau}(a + b\tau) + c$ for $a, b, c \geq 0$, then

$$Q(h, \tau, y_s, r + \phi(\tau^{n+1}), u + \phi(\tau^n)) - Q(h, \tau, y_s, r, v)$$
$$= \frac{1}{\Delta \tau} \left\{ \phi(\tau^{n+1}) - M^{-1}\phi(\tau^n) + M^{-1} \max_{k \in I(q)} \left[v^n(y, Q^n) - u^n(y, Q^n) \right] \right\}_s$$
$$\geq \frac{1}{\Delta \tau} \left[\phi(\tau^{n+1}) - M^{-1}\phi(\tau^n) \right]_s \quad (15)$$
$$= \frac{1}{\Delta \tau} \left[\phi(\tau^{n+1}) - \phi(\tau^n) \right] \geq b,$$

   where we assume that $M^{-1}\phi(\tau^n) = \phi(\tau^n)$. Actually this is true, since

$$M\phi(\tau) = \phi(\tau) - \frac{\sigma_0^2}{2} \Delta \tau e^{-2b\tau^{n+1}} A\phi(\tau) = \phi(\tau).$$

2. *Regularity*

   We now show that, for every h and $\phi \in V_j(G^j)$, the function:

$(\tau, y) \mapsto Q(h, \tau, y, \phi(\tau^{n+1}), \phi(\tau^n))$ is bounded and continuous in G^j and the function $r \mapsto Q(h, \tau, x, r, \phi(u^n))$ is uniformly continuous for bounded r, uniformly in $(\tau, x) \in G^j$.

Bounded: for every h, M^{-1} is bounded and for every $\phi^{n+1} \in V_j(G^j)$, ϕ^{n+1} is bounded. We know f is bounded and

$$
\left\| Q(h, \tau^{n+1}, y_s, \phi_m^{n+1}, [\phi^{n+1}]) \right\|_{L_\infty}
$$
$$
\leq \left\| \phi_m^{n+1}(y_s) \right\|_{L_\infty} + \left\| \left\{ M^{-1} \max_{k \in I(q)} \left(\phi_m^n(y; Q_m^n) + f(y, \tau^{n+1}; k) \right) \right\}_s \right\|_{L_\infty}. \tag{16}
$$

The function $(\tau, y) \mapsto Q(h, \tau, y, \phi(\tau^{n+1}), \phi(\tau^n))$ is bounded in G^j.

Continuous: since $\phi \in V_j(G^j)$, for any $(\tau^*, y^*) \in [\tau_0, \cdots, \tau_N] \times G^j$, if

$$
\left| (\tau, y) - (\tau^*, y^*) \right| \leq \delta,
$$

then

$$
\left\| \phi(\tau, y, q) - \phi(\tau^*, y^*, q) t \right\|_{L_\infty} \leq c_1 \epsilon(\delta),
$$

and

$$
\left\| f(y, \tau; k) - f(y^*, \tau^*; k) \right\|_{L_\infty} \leq c_2 \epsilon(\delta).
$$

Thus,

$$
\left| Q(h, \tau^{n+1}, y_s, \phi_m^{n+1}, [\phi^{n+1}]) - Q(h, \tau^*, y^*, \phi^*, [\phi^*]) \right|
$$
$$
\leq \left\| \phi(\tau, y, q_m) - \phi(\tau^*, y^*, q_m) \right\|_{L_\infty} +
$$
$$
\left| \left\{ M^{-1} \max_{k \in I(q)} \left[\phi(\tau, y, Q_m^n) - \phi(\tau^*, y^*, Q^*) + f(y_s, \tau; k) - f(y^*, \tau^*; k) \right] \right\}_s \right| \tag{17}
$$
$$
\leq c_1 \epsilon(\delta) + c_2 \epsilon(\delta).
$$

Uniformly continuous: for any bounded r_1, r_2, for any $\delta > 0$, if

$$
|r_1 - r_2| \leq \delta,
$$

then for any $(\tau, y) \in [\tau_0, \cdots, \tau_N] \times \varsigma^j$,

$$\left| Q(h, \tau, y_s, r_1, [\phi(\tau, y)]) - Q(h, \tau, y_s, r_2, [\phi(\tau, y)]) \right| = | r_1 - r_2 | \le \epsilon,$$

where $\epsilon = \delta$.

3. *Consistency*

For any $h = (\Delta \tau, \Delta y) > 0$, $(\tau, y) \in [\tau_0, \cdots, \tau_N] \times \varsigma^j$, and smooth function ϕ:

$$
\begin{aligned}
&\left| \phi_\tau + F(\tau, y_s, \phi, D\phi, D^2\phi) - Q(h, \tau, y_s, \phi_s^{n+1}, [\phi^{n+1}]) \right| \\
&= \left| \phi_{yy}^{n+1}(y_s) - \frac{d^2}{dx^2} \phi_h^{n+1}(y_s) + \max_{k \in l(q)} \left[\frac{d\phi}{d\tau} - \frac{\phi^{n+1} - \phi^n}{\Delta \tau} \right]_s \right| \\
&\le C_1 (\Delta y)^{p-2} \Box D_y^p \phi^{n+1} \Box_{L^2} + C_2 \Delta \tau \Box D_\tau^2 \phi^{n+1} \Box_{L^2}.
\end{aligned}
\tag{18}
$$

Furthermore, it is easy to show the stability condition

$$\| U^n \| \le \| f \|_{L_\infty}.$$

It follows immediately that Problem 4.2 has a unique solution. Therefore, we have the following convergence result.

Theorem 5.1 *Let U and w be the solutions to Problem 4.2 and Problem 4.1 respectively. There exists a constant C dependent only on μ, K in (K1),(A1) such that*

$$U - w \le C \max((\Delta y)^{1 - \frac{2}{p}}, \Delta \tau^{\frac{1}{4}})$$

and

$$U - w \ge -C \max((\Delta y)^{\frac{p-2}{3p-2}}, \Delta \tau^{\frac{1}{10}})$$

in G^j, where $\tilde{K} = |u|_1$.

Proof 5.1 First we notice that $|U_{0,h} - w_0| = 0$ and by Theorem 3.1 in Ref. [7] we have

$$U - w \le C \min_{\varepsilon > 0} \left(\varepsilon + E(\tilde{K}, h, \varepsilon) \right)$$

and

$$U - w \ge -C \min_{\varepsilon > 0} \left(\varepsilon^{1/3} + E(\tilde{K}, h, \varepsilon) \right)$$

where $E(\tilde{K}, h, \varepsilon) = \Delta y^{p-2} \varepsilon^{1-p} + \Delta \tau \varepsilon^{-3}$ and $\tilde{K} = |u|_1$. So we minimize w.r.t. ε the following functions

$$\varepsilon + \Delta y^{p-2} \varepsilon^{1-p} + \Delta \tau \varepsilon^{-3}$$

$$\varepsilon^{\frac{1}{3}} + \Delta y^{p-2} \varepsilon^{1-p} + \Delta \tau \varepsilon^{-3}.$$

By minimizing respectively in Δy, $\Delta \tau$, one finds that ε has to be like $\Delta y^{1-\frac{2}{p}}$, $\Delta \tau^{\frac{1}{4}}$ in the first case, and that $\varepsilon^{\frac{1}{3}}$ has to be like $\Delta y^{\frac{p-2}{3p-2}}$, $\Delta \tau^{\frac{1}{10}}$ in the second case. The result follows by taking $\varepsilon = \max(\Delta y^{1-\frac{2}{p}}, \Delta \tau^{\frac{1}{4}})$ in the first case and $\varepsilon^{\frac{1}{3}} = \max(\Delta y^{\frac{p-2}{3p-2}}, \Delta \tau^{\frac{1}{10}})$ in the second case.

6 Conclusion

This paper presented wavelet collocation methods for the numerical approximation of viscosity solutions of an HJB equation which arises in pricing swing options in a mean reverting world. The differential operator is formulated exactly and efficiently in the second generation interpolating wavelet spaces. The convergence was analyzed in the framework of viscosity solution theory.

References

[1] A. Lari-Lavassani, M. Simchi, A. Ware, A discrete valuation of swing options. *Canadian Applied Mathematics Quarterly*, **9(1)**, pp. 35–74, Spring 2001.
[2] P. Jaillet, E.R. Ronn, S. Tompaidis, Valuation of commodity-based swing options. *Management Science*, **50(7)**, pp. 909–921, July 2004.
[3] Joskow, Contract duration and relationship-specific investments: empirical evidence from coal markets. *American Economic Review*, **77**, pp. 168–185, 1987.
[4] U. Dörr, Valuation of Swing Options and Examination of Exercise Strategies by Monte Carlo Techniques. Master's thesis, University of Oxford, 2003.
[5] N. Meinshausen, B.M. Hambly, Monte-Carlo methods for the valuation of multiple-exercise options. *Mathematical Finance*, **14(4)**, pp. 557–583, 2004.
[6] M. Dahlgren, A continuous time model to price commodity-based swing options. *Review of Derivatives Research*, **8**, pp. 27–47, 2005.
[7] G. Barles, E. Jakobsen, Error bounds for monotone approximation schemes for Hamilton-Jacobi-Bellman equations. *SIAM Journal on Numerical Analysis*, **43(2)**, pp.540–558, 2005.

WIT Transactions on Information and Communication Technologies, Vol. 61, © 2014 WIT Press
www.witpress.com, ISSN 1743-3517 (on-line)

A new research of opportunistic spectrum access in cognitive networks

Zhang Li, Wei He, Yin Chen, Jinghua Huang
Faculty of Computer Science and Information Engineering, Hubei University, Wuhan, China

Abstract

Cognitive radio (CR) is a promising technology to handle the spectrum scarcity problem that was raised as the number of wireless devices in ad hoc networks increased. An analytical model was developed, which could evaluate the performance of a secondary user (SU) for opportunistic spectrum accessing in cognitive networks under non-saturation traffic conditions. Numerical results were given to show the performance of SUs in cognitive networks. In addition to using the unlicensed spectrum, by applying CR technology, the ad hoc devices would utilize the unused spectrum of the existing legacy systems in an opportunistic manner. Therefore, the network throughput would be increased. The results showed that the performance was improved in terms of blocking and dropping probabilities.

Keywords: cognitive network, wireless, secondary user.

1 Introduction

In recent years, the development of intelligent, adaptive wireless devices called cognitive radios (CRs), together with the introduction of secondary spectrum licensing, has led to a new paradigm in communications: cognitive networks. Cognitive networks are wireless networks that consist of several types of users: a primary user (PU) (the primary license holder of a spectrum band) and secondary users (SUs) (CRs) [1]. These cognitive users employ their cognitive abilities to communicate without harming the PUs [2]. Yet the study of cognitive networks is relatively new and many questions are to be answered. In this article we highlight some of the recent information theoretic limits, models, and design of these promising networks [3].

 WIT Transactions on Information and Communication Technologies, Vol. 61, © 2014 WIT Press
www.witpress.com, ISSN 1743-3517 (on-line)
doi:10.2495/MIIT130361

CRs—wireless devices with reconfigurable hardware and software (including transmission parameters and protocols)—are capable of delivering what these secondary devices would need: the ability to intelligently sense and adapt to their spectral environment [4]. By carefully sensing the PUs' presence and adapting their own transmission to guarantee a certain performance quality for the PUs, these cognitive devices could dramatically improve spectral efficiency [5]. Along with this newfound flexibility comes the challenge of understanding the limits of and designing protocols and transmission schemes to fully exploit these cognitive capabilities. In order to design practical and efficient protocols, the theoretical limits must be well understood [6].

CR is a promising technology to handle the spectrum scarcity problem that is raised as the number of wireless devices in ad hoc networks increases. CR is used to establish connections by using unused spectrum of today's legacy system for unlicensed users. An interesting overview of CR and current challenges in this technology was introduced in Ref. [7]. In CR networks, there are two types of users: the licensed or PUs that have the right to access the spectrum at any time, and the unlicensed or SUs that can access the spectrum in an opportunistic way without interfering the PUs.

A Markov chain analysis for spectrum access in licensed bands for CR was presented in Ref. [8]. The author only derived the blocking probability and dropping probability for the SUs operating in licensed band. In Ref. [9], a Markov chain model has been introduced to predict the behavior of open spectrum access in unlicensed bands, only. In Ref. [10], an efficient and fair MAC protocol as well as QoS provisioning for a CR device coexisting with the legacy users on both licensed and unlicensed bands, has been proposed. However, an analytical model was not investigated in Ref. [10]. There are several algorithms that be shown in Ref. [11]. The best approximation methods were discussed and had shown that the provided approximation method can achieve result very close to the result of the analytical model.

We present an analytical model to evaluate the performance of SUs operating under a heterogeneous spectrum environment of licensed and unlicensed bands. An SU has the choice to operate in any of those available bands. The reason that an SU operates in this heterogeneous spectrum environment is to increase the average spectrum usage for SUs. To achieve this goal, we assume that each SU is equipped with a CR that has the ability to detect the unused spectrum in a licensed band.

2 System model

In this section, in order to make the analytical model helpful and easy to discuss, assuming an idealistic system model to research performance of SUs is necessary. In order to rule out other factors of interference, we present an analytical model to evaluate the performance of SUs operating under a heterogeneous spectrum environment of licensed and unlicensed bands. An SU has the choice to operate in any of those available bands. The reason that an SU operates in this heterogeneous spectrum environment is to increase the average spectrum usage for SUs.

To achieve this goal, we assume that each SU is equipped with a CR that has the ability to detect the unused spectrum in a licensed band.

It is assumed for simplicity that the nodes of the CR ad hoc network under consideration are all homogeneous, statistically identical and independent. For each node, the following assumptions are made:

1. There are two types of available spectrum (channels), licensed and unlicensed spectrum. The licensed channels are referred to as primary channels (PCs), while the unlicensed channels are referred to as secondary channels (SCs).
2. The maximum numbers of PCs and SCs within the transmission range of a given node are assumed to be c1 and c2, respectively.
3. The PCs can be accessed by PUs and SUs. However, an SU using a PC is preempted in case of the appearance of the PU.
4. If there are free channels in both PCs and SCs, an SU has the choice to access one of those channels with equal probability. Otherwise, the SU will be blocked if both PCs and SCs are occupied.
5. If an SU connection is interrupted by a PU, then the SU will choose a free channel in either PCs or SCs. Otherwise, the SU will be dropped.
6. The total number of available channels for SUs depends on the number of busy PCs. This number is given as gi = c1 + c2 − i, where i is the number of busy PCs.
7. The arrival process of PUs and SUs is assumed to be Poisson with rate λ1 and λ2, respectively.
8. The call holding times of the PUs and SUs are assumed to be an exponential distribution with expectation 1/μ1 and 1/μ2, respectively.

3   Optimal sensing and access scheme

At first, let us understand the principle of Markov chain on the continuous time parameter. And then, according to system model assumption, using the principle of Markov chain we can get a series of balance equations. It is rather impractical to write all the balance equations in this paper and it is hard to summarize balance transition relations, as there are too many state boundaries for such a three-dimensional Markov chain. Therefore, it is very necessary to find an approximation method for the system states. At last, the best approximation methods will be discussed and shown named queuing algorithm. The provided approximation method can achieve result very close to the result of the analytical model.

For Markov chain on the continuous time parameter, if the continuous time parameter $\{X(t),\ t{\geq}0\}$, state space $E=\{0,1,2,\dots\}$, to any non-negative integer n, and any $0{<}t_1{<}t_2{<}\dots{<}t_n{<}t_{n+1}$ and $i_1,i_2,\dots i_n,i_{n+1}{\in}E$, there is

$$P\{X(t_{n+1})=i_{n+1}|x_{(tk)}=i_k,k=1,2,\dots,n\}=P\{X(t_{n+1})=i_{n+1}|x_{(tn)}=i_n\}, \qquad (1)$$

Therefore, $\{X(t), t \geq 0\}$ is Markov chain on the continuous time parameter. If (1) is just related to time interval t, but is not about starting time s, then $\{X(t), t \geq 0\}$ is continuous time parameters of homogeneous Markov chain.

If there is a system with a state set $E=\{0, 1, 2, ..., K\}$, let $N(t)$ be a system state at the time of t, and

$$P_{i,i+1}(\Delta t)=P\{N(t+\Delta t)=i+1|_{N(t)=i}\}=\lambda_i \Delta t+o(\Delta t), i=0, 1, 2, ..., K-1,$$

$$P_{i,i-1}(\Delta t)=P\{N(t+\Delta t)=i-1|_{N(t)=i}\}=\mu_i \Delta t+o(\Delta t), i=1, 2, ..., K,$$

$$P_{ij}(\Delta t)=P\{N(t+\Delta t)=j|_{N(t)=i}\}=o(\Delta t), |i-j| \geq 2, \tag{2}$$

When $\lambda_i>0$, $i=0, 1, ..., K-1$, $\mu_i>0$, $i=1, 2, ..., K$, therefore, $\{N(t), t \geq 0\}$ is birth and death process of the finite state $E=\{0, 1, 2, ..., K\}$ [12].

Understanding of the theoretical basis, we can presume

1. Let P_{1i} be the equilibrium probability distribution of $P_1(t)$.
2. Let $P_{2j|i}$ be the equilibrium conditional probability distribution of $P_2(t)$ given that i PUs are active.
3. Let P_{3k} be the equilibrium probability distribution of $P_3(t)$.
4. Many of the SUs are occupying the PCs; the others are occupying the SCs.
5. The $P_1(t)$ $P_2(t)$ $P_3(t)$ are a three-dimensional Markov process with state space

$$S = \left\{(i, j, k) \middle| 0 \leq i \leq c_1, 0 \leq j \leq c_1 - i, 0 \leq k \leq c_2\right\}.$$

Then, the joint probability $P_{i,j,k}$ can be written as

$$p_{i,j,k} = p_{2j|i} p_{1i} p_{3k} \tag{3}$$

First, the equilibrium conditional probability distribution P2j|i can be obtained as follows. Since the SUs will be affected by the PUs in PCs, the SUs can be regarded as M/M/c1 – i queueing system for i = 0, 1, 2, ..., c1. Thus, the conditional probability distribution P2j|i can be calculated by using the standard M/M/c1−i queueing system formula from Ref. [13]. That is

$$p_{2j|i} = \frac{1}{j!} \rho_2^j p_{20|i}, \quad 0 \leq j \leq c_1 - i, \rho_2 = \frac{\lambda_2}{\mu_2} \tag{4}$$

Second, we will obtain the steady state probability P1i of the number of PUs in progress. The number of ongoing PUs will not be affected by the SUs. Therefore, from the PUs' point of view, the existence of SUs in the system will be neglected. Hence, the number of PUs in progress can be regarded as M/M/c1 queueing system. Thus, the probability distribution P1i can be derived by using the standard M/M/c1 queueing system formula from Ref. [13]. That is,

$$P_{1i} = \frac{1}{i!} \rho_1^i P_{10}, \quad 0 \le i \le c_1, \rho_1 = \frac{\lambda_1}{\mu_1} \tag{5}$$

Finally, since the number of SUs in SCs is not affected by the PUs, the probability distribution of P3k can be calculated by using the standard M/M/c2 formula from Ref. [13]. That is,

$$P_{3k} = \frac{1}{i!} \rho_3^k P_{30}, \quad 0 \le i \le c_2, \rho_3 = \frac{\lambda_3}{\mu_3} \tag{6}$$

where $\rho_3 = \lambda_3/\mu_3$. Substituting for P2j|j, P1i and P3k from (4)–(6) into (3), we get

$$P_{i,j,k} = \frac{\rho_1^i \rho_2^j \rho_3^k}{i!j!k!} P_0, 0 \le i \le c_1, 0 \le j \le c_1 - i, 0 \le k \le c_2 \tag{7}$$

for $0 \le i \le c1$, $0 \le j \le c1 - i$ and $0 \le k \le c2$, where P0 = P20|iP10P30 and it is given by using the normalization condition

$$\sum_{i=0}^{c_1} \sum_{j=0}^{c_1-i} \sum_{k=0}^{c_2} P_{i,j,k} = 1$$

4   Performance metrics

Once the probabilities Pi,j,k are obtained, the blocking and dropping probabilities for SUs can be obtained. An SU gets blocked if upon its arrival, all the PCs and SCs are occupied. The blocking probability, Pb can be written as

$$P_b = \sum_{i=0}^{c_1} \lambda P_{i,c_1-i,c_2} \tag{8}$$

An SU is dropped if a PU arrives and transmits in the same channel that is already occupied by it and if there are no other free PCs and SCs. In the case, the dropping probability, Pd can be written as

$$P_b = \sum_{i=0}^{c_1-1} \frac{\lambda_1}{c_1 - i} P_{i,c_1-i,c_2} \tag{9}$$

The transmission of an SU is not completed when it is blocked upon the moment of its arrival or dropped during its transmission. Therefore, the SU non-

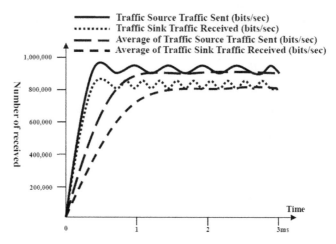

Figure 1: The network load and throughput.

completion probability Pnc can be written as Pnc = Pb+ (1 − Pb) Pd. Another important performance metric is the throughput of SUs, called T, that is defined as the average number of service completions for SUs per second. Therefore,

$$T = \sum_{i=0}^{c_1} \sum_{j=1}^{c_1-i} \sum_{k=1}^{c_2} (j + k)(1 - P_{nc})p_{i,j,k} \qquad (10)$$

5 Numerical results

We will use the previously derived analytical model to investigate the performance of SUs with different numbers of PCs, c_1. The number of SCs, c_2, is set to three channels since the IEEE 802.11b standard supports three nonoverlapping channels.

Figure 1 shows the performance metrics in terms of the arrival rate of PUs, λ_1, with different number of the PCs and SCs. The blocking probability increases with the increase of λ_1 due to the high traffic load of PUs. As the arrival rate of PUs increases, an SU has a higher possibility to be interrupted and hence the dropping rate is high.

Figure 2 depicts the throughput of SUs using the PCs only, $c_1 = 6$ and SUs using a heterogeneous spectrum environment of the PCs and SCs with the same number of channels. The throughput of SUs using the heterogeneous spectrum environment outperforms the other one. This can be explained as follows: as the arrival rate for the PU increases, the number of available channels for SUs decreases. Therefore, the throughput of SUs using the PCs only decreases. On the other hand, in heterogeneous spectrum environment, the interrupted SUs can switch to the SUs if there are free channels. Hence, those SUs will continue its transmission without interruption and therefore the throughput of SUs here is better than the throughput using PCs only.

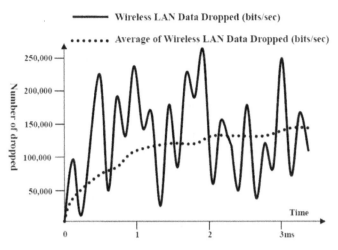

Figure 2: Dropping probability of SUs.

6 Conclusions

It is investigated that an analytical model using a three-dimensional Markov chain to evaluate the performance of SUs operating under a heterogeneous spectrum environment of licensed and unlicensed bands. Different performance metrics are obtained. As a result of using a heterogeneous environment of licensed and unlicensed bands, an improvement in terms of the blocking, dropping and throughput of SUs is obtained.

Acknowledgment

This research work was supported by Project of Department of Education of HuBei Province (Q20120112).

References

[1] C. Cordeiro, K. Challapali, D. Birru, et al., IEEE 802.22: an introduction to the first wireless standard based on cognitive radios. *Journal of Communications*, **1(1)**, pp. 38–47, 2006.

[2] Q. Zhao, L. Tong, A. Swami, et al., Decentralized cognitive mac for opportunistic spectrum access in ad hoc networks: a pomdp framework. *IEEE Journal on Selected Areas in Communications*, **25(3)**, pp. 589–600, 2007.

[3] L.C. Wang, C.W. Wang, F. Adachi, Load-balancing spectrum decision for cognitive radio networks. *IEEE Journal on Selected Areas in Communications*, **29(4)**, pp. 757–769, 2011.

[4]   Q. Xiao, Y. Li, M. Zhao, et al., Opportunistic channel selection approach under collision probability constraint in cognitive radio systems. *Computer Communications*, **32(18)**, pp. 1914–1922, 2009.

[5]   I.F. Akyildiz, W.Y. Lee, K.R. Chowdhury, Crahns: cognitive radio ad hoc networks. *Ad Hoc Networks*, **7(5)**, pp. 810–836, 2009.

[6]   N. Mittal, S. Krishnamurthya, R. Chandrasekarana, et al., On neighbor discovery in cognitive radio networks. *Journal of Parallel and Distributed Computing*, **69(7)**, pp. 623–637, 2009.

[7]   H. Tembine, E. Altman, R. El-Azouzi, et al., Bio-inspired delayed evolutionary game dynamics with networking applications. *Telecommunication Systems*, **47(1)**, pp. 137–152, 2011.

[8]   K. Subramanian, S. Suresh, A meta-cognitive sequential learning algorithm for neuro-fuzzy inference system. *Applied Soft Computing*, **12(11)**, pp. 3603–3614, 2012.

[9]   R. Savitha, S. Suresh, N. Sundararajan, Metacognitive learning in a fully complex-valued radial basis function neural network. *Neural Computation*, **24(5)**, pp. 1297–1328, 2012.

[10] D.E. Charilas, A.D. Panagopoulos, A survey on game theory applications in wireless networks. *Computer Networks*, **54(18)**, pp. 3421–3430, 2010.

[11] F.N. Pavlidou, G. Koltsidas, Game theory for routing modeling in communication networks—a survey. *Journal of Communications and Networks*, **10(3)**, pp. 268–286, 2008.

[12] R. Dwarakanath Vallam, A.A. Kanagasabapathy, C. Siva Ram Murthy, A non-cooperative game-theoretic approach to channel assignment in multi-channel multi-radio wireless networks. *Wireless Networks*, **17(2)**, pp. 411–435, 2011.

[13] M. Canales, J.R. Gállego, Potential game for joint channel and power allocation in cognitive radio networks. *IET Electronics Letters*, **46(24)**, pp. 1632–1634, 2010.

Research on the query co-occurrence networks

Lan Rao[1], Zhunchen Luo[2], Jintao Tang[2], Ting Wang[2]
[1]College of Humanities and Social Science, National University of Defense Technology, Changsha, China
[2]College of Computer, National University of Defense Technology, Changsha, China

Abstract

The co-occurrence of queries in the query logs can be characterized by complex networks analysis. In this paper, we first construct a query co-occurrence network from query logs. As there are a large number of named entities which are persons (NEP) in query logs, therefore we also construct an NEP co-occurrence network. Then we carry out comparative analysis of characteristics of complex networks in the query co-occurrence network, NEP co-occurrence network and word co-occurrence network. Experimental results show that all three networks display a typical small-world effect and the scale-free property.
Keywords: query log, complex networks, small world, scale-free.

1 Introduction

Networks are all around us. They can be classified into two parts: the first type of networks can be tangible objects in the Euclidean space, such as the Internet, electric power grids and subway systems; the other can be entities defined in an abstract space, such as networks of social relationship between individuals and networks of biochemical reactions in biological systems. However, there are thousands of odd phenomena in these networks, the forming and interaction of them are based on simple and powerful rules. A lot of work has been studied in different areas of networks. Here we study a new area of network which is formed based on co-occurrence of queries from query logs. This work can help us better understand the relationship between queries in search engine and potentially improve the performance of information retrieval.

 WIT Transactions on Information and Communication Technologies, Vol. 61, © 2014 WIT Press
www.witpress.com, ISSN 1743-3517 (on-line)
doi:10.2495/MIIT130371

Erdős and and Rényi firstly constructed a model for large called random networks [1]. They studied it exhaustively and rigorously and gave the network the name ER model by which it is most often known today. In the ER model, a random graph is likely to be connected only if at least $N*\ln(N)/2$ edges are present for large N. Put another way, if one increases the number of edges added randomly to a graph, then there is a sudden change in the connectedness property of the network. Since there is no large network, the verifying of prediction of the ER theory was difficult. However, driven by the computerization of data acquisition, it is available to collect the such topological information and understand the dynamical and topological stability of them [2,3].

Watts and Strogatz firstly proposed the small-world model which is a less sophisticated but more tractable model of a network with high transitivity [4]. This model starts a network built on a low-dimensional regular lattice. Then it adds or moves edges to create a "shortcuts," which joins remote parts of the lattice to one another. Barabási and Albert found World Wide Web has the property which the vertex connectivities follow a scale-free power-law distribution [5]. There are two generic mechanisms for this feature: (i) networks expand continuously by the addition of new vertices, and (ii) new vertices are more likely to attach to sites that are already well connected.

The above studies triggered many researchers to study networks in different areas. One of important area is language. The basic idea is that language can be seen as a complex adaptive system. This system solves the problem of developing a shared communication system.

With the rapid development of the Internet and richness of information resources, search engine has become the main way for people to obtain information. It is easy for people to issue some queries to retrieve webpages in search engines (e.g., Google, Bing, and Yahoo!). Therefore, the study of query logs has become a hot research area. As the networks constructed based on the co-occurrence of words in sentences, it also exists networks which constructed based on the co-occurrence of queries in query logs. Moreover, the queries contain a certain named entities which are persons (NEP). There also exist networks based on the co-occurrence of NEPs. Analysis of these two networks can bridge the gap between the characteristics of language in query logs and users' search behaviors. It can also help query expansion which could improve the performance of information retrieval. Therefore, in this paper we compare the characteristics of different networks among the co-occurrence of queries, NEPs from *SogouQ* query log and co-occurrence words in sentences from *People Daily Corpus* (see Section 4).

The rest of the paper is organized as follows: in Section 2, we give some concepts and definitions of complex networks. In Section 3, we introduce the method of constructing our networks. We give the experimental results in Section 4. Finally we conclude our study.

2 Basic concepts on complex networks

The previous research of networks is mainly studying the characteristics of small-world effect and scale-free property. Assume there is an undirected graph $G(V, E)$.

Where V is the set of nodes and E is the set of edges. The number of nodes is $|V|$ and the number of edges is $|E|$.

2.1 Small-world networks

Given a particular network, it would be interesting to know the minimum distance between every pair of nodes. Thus, we can define d_{ij} the minimum distance between the two nodes i and j. The degree of node i is $<k_i>$ which indicates the number of different nodes directly connected. A more useful magnitude to characterize the networks is the average path length d, defined as the mean value of the geodesics between every pair of nodes in the network:

$$d = \frac{1}{N(N-1)} \sum_{i,\, j \in N, i \neq j} d_{ij} \tag{1}$$

A graph in which, although most pairs of nodes are not directly connected to each other, they can nonetheless be in touch by a small number of steps is called a small-world network, since it captures this so-called phenomenon of strangers being linked by a mutual acquaintance (also known as six degrees of separation . Assume the average degree of nodes in a graph is $<k>$, if the graph is a small-world network, it follows:

$$d \approx \frac{\ln(n)}{\ln(<k>)} \tag{2}$$

Clustering of a node is the number of triangles in the graph, or in other words, how likely is that, if a node i has two neighbors, say j and k, then the nodes j and k are also linked to each other. First, given a node i and the subgraph of its k_i neighbors G_i, we can define the local clustering coefficient of node i as the ratio between the actual number of edges in the subgraph e_i, and the maximum possible number of them in G_i:

$$d = \frac{2e_i}{k_i(k_i-1)} = \frac{\sum_{j,m} a_{ij} a_{jm} a_{mi}}{k_i(k_i-1)} \tag{3}$$

where a_{ij} indicates whether the nodes i and j are directly connected or not ($a_{ij} = 1$ means they are directly connected, $a_{ij} = 0$ means they are not). Then we can define the clustering coefficient of the whole network, as the average of c_i over all the nodes in it:

$$C = \frac{1}{N} \sum_{i=1}^{N} c_i \tag{4}$$

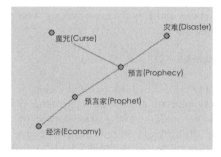

Figure 1: Subgraph of query co-occurrence network.

Notice that, by definition, both the local and the global clustering coefficient satisfy: $0 \leq c_i \leq 1$ and $0 \leq C \leq 1$. For a random network which includes N nodes, when the value of N is large, the value of C is much less than 1. But massive real complex networks exhibit significant aggregation effect, which have low values for the average path length, but relatively high values for the clustering coefficient.

2.2 Scale-free networks

A most basic topological characterization of the network as a whole is the degree distribution. We can define the degree distribution of the graph $\Pr(k)$, as the probability that a node randomly chosen from the network has k neighbors. If a graph has a power law distribution ($\Pr(k) \propto k^{-r}$), it is called a scale-free network.

The most notable characteristic in a scale-free network is the relative commonness of vertices with a degree that greatly exceeds the average. The highest-degree nodes are often called "hubs," and are thought to serve specific purposes in their networks, although this depends greatly on the domain. We will study whether the networks based on the co-occurrence of queries has this characteristic or not.

3   Query co-occurrence networks construction

The construction of word co-occurrence networks in the language are from large-scale corpus. Moreover many Asian languages such as Chinese do not delimit words by white-space, therefore it needs word segmentation. However, the construction of query co-occurrence networks is based on the co-occurrence of queries in query logs, the form of queries are usually words, phrases, or short sentences which are all meaningful words sequences. Hence, we do not use word segmentation for queries in networks construction.

3.1 Query co-occurrence networks

The method of constructing the query co-occurrence networks is simple. We first choose the queries which contain more than two words sequences in our Chinese

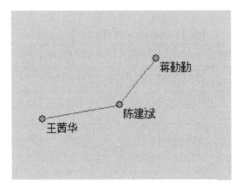

Figure 2: NEP co-occurrence network.

query log. The judgement of the query is whether it contains white-space or not. We take each of words sequence as the node in our graph. If two words sequence (two nodes) appear in a query, we build an edge in the graph. Fox example, there is a query "唐山 地震 (Tangshan Earthquake)." It contains two meaningful words sequences "唐山 (Tangshan)" and "地震 (Earthquake)." We take these two words sequence as two nodes in our graph and also create an edge to connect them. Figure 1 shows a subgraph of query co-occurrence network constructed by our query logs.

3.2 NEP co-occurrence networks

Users usually issue some NEPs to get information of people in search engine. Moreover, it has become a hot research area to study the relationship of people. Therefore, we construct the NEP co-occurrence networks which are based on the richness of NEPs in query logs and study the characteristics of them.

We choose the queries which contain more than two NEPs to construct the NEP co-occurrence networks in our Chinese query logs. Each query also needs to contain white-space. But it is difficult to judge whether each words sequence is NEP or not. Moreover, there is a large number of NEP in query logs. It is infeasible to manually label all the queries. Therefore, we use *Stanford Named Entity Recognizer*[1] to label these queries automatically. We take each of words sequence, which is identified as NEP, as the node in our graph. If two NEPs appear in a query, we build an edge in the graph. Fox example, there is a query "陈建斌 蒋勤勤 (Chen-Jianbin Jiang-qinqin)."[2] It includes two NEPs "陈建斌 (Chen-Jianbin)" and "蒋勤勤 (Jiang-qinqin)." We take these two NEPs as two nodes in our graph and create an edge to connect them. Figure 2 shows a subgraph of NEP co-occurrence networks constructed by our query logs.

---

[1] http://nlp.stanford.edu/software/CRF-NER.shtml.
[2] They are a couple and both are famous actors.

Table 1: Statistics of Three Networks.

	Query Co-occurrence Network	NEP Co-occurrence Network	Word Co-occurrence Network
N	0.45×10^5	1.50×10^3	0.20×10^5
E	0.46×10^5	1.03×10^3	0.30×10^6
$<k>$	2.04	1.37	30.19
C	$6.35*10^{-3}$	$1.25*10^{-2}$	$5.93*10^{-1}$
C_{random}	$3.08*10^{-5}$	$1.00*10^{-8}$	$1.51*10^{-3}$
d	5.66	4.57	2.22
d_{random}	14.09	14.63	3.21

4 Experiments

We use Search Engine *Click-through Log (SogouQ)*[3] as our corpus to construct the networks. SogouQ contains search engine click-through log data collected by sogou.com in June 2008. As the methods introduced in Section 3, we construct the query co-occurrence network and NEP co-occurrence network. Additionally the network, constructed based on the co-occurrence of words in sentences, is another important network which can potentially help query expansion improving information retrieval. Hence, we use *People Daily Corpus*[4] to construct word co-occurrence network. The judgement is whether two words appear in the same sentence. Then we use *Pajek*[5] to analysis these three networks.

Table 1 gives some statistics of three networks. Where N is the number of nodes, E is the number of edges, $<k>$ is the average degree of nodes, C is global clustering coefficient and d is average path length in a graph. Additionally C_{random} and d_{random} are clustering coefficient and average path length of random networks with the same N and E produced by *Pajek*.

In Table 1, we can see that the average path length of all three networks are shorter than the random networks with the same number of nodes and edges, but the global clustering coefficient of three networks are much bigger than the random networks. And these networks contain the characteristic of small-world networks. It shows that users, however, use a large number of queries to get information in search engines, the path from one query to another query is short in these graphs. Given a query, it is easy to associate with another query when a user issues it. Moreover, it also shows the speed of query expansion might be fast and it is not difficult to get rich expanded queries. All these can potentially help automatic query expansion, which can improve the performance of information retrieval.

---

[3] http://www.sogou.com/labs/dl/q-e.html.
[4] http://www.icl.pku.edu.cn/icl_res/.
[5] http://vlado.fmf.uni-lj.si/pub/networks/pajek/.

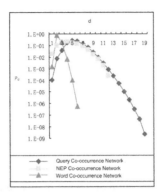

Figure 3: Distribution of distances in different networks.

Figure 3 gives the distribution of distances for two nodes in different networks. pd is the proportion of all pairs of nodes which the distance is d in a graph.[6] If the shorter of the distance of two words sequences (or NEPs), the closer of these two nodes. For example, in one network exists one path "走私-赖昌星-杨钰莹-照片 (Smuggling-Lai Changxing-Yang Yuying-Photo)." The relation between "走私 (Smuggling)" and "赖昌星 (Lai Changxing)" is closer than the relation between "走私 (Smuggling)" and "照片 (Photo)." We can see that the distance d is mainly distributed from 3 to 7 in networks which are constructed by our query log. And most distances for two nodes in NEP co-occurrence network are shorter than the distance of nodes in query co-occurrence network. It shows the relation of two NEPs are closer than two words sequences in query logs. Although most distances for two nodes in word co-occurrence network are shorter than the other two networks, it does not show the relation of two words in word co-occurrence network is closer, since these relations are mainly based on the grammar of language, but the relation of words sequences in query logs is based on semantic of language, which is more helpful for query expansion.

Figure 4 gives the distribution of degree in different networks. We can see that all the graphs have power law distribution which includes scale-free property. We also found the distribution of degree in word co-occurrence network has two parts, which is different from the other two networks constructed from our query log. The reason might be that the word co-occurrence network is constructed based on the grammar of language and query co-occurrence networks are constructed based on the semantic of language.

5 Conclusion

In this study, we use query logs to construct the query co-occurrence network and NEP co-occurrence network. We compare the characteristic of networks with the word co-occurrence network. We find all three networks display a typical small-world effect and the scale-free property.

---

[6] Here, we ignore all the nodes which are isolated in graphs.

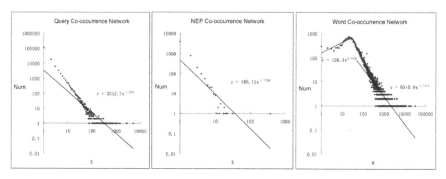

Figure 4: Distribution of degree in different networks.

Acknowledgment

This research is supported by the National Natural Science Foundation of China (Grant Nos. 61170156 and 61202337).

References

[1] P. Erdős, A. Rényi, On the evolution of random graphs. *Magyar Tud. Akad. Mat. Kutató Int. Közl*, **5**, pp. 17–61, 1960.
[2] L.A. Adamic, B.A. Huberman, Power-law distribution of the World Wide Web. *Science*, **287(24)**, p. 2115, 2000.
[3] M.E. Newman, The structure and function of complex networks. *SIAM Review*, **45**, pp. 167–256, 2003.
[4] D. Watts, S. Strogatz, The small world problem. *Collective Dynamics of Small-World Networks*, **393**, pp. 440–442, 1998.
[5] A.L. Barabási, R. Albert, Emergence of scaling in random networks. *Science*, **286**, pp. 509–512, 1999.

A novel method for analyzing nonlinear EEG signal using local SVM method

Lisha Sun[1], Zhifei Su[1], Minfen Shen[2]
[1]College of Engineering, Shantou University, Guangdong, China
[2]Shantou Polytechnic, Shantou, Guangdong, China

Abstract

Modeling of clinical electroencephalography (EEG) signals is an important problem in clinical diagnosis of brain diseases. The method using support vector machine (SVM) based on the structure risk minimization provides us an effective kind of learning machine. But solving the quadratic programming problem for training SVM becomes a bottle-neck of using SVM because of the long time of SVM training. In this paper, a local-SVM method is proposed for modeling EEG signals. The local method is presented for improving the speed of the prediction of EEG signals. Furthermore, this proposed model is used to detect epilepsy from EEG signals in which dynamic characteristics are different between normal and epilepsy EEG signals. The experimental results show that the training of the local-SVM obtains a good behavior. In addition, the local SVM method significantly improves the prediction and detection precision.

Keywords: EEG, signal processing, prediction, support, modeling.

1 Introduction

The electroencephalography (EEG) signals are very complicated pseudo-random signals and serve as windows for us to understand the cerebral activities because these signals are the synthetic reflection of the electricity activities of cerebral tissue and brain function status. If we can predict the variation of EEG signals, high-risk operation can be avoided when the patient incurs cerebral disease [1]. In fact, the EEG signal has the characteristics of chaos, that is, the learning machine is a common technique for modeling and predicting the chaotic signal.

In this paper, we are concerned with prediction performance of the learning machine. The traditional learning machines, such as BP neural network and RBF neural network, are based on the empirical risk minimization. In the case of finite training samples, there is a contradiction between the training precision and generalization. Sometimes reducing the training precision would increase the prediction risk because of the over-learning. In recent years, the support vector machine (SVM), according to statistical theory, has become a hot point and is widely used in classification and regression [2]. SVM applies structure risk minimization instead of empirical risk minimization. So it has better characteristic features of generalization, global optimization and sparse solution. SVM avoids the method selection and over-learning problems effectively and solves the problems of a non-linear, dimensionality curse and local minimum efficiently.

However in practice, globally training SVM will meet a great obstacle when the number of the training samples is large. To solve this problem, combining with some other optimization algorithms, we present a new method based on the idea of the local method, namely the local SVM. This new method inherits characteristics of the local method, which has the advantage of small samples, simplicity and high precision [3]. Combined with these characteristics, an accurate high-speed prediction method is expected to predict the EEG signals.

This paper is organized as follows. In Section 2, the ε-SVM for the prediction of chaotic signal was introduced. In Section 3, a local method was proposed to improve the training speed of SVM in prediction. In Section 4, the proposed method was applied to the Logistic chaotic sequence and real EEG signal. The conclusion was given in Section 5.

2   Modeling with SVM

Assuming the finite measured data samples $(\mathbf{x}_1, y_1), \cdots, (\mathbf{x}_l, y_l) \in (\mathbf{X} \times R)$ were obtained from a sample set $P(\mathbf{x}, y)(\mathbf{x} \in R^m, y \in R)$, which follows a certain distribution. The regression of SVM is to find a real function $f(\mathbf{x}) = \mathbf{w}\square\phi(\mathbf{x}_i) + b$ to fit these samples that make the risk function $R[f] = \int c(\mathbf{x}, y, f)dP(\mathbf{x}, y)$ minimum. Where c is the loss function, the error between the observed y and prediction $f(\mathbf{x})$ could be measured by a so called ε insensitive loss function described by Eq. (1):

$$\left| y_i - f(\mathbf{x}_i, \mathbf{x}) \right|_\varepsilon = \max\left\{ 0, \left| y_i - f(\mathbf{x}_i, \mathbf{x}) \right| - \varepsilon \right\} \tag{1}$$

In most cases, the probability density $P(\mathbf{x}, y)$ is not known. It cannot make the risk function minimum directly. Therefore, the minimum problem of Eq. (2) is proposed to substitute the risk function.

$$E(\mathbf{w}) = \frac{1}{2}(\mathbf{w}\square\mathbf{w}) + C\frac{1}{l}\sum_{i=1}^{l}\left| y_i - f(\mathbf{x}_i, \mathbf{x}) \right|_\varepsilon \tag{2}$$

Where $\left| y_i - f(\mathbf{x}_i, \mathbf{x}) \right|_\varepsilon = \max\left\{0, \left| y_i - f(\mathbf{x}_i, \mathbf{x}) \right| - \varepsilon \right\}$ is the ε insensitive loss function. The first term of the right side of Eq. (2) represents the complexity of $f(\mathbf{x})$, the second term represents the loss. C represents the compromise relationship between complexity and loss. It is equivalent to

$$
\begin{cases}
\min\limits_{w, \xi_i, \xi_i^*, b} \dfrac{1}{2}(\mathbf{w} \cdot \mathbf{w}) + C\dfrac{1}{l}\sum\limits_{i=1}^{l}(\xi_i + \xi_i^*) \\
s.t. \quad (\mathbf{w} \cdot \phi(\mathbf{x}_i) + b) - y_i \leq \varepsilon + \xi_i \\
\quad\quad y_i - (w \cdot \phi(\mathbf{x}_i) + b) \leq \varepsilon + \xi_i^* \\
\quad\quad \xi_i, \xi_i^* \geq 0
\end{cases}
\tag{3}
$$

It can yield the dual optimization problem:

$$
\begin{cases}
\max\limits_{\alpha, a^*} \sum\limits_{i=1}^{l}\left[\alpha_i^*(y_i - \varepsilon) - \alpha_i(y_i + \varepsilon)\right] \\
\quad - \dfrac{1}{2}\sum\limits_{i=1}^{l}\sum\limits_{j=1}^{l}(\alpha_i - \alpha_i^*)(\alpha_j - \alpha_i^*)K(\mathbf{x}_i, \mathbf{x}_j) \\
s.t. \quad \sum\limits_{i=1}^{l}(\alpha_i - \alpha_i^*) = 0 \quad 0 \leq \alpha_i, \alpha_i^* \leq C / l, i = 1\cdots l
\end{cases}
\tag{4}
$$

where $K(\mathbf{x}_i, \mathbf{x}_j) = \phi(\mathbf{x}_i)\phi(\mathbf{x}_j)$ is kernel. The linear kernels $K(x, y) = xy$, polynomial kernels $K(x, y) = (xy + 1)^d$ and RBF kernels $K(x, y) = \exp(-\left\| x - y \right\|_2^2 / \sigma^2)$ are commonly used. From Eq. (4), we can get the optimal solutions of α_i and α_i^*, denoted by $\bar{\alpha} = [\bar{\alpha}_1, \bar{\alpha}_1^*, \bar{\alpha}_2, \bar{\alpha}_2^*, \cdots, \bar{\alpha}_l, \bar{\alpha}_l^*]^T$. Then the dynamic system model can be obtained by solving the dual optimization problem. For the input vector $\mathbf{x}$, the prediction can be deduced from:

$$
f(\mathbf{x}) = \mathbf{w} \cdot \phi(\mathbf{x}) + \bar{b} = \sum\limits_{i-1}^{l}(\bar{\alpha}_i - \bar{\alpha}_i^*)K(\mathbf{x}_i, \mathbf{x}) + \bar{b}
\tag{5}
$$

where $\bar{b}$ can be gotten by Eq. (6) or Eq. (7). If $\bar{\alpha}_j$ is chosen, then

$$
\bar{b} = y_j - \sum\limits_{i=1}^{l}(\bar{\alpha}_i^* - \bar{\alpha}_i)K(\mathbf{x}_i, \mathbf{x}_j) + \varepsilon \quad \bar{\alpha}_j \in (0, C / l)
\tag{6}
$$

If $\bar{\alpha}_k^*$ is chosen, then $\bar{b} = y_k - \sum_{i=1}^{l} (\bar{\alpha}_i^* - \bar{\alpha}_i) K(\mathbf{x}_i, \mathbf{x}_k) - \varepsilon \bar{\alpha}_k^* \in (0, C / l)$ (7)

3 Local ε-SVM model

When the samples become large, training the SVM has become the bottle-neck of SVM application. Colin Campbell made an overview of existing training algorithm. In that overview, he mainly introduced sequential minimal optimization (SMO) algorithm. The algorithm aimed to improve the SVM training speed in the application of classification or regression. SMO is based on the decomposition. It iteratively selects two points and optimizing the target function with respect to them. Then the optimization problem becomes an analytic solution, so the problem of solving the quadratic programming is avoided. Although it needs more iterations, the iteration takes less computing time. Therefore, the total time consumed is reduced. The advantage of SMO is that there is no need to store the kernels matrix and there is no need to use a quadratic programming package. The SMO algorithm will be used in this paper.

Combining with the local method, this paper proposes a local ε-SVM. In the prediction process, the local method selects the vectors which are close to the target vector. Meanwhile, it uses these vectors to train the SVM by SMO algorithm. This increases the training speed because of the small samples. The following section introduces using the local ε-SVM for one-step prediction in chaotic signal.

Firstly, for a chaotic sequence $x(t)$, we need to select the embedding dimension m and delay time τ, reconstructing the phase space accordingly based on the Takens' embedding theorem. The final vector $\mathbf{X}(N)$ is used as the input target vector to predict the next point of the sequence, computing the distance between the target vector and preformed N-1 vectors as in Eq. (8)

$$d(i) = \|\mathbf{X}(i) - \mathbf{X}(N)\|, i = 1, 2, \ldots\ldots N - 1 \qquad (8)$$

Then, the p distances is selected to be closest to the vector $\mathbf{X}(N)$.

$$\mathbf{X}_r^n = [x(t_r), x(t_r + \tau), \cdots x(t_r + (m - 1)\tau)]^T, r = 1, 2, \cdots p \qquad (9)$$

$$D_r = x(t_r + T), r = 1, 2, \cdots p \qquad (10)$$

For one-step prediction, set $T = t_r + m\tau$.

$\mathbf{X}_r^n, r = 1 \cdots p$ is taken as the input vectors of the SVM and $D_r, r = 1, 2, \cdots p$ is taken as the output values gained from the training of the SVM. We can use $\mathbf{X}(N)$ as an input vectors for the SVM, then the prediction value $x(n+T)$ can be obtained. Finally, iterate the step above to obtain the prediction values for signal processing.

Table 1: MSE of Four Learning Machines.

	BP	RBF	Global ε-SVM	Local-SVM
MSE	3.0882 e-4	3.1979 e-4	3.6377 e-5	3.0000 e-5
Time (s)	–	–	24.13	11.97

4 Clinical EEG prediction

4.1 Simulation with logistic sequence

To verify the prediction performance, a 1000 point Logistic signal was generated from Eq. (11) for modeling and predicting.

$$x(n+1) = ax(n)(1-x(n)) \tag{11}$$

Initial value was 0.8 and a=4. The first 800 points were used for training the SVM, and the following 200 points were used for testing. According to the Takens' theorem, the embedding dimension was set m=3 and the delay time was set τ=1 to reconstruct the phase space. The hidden center of BP neural network and RBF neural network were both set to 10 and the training precision was 0.005. The parameters were set as C=1000 and ε=0.01 in training the ε-SVM. In the local SVM training, the close point was selected as p=20. The mean square error (MSE) was used here to evaluate the prediction performance as defined in Eq. (12):

$$e_{MSE} = \frac{1}{N} \sum_{k=1}^{N} \left| x(k) - \hat{x}(k) \right|^2 \tag{12}$$

Table 1 lists the prediction MSE of four learning machines. It is obvious that the MSE of SVM is less than the neural network. It shows that the SVM, which is based on the structure risk minimization, performs better than the neural network which is based on the empirical risk minimization.

On the Legend computer which has Pentium(R) 4 CPU 1.80GHz, 256M RAM memory, with the platform of matlab7.0, using the function "QUADPROG" which embeds in the matlab7.0 to solve the global ε-SVM directly, the training time was more than 24 h. In the same settings, training the local ε-SVM with the function "QUADPROG" needed 81 s. Also applying the SMO algorithm in the LIBSVM toolbox, the time for training global ε-SVM was 24.13 s. While for local ε-SVM, training 20 close samples only needed 0.0062 s, the total times for predicting 200 point including the time used in sorting and searching the close points is 11.97 s. Therefore, we can conclude that local ε-SVM has not only smaller prediction MSE, but also fast prediction speed. Figure 1 shows the result of prediction for logistic sequence.

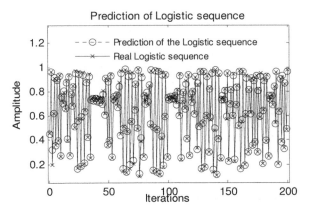

Figure 1: Prediction of logistic sequence based on local SVM.

4.2 Test with real EEG signal

To evaluate the performance of the proposed method, the EEG signal, taken from the Mental Health Center in Shantou University, is analyzed. The EEG signal records were collected from a normal person who was closing his/her eyes and kept silent and level-headed. Fourteen electrodes were placed according to the international standard 10–20 system. In this section, a segment of these real spontaneous EEG signals with 1000 data points was selected for the purpose. The first 800 points were used for training the SVM and the following 200 points were used for testing. The embedding dimension was selected as $m=5$ and delay time as $\tau=1$. Then a constructed phase space was constructed according to the Takens' theorem. The training parameters $C=1000$ and $\tau=0.01$ were set in both global ε-SVM and local ε-SVM. Close point was selected as $p=25$.

Table 2 lists the training MSE of two SVM and its iteration times using SMO in the LIBSVM toolbox. Figure 2 shows the prediction result of global and local SVM and their prediction errors are depicted in Figure 3. It is easy to see from Figure 2 that the prediction MSE of global SVM is 3.1084e-3 and the prediction MSE of local SVM is 2.2000e-3. The local SVM improves the prediction precision. Also, in Figure 3, there is some crackling noise in the global prediction, and the prediction at some peak points is not good. This may be caused by the noise in the EEG, or a different dynamic system model. In fact, the local method always selects the close points, that is to say it selects the same dynamic system model with the target vector $\mathbf{X}(N)$ more or less, therefore that its prediction MSE is less. In addition, because of the reducing number of the training samples in the local method, the training time at every prediction is cut down. Although it is necessary to train the SVM each time in every prediction process, it can still reduce the total training times. It shows that the time reduces almost 50 times from Table 2.

Table 2: Prediction MSE and Training Iteration Times.

Method	Global ε-SVM	Local ε-SVM
MSE	3.1084e-3	2.2000e-3
Time (s)	583.1	12.42

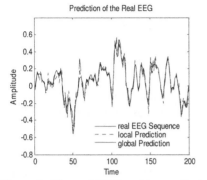

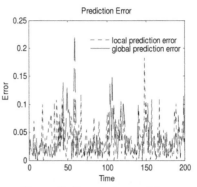

Figure 2: The real EEG and its prediction.

Figure 3: Comparison of the prediction MSE of the local SVM with the global SVM.

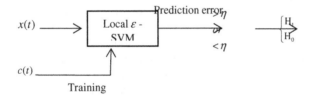

Figure 4: The epilepsy detection framework based on local ε-SVM.

4.3 Epilepsy detecting based on local ε-SVM

According to the dynamic characteristics difference between normal EEG signals and epilepsy signals, a new epilepsy detecting method based on local ε-SVM model is proposed in this paper. The detection framework is shown in Figure 4, which can be introduced as follows:

1. Both normal EEG signal and epilepsy signal are recorded through international 10-20 system with $c(t)$ and $s(t)$ for their representation.
2. Train the local ε-SVM model with normal EEG signals data $c(t)$, and then take the trained model as predictor.
3. Insert some epilepsy segments into the normal EEG signal to form a mixed signal $x(t)$. And take such a mixed signal as local ε-SVM model's input.

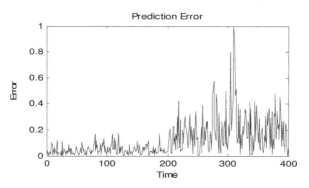

Figure 5: The prediction error in normal and epileptic EEG, the first 200 points are normal EEG prediction error, and the last 200 points are epileptic EEG prediction error.

4. Predict the mixed signals with local ε-SVM model. And compare the prediction error with threshold η. If the error is less than η, we think the input signal is H_0, namely: $x(t) = c(t)$. If not, the input signal is H_1, namely: $x(t) = s(t)$.

To evaluate the detection performance based on local ε-SVM model, we choose 1200 points EEG data for this job. Here, the first 1000 points are normal EEG signals and the last 200 points are the epilepsy signals. The first 800 points are used for the training model and the last 400 points are for the detection experiment. The detecting error result based on local ε-SVM model is shown in Figure 5. We can see from the figure that the detection error is obviously bigger in the last 200 points than the first 200 points. There are mainly two reasons for this: (i) The local ε-SVM model which is trained based on a normal EEG signal can exactly describe the characteristics and evolvement of the chaotic dynamical of EEG, so the detection error will be small in the non-epilepsy region. (ii) The chaotic dynamic characteristics have an obvious difference between epilepsy and normal EEG signal. Therefore, detection error will be bigger at the epilepsy region and the model we proposed is the effective model for epilepsy detecting.

5 Conclusion

This paper investigates the problem of prediction of EEG signals by using the SVM method. A local SVM procedure was proposed to deal with the problem of training global SVM when it comes to a large number of training samples. A local SVM based on the local procedures was proposed and combined with the existing training algorithms, such as SMO, to predict EEG signals. The simulation results indicated that the presented local SVM can not only increase the training speed but also effectively reduced the prediction MSE, and is therefore a good epilepsy detector.

Acknowledgment

This project is financially supported by the National Natural Science Foundation of China (NSFC 61072037), Guangdong Chang-Xue-Yang Base Foundation (2011-2014), and the Foundation of Sci-Tech Plan of Guangdong (2012-2015).

References

[1] A.J. Smola, B. Scholkopf, A tutorial on support vector regression. *Statistics and Computing*, **14**, pp. 199–222, 1998.

[2] C.J.C. Burges, A tutorial on support vector machines for pattern recognition. *Data Mining and Knowledge Discovery*, **2(2)**, pp. 121–167, 1998.

[3] J.S. Zhang, J.J. Dang, H.C. Li, Spatiotemporal chaos sequence prediction using local support vector machine. *Acta Physica Sinica*, **56**, pp. 67–77, 2007 (in Chinese).

Energy-aware scheduling for multicore real-time systems

Youlin Ruan, Xiuming Chen, Yunyun Qiu, Dewei Peng
Key Laboratory of Fiber Optic Sensing Technology and Information Processing, Ministry of Education, Wuhan University of Technology, Wuhan, China

Abstract

How to reduce the system energy consumption as much as possible while meet the time constraints is becoming an urgent problem of real-time scheduling for multicore systems. This paper proposed a new energy-efficient scheduling algorithm, which is based on the reduction of the energy consumption caused by switching frequency of the processor and slack time reclamation. First of all, use the ratio of pre-executing tasks to get average task utilization rate to estimate the speed of the post-executing task. Then map the post-executing task to the processor which has the most similar to the estimate speed, to reduce the energy consumption of changing the speed. In each core, the dynamic slack time is fairly shared by following two tasks. Simulation results show that the proposed scheduling algorithm obtains a better effect in energy-saving than other algorithms.

Keywords: multicore systems, energy-aware scheduling, slack time reclamation.

1 Introduction

Multicore processors can achieve higher throughput with the same clock frequency. On the other hand, increased power consumption generates more heat, which causes heat dissipation to be a problem since it requires more expensive packaging and cooling technology and decreases reliability. To reduce processor power consumption, many hardware techniques have been proposed, such as shutting down unused parts or reducing the power level of non-fully utilized functional units [1, 2]. Processors that have multiple supply voltages have become available in recent years, which can make power management at the processor level possible.

WIT Transactions on Information and Communication Technologies, Vol. 61, © 2014 WIT Press
www.witpress.com, ISSN 1743-3517 (on-line)
doi:10.2495/MIIT130391

Using this feature, several software techniques have been proposed to adjust the supply voltage, especially for mobile or uniprocessor systems. Many up-to-date processors also use dynamic voltage scaling (DVS). DVS adjusts the clock frequency and operating voltage on the fly to meet changes in the performance demand. Existing multicore real-time scheduling methods are classified as being either partitioned or global approaches. The task partitioning has an important effect on both schedulability and power consumption.

DVS is only capable to reduce the dynamic component of power consumption, which depends on f and Vdd. The increasing portion of static power in the total power dissipation of upcoming manufacturing technologies has led several researchers to exploring the real limits of using DVS to reduce energy consumption. Cho and Melhem [3, 4] derive analytical models to study the potential of DPM and DVS to reduce energy consumption for parallelizable applications on multicore systems. In their analysis, they consider two different scenarios: one where just DVS is supported and the other where both DPM and DVS are available. The obtained models reveal that substantially greater power savings can be obtained in the second scenario where individual processors can be turned off. LeSueur and Heiser [5] take this observation one step further by illustrating that the energy savings benefits of DVS are diminishing in recent processors due to rising static power consumption and reduced dynamic power range. Lower frequencies result in less frequency-dependent active energy consumption. But with reduced speed, the application will run longer and thus consume more static energy and frequency-independent dynamic energy. Zhang [6] proposes a global EDF-based energy-aware scheduling algorithm for real-time tasks in multi-core system. The proposed algorithm can reduce the execution speed of task in multicore system and reach a reasonable compromise between real-time constraints and energy savings, as it introduces a speed scale factor for utilizing the slack time and combines dynamic power management with DVS.

This paper presents a new multicore energy-efficient scheduling algorithm, which is based on the reduction of the energy consumption caused by switching frequency of the processor and slack time reclamation. The fundamental idea of our method is to reduction of the energy consumption caused by switching frequency of the processor. First of all, use the ratio of pre-executing tasks to get average task utilization rate to estimate the speed of the post-executing task. Then map the post-executing task to the processor which has the most similar to the estimate speed, to reduce the energy consumption of changing the speed. Then the current slack time is fairly shared by two tasks. It reduces the processor speed of the processor and minimizes the energy consumption. Through the theory and performance evaluation, compared to the other major algorithms, the new algorithm obtains better energy-saving effect. Experimental results show that the proposed algorithm obtain a better effect in energy-saving than other methods.

This paper is motivated by the energy-aware scheduling of tasks in reality, where tasks often have different power characteristics. We aim to the strategy of tasks assignment, and how to dynamic adjust speed to save energy consumption. The paper is organized as follows. In the next section, Section 2 describes the task model, energy model, and power management schemes. A new energy-aware multicore scheduling algorithm is addressed in Section 3. Simulation and comparison are given and analyzed in Section 4. Finally, we conclude our paper in Section 5.

2 System models

2.1 Energy model

For processors based on CMOS technology, the power consumption is dominated by dynamic power dissipation, which is further divided into two parts: *frequency-independent* active power and *frequency-dependent* active power.

$$p = p^{dep}(s) + p^{ind} \tag{1}$$

where p^{ind} is the frequency-independent active power and $p^{dep}(s)$ is the frequency-dependent active power. Frequency-independent active power p^{ind} consists of part of memory and processor power as well as any power that can be efficiently removed by putting systems into sleep states and is independent of system supply voltages and processing frequencies. Frequency-dependent active power $p^{dep}(s)$ includes processor's dynamic power and any power that depends on system supply voltages and processing frequencies. Generally speaking, $p^{dep}(s) = s^3$. Consequently, the total energy consumption of a *running* application at frequency f in the deadline D can be modelled as:

$$E(s) = p(s) * \frac{\alpha}{f} = \left(s^3 + \beta\right) * \frac{\alpha}{f} \tag{2}$$

From above equation, lower frequencies result in less frequency-dependent active energy consumption. But with reduced speed, the application will run longer and thus consume more static energy and frequency-independent active energy. Hence, in general, an energy-efficient frequency, below which voltage scaling start to consume more total energy, it is easy to find out that the *energy efficient frequency* is $s_{critical} = \sqrt[3]{\beta/2}$.

2.2 Task model

We consider a set of real-time tasks $T = \{ \tau_1, \tau_2, ..., \tau_n \}$, where n is the number of tasks, and a homogeneous multicore processor system $C = \{c_1, c_2, ..., c_m\}$, where m is the number of cores. Each task τ_i is characterized by $(\omega_i, \alpha_i, D_i)$, where ω_i and α_i are the worst case execution time and actual execution time of task τ_i, and D_i is the period of task τ_i. We assume that the value of ω_i and D_i are known before execution, while α_i is determined at run time. We assume that the period is equal to the relative implicit deadline.

3 The proposed algorithm

Partitioned scheduling provides scalability and low overhead due to a lack of centralized data structures that can produce contention and cross-core data migration. Partitioned approach consists of the following two steps:

Step 1: Assign each task to a core where the task is able to meet its deadline and save energy. Tasks may be sorted in order of some criteria (e.g., utilization, deadline).

Step 2: After core assignment, apply a uniprocessor scheduling algorithm and slack time reclamation to schedule assigned tasks within the time line of each core.

Our aim of the algorithm is that the tasks can be scheduled in a feasible manner and the total energy consumption is minimal.

At step 1, task partitioning is performed in order to assign tasks to appropriate cores. There are several heuristics to solve the bin packing problem. But these methods cannot consider *energy-efficient frequency* and energy consumption caused by switching frequency of the cores. At step 2, we employ a well-known slack time reclamation mechanism HR-2 [7] which provides good energy performance.

From the idea described above, we propose a new multicore energy-efficient scheduling algorithm ESPSR, which is based on the slack time reclamation and reduction of the energy consumption caused by switching frequency of the processor. The fundamental idea of our method is to reduction of the energy consumption caused by switching frequency of the processor. First of all, use the ratio of pre-executing tasks to get average task utilization rate to estimate the speed of the post-executing task. Then map the post-executing task to the processor which has the most similar to the estimate speed, to reduce the energy consumption of changing the speed. Then the current slack time is fairly shared by two tasks. It reduces the processor speed of the processor and minimizes the energy consumption.

ESPSR consists of the following three steps:

1. Estimate the speed of each task:

$$s_i^* = \overline{\lambda} = \sum_{j=1}^{i-1} \lambda_j \ / \ (i-1)\left(2 \le i \le m\right)$$

2. Task partitioning: each task τ_i is assigned to the core in which its current speed is closest approach to estimate speed of τ_1. That to say, if $\Delta s = \left| s_i^* - s_k \right|$ is minimum then map task τ_i to core p_k;

3. Slack reclamation: for the each core, the dynamic slack time is fairly shared by following two tasks.

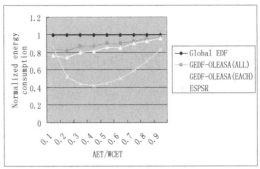

(a) Total utilization=0.1

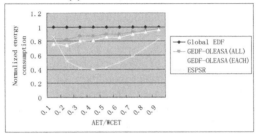

(b) Total utilization=0.2

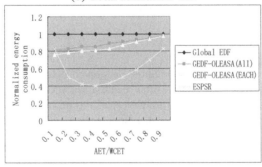

(c) Total utilization=0.4

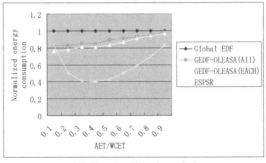

(d) Total utilization=0.6

Figure 1: Comparison of algorithms with energy consumption.

4 Performance evaluation

In this section, we present results of simulations performed to compare our algorithms ESPSR, with Global EDF, GEDF-OLEASA (ALL), and GEDF-OLEASA (EACH).

We have generated a total of 1000 task sets by varying the number of cores m, the total utilization of the task set $U=U_{total}$ and the number of tasks n. Period tasks have three types of tasks with short period (1–10 ms), middle period (10–100 ms) and long period (100–1000 ms). Utilization of tasks can be generated by UUnifast [7], and the WCET of task can be computed by utilization and period. Thus, $\omega_i = u_i * T_i$. The deadline of tasks are uniformly distributed in the range [ω_i, $2T_i$]. Aperiodic tasks have been generated by same method, but the WCET of task should be computed by utilization and deadline. Thus, $\omega_i = u_i * D_i$.

Figure 1 shows the performance comparison of the methods using task utilization factor of 0.1, 0.2, 0.4, 0.6, respectively for two cores, and AET/WCET varies from 0.1 to 0.9, step is 0.1. Our experiments confirmed that ESPSR provides better energy saving except condition of AET/WCET=0.1. When AET/WCET=0.4, our algorithm can save the most energy performance than other algorithms. Because s^* to become 0.4 when AET/WCET=0.4, however, $s_{critical} = 0.37$ in our experiment. Thus, s^* be close to $s_{critical}$. Therefore, no switching frequency of the processor and *energy efficient frequency* can save most energy consumption. Thus, energy is minimum.

5 Conclusions

In this paper, we present a new method for power-aware multicore scheduling. Our solution is based on the slack time reclamation and reduction of the energy consumption caused by switching frequency of the processor. Simulation results show that our strategy is better than other major approaches.

Acknowledgment

The research work was supported by National Natural Science Foundation of China under Grant No. 61173045.

References

[1] A.P. Chandrakasan, S. Sheng, R.W. Brodersen, Low-power CMOS digital design. *IEEE Journal of Solid-State Circuit*, **27(4)**, pp. 473–484, 1992.
[2] F. Yao, A. Demers, S. Shenker, A scheduling model for reduced CPU energy. In: P. Hájek, J. Wiedermann (eds.), *Proceedings of 36th Symposium on Foundations of Computer Science*. IEEE, Milwaukee, pp. 374–382, 1995.
[3] S. Cho, R.G. Melhem, Corollaries to amdahl's law for energy. *IEEE Computer Architecture Letters*, **7(1)**, pp. 25–28, 2007.

[4] Sangyeun Cho, Rami G. Melhem, On the interplay of parallelization, program performance, and energy consumption. *IEEE Transactions on Parallel and Distributed Systems*, **21(3)**, pp. 342–353, 2010.

[5] E. Le Sueur, G. Heiser, Dynamic voltage and frequency scaling: the laws of diminishing returns. In: Frank Bellosa, Trishul Chilimbi (eds.), *Proceedings of the 2010 Workshop on Power Aware Computing and Systems (HotPower'10)*. USENIX Association, Berkeley, CA, pp. 1–8, 2010.

[6] DongSong Zhang, Tong Wu, FangYuan Chen, et al., Global EDF-based on-line energy-aware real-time scheduling algorithm in multi-core systems. *Journal of Software*, **23(4)**, pp. 996–1009, 2012.

[7] J.J. Chen, C.Y. Yang, T.W. Kuo, Slack reclamation for real-time scheduling over dynamic voltage scaling multiprocessors. In: Bob Werner (ed.), *Proceedings of the IEEE International Conference on Sensor Networks, Ubiquitous, and Trustworthy Computing*. IEEE, Taichung, pp. 408–417, 2006.

Index screening model construction of discipline evaluation based on combination of discrimination degree and importance

Xue Wang, Yuanming Ding

Department of Information Engineering, Dalian University, Dalian, China

Abstract

To screen index reasonably and correctly is the basis of insuring the evaluation results accurate. However, most of the current studies on index screening remain at the application level with less theoretical research, which focus on how to eliminate the index pertinence. For this reason, on the basis of analyzing the entropy theory, in this paper, the idea of entropy weight empowerment is used for the quantification of indicator "discrimination." The multiplication synthesis thought is borrowed to make a combination of the index discrimination and importance, and the definition and calculation formula of "influence degree" are given. In addition, the index selection model based on a combination of index importance and discrimination is constructed. This model can establish index system for the performance evaluation of discipline construction and provide basis and evidence for index empowerment.

Keywords: index screening, index empowerment, maximum entropy, performance evaluation, discipline construction.

1 Introduction

Currently, some special evaluation agencies have been developed in western countries, and they evaluate various disciplines regularly. For example, doctorate is evaluated by "American Research Council," and "the new U.S. Weekly" makes evaluation and taxis for disciplines and institutes regularly [1]. A lot of research work on discipline construction and evaluation has been carried out in our country. The Education Ministry has made examination and evaluation for the national key disciplines for three times which has achieved significant results [2]. However, generally accepted evaluation index system and evaluation method of discipline construction have not been developed due to the fact that factors affecting the discipline construction evaluation are complex. So to build a discipline performance evaluation model can provide evidence for allocating discipline resources scientifically and effectively.

In the evaluation, the index system of an evaluated object should be able to reflect the main factors that influence the system performance. And how to screen these factors is the key to ensure the performance evaluation results reasonable and accurate. Reasonable index screening and optimization can prevent the index proliferation and avoid structure distortion; can fully characterize the effectiveness of evaluation index and index system; and can guarantee the reliability of evaluation index system. Therefore, to screen representative, independent and informative index correctly and rationally is the key to build an index system, which has a very important significance.

However, most of the current studies of evaluation index system emphasize on practical application, which focus on constructing the corresponding index system of specific evaluation objects. Theory research on assessment index is rare. The basic methods of index screening include factor analysis, grey correlation analysis, correlation coefficient method, rough set theory analysis, and principal component analysis [3–8]. Although these methods have made researches on index screening problem from different angles and do made some achievements, most researches still focus on the index correlation elimination and rarely involve other areas.

Recently, researches on multi-objective index screening models mainly concentrate on the index "importance" principle based screening methods. The AHP evaluation indication screening method based on index weight coefficients [9] make a screening using the index importance, or it makes a primary screening using the indication importance, then eliminates the correlation between indexes using objective methods, such as the principal component analysis method and factor analysis method [10]. However, these methods only consider the importance of indexes, ignoring the discrimination of indexes. Some indexes with strong distinction are washed out and as a result, the evaluation results of the evaluated objects are very close to each other. Although "discrimination degree" is difficult to quantitative, there are also a small number of discrimination degree based screening methods such as, the minimum variance method and minimax deviation method. But these methods only consider the index "discrimination," ignoring the index "importance." Some very important indexes may be washed out, resulting in the serious distortion of evaluation results. The ideal case is to achieve the reasonable combination of discrimination degree and importance. While this operation is difficult in actual situation, and one of the reasons is that "discrimination degree" is hard to quantify.

Index system construction and index empowerment, in fact, is a progress which makes the evaluated index (reflecting the properties of an evaluated object) in order from a disorder state. And this comes to coincide with the correlative thought of "entropy." The entropy value does reflect the disorder strength within the system. Among the existing theories, entropy can be considered to be the best measure of "uncertainty." With the further development of entropy theory, "entropy" will have a broader prospect in the field of performance evaluation. Therefore, this paper, in the basis of analyzing the entropy weight idea, quantitative method of index discrimination degree is given. Innovatively, the discrimination degree and importance are combined organically using the idea of multiplication synthesis in combination weighting method. The index screening model based on the combination of index importance and discrimination degree is established, which provides a new method of index screening.

2 Index screening model based on the combination of importance and discrimination degree

In the situation where exits multiple evaluated objects, the "discrimination degree" and "importance" of index are two indispensable factors in screening process. The most reasonable approach is to achieve the rational integration of these both, making them harmonized in the screening process.

2.1 The importance and discrimination of index

2.1.1 The importance of index

The importance of index is a critical factor in the progress of index screening. In the performance evaluation progress, it is difficult to quantify the importance of an index, and the evaluators can only make a qualitative understanding. And in some cases, for the same evaluated object, analyzed from different sides, the importance degrees of relative indexes can be different.

2.1.2 The discrimination of index

The index "discrimination" denotes its ability to distinguish various evaluated objects, and it is defined as "discrimination" in this paper.

In the performance evaluation question of multi-object, the discrimination abilities of various indexes in the index system largely determine whether the evaluation results are reasonable or not. If an index shows no difference to all evaluated objects, and then it has no existing value and significance to the evaluation object set. Currently, most objective empowerment methods do take the discrimination ability as the sole basis of index empowerment. Although this is unreasonable, from another perspective, it also reflects that the index "discrimination" is a very important factor in index screening.

2.2 Entropy ideas

Entropy weight means entropy value empowerment, and its basic principle is that the weights of each index are decided by the amount of their contained information. The formula is as follows:

$$w_j = \frac{1 - H_j}{n - \sum_{j=1}^{n} H_j} \tag{1}$$

Among which H_j is the entropy of jth index.

According to the view of information theory, we can conclude that the greater the index "discrimination" is, the greater the amount of its contained information is. It also means that the greater the index discrimination is, the greater its discriminating effect is. It can be interpreted as if an index shows no difference to all evaluated objects, and it means the index cannot discriminate various evaluated objects. Then the weight coefficient of this index will be set as 0; and if the index shows significant differences to all evaluated objects, well then the index will play an important role in the evaluation and sorting of the evaluated objects and its weight coefficient should also be big. Namely, the sizes of weight coefficients are ascertained by the difference sizes of various evaluated objects under this index.

Through the analysis above, it is not difficult to find that the sizes of entropy weight actually reflect the discrimination ability of this index to the evaluated objects. And the entropy weight model provides a quantitative approach for "discrimination" calculation.

Assuming that in a multi-object performance evaluation process, there are m evaluated objects, n primary evaluated indexes. In the (m, n) performance evaluation problem, if the entropy value of the jth index is H_j, and entropy weight is w_j, then its discrimination degree is defined as η_j, which is calculated as follows:

$$\eta_j = \frac{w_j}{H_j} = \frac{1 - H_j}{(n - \sum_{j=1}^{n} H_j) H_j} \tag{2}$$

2.3 Index discrimination calculation model

Using the "discrimination" thoughts, the number of indexes can be condensed, and the calculation progress can be summarized as the following steps:

Step 1: Build the evaluated matrix

$$R' = \begin{bmatrix} r'_{11} & r'_{12} & \cdots & r'_{1n} \\ r'_{21} & r'_{22} & \cdots & r'_{2n} \\ \vdots & \vdots & \vdots & \vdots \\ r'_{m1} & r'_{m2} & \cdots & r'_{mn} \end{bmatrix} \tag{3}$$

Step 2: Standardize the evaluated matrix and get the standard matrix

$$R = \left(r_{ij}\right)_{m \times n} \tag{4}$$

$$r_{ij} = \frac{r_{ij}' - \min\limits_{i}\{r_{ij}'\}}{\max\limits_{i}\{r_{ij}'\} - \min\limits_{i}\{r_{ij}'\}} \tag{5}$$

Step 3: Calculate the entropy of the *j*th index

$$H_j = -k \sum_{i=1}^{m} f_{ij} \ln f_{ij} \tag{6}$$

Among which, $k = 1 / \ln m$, $f_{ij} = r_{ij} / \sum\limits_{i=1}^{m} r_{ij}$, and when $f_{ij} = 0$, $f_{ij} \ln f_{ij} = 0$.

Step 4: Calculate the entropy weight of *j* index
Calculate the entropy of the *j*th index using formula (1).
Step 5: Calculate the discrimination of index *j*
Calculate the discrimination degree of the *j*th index using formula (2).

2.4 Influence degree calculation model

In the index screening, firstly according to opinions of expert, the initial index screening is completed using the scoring method. While in order to simplify the structure of the index system without losing the integrity of the architecture, the best result is that the indexes with small importance and small discrimination degree are washed out. Here, the idea of multiplication synthesis in combination weighting method is borrowed to define the index "influence degree." The influence degree is the combination of importance and discrimination degree of the index. The larger the importance and discrimination are, the larger the influence degree of the index to system performance will be. Contrarily, the smaller the importance and discrimination are, the smaller the influence degree of the index to system performance will be. The calculation of "influence degree" is as follows:

$$\vartheta_j = \alpha v_j + \beta \eta_j \tag{7}$$

Among which, ϑ_j is the influence degree of the *i*th index. v_j is the importance of the *j*th index, η_j is the discrimination degree of the *j*th index; α, β are the influence genes of influence and discrimination degree, respectively.

3 The application of index screening model

Discipline construction is a fundamental build of higher education institution, and it is the foundation of school reform and development. The construction of

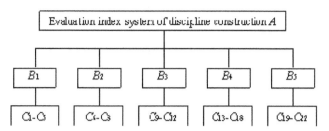

Figure 1: Evaluation index structure of discipline construction.

discipline evaluation index system is the basis of university construction evaluation, and the index system is reasonable or not directly determines the performance evaluation results. Using the index screening model above, this paper screens the second-level indexes of the discipline construction evaluation system.

On the basis of access to relevant information, through the questionnaire method, and with the experience and views of relevant experts, the primary screening of discipline construction evaluation index system is completed. The first-level index of discipline construction evaluation index system is constructed by decomposition method. As shown in Figure 1, the first-level index set of discipline construction is {faculty building B_1, personnel training B_2, disciplinary research B_3, academic platform B_4, and academic exchanges B_5}.

The second-level index set of scientific research includes: monographs, patents, SCI, EI, significant nuclear Journal, general nuclear Journal, the importance degrees of each index are: 0.36, 0.21, 0.15, 0.11, 0.11, and 0.06.

The second-level index set of faculty building includes: academicians, Cheung Kong Scholar, National Talent Project training object, professors, provincial engineering talent cultivation object, associate professor, and the importance degrees of each index are: 0.41, 0.20, 0.17, 0.09, 0.07, and 0.06.

The second-level index set of personnel training includes: each to obtain a provincial outstanding graduate title, each to obtain a city outstanding graduate title, each graduate doctoral, each graduate master, each graduate undergraduate, and the importance degrees of each index are: 0.51, 0.25, 0.15, 0.06, and 0.03.

The second-level index set of academic exchanges includes: the times of holding international academic conferences, the times of holding national academic conferences, the number of positive-vice chairman of national learn, the number of positive-vice chairman of provincial learn, the number of attending international conference, the number of attending national conference, and the importance degrees are: 0.35, 0.24, 0.22, 0.13, 0.04, and 0.02.

The second-level index set of disciplinary platform construction includes: international key laboratory, international innovation team, doctoral degree programs, provincial key laboratory, provincial innovation team, master degree programs, university innovation group, and the importance degrees of various indexes are: 0.25, 0.23, 0.16, 0.14, 0.12, 0.07, and 0.03.

Since the total evaluated objectives involve many factors, it is requested that each index subset should be concise. For the second-level index subsets, they need to be further cut to improve the evaluation system performance. Now then, taking the first-level index scientific research for example, indexes are screened using the index screening model constructed above in this paper. This paper screens five evaluated objects as an evaluated object set, denoted by $Q = \{Q_1, Q_2, Q_3, Q_4, Q_5\}$, and the indexes of each evaluated object are as shown in Table 1.

According to the calculation steps of index discrimination above, the entropy, weight, discrimination degree and influence degree of the second-level index scientific research can be calculated as follows:

$$H_j = (0.8043, 0.7936, 0.8338, 0.7565, 0.7066, 0.7402)$$
$$w_j = (0.1434, 0.1512, 0.1218, 0.1711, 0.2149, 0.1903)$$
$$\eta_j = (0.1783, 0.1905, 0.1461, 0.2262, 0.3041, 0.2571)$$
$$\vartheta_j = (0.2692, 0.2002, 0.1481, 0.1681, 0.2070, 0.1568)$$

In order to make the index system calculation simply and conveniently, if the second-level index is required to retain four indexes, it can be seen from the calculation results above, the influence values of the third and sixth indexes are smaller which can be washed out. It denotes that in the index system established.

Table 1: Performance Index Parameters of Discipline Construction Evaluation.

Third-Level Index	Q_1	Q_2	Q_3	Q_4	Q_5	Third-Level Index	Q_1	Q_2	Q_3	Q_4	Q_5
Academician C_1	2	0	1	1	0	Important journals C_{12}	21	26	51	34	17
Changjiang scholar C_2	1	2	0	1	0	National key laboratory C_{13}	4	3	1	2	1
National talent project C_3	2	3	1	1	2	National innovation team C_{14}	2	1	0	2	1
Professor C_4	12	18	21	14	16	Doctoral section C_{15}	3	1	2	3	2
Provincial talent project C_5	5	3	1	2	4	Provincial key laboratories C_{16}	5	4	2	3	2
Doctor C_6	20	16	12	18	10	Provincial innovation team C_{17}	2	3	2	1	1
Graduate student C_7	85	64	73	54	46	Master section C_{18}	4	2	3	3	2
Undergraduate C_8	402	310	274	187	216	International academic conference C_{19}	4	1	2	3	1
Monographs C_9	5	3	6	5	2	National academic conference C_{20}	34	26	28	31	29
Patents C_{10}	4	3	5	3	2	Deputy chairman of national institute C_{21}	4	2	3	0	1
EI C_{11}	29	27	13	15	31	Deputy chairman of provincial institute C_{22}	7	4	5	2	3

According to the evaluated object $Q = \{Q_1, Q_2, Q_3, Q_4, Q_5\}$, the second-level indexes of scientific research include monographs, patents, EI and important journals.

In accordance with the method described above, the second-level indexes in other four first-level indexes can be screened in the same way.

4 Conclusions

For multiple evaluated objects, the "discrimination degree" and "importance" of the index are two indispensable factors in screening process. This paper defines the index discrimination using the entropy and entropy weight values of evaluated index, and makes a combination of the "discrimination degree" and "importance" of the evaluated object, establishing the index screening model. Finally, taking the disciplinary construction evaluation of higher education institution as an example, the second-level index of the index system is screened using this model.

Acknowledgment

This article is the results of the University Educational Quality Project of Liaoning Province (No. 2012106).

References

[1] S.E. Judith, Accreditation and quality in the united states: practice and pressure. *Global Perspectives on Quality in Higher Education*, (**4**), pp. 56–64, 2001.

[2] Y. Zhu, Thinking on further improvement of China first-class discipline ranking assessment. *Sciences Research Management*, **27**(**1**), pp. 156–159, 2006.

[3] Shamilov, Aladdin, A development of entropy optimization methods. *WSEAS Transactions on Mathematics*, pp. 568–575, 2007.

[4] P. Embrechts, F. Lindskog, Modeling dependence with copulas and application to risk management. *Handbook of Heavy Tailed Distributions in Finance*, pp. 329–384, 2003.

[5] W. Shen, J. Liu, Application of the gray relevancy method to college teachers performance assessment humanities and social science. *Science and Technology Management Research*, **30**(**22**), pp. 237–240, 2010.

[6] M. LV, Y. Du, C. Rong, et al., Set pair analysis method in lake's eutrophication assessment based on correlation weight method. *South to North Water Science & Technology*, **19**(**5**), pp. 129–133, 2011.

[7] Abdou, Samir, Savoy, Statistical and comparative evaluation of various indexing and search models. *Lecture Notes in Computer Science*, pp. 362–373, 2006.

[8] S.Q. Yin, W.L. Chen, W. Wang, Network teaching intelligent evaluation method research on fuzzy comprehensive judgment. *ICIC Express Letters*, **5(4)**, pp. 1255–1260, 2011.

[9] R.Y. Zhou, N.X. Zhang, Y. Zhou, ANN assessment model and its application based on AHP and the sieving of important index. *China Safety Science Journal*, **17(4)**, pp. 43–47, 2007.

[10] W.S. Li, Comprehensive index evaluation method and its application on water quality based on factor analysis. *Journal of North University of China (Natural Science Edition)*, **32(2)**, pp. 207–211, 2011.

Gateway deployment optimization in wireless mesh backbone networks using directional antenna based on delaunay graph

Chengxin Guo, Taoshen Li, Zhihui Ge
Department of Computer, Electronics and Information, Guangxi University, Nanning, China

Abstract

The deployment optimization research is one of the key issues of wireless mesh network. A delaunay graph-based gateway deployment optimization algorithm of wireless mesh backbone network using directional antenna was proposed. Firstly, according to the whole traffic of all mesh routers and the maximum traffic of gateway, this algorithm divided the network into several clusters forming delaunay subgraph. Secondly, in the subgraph, this algorithm found out the three nodes that were closest to the center point by the euclidean distance, and they formed the gateway candidate set. The node had the shortest path to the other nodes in this set was chosen from the gateway candidate setting as the gateway location to deploy. Finally, this algorithm achieved gateways of the network chosen from each cluster. The simulation results show that this algorithm can minimize the number of gateway and its total path length from mesh router to gateway is better than random algorithm.

Keywords: wireless mesh network, gateway deployment, directional antenna, delaunay graph.

1 Introduction

As the key technology of next generation wireless networks, wireless mesh network (WMN) with the characteristics of dynamic self-organization self-healing has a great advantage on flexible networking, easy maintenance, wide range of network covering and it meets people's requirements of high-rate high-capacity Internet access, which makes WMN become one of the hotspots of many researchers [1]. WMN is a multi-hop wireless transmission network, including three types of nodes: gateway, mesh routers (MR) and mesh clients (MC). The wireless mesh backbone network which consists of gateways and MRs is responsible for providing network services to clients. Because of the network traffic aggregation, gateways become the bottlenecks of the network which makes gateway deployment significantly affect the performance of WMNs.

Gateway deployment optimization with multi-objective in WMN is an NP-Hard problem [2]. In previous study, gateway deployment problem was formulated as a linear programming problem. Several algorithms are come out to optimize this problem. In Ref. [2], He and Xie have presented two heuristic algorithms based on the R-hop adjacency matrix of network to minimize the number of gateways and the number of hops from MR to gateway (MR-GW). A new concept of limited dominating set (LDS) in graph is presented to addresses the gateway deployment problem with certain QoS to minimize the cost of gateway deployment in Refs. [2, 3]. In Ref. [3], heuristic algorithm WMB-LDS algorithm based on the performance/cost ratio of gateway and GA_LDS algorithm based on genetic algorithm optimization were proposed. The WMB_LDS algorithm has lower computing complexity and the GA_LDS algorithm can achieve more optimal solution with more computation time. Jian Peng et al. [4] proposed GREEDY_LDSC algorithm and GREEDY_LDSI algorithm to increase cost-effective and reduced costs of gateway deployment respectively. A greedy algorithm based on the weight of the load of network was proposed in Ref. [5] to minimize the number of gateway while reducing link interference, which made load balance between gateways. These researches on gateway deployment optimization mentioned above are all based on omni-directional antenna which makes communications interference inevitable.

Compared to omni-directional antenna, the use of directional antennas can improve the performance of the WMN, including the reduction of interference between nodes and it can also improve the spatial reuse as well as increase network throughput and so on.

On the other hand, researchers have found that delaunay triangulation could be widely used in the deployment of wireless network like wireless sensor network because of its excellent mathematical properties that could increase network coverage and minimize network deployment costs. In this paper, the gateway placement problem of wireless mesh backbone network using directional antenna is investigated. By using delaunay triangulation as network topology, we develop a delaunay graph-based gateway deployment optimization algorithm of wireless mesh backbone network using directional antenna.

This paper is organized as follows. Section 2 presents problem descriptions and network model. In Section 3, we develop a gateway deployment algorithm for WMN based on delaunay graph. Section 4 gives performance analysis and simulation result of the algorithm. Finally, Section 5 concludes the paper.

2 Problem descriptions and network model

2.1 Problem descriptions

In this paper, WMN backbone in which each node is deployed appropriate number of directional antennas is optimized. Taking into account meet users' request for bandwidth and network performance, WMN is divided into disjoint clusters. The gateway deployment algorithm to reduce the deployment costs and the delay from MR to gateway (MR-GW) is proposed while balancing the load between gateways and controlling the media contention between nodes. Because of the high cost of gateway, the number of gateways can be used to represent the cost of gateway deployment. The delay from MR to the gateway is equivalent to the path length of MR-GW. Therefore, the goal of our algorithms is to minimize the number of gateways and the path length of MR-GW. Besides, the load balance among gateways and the node contention controlling are achieved through a reasonable division of total traffic of MR and the constraint of the number of node that attach to some gateway.

2.2 Network model

We model a wireless mesh backbone network as an undirected delaunay graph $G(V, E)$, $V=\{v_1, v_2, \ldots, v_n\}$ is the set of n network nodes, representing MRs and GWs. E is the set of link in the network. The coordinates of a node can be represented by (x, y). The Euclidean distance between node v_i and v_j is $L(i, j) = \sqrt{(x_i, x_j)^2 + (y_i, y_j)^2}$, setting that the maximum transmission distance of directional antenna is L_{max}, in order to reduce the interference between antennas, setting a minimum distance between nodes is L_{min}. Therefore, the radio link set $E=\{(v_i, v_j) | L_{min} \leqslant L_{min}(i,j) \leqslant L_{max}, i \neq j\}$, and the adjacency matrix of G is

$$A = \begin{pmatrix} a_{1,1} & \cdots & a_{1,n} \\ \vdots & \ddots & \vdots \\ a_{n,1} & \cdots & a_{n,n} \end{pmatrix},$$ where $a_{i,j}$ represents whether there is a radio link between

nodes v_i and v_j, if $(v_i, v_j) \in E$, then $a_{i,j} = 1$, otherwise $a_{i,j} = 0$. The link distance between nodes is expressed as ω which is equal to the Euclidean distance between the two nodes, the gateway node is set as V_G and the non-gateway nodes represent a collection V_{NG}.

Vector $Z=\{z_1, z_2, \ldots, z_n\}$ represents that which node is selected as a gateway, when a node v_i is selected as the gateway, $z_i = 1$, otherwise $z_i = 0$. T_i denotes the maximum traffic of node v_i. In this paper, the WMN is divided into several clusters, and each cluster has only one gateway (cluster's head) serving the nodes inside the cluster. Cluster C is a subgraph of G, $C(V', E') \subseteq G(V, E), V' \subseteq V, E' \subseteq E$, C_g represents the cluster whose root node is gateway v_g and $|C_g|$ denotes the node number of C_g. $\lambda(i, j)$ indicates that the node v_i connects to the gateway v_j via a or multi-hop, $\delta(i, j)$ represents the shortest distance between node v_i and v_j with single hop or multi-hop, T_g represents the maximum traffic of gateway v_g, S represents the maximum number of nodes inside the cluster. The discussed model is given below:

$$\min \sum_{i=1}^{n} z_i \tag{1}$$

$$\min \sum_{i}^{n} \sum_{j}^{n} \delta(i, j) * \lambda(i, j) \tag{2}$$

Subject to:

$$\sum_{v_j \in V_G} \lambda(i, j) = 1, \forall v_i \in V_{NG} \tag{3}$$

$$|C_g| \leq S \tag{4}$$

$$\sum_{i=1}^{S} T_i \leq T_g, v_i \in C_g \tag{5}$$

In this model, (1) means that a minimum number of nodes selected as the gateway among n nodes is achieved. And (2), the total distance of MR-GW is minimized. These two objectives are subjected to the following constraints. Eq. (3) ensures that each node v_i is attached to only one gateway v_j. Inequality (4) guarantees that the number of nodes inside each cluster is within maximum number S. Inequality (5) ensures the gateway maximum traffic capacity as the upper bound of the traffic in each cluster.

3 Gateway deployment algorithm based on delaunay graph

The gateway deployment optimization problem is treated as a linear programming problem. According to the centrality of graph theory, we propose a gateway deployment algorithm based on Delaunay graph. According to the closeness centrality of graph theory, tightness is a kind of measurement of centrality of a node in a graph. In the analysis of a network, tightness of a node is defined as the reciprocal of the total path of the node to other nodes. Therefore, the closer to the center a node is, the smaller total path of the node to other nodes it has. This algorithm design idea is: in the subgraph subjected to the constraint of traffic flow and the number of nodes that gateway serve, we figure out the central node or nodes close to the center through greedy algorithm to achieve the shortest path MR to the gateway, and then achieve the shortest total MR-GW distance of the whole network. Another objective of the proposed algorithm is to achieve the minimum number of gateways based on a reasonable network division of network traffic flow subjected to the QoS constraints.

Thus, our gateway deployment algorithm based on delaunay graph for WMN is as follows:

Step 1: Collect the network information (including the maximum traffic flow and coordinates of nodes), and then we get the delaunay topology of WMN. The overall traffic flow of the network is calculated to decide whether the network is divided.

Step 2: Start breadth-first traversal in the network from the node lower left, when the traffic flow of traversed node reaches maximum limit of gateway or the number of traversed node reaches *S*, the delaunay subgraph is formed.

Step 3: The center coordinates of the subgraph is found out based on the coordinates of nodes in the subgraph so that we can get the Euclidean distance of each node to the center point and the shortest three nodes are found out. The one of these three nodes has the shortest total distance to other nodes is selected as the gateway of the subgraph. The traversed nodes are removed from the adjacency matrix.

Step 4: Repeat Step 2 and Step 3 in the rest of the adjacency matrix until all gateways needed in the network are selected.

Step 5: Output the coordinates of the selected gateway node.

The pseudo code of the main algorithm presents as following:

Input: The Delaunay subgraph C based on breadth-first traversal and constraints

Output: The coordinate of gateway g

1. CountCenterPoint(C); // Calculate the center coordinate of subgraph C
2. **For** all $v_i \in C$
3. Candidate(C)=CountDistanceToCenter(v_i);// Calculate the distance node v_i to the center and select the shortest three nodes as the candidate set
4. **end For**
5. **For** all v_i in Candidate(C)
6. ThreeNodes(C)=CountDistanceToOtherPoint(v_i);// Calculate the shortest distance each node in candidate to other nodes
7. **end For**
8. g = Shortest(ThreeNodes(C));//The node has the shortest total distance is selected as the gateway
9. return g

4 Performance analysis and simulation result

In this paper, we assess the performance simulation of the algorithm with MATLAB and analyze the result. In the simulation experiment, each node communicates with the gateway node with the shortest path. All nodes are

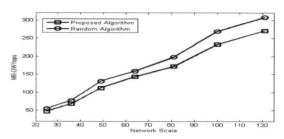

Figure 1: MR-GW hops by varying network scale.

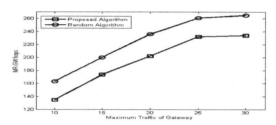

Figure 2: MR-GW hops by varying maximum gateway's traffic.

randomly and uniformly distributed so that the distance between the nodes is approximately equal which make us use total number of MR-GW hops to represent the total MR-GW distance. In order to simplify the calculation, we set that all MR node's local traffic is 1 and the maximum traffic T_g of gateway v_g is 25. The maximum traffic of gateway is equal to the maximum number of nodes it serves, which means the cluster's maximum number of node is 25. Firstly, delaunay graph is generated according to the coordinates of nodes. Then we find the location of gateway of proposed algorithm and random algorithm respectively and compare the total MR-GW hops of them. We first make a comparison under different number of nodes of WMN. The simulation result is shown in Figure 1.

As can be seen from Figure 1, when the number of nodes increases, the total MR-GW hops of our algorithm is always less than the one of random algorithm, and with the number of nodes increases, the difference becomes more apparent.

Different maximum traffic of gateway also has influence on the MR-GW hops. We keep the WMN stay 100 nodes and the network topology steady, and then investigate the relation between the maximum traffic of gateway and the total MR-GW hops. Figure 2 gives the simulation result.

In Figure 2, with the maximum traffic of gateway T_g increases, the total MR-GW hops also increases. The reason is that the algorithm limits the number of nodes of cluster with T_g. While T_g is small, less nodes are in the cluster which make the number of cluster increase so that the total MR-GW hops reduces; when T_g increases, more nodes are in the cluster and the number of clusters increases which results in the increase of the total MR-GW hops. As shown in Figure 2, when T_g increases from 25 to 30, the total MR-GW of hops has no apparent increase. That is because the network is divided based on T_g which make the number of gateway is $\lceil n/T_g \rceil$. That's the minimum number of gateway that satisfies user's requirement within the load capacity of gateways. So whether T_g is 25 or 30, the number of gateways is 4 and the total MR-GW hops has no significant increase.

Above all, the proposed algorithm divides the network reasonably based on biggest traffic of gateway. Subjected to a certain QoS constraints, the proposed algorithm achieves the minimum number of gateways and the shortest total MR-GW distances while guaranteeing the requirement of user within the load of gateway.

5 Conclusion

In this paper, the gateway deployment optimization problem of wireless mesh backbone network using directional antenna is studied. We applies delaunay graph for gateway deployment and propose the gateway deployment optimization algorithm based on delaunay graph. Firstly, the WMN is divided into several clusters based on the network traffic of node. Then, according to centrality of graph theory, the node that has the shortest total distance to other nodes is selected as the gateway. Simulation results show that, in a certain QoS constraint, the proposed algorithm can achieve a minimum number of gateways and the shortest MR-GW total distance.

The next step is to investigate the optimization of the wireless mesh network deployment. The topology of WMN is simplified by limiting the degree of each node while guaranteeing network's connectivity so that the number of directional antenna deployed on nodes is reduced. In other words, the cost of WMN deployment is reduced.

Acknowledgment

The research is supported by the National Natural Science Foundation of China under Grant Nos. 61363067, 60963022; the Natural Science Foundation of Guangxi in China under Grant No. 2012GXNSFAA053226.

References

[1] I.F. Akyildiz, , X.D. Wang, W.L. Wang, Wireless Mesh networks: a survey. *Computer Networks*, **47(4)**, pp. 445–487, 2005.

[2] B. He, B. Xie, D.P. Agrawal, Optimizing deployment of Internet gateway in Wireless Mesh Networks. *Computer Communications*, **31(7)**, pp. 1259–1275, 2008.

[3] Z.G. Chen, F. Zeng, Minimum-cost gateway placement in wireless mesh networks with QoS constraints. *Communication Networks and Distributed Systems*, **4(4)**, pp. 389–406, 2010.

[4] P. Jian, H.M. Qi, Z.G. Chen, Research of a gateway deployment algorithm for wireless mesh networks based on the limited dominating set. *Computer Engineering & Science*, **33(8)**, pp. 14–18, 2011 (in Chinese).

[5] W.J. Wu, M. Yang, J.Z. Luo, et al., A gateway placement scheme with interference constraints and load balance in wireless mesh networks. *Chinese Journal of Computers*, **35(5)**, pp. 883–897, 2012 (in Chinese).

Matrix iterative reasoning method of causality diagram

Xinyuan Liang
College of Computer Science, Chongqing Technology and Business University, Chongqing, China

Abstract

An approximate reasoning method is presented to solve nondeterministic polynomial hard problem of accurate reasoning in causality diagram. Firstly, this paper discussed AND-gate and OR-gate operator. After analyzing the mechanism of the probability computing and transferring in causality diagram from the point of view of graph theory, an idea to break down the circuit by matrix was introduced. A matrix iterative reasoning method was proposed and computing time complexity of the method was discussed. Lastly, an example demonstrates the effect of the reasoning algorithm. The research shows that the iterative reasoning algorithm of causality diagram is so effective, its reasoning process is rigorous, and the result coincides with the reality. The algorithm is an effective approximating reasoning method for its polynomial time complexity.

Keywords: causality diagram, iteration, reasoning algorithm, matrix, graph.

1 Introduction

Causality diagram (CD) is a method of reasoning and knowledge representation based on probability theory [1]. The main purpose of the reasoning with causality diagram is to work out the posterior probability of a certain event with its known evidence, where evidence means that some basic events or middle events have happened. The probabilities of the basic events and the linkage events in causality diagram are supposed to be known and independent. During the course of reasoning the middle event should be firstly converted into the logic expression of the basic events and linkage events, then the probabilities of the middle events can be worked out. In order to simplify reasoning computation, causality diagram needs to be compiled to gain the expressions of all middle events (i.e., the right of

 WIT Transactions on Information and Communication Technologies, Vol. 61, © 2014 WIT Press
www.witpress.com, ISSN 1743-3517 (on-line)
doi:10.2495/MIIT130421

the logic expression is basic event and linkage event). The reasoning process of causality diagram is in four steps, i.e., calculating the CSs-1 (level-1 cut sets), calculating the CSs-f (final level cut sets), calculating the DCSs-f (final level disjoint cut sets), and calculating posterior probability [2].

Causality diagram is a probabilistic reasoning method that previous work mainly dealt with accurate probability [3]. In fact, it is difficult to dispose in reality because accurate reasoning of Causality diagram is usually NP-hard [4]. It is necessary to introduce approximate reasoning method into causality diagram. This paper proposed an iterative reasoning algorithm for approximate reasoning. The principle idea of iterative reasoning algorithm is calculating the probabilities of middle events through multiplying linkage strength matrix by probability vector and realizing compiling, disjointing, and calculating probability through matrix computing.

The paper is organized as follows. In the next section, we discuss the model that we research in this paper. In Section 3, the reasoning theory of causality diagram based on matrix compiling is presented. Section 4 presents the iterative reasoning algorithm steps based on matrix compiling theory. In Section 5, computing time complexity of the iterative reasoning method is discussed. The computational simulation is made to illustrate the efficiency of the algorithm in Section 6. Finally, we conclude our paper in Section 7.

2 Discussed problems

Convention reasoning of causality diagram is usually NP-hard which order of DCSs-f is, where M is the number of middle events, m is the mean number of basic events of every middle event, R is the mean number of every Cut Set (CS). So the computing workload is very large, and the computing time complexity is very high [5]. Omitting disjoint process, this paper adopts approximate computing by matrix. Its main idea of iterative reasoning algorithm is calculating the probabilities of middle events through multiplying linkage strength matrix by probability vector.

$X = \bigcup_{i=1}^{m} cs_i$ denotes the CSs-f logical formula of a middle event X, where

$cs_i = \bigcap_{j=1}^{n_i} V^{C_i(j)}$ denotes an union random event, m is the number of CS, n_i denotes

the number of nodes in cs_i, $C_i(j)$ is a function which translates subscripts of cs_i into that of nodes in causality diagram.

The purpose of disjoint is that translate OR operator of CSs-f into + operator. The method transforms logical formula into the union of the exclusively OR operator by the formula (1).

$$X = cs_1 + cs_2 \overline{cs_1} + cs_3 \overline{cs_1} \overline{cs_2} + \cdots + cs_m \overline{cs_1} \overline{cs_2} \cdots \overline{cs_{m-1}} \tag{1}$$

where the operator "+" means the exclusively OR operator. After removing again all complement operator, the formula transforms complement state of a node into the union state of the rest node, and expands to get the standard form of DCSs-f.

Now, we discuss the disjointing and calculating probability of causality diagram through matrix computing. The disjointing and calculating probability is combined together in iterative reasoning through multiplying linkage strength matrix by probability vector.

$$V^* = P * V = \begin{bmatrix} p_{11} & p_{21} & \cdots & p_{n1} \\ p_{12} & p_{22} & \cdots & p_{n2} \\ \cdots & \cdots & \cdots & \cdots \\ p_{1n} & p_{2n} & \cdots & p_{nn} \end{bmatrix} \begin{bmatrix} v_1 \\ v_2 \\ \cdots \\ v_n \end{bmatrix} = (v_i)_{n \times 1}, v_i = \sum_{j=1}^{n} p_{ji} v_j \qquad (2)$$

The default relation between the nodes of causality diagram is logical OR relation. Suppose $V_i = \bigcup_{j=1}^{k} P_{ji} V_j 1$, where V_j is any type node. Based on the diamond expression of minicausality tree [6], we have

$$v_i = \Pr(V_i) = \sum_{j=1}^{k} p_{ji} v_j \qquad (3)$$

But the OR relationship of the set need disjoint form to compute probability. According to disjoint form (2), (3) should be written as follows.

$$\Pr(V_i) = \Pr(V_1 \cup V_2) = \Pr(V_1 + V_2 \overline{V_1}) = \Pr(V_1) + \Pr(V_2)(1 - \Pr(V_1))$$

$$v_i = \Pr(V_i) = p_{1i} v_1 + p_{2i} v_2 (1 - p_{1i} v_1) + \cdots + p_{ki} v_k \prod_{j=1}^{k-1} (1 - p_{ji} v_j) \qquad (4)$$

We can find the difference between usual multiplication and multiplication in iterative reasoning algorithm. We refer to Eq. (4) as OR operator of iterative reasoning. $\Pr\{V_i\}$ can be calculated through Eq. (4) if $\Pr\{V_j\}$ is known.

The probability of OR-gate can be expressed in the form of the sum of product i Causality Diagram. However, this form is not adaptive to AND-gate so that it needs to deal with by converting into the OR-gate.

Suppose AND-gate $G = V_1 \cap V_2$, we have $G = V_1 \cap V_2 = \overline{\overline{V_1} \cup \overline{V_2}} 1$

So, we have

$$v(G) = \Pr(G) = \Pr(V_1 \cap V_2) = \Pr(\overline{\overline{V_1} \cup \overline{V_2}}) = 1 - \Pr(\overline{V_1} \cup \overline{V_2})$$

In a general, if $G_i = P_{1i} V_1 \cap P_{2i} V_2 \cdots \cap P_{ki} V_k$, we have

$$v(G_i) = \Pr(G_i) = \Pr(P_{1i} V_1 \cap P_{2i} V_2 \cdots \cap P_{ki} V_k)$$
$$= \Pr(\overline{\overline{P_{1i} V_1} \cup \overline{P_{2i} V_2} \cdots \cup \overline{P_{ki} V_k}}) = 1 - \Pr(\overline{P_{1i} V_1} \cup \overline{P_{2i} V_2} \cdots \cup \overline{P_{ki} V_k}) \qquad (5)$$

We can find the processing method to AND-gate from Eq. (5), that is, adopting Eq. (4) to compute probability after converting AND-gate into OR-gate. We refer to Eq. (5) as AND-operator of iterative reasoning.

Equation (4) actually performed disjointing union set so as to combine the disjointing into computing probability. Therefore, Eqs. (4) and (5) can calculate all probabilities of the middle events of causality diagram.

3 Matrix compiling

Now, we discuss the compiling process by matrix. In fact, Eqs. (4) and (5) logically spread out the middle event and get CSs-1. However, it is necessary to farther spread and decompose causality circuit to gain CSs-f. So some definitions are necessary to give as follows.

Theorem 1 If DP_{1k} is the only path with linkage event $P_{i,i+1}(i=1,2,\cdots,k-1)$ from V_1 to V_k, the length is L, we have

$$\Pr(V_k) = \Pr(V^I(DP)) = \prod_{i=1}^{L-1} p_{i,i+1} \Pr(V^O(DP)) = \prod_{i=1}^{L-1} p_{i,i+1} \Pr(V_1) \qquad (6)$$

The length of the longest basic path is no more than the basic number of nodes [7]. Thus,

Theorem 2 If M is the number of the middle event nodes in causality diagram D. Then the length of longest path in corresponding causality tree is no more than M.

Theorem 3 P is linkage strength matrix of causality diagram, m, n is natural number, then

(1) $P^m * P^n = P^{m+n}$;

(2) $(P^m)^n = P^{mn}$.

Theorem 4 Let $pr_{ij} \in P^k$, $pr_{ij} > 0$ denotes that there are k paths from V_j to V_i and the convergent linkage strength is pr_{ij}, then $\Pr(V_i) = pr_{ij} \Pr(V_j)$.

We can conclude that P^k denotes reachability among nodes in causality diagram through only k edges from Theorem 3.

Theorem 5 Let M is the number of the middle event in causality diagram D, then the iterative steps that we can gain the final probability values of all middle events is no more than M.

Let the number of the middle event in causality diagram D is M. So, we can get the CSs-f of all middle events after no more than M iterative steps.

Theorem 6 If M is the number of the middle event in causality diagram D, then the iterative steps that we can gain the CSs-f of all middle events is no more than M.

Theorem 7 If M is the number of the middle event in causality diagram D, then we can gain the CSs-f of all middle events at most after using M-edge reachable matrix.

Based on above analyses, let the number of the middle event in causality diagram D is M, the matrix method of decomposing circuit is as follows:

(1) We let $pr_{ii} = 0$ in the computing process of reachable matrix.
(2) Number k in k-edge reachable matrix that we use to decompose circuit is no more than M.

The first step gets rid of all circuits which lengths are no more than M, as well the second step gets rid of all circuits which lengths are more than M, that is, the two steps get rid of all circuits. The computing efficiency of the decomposing circuit method is very high.

Through above-mentioned discussion, adopting matrix compiles causality diagram and decomposes all logical circuits of causality diagram.

Theorem 8 Let the number of the middle event in causality diagram D is M, then we can gain the probability values of all middle events at most after using M-edge reachable matrix.

That is, the linkage strengths of Eqs. (4) and (5) are in reachable matrix.

Theorem 9 Let the number of the middle event in Causality diagram D is M, $V^k (1 \le k \le M)$ means probability vector which is gained passing through only just k edges, then we can gain the final probability values as follow.

$$V = V^1 + V^2(1 - V^1) + \cdots + V^M \prod_{k=1}^{M-1} (1 - V^{M-1}) \tag{7}$$

4 Iterative reasoning algorithm

Iterative process needs three elements, such as initial value, iterative updating and end condition [6]. Based on above-mentioned analysis of iterative reasoning process, we can conclude that the initial value is V_0, the iterative updating rules is Eqs. (6) and (7), and the end conditions is the numbers of the middle events. Therefore, the iterative reasoning algorithm of causality diagram is given as follow.

Step 1: Constructing N-order linkage strength matrix P and initial vector V_0 based on the Causality diagram Model and its probabilities of the basic events.
Step 2: Consequently computing the k-edge reachable matrix $PR_k (2 \le k \le m + r)$ through applying matrix method of decomposing logically circuits;
Step 3: $k = 1$;
Step 4: Letting $V_k = 0$, then computing V_k according to the node probabilities in V_{k-1};
Step 5: $i = 1$;
Step 6: If node V_i is logical AND-gate, then goto step 8;
Step 7: Adopting (4) to calculate probability V_i of node V_i;
Step 8: Converting AND-gate into OR-gate and applying (5) to compute probability V_i of node V_i;

Step 9: If $i \leq N$, turning to step6;

Step 10: Gaining probability vector;

Step 11: If $k \leq m + r$, turning to step4

Step 12: Disjointing the all edges probability vectors V_k so as to get the probability vector of Causality, that is, Get all probabilities of the middle events including logical gate event.

Step 13: The reasoning is over, Algorithm stop.

5   Analyses and discussions of algorithm

Iterative reasoning algorithm combines decomposing circuit, gaining CSs-f, gaining DCSs-f and calculating probability into the matrix multiplication. Now we discuss the computing complexity of the iterative reasoning. M denotes numbers of middle events, n is number of basic event, and N denotes number of all nodes. The second step carries on decomposing circuit through reachable matrix with the computing time complexity $O(N^3)$. Through step 3 to step 12, we can gain CSs-f , DCSs-f and probability by the matrix multiplication. The time complexity from step 3 to step 11 is $O(N^3)$, as well as 12 with $O(N^2)$. The computing time complexity of iterative reasoning algorithm of causality diagram is $O(N^3)$, i.e., it is a polynomial time complexity. Its complexity is sharply descend comparing with conventional reasoning algorithm which complexity is $O((R)^{(M\,!(M/n))})$ so that it reduce NP-hard problem to polynomial time complexity and improve reasoning efficiency. Therefore, the iterative reasoning algorithm based on matrix which is proposed in this paper is a high efficient reasoning algorithm; it is very valuable to theory and application of causality diagram.

6   Computational examples and analysis

In order to illustrate the feasibility and effectiveness of the algorithm, we construct an example according to examples in literature [8] (Figure 1).

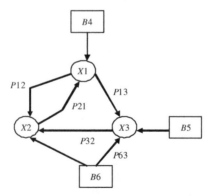

Figure 1: An example causality diagram.

Table 1: Probability Vector Table.

Event	V_1	V_2	V_3	V_4	V_5	V_6	V
X_1	0.2	0.0682	0	0	0	0	0.2546
X_2	0.3	0.1082	0.0006	0	0	0	0.3761
X_3	0.436	0.1021	0	0	0	0	0.4936

Table 2: Results Comparison of Iterative Reasoning and Conventional Reasoning.

Event	Conventional Reasoning	Iterative Reasoning	Error	Error Rate (%)
X_1	0.253376	0.2546	−0.001184	−0.46729
X_2	0.386352	0.3761	0.01023744	2.649771
X_3	0.512416	0.4936	0.0188316	3.675061
sum	1.152144	1.124259	0.02788504	2.420274

All probability values of the basic events and the linkage events are as follows. $P_{12} = 0.3, P_{13} = 0.4, P_{21} = 0.2, P_{32} = 0.1, P_{63} = 0.2$, we can get linkage strength matrix.

Initial probability vector V_0=[0 0 0 0.2 0.3 0.4]'.

Through the iterative reasoning algorithm of causality diagram, we can obtain the following results.

Table 1 shows the probability vector $V^k (1 \leq k \leq 6)$ by passing through k edges and the probability vector V of causality diagram by disjoint so as to gain the probabilities of the middle events. For the sake of analysis, we gain $V^k (4 \leq k \leq 6)$, that the probability is very small or even zero so that it should be omitted. This further explains that the iterative algorithm is effective to reason when the iteration time of algorithm is the number of the middle events.

Table 2 gives the comparison of the result probabilities of iterative reasoning with conventional reasoning. Result analysis illuminates that the results of iterative reasoning and conventional reasoning are very close, that is, the error is very small and in the acceptable range. We can see that the iterative reasoning algorithm can get the right result and the effect is very good, so it is an efficient algorithm for approximate reasoning.

7   Conclusions

Causality diagram is a probabilistic reasoning method that previous work mainly dealt with accurate reasoning. However, accurate reasoning is NP hard. So the approximate reasoning becomes an important reasoning method of causality diagram. Firstly, this paper discussed AND-gate and OR-gate operator. After analyzing the mechanism of the probability computing and transferring in causality diagram from the point of view of graph theory, an idea to break down the circuit by matrix was introduced, and an iterative reasoning algorithm based on reachable matrix was proposed. The iterative algorithm is effective to reason when the iteration time of algorithm is the number of the middle events, so that it is an effective approximating reasoning algorithm for its polynomial time complexity. An example demonstrates the effect of the reasoning algorithm in Section 6. Result analysis illuminates that the results of iterative reasoning and conventional reasoning are very close. In this paper, this work which provides an approximate reasoning method for causality diagram is important to develop the theory and application of causality diagram.

Acknowledgment

The work described here was supported by Science Technology Project of Chongqing Education Committee under Grant No. KJ120718 and Natural Science Foundation Project of Chongqing Municipal under Grant No. CSTC 2010BB2259.

References

[1] Qin Zhang, Probabilistic reasoning based on dynamic causality tree/diagrams. *Reliability Engineering and System Safety*, **46(3)**, pp. 209–220, 1994.

[2] Qin Zhang, A new methodology to deal with dynamical uncertain causalities (I): the static discrete DAG case. *Chinese Journal of Computers*, **33(4)**, pp. 625–651, 2010 (in Chinese).

[3] Hongchun Wang, An efficient dimension-adaptive uncertainty propagation approach. *Applied Mathematics and Computation*, **218(7)**, pp. 3230–3237, 2011.

[4] Xinhua Fan, Qin Zhang, Maosong Sun, et al., Reasoning algorithm in multi-value causality diagram. *Chinese Journal of Computers*, **16(3)**, pp. 310–323, 2003 (in Chinese).

[5] Qin Zhang, Xuegao An, Jin Gu, et al., Application of FBOLES – a prototype expert system for fault diagnosis in nuclear power plants. *Reliability Engineering and System Safety*, **34(2)**, pp. 225–235, 1991.

[6] Qin Zhang, Dynamic uncertain causality graph for knowledge representation and reasoning: discrete DAG cases. *Journal of Computer Science and Technology*, **27(1)**, pp. 1–23, 2012.

[7] Shu-gui Du, An algorithm for finding all directed circuits and directed walk from its digraph. *Journal of Circuits and Systems*, **4(4)**, pp. 83–85, 1999 (in Chinese).

[8] S.T. Ding, M.Y. Bao, Causality diagram based safety analysis of micro turbojet engine. *Transactions of Nanjing University of Aeronautics and Astronautics*, **28(3)**, pp. 262–268, 2011.

Current research and developing trend of oil condition monitoring

Xinyuan Liang
Engineering Research Center for Waste Oil Recovery Technology and Equipment of Ministry of Education, Chongqing Technology and Business University, Chongqing, China
College of Computer Science, Chongqing Technology and Business University, Chongqing, China

Abstract

It is very important for oil condition monitoring because oil is the blood of machine equipment, and its condition have very serious influence on machine running. After reviewing the current research of oil condition monitoring, the developing trend of oil condition monitoring was discussed in this paper. The research shows that on-line monitoring is the developing trend of oil condition monitoring.

Keywords: oil, condition, monitoring, current research, trend.

1 Introduction

The oil, which mainly includes lubricating oil, hydraulic oil, cooling fluid or cooling oil etc., is the blood of mechanical device. Lubricating oil in machinery equipment plays important roles, such as sealing, lubricating, less grinding, cooling, cleaning, reducing vibration, anti-corrupting, and so on. Hydraulic oil which is the liquid medium using of liquid pressure energy in the hydraulic system, plays in important affections, such as transferring energy, system lubricating, cooling, preventing corrosion and rusting, and so on. Cooling fluid is the special-purpose cooling medium of the cooling system, and its superiority is super more than that of tap water, distilled water and antifreeze fluid with poor quality.

Performance indicators of various oil products should meet the quality requirements of its products, the oil can only qualified to play a good role on the device. In use for some time, due to high temperature, high shear, the outside impurities and its reaction of oxidation and other reasons, the physical and chemical properties of oil, such as additive content, viscosity, flash point, total acid number, impurity content and moisture content etc. will be changed so as to drop the use performance. While the changing beyond a certain limit, the oil will lose its performance, so oil must be timely stopped and replaced. Using the deterioration oil will lead to a sharply increased deposits, decreased engine power performance, decreased equipment performance, and parts increased wearing, and even cause serious system failure so as to result in disastrous consequences for the machinery equipment [1]. Conversely, if the oil is used in normal performance, the renewal of oil will result in waste of resources. Therefore, in order to avoid these problems and determine a reasonable oil change time, it is necessary to real-time monitor of oil condition, which measures the extent of oil deterioration and oil quality through a certain monitoring data.

The paper is organized as follows. In the next section, we review the current research of oil condition monitoring. In Section 3, t the developing trend of oil condition monitoring is concluded. Finally, we conclude our paper in section 4.

2   Current research of oil condition monitoring

Oil contaminants include wear particles of parts, corrosion products, as well as gum, asphalt, sludge and other combustion products through a series of physical and chemical changes of lubricants and additives. To some extent, a variety of pollutants are all associated with the use state of mechanical equipment and oil, because lubrication oil in use bears with very rich tribological state information from the surface of the machine's campaign deputy. Usually, the oil analysis mainly carries on, pollution measurement and the analysis of partial physics and chemistry performance. The analysis of metal particle is most important in oil analysis because it can detect, locate and forecast the failure of machine parts soaked by oil. At present, the analysis of metal particle in the oil is mainly completed by all kinds of spectroscope instruments and ferrograph instruments, dustiness analysis is mainly completed by all kinds of pollution particle counter, and the determination instrument of physics and chemistry performance has the viscometer, the moisture meter, the pH meter, the flash point tester and so on.

(1) International Current Research of Oil Condition Monitoring
In 1941, American railway industry took the lead in using spectral analysis method to railway locomotive for oil analysis and had made tremendous benefit. In 1950s, the U.S. Navy began to implement the oil spectrum analysis of the jet engines. In the late 1950s and early 1960s, the U.S. Army and Air Force carry out furnishing oil monitoring equipment at large. With the advent of ferrography technology, oil monitoring technology in the United States, Germany, Japan and other developed countries have developed rapidly. In 1970s, the U.S. Navy began to implement oil monitoring for shipboard equipment.

In 1980s, through jointly endeavoring and actively exploring by the academia and industry, the oil monitoring technology has become the main method of the system of equipment diagnostics. In 1990s, the gas chromatography and mass spectrograph have been used to measure the composition changes of lubricating oil. Furthermore, the oil detection technology has developed toward the directions, such as, the integration of a variety of methods, the off-line methods, the on-line methods, the intelligent apparatus, and so on. To 90 years, only U.S. Navy has 12,000 kinds of aviation parts and 20,000 kinds of marine parts in oil monitoring. Ford International Inc. of U.S.A in the early 1990s developed the system which can monitor the oil decay by measuring the relationship between the viscosity and the conductivity of insulation of the lubricant oil, but the accuracy of the test system was less and difficult to apply to the actual instance.

Since the twenty-first century, while the oil pollution analysis technology has matured and perfected, people have paid more and more attention on the application of condition monitoring and fault diagnosis for the equipment; matching the low-cost, full-featured, and stable performance instrument, the technology has become the preferred method of general enterprise. In developed countries the oil pollution monitoring have been applied in the condition monitoring for rotating machinery, reciprocating machinery, machine processing equipment, electrical equipment and engineering machinery, and so on. With simple detecting principle, the detector method for degree of oil contamination represented the future development direction of practical rapid oil contamination detector. With scientific and technological progress and development, new instruments for monitoring and fault diagnosis of the equipment had been successfully developed and manufactured, which made the constantly perfection and development of the relatively new application technology of oil pollution monitoring. In the United States, Germany, Japan and other developed countries, the oil quality monitoring technology has been applied to vehicles, and some vehicle, has equipped it as a general configuration to ensure the replacement of lubricant according to the quality of oil in use [2].

In the development process of oil testing technology, the oil joint analysis technology gradually developed.

In January 1976, joint oil analysis program (JOAP) was mandatorily set up according to U.S. military demand. By October 2002, JOAP in 18 countries had established more than 300 laboratories, and it had more than 440 sets of the oil spectrum analyzer and had promulgated a series of technical specifications of oil monitoring, which may effectively monitor the military equipment, such as, aircraft, ships, helicopters, tanks and armored vehicles and radar equipment, and so on. JOAP formed by the armed forces had dual leadership by this service and joint organization. The laboratory distributed according to the regional distribution, not according to the administrative division of the army. Due to the implementation of the joint oil analysis program, inter-service joint guarantee was achieved, and the distribution of JOAP laboratories become more reasonable; Furthermore, JOAP had promoted the exchange of information to avoid a lot of duplication effort, and had achieved significant military and economic effects.

(2) Chinese Current Research of Oil Condition Monitoring

Since the early 1980s China gradually carried out the oil pollution control technology and management measures in all industrial departments. Chinese oil monitoring technology development initially focused on the application research of iron spectrum analysis technology. Its period of rapid development is from the early 1980s to early 1990s, the application research of the oil pollution control technology had been gradually performed in industrial departments, such as, machinery, coal, aviation and shipbuilding, etc.

First, the academic research of oil detection technology rapid developed. Since the First National Symposium on Iron Spectrum was held on October, 1986 in Guangzhou, China, Chinese oil monitoring technology had developed to some extent. In order to adapt to the needs of the international standard, The Iron Spectrum Technology Committee was renamed the Oil Monitoring Committee in the Fifth National Symposium on Iron Spectrum, and its sixth national meeting of the oil monitoring technology was held on November, 2002 in Shanghai, China. Six conference proceedings were published, which showed that the abundant Chinese scientific research and extensive application on industry had been made in this area. Since 1994, the formulation of integrated diagnosis gradually increased. After the fifth session in 1999, the papers about tribological diagnostic techniques based on oil monitoring technology gradually increased in the relevant journals.

Second, China research and development of oil analysis and monitoring equipment has made great progress. By 1985, Chinese iron spectrometer, including the domestic product, has nearly 100 units, with worth 300 to 500 million RMB. For example, there were PCC-type portable oil pollution detector, THY-18F-type oil detector, and OLF-4 four-channel on-line ferrography developed by Xi'an Jiaotong University, and so on.

Since the early 1980s, China has carried out the oil analysis on the aircraft, ships, vehicles and other large-scale projects implemented; China has established a large number of oil analysis laboratory, and some departments and industry have also built a professional oil monitoring technology center; furthermore China has issued a series of oil analysis industry standards and obtained a large number of high-level research.

However, there is still a considerable gap between technology and management level of oil pollution control in China and that in major developed countries, which the oil contamination degree is generally 3-4 times higher than developed countries so that the high failure rate and short component life have seriously affected the performance of full equipment. Thus, Chinese research on the oil pollution control which is still a weak link should be strengthened and improved [3]. From the early 1980s to the early 1990s, Chinese oil monitoring technology had always been focused on the analysis of iron spectrum or the joint analysis of iron spectrum and spectrum with a single mean, and the researchers had put too much emphasis on the trend analysis of wear element and wears particle analysis. In recent years, most people still focused on researching and finding the phenomenon about abnormal wear of equipment.

At present, China has basically adopted the traditional model of replacement oil according to observing or schedule, that is, the change time of lubricant oil is determined by virtue of observation, experience and subjective judgments or change cycle.

Chinese oil analysis mainly depends on the professional oil analysis laboratory, which the main object is the analysis of lubrication systems and hydraulic systems various types of large machinery, with the mainly instrument of spectrum analyzers and contamination degree detector, the evaluation method of lubricant oil has on-line mode and off-line mode. Currently, the project mainly uses off-line technology for the monitoring of oil performance and status, which oil samples by on-site collection are sent to the monitoring center for the test of physical and chemical properties.

These instruments with huge volume are only used for off-line analysis in the laboratory environment, not suitable for on-line or on-site analysis test; its process takes a long time to sample from the field to the laboratory, which does not meet the requirements of real-time; These instruments which are generally more expensive with high test cost and high technical requirements for maintenance and operation are not applicable to the scene monitoring.

The traditional oil monitoring technology mainly adopts off-line sampling analysis method which requires expensive precision instruments and testing for a long time. With the development of modern industry, modern mechanical systems become more complex, sophisticated and high-performance, and the oil monitoring requirements get more and more high so that the traditional oil monitoring technology is not conducive to mechanical systems for early diagnosis and prevention of failure, and not suitable for engineering field use. Such systems are characterized by timely information to reflect mechanical equipment, mobility, simple operation, suitable field, and easily equipped with large quantities for its low price.

Because the oil off-line detection equipment can't meet the requirements of real-time oil monitoring, on-line detection technology and portable testing equipment come into being.

At present, the oil detection technology mainly includes spectroscopy analysis, infrared spectroscopy analysis, iron spectral analysis, particle counting, and analysis of physical and chemical indicators. Spectral analysis method includes atomic emission spectrometry, atomic absorption spectrometry, infrared spectroscopy and X-ray fluorescence spectrometry.

3   Trend of oil condition monitoring

In recent years, all kinds of mechanical equipment were advanced and complex, so the new requirements of oil analysis technology were put forward. The rapid technology development of electronics, information, artificial intelligence and micro machining etc and the development of the fault diagnosis theory has laid the foundation for innovation of oil monitoring technology. Since the 21st century, with the unceasing development of oil monitoring technology, the oil monitoring has developed from the conventional detection by physical and chemical indexes and iron spectral detection to joint analysis by five monitoring technologies, including physical and chemical analysis, contamination degree detecting, infrared spectrum analysis, the emission spectrum analysis, and iron spectral analysis. The development of monitoring tester turns toward the direction of miniaturization and develop, and the detection mode develops from off-line monitoring to on-line monitoring. The main developing trend of oil condition monitoring is as follows.

(1) Development of embedded sensors, on-line monitoring equipment and on-line monitoring system.

By the use of electronic technology and signal processing technology, developed countries have developed many kinds of new embedded sensors for oil analysis so as to save analysis time and ensure the timeliness of diagnosis. There are some successfully applied instruments, such as, the on-line analysis instrument for lubricant wear metal by X-ray fluorescence manufactured by in the U.S. Based on all kinds of embedded sensors for oil analysis, various countries has developed the on-line oil monitoring system for different types of weapons and equipments.

(2) Development of portable and micro instrument.

In recent years, small portable devices used for oil on-line monitoring have been researched and developed, and various countries have developed a variety of portable general-purpose instruments for oil analysis in the field use and compensate for the lack of on-line oil monitoring system. These instruments are characterized by low cost, small size, light weight, portable, simple operation and fast detection, so they are applicable to field conditions for low environmental requirements and the simple and rapid characteristics. Moreover, Li Jianbo and Wan Jia-fu put forward the digital detector of lube oil based on single chip computer [4]. However, without achieving real-time requirements, these portable instruments can't continuously monitor the performance parameters of the oil to know its use state, so its uses have also been limited under certain conditions.

(3) Development of comprehensive instrument with multi-parameter and multi-function.

It needs a large amount of manpower, material and time to do multi-parameter testing for an oil sample through traditional single-function instruments due to requiring a variety of instruments. To better determine the performance and status of oil, it is necessary for multi-parameter and multi-dimensional analysis, which can measure oil solid particles, water, air, oxides and so on. Therefore, the development of comprehensive instrument with multi-parameter and multi-function is universal concerned by various countries. In 2001, the United Kingdom Foster-Miller Company had successfully developed the oil condition monitoring device [5], which can simultaneously measure the total acid oil, moisture, thermal oxidation decomposition, coolant dilution, coke deposition, nitrification, vulcanization, additive loss. The instrument has been used in the U.S. Navy Nimitz-class Aircraft Carrier.

(4) Development of intelligent and automotive instrument and system by intelligent information technology.

With the development of computer technology, the pursuit goals of oil monitoring technology is to develop the database, data processing procedures, auxiliary diagnosis system and the intelligent expert system for fault diagnosis with comprehensive technology of oil monitoring. According to oil analysis data, automatic fault location and analysis of particle morphology is the bottleneck of oil analysis. Due to the development of artificial intelligence technology and image recognition technology, the solutions to the two issues have made breakthrough progress in recent years. The abrasive image database has been developed in research on automatic identification technology for abrasive image which also depends on the development of computer vision technology. Xiao Jianwei et al. proposed the lubricating oil monitoring technology based upon grey theory [6]; Zhang Xianming et al. put forward the oil contamination monitoring system based on the image analysis and processing [7].

(5) Providing remote service of diagnosis and oil analysis by network.

Information technology and network technology is so advanced and maturity to provide users with on-line oil analysis services. The establishment of a remote detecting service system not only accelerates technical cooperation and information exchange, but also provides strong technical support for oil detecting analysis of hydraulic equipment far away from the technology center. Long Xiaoguang et al. developed the on-line query system of oil monitoring to real-time process remote oil diagnostic information [8]. The foundation of a remote detecting and analyzing service system not only accelerates technical cooperation and information exchange, but also provides strong technical support for oil analysis service for the equipment such as ships and warships far away from the technology base.

(6) Performing a comprehensive condition monitoring of machines with the integration of information by other monitoring method.

The multi-sensor information fusion thought among the oil monitoring methods and between the oil monitoring method with other monitoring method, such as vibration monitor, temperature monitor and performance parameter monitor etc. is applied and developed to improve the accuracy of oil monitoring. Using information fusion technology, overall information data which are gained through many kinds of detecting methods, such as, oil pollution, pressure, current capacity, and vibration etc, could implement a comprehensive condition examination for hydraulic system. With the widespread use of information fusion technology in oil analysis, developed country made comprehensive use of many kinds of monitor methods including oil analysis and vibration analysis and other monitoring tools in monitoring the machinery and equipment.

From the above analysis, we can see that on-line testing technique is the development trend of oil testing technology. The on-line oil detection technology can real-timely monitor the oil quality and grasp the reasonable time to replace oil so as to realize the energy-saving and emission-reduction. Based on the wear debris analysis, the real-time wear status of equipment is used to forecast failures and predictive maintenance, obviously enhance normal operation life of machinery and equipment. The technology can promote the key technology of the large-scale machinery equipment, greatly boost the reliability and service life, and vastly upgrade the level of equipment manufacturing industry. Therefore, the on-line oil detection technology has widely application prospects. The on-line detection technology is the research hotspot of oil analysis in recent years.

4 Conclusions

The technology and its application of on-line oil detection is a research hot of the current oil treatment technology, and the research has the important academic significance and the application value. After reviewing the current research of oil condition monitoring, the developing trend of oil condition monitoring is concluded in this paper. Furthermore, this paper especially pointed out that on-line monitoring is the developing trend of oil condition monitoring. The on-line oil monitoring technology may be widely applied on he oil monitoring, pollution analysis and the use of maintenance measures of the high-speed precision numerically-controlled machine tool, the heavy equipment, the numerical control system and the functional unit. The technology research of on-line oil monitoring may greatly improve the detection efficiency, and reduce detecting costs and maintenance costs, so as to greatly improve the level of the oil handling technology.

Acknowledgments

The work described here was supported by Science Technology Project of Chongqing Education Committee under Grant No. KJ120718 and Natural Science Foundation Project of Chongqing Municipal under Grant No. CSTC 2010BB2259.

References

[1] Yumei Liu, Qingnian Wang, Xiaoning Cao, et al., Vehicle lubrication oil on-line monitoring method and monitoring system. *Journal of Jilin University*, **39(6)**, pp. 1441–1145, 2009 (in Chinese).

[2] Jinlong Xu, Oil sensor development of foreign automotive engine. *Lubricating Oil*, **20(3)**, pp. 2–4, 2000 (in Chinese).

[3] Hongshu Zhou, History and current status of oil monitoring and its prospects in China. *Material Protection*, **16(7)**, pp. 154–156, 2004 (in Chinese).

[4] Jianbo Li, Jiafu Wan, Digital detector of lube oil based on single chip computer. *Coal Mine Machinery*, **30(1)**, pp. 207–208, 2009 (in Chinese).

[5] R. Rowe, P. Henning, R. Damren, et al., On-line oil condition monitor. *JOAP International Condition Monitoring Conference*, Mobile, Alabama, pp. 20–25, 2002.

[6] Jianwei Xiao, Dingxin Yang, Zheng Hu, et al., Research of oil monitoring technology based upon grey theory and dielectric constant measurement. *Synthetic Lubricants*, **36(4)**, pp. 15–18, 2009 (in Chinese).

[7] Xianming Zhang, Yumei Jia, Chuan Li, et al., Image processing system of oil contamination level. *Instrument Technique and Sensor*, **14(2)**, pp. 84–86, 2008 (in Chinese).

[8] Wenhe Lv, Development of moisture percentage on-line monitoring system for high speed wire rod mill. *Mechanical Engineering & Automation*, **28(6)**, pp. 108–109, 2008 (in Chinese).

A semantic extension with ontology-learning to improve a information retrieval system

Rui Zhang[1,2], Hong Liu[2]
[1]*Department of Computer, Shandong Normal University, Jinan, 250014, China*
[2]*Shandong Institute of Medicine and Health Information, Jinan, 250014, China*

Abstract

The traditional keyword-based retrieval has failed to extract hidden knowledge in uncertain and imprecise data. In order to solve the problem, we presented a sematic extension retrieval framework with ontology learning. The framework extended the query and gave the full-text retrieval results by calculating the semantic relatedness and the document ontology weight. At the same time, the ontology leaning used the artificial bee colony algorithm to extract the semantic knowledge implied in the literature. We tested the system in enzyme ontology. The results show the improvement of the precision and recall compared with the keyword-based retrieval.
Keywords: semantic extension, ontology leaning, artificial bee colony algorithm

1 Introduction

The semantic extension is a method of analysis query by adding the related words to the initial keyword with the domain ontology model. This method can get more accurate and more comprehensive results compared with the traditional keyword retrieval. Diaz-Galiano [1] used the descriptors of MeSH to expand the queries by adding medical information such as MeSH headings and the synonym of the term, and evaluated the system's effectiveness with mean uninterpolated average precision (MAP). Segura [2] presented a simple method which extends the query word with the adjacent concept at the base of gene ontology. But the type of the expansion is divided into three: is a part of and specific relationship. The specific relationship includes negative and positive regulations. Robles [3] made the domain ontology into a graph. The expert defined the weight of each relationship and calculated the ratio of the shortest distance and the longest distance after expansion. If the value was closed to 1, the concept did not add to the query. Jing [4] extended the query with domain knowledge dictionary. The recall ratio is improved. The result was calculated by the correlation of expansion of the query and the correlation of the mapping in ontology. Hu [5] built and extended the retrieval intention tree of initial query by calculating the concept similarity through ontology model and extended the query word with the shortest pathway.

Consequently, the technique of semantic expansion uses different forms and methods for query expansion by expanding the search word with the upper and lower ontology concepts. The retrieval results showed the semantic extension can raise the recall effectively, but the precision was improved a little. So the way of query extension need to calculate based on the domain ontology in order to control the scope and effectiveness of the semantic extension. The methods depend on the different domain ontology bases. For example, a method [2] was used in gene ontology. If the domain ontology can get learning ability from the literature resources, the semantic expansion will be improved.

We present a semantic extension full-text retrieval system with ontology learning and its application in the enzyme domain. The ontology learning extracts the concept from literature with the artificial bee colony algorithm. This can solve the matching query problem better and enhance the ability of analysis the latent semantic in the literature.

2 The framework of the system

In this study, a new semantic extension information retrieval mechanism has been developed. This model includes three parts: ontology annotation full-text index, full-text retrieval based on semantic extension and the ontology learning using the artificial bee colony algorithm. The ontology annotation, semantic extension, and ontology learning has been utilized as the technical basis to design the mechanism, through which the user can perform semantic-basic information retrieval in the following processes: (1) The ontology learning extracts the complex concept by using the artificial bee colony algorithm to search in the corpus. The expert adds the candidate domain concepts into the domain ontology. (2) The ontology annotation [6] make the document into the index based on enzyme domain, this is the foundation of the full-text retrieval. (3) The full-text retrieval expends the query word and make the full-text research, and the result is reordered by the semantic relatedness. The semantic extension information retrieval system based on ontology learning is shown in Figure 1.

Index writer adds the documents to the index and prepares for the analyzer doing ontology annotation. The index writer is the core component to construct the index.

Index reader reads the index and gets ready for the full-text retrieval. The index reader is the core component to retrieve.

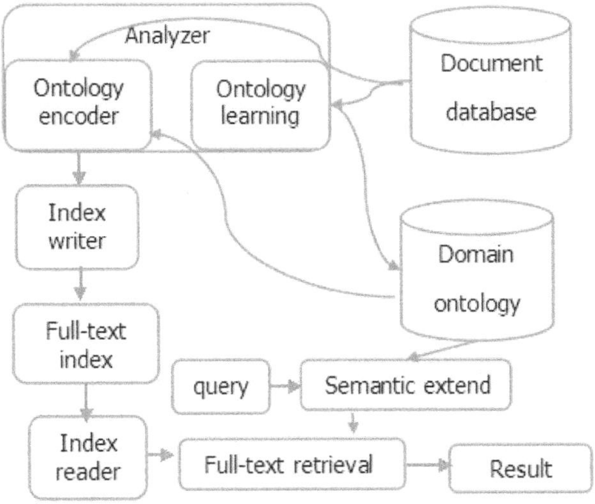

Figure 1: Architecture of semantic extension information retrieval system based on ontology learning.

Analyzer pretreatments the content of the documents by ontology annotation, send the content to the index writer, and also matches the query keyword to domain ontology.

Ontology encoder is the subcomponent of the analyzer. It encodes the elements in the domain ontology into an efficient multi-tree. The multi-tree is used for ontology annotation and matching the query keyword to domain ontology.

Ontology learning is another component of the analyzer. It extracts the domain concepts from the corpus. The domain ontology will grow in maturity with the increase of the documents. So the query expand can interpret the semantic of the query keyword more accurately. This makes the system gaining capability of learning.

Semantic extends the query which has matched to domain ontology, adds the hyponymy word to the query forming the new query vector.

Full-text retrieval makes the full-text retrieval and reorder the result finally.

3   The ontology learning with ABC

3.1 The fitness function

In this study, we define the function with the domain relevancy. The main idea is that a word may be a domain terminology: if the probability of the word existing in the front-ground corpus   is higher than the probability of the word existing in the back-ground corpus.

The domain relevancy is the relevancy of the concepts in domain. The domain sets set = $\{D_1,...,D_k\}$, the domain relevancy of a terminology t to a domain D_k is defined as followed:

$$f(t) = \lg\left(\frac{P(t \mid Cf_k)}{P(t \mid Cb_k)}\right) \times \lg(TF_{t,k})$$

The conditional probability $P(t|Cf_k)$ is the probability of t in the front-ground corpus Cf_k; $P(t|Cb_k)$ is the probability of t in the back-ground corpus Cb_k.

$$E(P(t \mid Cf_k)) = \frac{TF_{t,k}}{mf_k}$$

$$E(P(t \mid Cb_k)) = \frac{\sum_{Cf_j \in Cb_k} tf_{t,j}}{mb_k}$$

$TF_{t,i}$ is the frequency of t in front-ground corpus Cf_k , mf_i is the numbers of documents in Cf_i, mb_k is the numbers of documents in back-ground corpus Cb_k, $tf_{t,j}$ is the number of a word t appear in the documents c_j.

3.2 The ABC

We use the ABC algorithm to search the domain concepts in the corpus. The artificial bee colony algorithm is a new population-based metaheuristic approach. This approach is inspired by the intelligent foraging behavior of honeybee swarm.

In this study, the algorithm searches the words relevant to domain knowledge automatically by adopting the optimization principle. The process of searching for concepts is like looking for high yield of the food source. The scout employed foraging bees are those bees those are currently searching for new food sources. It can enlarge solution. The onlookers employed foraging bees are waiting for the information to be shared by the employed bees about their food sources. It can speed up the convergence of the algorithm. The food source is the possible solution to the problem.The nectar amount is the fitness function of the algorithm.

The procedure of the algorithm is as follows:

Step 1: The algorithm starts by associating all employed bees with randomly generated food sources (solution).

$$x_i^j = x_{min}^j + rand(0,1) * (x_{max}^j - x_{min}^j)$$

Step 2: The scout employed foraging bees search the neighborhood of initial solution and calculate the fitness function of the individual.

$$x_i^j = x_i^j + rand(-1,1) * (x_i^j - x_k^j)$$

Step 3: If the fitness function is below the threshold 0,we need to give it up and go to step 1 to generate the new individuals randomly.
Step 4: If it do not satisfy the end condition, then go to step 2.
Step 5: Output of the optimum solution.

4   Semantic extension and full-text retrieval

The semantic extension strategy has two parts: extending the keyword and reordering the results. First, the terminology in the ontology was found to match the keywords submitted by the users, search the instance, and attribute of the keyword in the ontology concept node, and extend the hyponymy word as a new query vector to retrieve the full text in the document database. Last, the semantic relatedness and the document ontology weight were computed as the parameter to filter out the irrelevant results.

4.1 Semantic relatedness

Make the set of constraint relations between ontology elements as a vector system, O = [F C S I R A]. F represents the concept of parent class collection, C represents the concept of the class collection, S represents the concept of the subclass collection, I represents the concept of the instance collection, R represents the concept of the relation collection, A represents the concept of the attribute collection. Each vector values a binary function{0 1}. If the vector shows significantly, then take 1, else take 0. For initial keyword Gi, let the m represents the number of vectors value is 1; for extended keyword Ei, let the n represents the number of vectors value is 1. Make the initial keyword and extended keyword transformed into vector matrix, the formula of semantic relatedness is defined as follows:

$$relatedness = \frac{1}{2}\left[\frac{l}{m} + \frac{l}{n}\right]$$

4.2 Document ontology weight

The document ontology weight is associated with the domain ontology. The element in different domain ontology has different weight. The weight of the class ra, instance ri and attribute ra can be described as follows:

1.   The weight of the concept root node is 1.
2.   If C has subclass c' ,then $rc\ = \Sigma\ rc'$
3.   If I is the instance of the subclass c', then $rc' = \Sigma ri$.

4.   If a class or subclass have m attributes, then $\sum_{j=1}^{m} ra_j = 1$

The value of document ontology weight is the sum of the weight of the ontology elements in the document:

$$rd = \sum_{m=1}^{m} rc_m + \sum_{n=1}^{n} ri_n + \sum_{p=1}^{p} ra_p$$

4.3 Full-text retrieval

The full-text retrieval is achieved by the information retrieval of vector space model. The document d is closer to the query condition q, the higher score of the document gets. The computational formula is as follows:

$$score(q,d) = \arctan(a\square relateness)queryNorm(q)\sum_{t\in q}\left(tf\,(t\in d\,)\square idf\,(t)^2\square norm(t,d)\right)$$

1. $tf\,(t\in d)$ is the frequency of each word existed in the documents. The frequency of query keyword is higher, the higher score of the documents gets. The computational formula is : $f\,(t\in d) = frequency^{1/2}$

2. $idf\,(t)$ is the inverse document frequency. This function indicates the keyword exist on how many documents in the whole document database. The occurrence number is less, the higher score the document gets. The computational formula is :

$$idf\,(t) = 1 + \log\left(\frac{numdocs}{docFreq + 1}\right) \tag{1}$$

3. $queryNorm\,(q)$ is the function of the regulatory factor. It computed in the search, the computational formula is as follows:

$$queryNorm(q) = queryNorm(sumOfSquaredWeights) = \frac{1}{sumOfSquaredWeight^{1/2}} \tag{2}$$

$$sumOfSquaredWeights = q.getBoost()^2\sum_{t\in q}\left(idf\,(t)\square t.getBoost()\right)^2 \tag{3}$$

4. $norm(t,d)$ is the function encapsulates the boost in the index process. The document boost is the weight of the ontology elements in the documents, which is mentioned above. The field boost is the score of the keyword in different fields, for example, the keyword exists in the title has a higher

score than in the document content. *lengthNorm(field)* is the parameter in the process of the index.

$$norm(t, d) = doc.getBoost()lengthNorm(field) \prod_{f \in d} f.getBoost()$$

5. *arctan(a×relateness)* is the function which can adjust the document that is not consistent with the user's needs. At some point of the semantic extension, the interrelated documents are increasing, so the precision ratio is reduced. In this study, a limit is to be made when the semantic relatedness have increased to a certain extent. Those uncorrelated documents will get the low weight and list it at the back of the search results.

5 Experiment analysis

To evaluate the proposed mechanism in this study, a semantic-enable document information retrieval system was implemented, and the results were then compared to the traditional keyword-based retrieval to analyze the strengths and weaknesses. The retrieval system was implemented in Eclipse3.2 JDK1.6 and executed on a windows server 2003 Enterprise Edition Service Pack 2 and SQL SERVER 2000 environment with 1.86 GHz Intel (R) Core (TM) 2 CPU and 1.50 GB of memory. The traditional keyword-based retrieval was implemented in the SQL sentence of %like. Due to the restriction, a total of 1000 related papers were collected in document database. The experiment includes three parts: the results of the concepts extraction, the comparison of precision and recall, and the comparison of performance.

5.1 The results of the concepts extraction

We select a hundred documents about the domain enzyme as the front-ground corpus and twelve corpus of the Chinese classification text corpus TanCorpV1.0 as the background.

First, we used the word segmentation to deleting the stop word and mural in the 100 documents about enzyme. And then we get the 368 concepts by using the ontology learning algorithm. The frequency of the word "enzyme" is the most high.

5.2 The precision and recall ratio

The precision and recall ratio of the two retrieval methods are shown in Figure 2. The results are the arithmetical average of many queries and also with the semantic relatedness.

In contrast to a traditional keyword-based retrieval, the semantic extend retrieval is not improved greatly in the precision ratio but has greatly improved in recall ratio. This may be because the semantic extension facilitates the retrieval

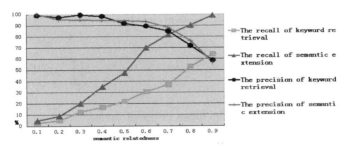

Figure 2: The contrast of the retrieval efficiency.

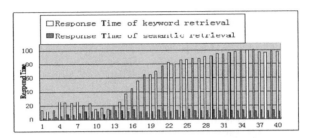

Figure 3: The contrast of the respond time.

of semantic features. And if the ability of ontology learning can get strengthened, the precision ratio will be improved as well.

5.3 Performance testing

This experiment uses Load Runner to test the response time of the two methods by simulated users to query 40 times with the two retrieval method and analyze the results.

The average response time of the keyword retrieval is 61.39 s. And the response time of the query was getting slower and slower. This shows that the query performance is unstable and the concurrent processing capability is poor. The average response time of the semantic extension retrieval is 11.04 s, far below that of the keyword retrieval. And the respond time is stable, as shown in Figure 3.

The results demonstrated that the accuracy and the performance of the semantic extension retrieval is better than that of the keyword retrieval.

6 Conclusions

In this study, the system was implemented and has two significant novelties: learn the concepts from the corpus with the artificial bee colony algorithm and match the query word for semantic extension. The semantic extension strategy analyzes the latent semantic in the query word and control excessive semantic extension, there by solving the problem of insufficient retrieval information. The ontology learning algorithm get the domain concepts from the corpus perfecting the domain ontology. This can strengthen the whole framework's ability of analyzing the latent semantics in the documents. The experiments in this study also demonstrated that the accuracy and the performance of the system are improved with the contrast of the traditional keyword-based search.

Acknowledgments

This work was supported in part by the Shandong Science and technology plan under Grant (2010G0020121).

References

[1] M.C. Díaz-Galiano, Query expansion with a medical ontology to improve a multimodal information retrieval system. *Computers in Biology and Medicine*, **39**, pp. 396–403, 2009.
[2] N. Alejandra Segura, An empirical analysis of ontology-based query expansion for learning resource searches using MERLOT and the Gene ontology. *Knowledge-Based Systems*, **24(1)**, pp. 119–133, 2011.
[3] Karina Robles, Towards an ontology-based retrieval of UML Class Diagrams. *Information and Software Technology*, **54(1)**, pp. 72–86, 2012.
[4] W. Jing, A retrieval method of semantic extend based on ontology knowledge base. *Computer Engineering*, **38(6)**, pp. 19–24, 2012.
[5] H. Chuan Lie, A query expansion based on ontology. *Computer System and Application*, **21(7)**, pp. 83–89, 2012.
[6] Kazuhiro Seki, Gene ontology annotation as text categorization: An empirical study. *Information Processing & Management*, **44(5)**, pp. 1754–1770, 2008.

Stability and existence of solution for impulsive differential equations with delays

Yanling Li, Man Hua
School of Computer Science, Civil Aviation Flight University of China, Guanghan, Sichuan, 618307, China

Abstract

In this paper, we employ iterative analysis method to obtain both the existence and the stability of first-order functional differential equations with impulses for periodic boundary value problem. Some new results are obtained.

Keywords: iterative analysis, periodic boundary value problem, existence, stability

1 Introduction

The monotone iterative technique coupled with lower and upper solutions and coincidence degree theory are powerful methods in dealing with the existence of solutions to nonlinear differential equations. The theory of periodic boundary value problem has been studied in Ref. [1]. The stability theory of differential equations has been developed by a large number of mathematicians, see Ref. [2], and their studies have been attached much attention. They have been successful in different approaches based on Lyapunov direct method and comparison technique. Although Lyapunov direct method has generality from the theoretical standpoint, it is not convenient for practical use sometimes. In this paper, we employ iterative analysis method which is different from the above two methods to obtain both the existence and the stability of first-order functional differential equations with impulses for periodic boundary value problem.

In this paper, we consider the following periodic boundary value problem (PBVP) for first-order impulsive functional differential equations:

$$u'(t) + \lambda u(t) = f\left(t, u(t-\tau)\right), \quad t \neq t_k, t \in J = [0, T] \tag{1}$$

$$\Delta u\left(t_{k}\right)=I_{k}\left(u\left(t_{k}\right)\right), k=1,2,\cdots,m, \qquad (2)$$

$$u(0)=u(T)=u_{0}, \qquad (3)$$

$$u(t)=0, \quad t\in(-\tau,0), \qquad (4)$$

where $f\in C(J\times R,R), \lambda\in R$, $J=[0, T]$, $J^{+}=[-\tau , T]$, $T > 0$, $\tau > 0$, $0=t_{0}<t_{1}<\cdots<t_{m}<t_{m+1}=T$, $I_{k}\in C(R,R)$, $\Delta u\left(t_{k}\right)=u\left(t_{k}^{+}\right)-u\left(t_{k}^{-}\right)$, $t_{k+1}-t_{k}=\tau$ for all $k=1,\dots,m$.

The contents of this paper are following: in Section 2, some notations and preliminaries are introduced, in Section 3, we obtain the existence and stability of solutions of the impulsive functional differential equations using the iterative method.

2 Preliminaries

Let $J^{-}=J^{+}-\{t_{1},t_{2},\cdots,t_{m}\}, PC(J^{+},R)=\{u:J^{+}\rightarrow R;u(t)$ is continuous everywhere except for some $t_{k},$ at which $u\left(t_{k}^{+}\right)$ and $u\left(t_{k}^{-}\right)$ exist, and $u\left(t_{k}^{-}\right)=u(t_{k}),k=1,\cdots,m\}$.

And let $E_{0}=\{u\in PC(J^{+},R):u(t)=0,t\in[-\tau,0]\}$, with norm $\|u\|_{E_{0}}=\sup\{|u(t)|:t\in J^{+}\}$.

The following are the basic hypothesis:

$(H_{1})f(t,0)=0,$ there exists $L(t)>0$ such that $|f(t,u_{1})-f(t,u_{2})|\leq L(t)|u_{1}-u_{2}|$;

$(H_{2})I_{k}(0)=0,$ there exist $q_{k}>0$ such that $|I_{k}(u_{1})-I_{k}(u_{2})|\leq q_{k}|u_{1}-u_{2}|$.

We denote $B=\sum_{k=1}^{m}q_{k}$ $C=\dfrac{e^{|\lambda|T}(B+D)}{|1-e^{-\lambda T}|}$ $D=\int_{0}^{T}L(s)ds$ $A=\dfrac{De^{|\lambda|T}}{|1-e^{-\lambda T}|}$

(H$_3$) Suppose that $0<C<1$ is always satisfied.

Lemma: The solution of the problem (1)–(4) can be presented as:

$$u(t)=\begin{cases}\int_{0}^{T}g(t,s)f(s,u(s-\tau))ds+\sum_{k=1}^{m}g(t,t_{k})I_{k}(u(t_{k})), & t\in J,\\0, & t\in[-\tau,0),\end{cases}$$

where

$$g(t,s) = \frac{1}{1-e^{-\lambda T}} \begin{cases} e^{-\lambda(t-s)}, & 0 \le s < t \le T, \\ e^{-\lambda(T+t-s)}, & 0 \le t \le s \le T. \end{cases}$$

Proof. Set $y(t) = e^{\lambda t} u(t)$ for $t \in J$. Thus, $y(t)$ satisfies the impulsive boundary value problem:

$$y'(t) = e^{\lambda t} f^* \left(t, y(t-\tau) \right), \qquad y(0) = e^{-\lambda T} y(T),$$

$$y\left(t_k^+\right) = y\left(t_k^-\right) + I_k^* \left(y(t_k) \right),$$

where $f^*\left(t, y(t-\tau)\right) = f\left(t, e^{-\lambda(t-\tau)} y(t-\tau)\right)$, and $I_k^*\left(y(t_k)\right) = e^{\lambda t_k} I_k\left(e^{-\lambda t_k} y(t_k)\right)$.

For $t \in [0, t_1]$, there is no impulsive effect in this interval, then we can obtain:

$$y(t) = y(0) + \int_0^t e^{\lambda s} f^*\left(s, y(s-\tau)\right) ds.$$

then,

$$y\left(t_1^-\right) = y(0) + \int_0^{t_1} e^{\lambda s} f^*\left(s, y(s-\tau)\right) ds, \tag{5}$$

we consider Cauchy problem (1), (2), and (5) on $(t_1; t_2]$, then we have

$$y(t) = y\left(t_1^-\right) + \int_{t_1}^t e^{\lambda s} f^*\left(s, y(s-\tau)\right) ds + I_1^*\left(y(t_1)\right)$$
$$= y(0) + \int_0^t e^{\lambda s} f^*\left(s, y(s-\tau)\right) ds + I_1^*\left(y(t_1)\right).$$

The procedure can be repeated on $(t_2, t_3], (t_3, t_4], \cdots, (t_p, T]$, then we can get:

$$y(t) = y(0) + \int_0^t e^{\lambda s} f^*\left(s, y(s-\tau)\right) ds + \sum_{k:t_k \in (0,t)} I_k^*\left(y(t_k)\right), \qquad t \in J. \tag{6}$$

Using this expression for $t = T$, we then get

$$y(0) = \frac{1}{e^{\lambda T} - 1} \int_0^T e^{\lambda s} f^*\left(s, y(s)\right) ds + \frac{1}{e^{\lambda T} - 1} \sum_{j=1}^p I_j^*\left(y(t_j)\right).$$

Substituting this value into (6), we obtain that for every $t \in J$

$$
\begin{aligned}
u(t) &= \frac{e^{-\lambda t}}{e^{\lambda T} - 1} \int_0^T e^{\lambda s} f^*\left(s, y(s-\tau)\right) ds + \int_0^t e^{-\lambda(t-s)} f^*\left(s, y(s-\tau)\right) ds \\
&\quad + \frac{e^{-\lambda t}}{e^{\lambda T} - 1} \sum_{k=1}^m I_k^*\left(y(t_k)\right) + e^{-\lambda t} \sum_{k:t_k \in (0,t)} I^*_k\left(y(t_k)\right) \\
&= \int_0^T \frac{e^{-\lambda(t-s)}}{e^{\lambda T} - 1} f\left(s, u(s-\tau)\right) ds + \int_0^t e^{-\lambda(t-s)} f\left(s, u(s-\tau)\right) ds \\
&\quad + \sum_{k=1}^m \frac{e^{-\lambda(t-t_k)}}{e^{\lambda T} - 1} I_k\left(u(t_k)\right) + e^{-\lambda t} \sum_{k:t_k \in (0,t)} e^{-\lambda t_k} I_k\left(u(t_k)\right) \\
&= \int_0^T g(t,s) f\left(s, u(s-\tau)\right) ds + \sum_{k=1}^m g(t,t_k) I_k\left(u(t_k)\right).
\end{aligned}
$$

Then the proof of the lemma is complete.

3 Main results

Theorem 1: Suppose that the hypotheses (H_1)–(H_3) hold, then the PBVP (1)–(4) has a unique solution $u(t)$ on $[-\tau, T]$, and

$$
\left\| u(t) \right\|_{E_0} \leq \frac{2A|u_0|}{1 - C}. \tag{7}
$$

Proof. We define the iteration

$$
u^{(k)}(t) = \begin{cases} \int_{-\tau}^{T-\tau} g(t, s+\tau) f\left(s+\tau, u^{(k-1)}(s)\right) ds + \sum_{k=1}^m g(t, t_k) I_k\left(u^{(k-1)}(t_k)\right), & t \in J, \\ 0, & t \in [-\tau, 0). \end{cases}
$$

$$
u^{(0)}(t) = \begin{cases} \int_{-\tau}^{T-\tau} g(t, s+\tau) f\left(s+\tau, u(0)\right) ds, & t \in J, \\ 0, & t \in [-\tau, 0). \end{cases}
$$

then,

$$
\left\| u^{(0)} \right\|_{E_0} = \sup_{t \in [-\tau, T]} \left| u^{(0)}(t) \right| \leq \frac{e^{\lambda T}}{\left| 1 - e^{-\lambda T} \right|} \int_{-\tau}^{T-\tau} L(s+\tau) ds \cdot |u_0| = \frac{e^{\lambda T}}{\left| 1 - e^{-\lambda T} \right|} \int_0^T L(s) ds \cdot |u_0| = A|u_0|.
$$

$$\left\|u^{(1)}\right\|_{E_0} \leq \sup_{t \in [-\tau, T]} \left\{ \int_{-\tau}^{T-\tau} \left|g(t, s+\tau)\right| \cdot L(s+\tau) \cdot \left|u^{(0)}(s)\right| ds + \sum_{k=1}^{m} \left|g(t, t_k)\right| \cdot q_k \cdot \left|u^{(0)}(t_k)\right| \right\}$$

$$\leq \frac{e^{|\lambda|T}}{\left|1-e^{-\lambda T}\right|} \left(D \left\|u^{(0)}\right\|_{E_0} + B \left\|u^{(0)}\right\|_{E_0} \right) = AC|u_0|.$$

$$\left\|u^{(2)}\right\|_{E_0} \leq \sup_{t \in [-\tau, T]} \left\{ \int_{-\tau}^{T-\tau} \left|g(t, s+\tau)\right| \cdot L(s+\tau) \cdot \left|u^{(1)}(s)\right| ds + \sum_{k=1}^{m} \left|g(t, t_k)\right| \cdot q_k \cdot \left|u^{(1)}(t_k)\right| \right\}$$

$$\leq \frac{e^{|\lambda|T}}{\left|1-e^{-\lambda T}\right|} \left(D \left\|u^{(1)}\right\|_{E_0} + B \left\|u^{(1)}\right\|_{E_0} \right) = AC^2|u_0|.$$

Applying induction, we can get the following inequality for any j

$$\left\|u^{(j)}\right\|_{E_0} \leq AC^j |u_0|, \ j = 0, 1, \cdots .$$

From the above, it follows:

$$\left\|u^{(1)} - u^{(0)}\right\|_{E_0} = \sup_{t \in [-\tau, T]} \left|u^{(1)}(t) - u^{(0)}(t)\right|$$

$$\leq \frac{e^{|\lambda|T}}{\left|1-e^{-\lambda T}\right|} \int_{-\tau}^{T-\tau} L(s+\tau) \cdot \left(\left\|u^{(0)}\right\|_{E_0} + |u_0| \right) ds + \frac{e^{|\lambda|T} B}{\left|1-e^{-\lambda T}\right|} \cdot \left\|u^{(0)}\right\|_{E_0}$$

$$\leq \frac{e^{|\lambda|T}}{\left|1-e^{-\lambda T}\right|} \left(AD|u_0| + D|u_0| + AB|u_0| \right) = A(1+C)|u_0|.$$

$$\left\|u^{(2)} - u^{(1)}\right\|_{E_0} = \sup_{t \in [-\tau, T]} \left|u^{(2)}(t) - u^{(1)}(t)\right|$$

$$\leq \frac{e^{|\lambda|T}}{\left|1-e^{-\lambda T}\right|} \int_{-\tau}^{T-\tau} L(s+\tau) \cdot \left\|u^{(1)} - u^{(0)}\right\|_{E_0} ds + \frac{e^{|\lambda|T} B}{\left|1-e^{-\lambda T}\right|} \cdot \left\|u^{(1)} - u^{(0)}\right\|_{E_0}$$

$$\leq \frac{e^{|\lambda|T}}{\left|1-e^{-\lambda T}\right|} (B+D) \left\|u^{(1)} - u^{(0)}\right\|_{E_0} = A(1+C)C|u_0|.$$

$$\left\|u^{(3)} - u^{(2)}\right\|_{E_0} = \sup_{t \in [-\tau, T]} \left|u^{(3)}(t) - u^{(2)}(t)\right|$$

$$\leq \frac{e^{|\lambda|T}}{\left|1-e^{-\lambda T}\right|} \int_{-\tau}^{T-\tau} L(s+\tau) \cdot \left\|u^{(2)} - u^{(1)}\right\|_{E_0} ds + \frac{e^{|\lambda|T} B}{\left|1-e^{-\lambda T}\right|} \cdot \left\|u^{(2)} - u^{(1)}\right\|_{E_0}$$

$$= A(1+C)C^2|u_0|.$$

Applying induction, we can obtain:

$$\left\| u^{(j+1)} - u^{(j)} \right\|_{E_0} \le A(1+C)C^j |u_0|, \, j = 0,1,\cdots .$$

then,

$$\left| u^{(n+1)}(t) \right| \le \sum_{j=0}^{n} \left| u^{(j+1)}(t) - u^{(j)}(t) \right| + \left| u^{(0)}(t) \right|,$$

$$\left\| u^{(n+1)} \right\|_{E_0} = \sup_{t \in [-\tau, T]} \left| u^{(n+1)}(t) \right| \le \sum_{j=0}^{n} A(1+C)C^j |u_0| + A|u_0| \le \frac{2A|u_0|}{1-C}.$$

$\forall p \in N, m + p \ge m$, we have

$$\left\| u^{(m+p)}(t) - u^{(m)}(t) \right\|_{E_0} \le \sum_{j=m+1}^{m+p} \left| u^{(j)}(t) - u^{(j-1)}(t) \right| \le A(1+C) \cdot \frac{C^m}{1-C} \cdot |u_0|.$$

Therefore, the sequence $\left\{ u^{(k)}(t) \right\}$ is uniformly convergent on $[-\tau, T]$, let,

$$\lim_{k \to \infty} u^{(k)}(t) = u(t),$$

obviously, $u(t)$ is a solution of PBVP (1)–(4) which satisfies the equality (7).

Next, we will show the uniqueness. Suppose v is another solution of PBVP (1)–(3), then,

$$\left\| u - v \right\|_{E_0} = \sup_{t \in [-\tau, T]} \left| u(t) - v(t) \right| \le \frac{e^{|A|T}}{\left| 1 - e^{-\lambda T} \right|} \int_{-\tau}^{T-\tau} L(s) \cdot \left\| u - v \right\|_{E_0} ds + \frac{B e^{|A|T}}{\left| 1 - e^{-\lambda T} \right|} \cdot \left\| u - v \right\|_{E_0}$$

$$= \frac{e^{|A|T}(B+D)}{\left| 1 - e^{-\lambda T} \right|} \left\| u - v \right\|_{E_0}.$$

From this, it is easy to see that the solution is unique.

The proof of Theorem 1 is complete.

From (H_1), $f(t, 0) = 0$, $I_j(0) = 0$, if $u_0 = 0$, then $u(t) = 0$ is a solution of (1)–(4) which we call as the trivial solution.

Definition: The trivial solution of (1)–(4) is stable if for any $\varepsilon > 0$, there exists a $\delta(\varepsilon, t_0) > 0$, such that $|u(t_0)| < \delta$ implies that $|u(t, t_0, u(t_0))| < \varepsilon$ for $t \ge t_0$. If δ is independent to t_0, we say the trivial solution of (1)–(4) is uniformly stable.

Theorem 2: Suppose that the hypotheses (H_1)–(H_3) hold, then the trivial solution of the Cauchy problem for the impulsive equation (1)–(4) is uniformly stable.

Proof. If the trivial solution of (1)–(4) is not stable, then we have that $\exists \varepsilon_1 > 0$, $\forall \delta(\varepsilon_1, t_0) > 0, \exists t_1 \geq t_0$,

$$\left| u(t_1, t_0, u(t_0)) \right| \geq \varepsilon_1 \ as \ \left| u(t_0) \right| < \delta(\varepsilon_1, t_0). \tag{8}$$

From Theorem 2, we have $\left\| u(t) \right\|_{E_0} \leq \dfrac{2A|u_0|}{1-C}$. Let $\delta(\varepsilon_1, t_0) = \dfrac{1-C}{2A}\varepsilon_1$, then we get that $\left\| u(t) \right\|_{E_0} \leq \varepsilon_1 \ as \ \left| u(t_0) \right| < \delta(\varepsilon_1, t_0)$. So we get a contradiction with Eq. (8).

Therefore, the proof of Theorem 2 is complete.

Acknowledgments

This work is supported by National Natural Science Foundation of China (No.60879023) and GPMR200916.

References

[1] M.U. Akhmetov, A. Zafer, Stability of the zero solution of impulsive differential equations by the Lyapunov second method. *Journal of Mathematics and Analytical Application,* **248**, pp. 69–82, 2000.
[2] A. Cabada, D.R. Vivero, Existence and uniqueness of solutions of higher order antiperiodic dynamic equations. *Advances in Differential Equation,* **4**, pp. 291–310, 2000.

A hybrid encryption scheme for RFID system

Yunfeng Wang, Xing Zheng, Jing wang, Donghui Guo
Department of Electronic Engineering, School of Information Science and Engineering, Xiamen University, Xiamen, 361005, China

Abstract

Radio-frequency identification (RFID) is a wireless technology that utilizes radio communication to identify objects. It is applied to tag and smart card systems widespread. After authentication, data is transmitted in plaintext or ciphertext which is the encrypted result with the same key in one system between database and reader or between reader and tag/smart card which is one of the main safety drawbacks in RFID application systems. A hybrid encryption scheme is proposed for RFID system in order to overcome this drawback. It applies asymmetric algorithm to handing over keys and symmetric algorithm to encrypting information. Moreover, an IC implementation of the hybrid encryption scheme is advanced, and one minimum Mifare1 RFID system with this scheme is designed.

Keywords: radio-frequency identification (RFID), information security, hybrid encryption scheme, key delivery

1 Introduction

Radio-frequency identification (RFID) is a rapidly growing technology enabling automatic objects identification. An RFID system is composed of three main components: tags/smart cards, readers, back-end database. An RFID tag/smart card typically consists of an integrated circuit for handling data and an antenna for receiving and transmitting a radio-frequency signal. A reader can read or write information content in tags/smarts cards by radio-frequency signals without physical contact at a distance of several meters. Back-end database manages the RFID system and processes the acquired data. Due to their convenience in identifying an object, RFID have been widely applied in various applications [1].

Owing to the radio transmission nature of RFID, the information traveling in the air the tag and the reader could easily be intercepted and eavesdropped. Some relative literatures have pointed out that RFID system could be vulnerable to the threats such as impersonation attack, replay attack, DoS (denial of service) attack, no forward, privacy concern [2,3]. As RFID has been prevailing, the issues of security and privacy have raised many concerns.

Recent works [4–7] attempt to solve the RFID security and privacy problem by utilizing authentication protocol, which grant access to the tag/smart card content only to a legitimate reader and, at the same time, guarantee the reader of the identity of the tag/smart card. After authenticating, message is transmitted in plaintext between database and reader or between reader and tag/smart card. The transmitted data could be eavesdropped easily because of traveling in air between reader and tag/smart card. And most connections between database and reader are also not safe. Some literatures apply encryption to protecting the transmitted data from being eavesdropped, and the most representative schemes are ISO9798-2 and re-encryption protocols. However, they all have the same security drawback, which is that all readers and tags/smart cards share the same key in one RFID system so that all readers can read or write all tags/smart cards. If the key is leaked, the total system is not secured. This paper proposes a hybrid encryption scheme to overcome this security drawback. Every tag/smart cards and every reader has itself key.

2 The hybrid encryption scheme

2.1 RDID system

As shown in Figure 1, an RFID system consists of tags/smart cards, readers, and a back-end database. A tag/smart card contains a microchip, capacitors, and an antenna coil which is embedded into an encapsulation material, for example, a coin, a glass body, plastic substrate, smart label, or a standard ID-1 card. The tags/smart cards communicate via radio signals with a reader, which is a central component of an RFID system, can read or write the tag/smart card data. A reader can either be a peripheral or a handheld device. Another possibility is that it is integrated into a fixed, installed system. The reader usually sends the collected tag/smart card data to a back-end database for further processing. Peripheral readers are directly attached to the back-end database (e.g., via RS 232 or USB interfaces) and standalone readers (e.g., handheld devices) can connect via standard network protocols to the back-end database, for example, via Ethernet (or a wireless link) and TCP/IP.

Attacker can intercept the transmitted information through two channels among the tag, the reader, and the back-end database. Some RFID security protocol assumes the connection between the reader and the back-end database. However, the assumption usually is dropped. Obviously, the RFID information security and privacy could not achieve simply by authentication. Furthermore, the RFID security protocol must take into account the computation and power of tags/smart cards.

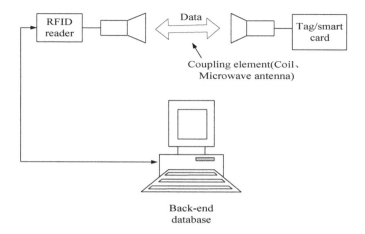

Figure 1: Overview of an RFID system.

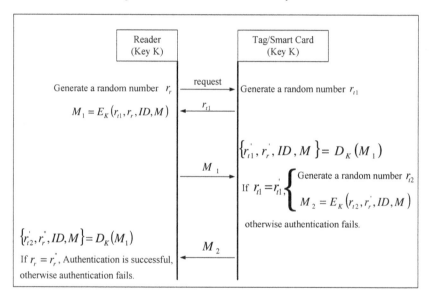

Figure 2: ISO9798-2 RFID security protocol.

2.2 Review of ISO9798-2 and re-encryption protocols

Encryption associated with authentication seems to shed new light on enhancing RFID security. As shown in Figure 2, ISO9798-2 [8] is a bilateral challenge–response authentication-encryption protocol with symmetric algorithm. After authentication, information is transmitted between legitimate reader and tat/smart card. The plaintext message is denoted as M, and ciphertext message is denoted as C. The sender uses $C = E_K(M)$ to encrypt message, and the receiver uses $M =$

Table 1: The Notations Used by Protocol.

Notation	Description
K_{E_db} and K_{D_db}	The key pair of back-end database known only by back-end database itself
$K_{E\_r_i}$ and $K_{D\_r_i}$	The key pair of reader i, $K_{E\_r_i}$ known by back-end database, $K_{D\_r_i}$ known by reader i
K_{t_j}	The key of tag/smart card j known by back-end database itself
$E_{K_E}(M)$	Encryption of asymmetric algorithm
$D_{K_D}(C)$	Decryption of asymmetric algorithm
$E_K(M)$	Encryption of symmetric algorithm
$D_K(C)$	Decryption of symmetric algorithm

$D_K(C)$ to decrypt message. Attackers do not know the key, so they cannot understand message.

During communication, ISO9798-2 protocol requests that tags/smart card perform encryption and decryption. Re-encryption protocols [9] are based on asymmetric algorithm. It uses the encryption key K_E and $C = E_{K_E}(M)$ to encrypt message, and the write C to the tag/ smart card. Then only legitimate reader knowing decryption key K_D can decrypt C by K_D and $M = D_{K_D}(C)$.

However, both ISO9798-2-like protocols and re-encryption protocols request that all readers and tags/smart cards share the same key or the same public/private key pair in one RFID application system so that all readers can read or write all tags/smarts cards. Moreover, the two types of protocols ignore that the attacker can intercept information through the channel between the back-end database and the reader. Once the key or the key pair is compromised, the attacker can understand all information intercepted.

2.3 The hybrid cryptographic protocol

In order to protect RFID system against the described threats, a hybrid cryptographic protocol is proposed. The notations used by protocol are listed in Table 1. The protocol consists of two phases: the initialization phase and the communication phase.

The initialization phase is depicted in Figure 3. At first, the back-end database choose a key pair $K_{E\_r_i}$, $K_{D\_r_i}$ for reader i and performs $K_{E\_db\_c} = E_{K_{E\_r_i}}(K_{E\_db})$ with $K_{E\_r_i}$, write the result $K_{E\_db\_c}$ into reader i.

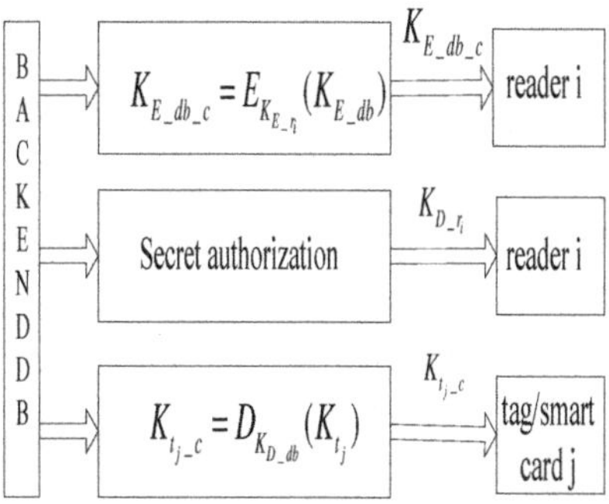

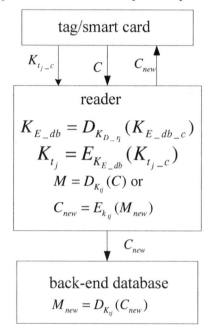

Figure 3: The initialization phase of protocol.

$$K_{E\_db} = D_{K_{D\_r_i}}(K_{E\_db\_c})$$

$$K_{t_j} = E_{K_{E\_db}}(K_{t_j\_c})$$

$$M = D_{K_{ij}}(C) \text{ or}$$

$$C_{new} = E_{k_{ij}}(M_{new})$$

$$M_{new} = D_{K_{ij}}(C_{new})$$

Figure 4: The communication phase of protocol.

Then it authorizes $K_{D\_r_i}$ to reader i, and the $K_{D\_r_i}$ is the reader's ID, must be kept from being known by others. Finally, the back-end database performs $K_{t_j\_c} = D_{K_{D\_db}}(K_{t_j})$ with K_{D_db}, and writes $K_{t_j\_c}$ into tag/smart card j.

The communication phase of hybrid cryptographic protocol is described in Figure 4. Ciphertext C only is stored in the tag/smart card. The interactions between the tag/smart card, the reader, and the back-end database are described as follows:

(1) The tag/smart card to the reader: if to write the tag/smart card, $K_{t_j\_c}$ is sent to the reader, and if to read the tag/smart card, C and $K_{t_j\_c}$ are sent to the reader.

(2) The reader utilizes asymmetric algorithm to achieve K_{E_db} and K_{t_j} in turn. If to read the tag/smart card, the reader uses symmetric algorithm to achieve M, and if to write the tag/smart card, uses symmetric algorithm to achieve C_{new}, the sent C_{new} to the tag/smart card and back-end database.

(3) If to write the tag/smart card, the back-end database achieves M_{new} by symmetric algorithm and records it.

3 Hardware implementation and discussion

The hybrid encryption scheme involves symmetric algorithm and asymmetric algorithm. However, the RFID reader usually is an embedded system, perhaps takes a long time to operate symmetric algorithm and asymmetric algorithm. Then an integrated circuit (IC) for the hybrid encryption scheme is designed, which can be embedded in the reader to accelerate operation. RSA and AES, the most famous and widely used asymmetric algorithm and symmetric algorithm, are chosen.

The architecture of IC is shown in Figure 5. The reconfigurable technology is used so that IC can be applied in RFID systems with different security levels. Reconfigurable RSA is designed to fit four different key length including 256 bits, 512 bits, 1024 bits, 2048 bits, and AES is design to fit three different key length including 128 bits, 192 bits, and 256 bits.

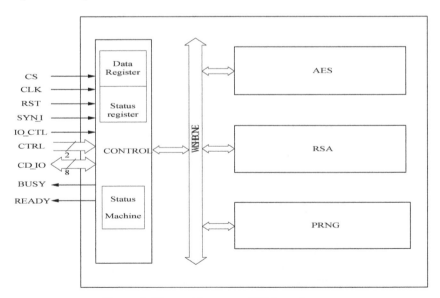

Figure 5: The architecture of IC for scheme.

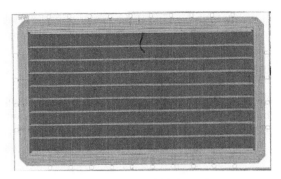

Figure 6: The photo of IC for scheme.

Table 2: The Data Throughput of Different Operation at 100 MHz Frequency.

Operation Model	Data Throughput
AES with 128 bits key	100 Mbps
AES with 192 bits key	84 Mbps
AES with 256 bits key	72 Mbps
RSA with 256 bits key	182.8 kbps
RSA with 512 bits key	91.7 kbps
RSA with 1024 bits key	46 kbps
RSA with 2048 bits key	23 kbps

The photo of IC is seen in Figure 6. The die size is 5 mm × 2.5 mm. And it has a maximum clock frequency of 150 MHz. When IC is driven by 100 MHz clock, the data throughput is listed in Table 2.

An RFID reader board is designed by using the IC, and one minimum Mifare1 RFID system is implemented as shown in Figure 7. The performances of this system demonstrate the scheme can protect information among RFID system form being eavesdropped.

4 Conclusions

Effective security protocol for RFID should take into account that the primary purpose of the RFID technology is the realization of cheap and automated identification. All encryptions and decryptions only are operated at the reader and the database in the hybrid encryption scheme, which does not increases tag/smart card costs. This scheme can combine with other authentication protocol, legitimate tags/smart cards and readers have different keys, and all legal readers can access to all legal tags/smart cards. Moreover, every reader possesses itself key pair, which can be used to achieve digital signature by combining

WIT Transactions on Information and Communication Technologies, Vol. 61, © 2014 WIT Press
www.witpress.com, ISSN 1743-3517 (on-line)

asymmetric cipher with hash function if the reader writes message to tags/smart cards, so that the malicious writing of the legal reader can be monitored.

Acknowledgments

This research was supported in part by the Natural Science Foundation of Fujian Province of China (No.2010J05143) and the Chinese Fundamental Research Funds for the Central Universities (Xiamen University: No.2010121060).

References

[1] J. Lyu, S.Y. Chang, T.L. Chen, Integrating RFID with quality assurance system–framework and applications. *Expert Systems with Applications*, **3**, pp. 10877–10882, 2009.

[2] N.Y. Lee, Z.J. Lin, Efficient identification mechanism for RFID system. *Journal of Industrial and Business Management*, **3**, pp. –110, 2007.

[3] M. Ohkubo, K. Suzuki, S. Kinoshita, RFID privacy issues and technical challenges. *Communications of the ACM*, **48**, pp. 66–71, 2005.

[4] BooJoong Kang, Hye Seon Kim, Eui-Hyung Kim, Hyong-Shik Kim, Eul Gyu Im, RFID authentication protocol for low-cost RFID tags. *Information*, **14**, pp. 2041–2060, 2011.

[5] Jihwan Lim, Sangjin Kim, Heekuck Oh, A new dynamic ID-based RFID mutual authentication protocol providing perfect synchronization. *Information*, **15**, pp. 639–656, 2012.

[6] Mande Xie, EEORP: Energy-efficient online reprogramming protocol for wireless sensor networks. *Applied Mathematics & Information Sciences (AMIS)*, **5**, pp. 89–96, 2011.

[7] H.Y. Chien, C.H. Chen, Mutual authentication protocol for RFID conforming to EPC class 1 generation 2 standards. *Computer Standards and Interfaces*, **29**, pp. 254–259, 2007.

TRSD: time reserved and same direction based parking space discovery system on VANETs

Xiaolu Zhang, Demin Li, Peng Li, Jianbin Chen
College of Information Science and Technology, Donghua University, Shanghai, 201620, China

Abstract

Nowadays, parking is more and more difficult in large cities because of the rapid increase of vehicles. In this paper, we provide the system of parking space discovery based on VANETs. We discuss a method of parking space discovery by multi-hops on VANETs. We use direction-based method in the parking space discovery process to reduce the amount of packets transmitting and set reserved time for vehicles searching for parking spaces to improve the utilization ratio of parking spaces. We also give the simulation of our method by NS2, and it shows its good performance on the reduction of broadcast packets. At last we suggest important future work, such as the competition among vehicles and Parking Space Units (PSUs).

Keywords: multi-hops VANETs, direction-based, reserved time

1 Introduction

As the number of vehicles on the road is rapidly increasing, there are more and more traffic problems. It maybe impossible to expand parking space in short time. So, using the Internet, communications, and management technology on the base of the existing parking spaces to enhance the use of parking spaces has important practical significance. Smart parking is a parking system using these technology based on vehicular ad hoc network.

Vehicular ad hoc networks (VANETs) are ad hoc network designed for communication between vehicles. VANETs enable the driver to get other vehicles' information and real-time traffic information within the communication range. However, routing in VANETs is different from that in ad hoc network due to the characteristics of VANETs, for example, high dynamic mobility constraints and high speed of vehicles [1].

In particular, many researches on parking space discovery based on VANETs are emerging. Common to these researches are the exploitation of wireless communications and information sensing technologies to collect and broadcast or share information about the availabilities of parking space and the demand of it within the search area. In Ref. [2], Basu and Little proposed a multi-hop wireless parking meter network (PMNET) for drivers to locate and navigate to available parking spaces. However, they use multi-hop dissemination of information only among interlinked parking meters. And the requests from vehicles to parking meter via single-hop communication. In Ref. [3], Alhammad et al. proposed a novel VANET based on an on-street parking system that exploits the concept of InfoStations (ISs) and context-aware systems to locate and reserve a parking space. All parking zones have an assigned IS that provides wireless coverage to that parking zone. So, vehicles communicate with these ISs to get parking spaces information which makes the cost of these ISs quite higher and the service area limited. In Ref. [5], Bavkar et al. proposed a new VANET-based parking system. Road Site Units (RSUs) installed across a parking lot can cover the whole parking lot and provide convenience services for drivers. However, in this system, they need stationary and high-power RSU which is deployed in the parking area.

According to researches on parking space discovery, we can see most researches are based on assistant equipments such as RSU and ignore the use of multi-hop communication among vehicles. So, our paper focuses on VANET-based technologies to gather the availability of parking spaces by multi-hops to solve and to reduce the mass broadcasts which may cause broadcast storm and affect the latency of parking space information gathering, we propose the direction-based method to spread messages for parking space discovery. We also propose setting reserved time for the vehicle asking for a parking space to improve the performance of this system. To discuss conveniently, we just focus on the research which vehicles and parking space are on the same straight road.

The contributions of this paper are as follows: (1) The system in this paper can provide real-time parking space information to divers. With the real-time parking space information, the drivers can get the vacant parking space quickly. Therefore, we can reduce the waste of the gasoline and time. (2) In the system, nodes which only have the same direction with the requesting nodes can transmit the related information. By this way, we greatly reduce the mass broadcasts found in other parking space discovery method, and reduce the latency of parking space information gathering. (3) In the system, we set reserved time for the vehicle asking for a parking space in case that the vehicle driver changes his/her mind which will result in wasting the parking space resources.

The rest of this paper is organized as follows. Section 2 describes some formulation of the parking space discovery process, gives some basic assumption, and presents the mathematical method used in this paper. In Section 3, we explain our method in detail, and this is also the most important part of this paper. Section 4 proves the performance of the parking space discovery method. Section 5 summarizes the paper and gives the future work.

2 Problem formulation

2.1 Statements

We state our problem as follows.

On each parking space, they have their own PSU which is used to broadcast the information of their parking space. The power of PSU does not need be too high and the communication range is usually about several hundred meters. So, the cost is not high. We assume that all vehicles are equipped with GPS and a navigation system, so that every vehicle knows information of itself (position, speed, direction). It is a reasonable hypothesis since the GPS and navigation systems are becoming standard onboard equipments in vehicles. We also assume that vehicle should be equipped with wireless communication devices and optional sensors for reporting vehicles condition. Vehicle can exchange information with other vehicle as well as parking-space infrastructure within their radio ranges, and they have the same transmission range length.

When a vehicle is searching for a parking space, it can communicate with other vehicles by single/multi-hops or communicate with the PSU in its communication range. And the radio range for VANET is several hundred meters, typically between 200 and 300 m.

2.2 Theoretical method

In Figure 1, point A_0 means vehicle A's position at time t_0, which is $A_0(x_{A0}, y_{A0})$, point A_1 means vehicle A's position at time t_1, which is $A_1(x_{A1}, y_{A1})$, point B_1 means vehicle B's position at time t_1, which is $B_1(x_{B1}, y_{B1})$, and point C_1 means vehicle C's position at time t_1, which is $C_1(x_{C1}, y_{C1})$, and $t_1 > t_0$. Vehicle B has the same direction with vehicle A, and vehicle C has the opposite direction with vehicle A. We assume that in the short time interval $(t_1 - t_0)$, all the vehicles are running uniform motion in straight line.

So, we can get running direction θ_B between vehicle B and vehicle A as follows:

$$\theta_B = \arccos \frac{(A_0A_1)^2 + (A_1B_1)^2 - (A_0B_1)^2}{2(A_0A_1)(A_1B_1)} \tag{1}$$

And the direction θ_C between vehicle C and vehicle A runs in Eq. (2).

$$\theta_C = \arccos \frac{(A_0A_1)^2 + (A_1C_1)^2 - (A_0C_1)^2}{2(A_0A_1)(A_1C_1)} \tag{2}$$

We can see that for $\theta_B \geq \dfrac{\pi}{2}$, that means, vehicle B and vehicle A have the same direction, and at time t_1, vehicle B is in front of vehicle A. And for

$\theta_C < \dfrac{\pi}{2}$, we can think vehicle C and vehicle A has the opposite directions. In the calculation, we may get the opposite judgment, but we can easily prove that these vehicles are not best proper candidates.

3 Parking space discovery system setup

This system model we considered only consists of PSU and vehicles. The details of parking space discovery system are as *3.1–3.5*, and Figure 2 shows the parking space discovery process of vehicles.

Once a driver wants to look for a parking space, he/she has to set a periodic time T_0 to control the time of sending request to get the best proper vehicle to transfer its message during T_0. And we also set reserved time *Period* for the requesting vehicle. If the vehicle does not reach the appointed parking space during the *Period* time, PSU will cancel the reserved parking space. To reduce the energy of PSU, we set it sleep mode when the parking space is full. So, at this time, no signal will be received by any vehicles. But, when there are some parking spaces, the PSU will be open.

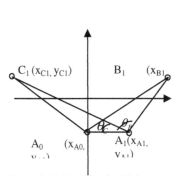

Figure 1: Judgment of vehicles.

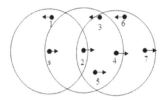

Figure 3: The process of choosing the media vehicle.

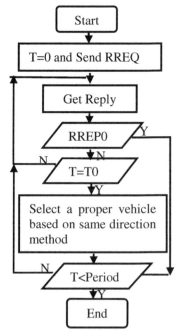

Figure 2: The parking space discovery process of the original

3.1 Send parking space request

The driver who wants to park his/her vehicle, will broadcast parking space request which is called RREQ. RREQ(*ID, car_ID, (x,y), t, Destination, original_info*), and original_info(*car_ID, (x,y), t, Destination, Period*). *ID* means RREQ's times. If *ID*=1, means the initial broadcasting, if *ID*=2,means the indirect broadcasting, that is to say, the requesting car need to get PSU information by multi-hops. And *car_ID* is the vehicle's unique identifier, *(x,y)* means the vehicle's current position, *t* means the time the vehicle starts to send message, *Destination* means the requesting vehicle's final destination, *original_info* stores the information of the original requesting vehicle, *Period* means the time that the requesting vehicle wants the PSU to reserve for it.

3.2 Receiving the parking space request

If PSU in the requesting vehicle's communication range receives the RREQ directly, then go to *3.4.*, else the requesting vehicle will find its parking space by multi-hops using other vehicles. When other vehicles within the range get the RREQ, they check whether they have received the packet. If they have received and dealt with the packet, then discard it. Next, vehicles check RREQ, and judge whether the packet has been out of date according to *t* and *Period* in *original_info*, if the RREQ is out of date, they discard it too. Else, they store RREQ, and send a reply which is called RREP1 to the original requesting vehicle. And RREP1 contains (*ID, car_ID, (x,y), t, Destination, original_info*). All these information has the same meaning of RREQ.

3.3 Choosing the media-vehicle based on direction judgment

When the requesting vehicle gets requesting reply which is called RREP1, it analyzes these RREP1s using Eqs. (1), (2) to judge the direction, and choose from these vehicles who has the same direction with the requesting vehicle, then choose the farthest one from itself. And the original requesting vehicle sends RREQ to it, and at this time *ID* equals 2. The selected one become the second original requesting vehicle, and then broadcast the parking space request from the beginning.

3.4 Received the parking space request by PSU directly

When a PSU receives an RREQ directly, that is to say, the ID equals 1, it checks that if the vehicle has been allocated for a parking space. If the vehicle has been allocated, then the PSU sends an RREP0 directly, else the proper PSU reserves a parking space to the vehicle, and sends an RREP0 to the requesting vehicle. At last, the requesting vehicle receives the RREP0, and finds its parking space. Here, the RREP0 is as follows: RREP0(*ps_id, (x,y), t, (x_v,y_v), ps_information, original_info*). This is the reply of PSU, *ps_id* is the id of the PSU of the parking space, *(x,y)* is the position of the parking space, *t* is the time the PSU starts sending the reply, *(x_v,y_v)* is the position the PSU directly received from the requesting vehicle's, *ps_information,* information about the parking space, *original_info,* is the information of the original requesting vehicle.

3.5 Sending parking space information indirectly by direction judgment

The PSU receives an RREQ indirectly that means ID equals 2. PSU sends parking space information which is called RREP0 to the requesting vehicle. Vehicles which directly receive RREP0 check whether it is the original requesting vehicle. If the original requesting vehicle is founded, the process is over. Else vehicles which get the RREP0 check whether they have received the packet before. If they have received and dealt with the packet, then discard it. Next, vehicles check RREQ, and judge whether the packet has been out of date according to the *t* and *Period* in *original_info,* if the RREP0 is out of date, they discard it too. Else, according to Eqs. (1), (2) to choose the vehicle which has the opposite direction with the requesting vehicle that sent RREQ to PSU and is the farthest from the PSU to transmit the RREP0.

Figure 3 shows the process of the requesting vehicle choosing the media-vehicle. In Figure 3, node S is the requesting vehicle, after researching and processing, it chooses node 2 to transmit its request, and node 2 chooses node 4, node 4 chooses node 7.

4   Simulation analysis

In this study, performance of parking space discovery system is measured using the packet delivery radios (PDR) and average end-to-end delay [4].
Packet delivery radios: packet delivery radio is the radio of the packets that successfully reach destination to evaluate the performance of the simulation.

*PDR=Total number of packets delivered/Total number of packets transferred*100*

Average end-to-end delay: this metric gives the delay, from the beginning of original requesting vehicle transferring parking space request to the end of receiving the allocation information sending by the PSU.

At present, there are many routing protocols for vehicular ad hoc networks, such as VADD, GPSR* and so on. Our parking space discovery system is compared with the classical protocol, VADD [6].

We set twelve vehicles moving on the road and one PSU in the parking space. And among these vehicles, one vehicle is searching for the PSU. The parameters for the simulation environment are in Table 1. We carry out the evaluation using the network simulator NS2. The results of end-to-end delay' and PDR' simulations of VADD and TRSD are presented in Figures 4 and 5.

From Figure 4, we see that the latency of TRSQ is slower than that of VADD when the interval time of packets is quite slow and even when the interval time of packets is high, the latency is almost the same. So, there is almost no sideeffects on time latency according to Figure 4. In Figure 5, we can notice that the number of PDR of TRSQ is higher than that of VADD especially from the

Table 1: Simulation Setup.

Parameters	Value
Simulation area	1500 m × 200 m
Number of vehicles	12
Number of Parking Space Unit(PSU)	1
Transmission range of every vehicle	200 m
Transmission range of every PSU	200 m
Simulation time	200 s
Vehicle velocity	7-15 m/s
Date packet size	512 bytes

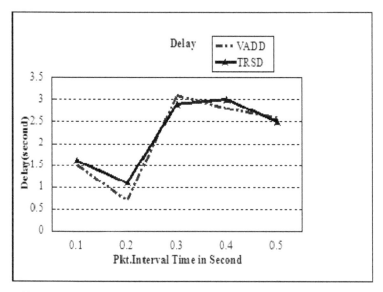

Figure 4: End-to-end delay versus packet interval time in second.

interval time of packets of 0.3 s. It is obvious since TRSD rebroadcast its RREQ only to the node having the same direction and farthest from the requesting node. From Figures 4 and 5, we see in the process of parking space discovery, TRSD has more advantages. It can reduce lots of meaningless packets, prevent the useless data storm, and reduce resource usage and so on.

5 Conclusion and future work

In this paper, we proposed a parking space discovery system. Vehicles can get real-time parking space information by multi-hops on VANETs. The node only having the same direction with the requesting node and is the farthest one within its communication range can transmit the message. By simulation, we found this system can reduce lots of useless information and quite useful in the process of

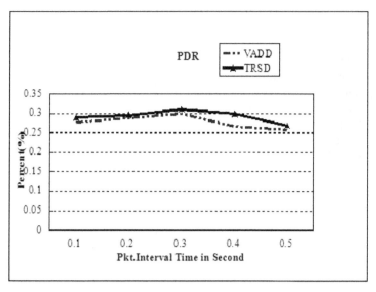

Figure 5: PDR versus packet interval time in second.

parking space discovery. And we set reserved time for requesting vehicles which will reduce large repeat updating broadcasts and improve the utilization ratio of parking spaces. There are many problems in the parking space discovery such as the competition among vehicles and parking spaces. In this paper, we also have some problems on information gathering. We will improve these in our future jobs.

Acknowledgment

This work is supported by National Natural Science Foundation of China (NSFC) granted number 71171045.

References

[1] A.K. Verma, T. Sivakumar, A reliable routing protocol for VANETs (RRPV). *International Journal of Scientific & Engineering Research*, **4(6)**, pp. 1099–1103, 2013.
[2] P. Basu, T.D.C. Little, Wireless ad hoc discovery of parking meters. *MobiSysWorkshop on Applications of Mobile Embedded Systems, WAMES'04*, Boston, MA, pp. 8–11, 2004.
[3] A. Alhammad, F. Siewe, A.H. Al-Bayatti, An InfoStation-based context-aware on-street parking system. *Computer Systems and Industrial Informatics(ICCSII), 2012 International Conference on. IEEE*, Sharjah, pp. 1–6, 2012.

[4] T. Delot, S. Ilarri, S. Lecomte, et al., Sharing with caution: Managing parking spaces in vehicular networks. *Mobile Information Systems*, **9(1)**, pp. 69–98, 2013.

[5] D.M. Bavkar, V.D. Khairnar, V.B. Gaikwad, PAV: Parking allotment for vehicles using VANET. *International Journal of Latest Trends in Engineering and Technology (IJLTET)*, **1(2)**, pp. 68–76, 2013.

[6] J. Zhao, G. Cao, VADD: Vehicle-assisted data delivery in vehicular ad hoc networks. *Vehicular Technology, IEEE Transactions on*, **57(3)**, pp. 1910–1922, 2008.

A portable mass storage based on Sl811hst

Jianfeng Xue, Jianrui Zhang
*Department of Electronic Engineering, North China Institute of
Aerospace Engineering, Langfang, 065000, China*

Abstract

A portable mass storage, accomplished by the USB host and the SCM without a computer, has been introduced. In the design of the hardware, the sketch map of the communication between the USB host and the SCM is given in detail; and then the design of the software, the particular flow map of the USB read and write, which is finished by the USB host and the SCM, is given. Furthermore, through the use in the portable intelligent flowmeter, which is researched and developed by the writer, not only the portability and the reliability have been proved, but a good foreground has also been predicted.

Keywords: sl811hst, scm, usb interface, ,flash disk read and write

1 Introduction

With the development of demand, many electronic products are required to provide USB host interface to perform a variety of functions, such as mobile hard disk, U disk read and write, through the USB interface with other equipment connection and so on, but most of the time and the computer connection is very inconvenient, impeded the work process. Especially in the survey work of the workers to go out to work, a large amount of data storage is more to let a person not know what course to take. A portable USB device to read and write is imminent.

In this paper, to solve these problems, introduced a scheme based on single chip microcomputer and SL811HST, and briefly tells its application in actual measurement. It is not only small volume, convenient to carry, and powerful, can read and write the correct all kinds of USB devices, such as U disk, mobile hard disk, so as to realize a portable mass storage of data [1–3].

WIT Transactions on Information and Communication Technologies, Vol. 61, © 2014 WIT Press
www.witpress.com, ISSN 1743-3517 (on-line)
doi:10.2495/MIIT130481

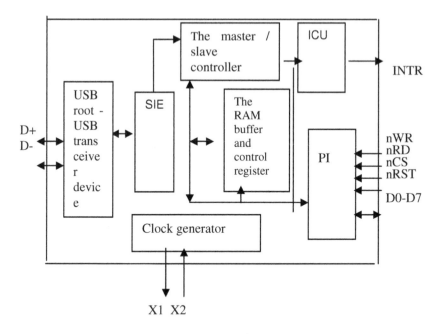

Figure 1: SL811HST diagram.

2 Discussed problems

SL811HST is an embedded chip CYPRESS produced by a compliance with the USB1.1 agreement, can work in the Host and Slave are two kinds of mode, with USB low speed communication equipment, but also with the high-speed USB device communication. The characteristics of the chip are: automatic detection device is connected with low or high speed devices; 8 bit bidirectional data bus; on-chip SIE transceiver (serial interface engine) to achieve a complete USB protocol layer functions, including: synchronous mode identification, and string conversion, bits, filling/solution filled, PID confirmation/generation address recognition, and handshake signal identification/generation; SOF automatically generates the token packet, and the need to automatically generate a token packet, the packet of CRC5/CRC16 data; internal 256 byte RAM, support the ping-pong operation; support for SUSPEND/RESUME, WAKE UP, LOW-POWER model; through the interrupt support, can easily work with a microprocessor, microcontroller and DSP communication, can be directly connected to the ISA, PCMCIA, and other bus, and the functional block diagram is shown in Figure 1.

3 The hardware design of U disk read and write the host

SL811HST as a USB host chip, can be used with microprocessors, microcontrollers, DSP and other host chip communication. This paper takes its

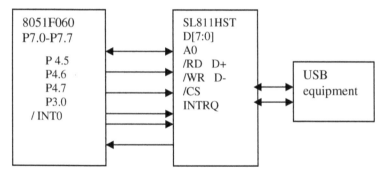

Figure 2: Single-chip computer and SL811HST interface.

communication with Cygnal company as an example, introduces its main chip and the communication process. The connection between the chip and C8051F060 is shown in Figure 2.

In the design of the hardware, although SL811HST can also use the 12M crystal, but in the practical application, if the crystal quality is not good or instability, will cause the circuit unstable, so we choose 48M active crystal because the SL811HST interrupt request is high, therefore need to reverse its transformation into a low level in order to meet the requirements of SCM level; in the time of program design, if the application variables or data to be transmitted is too long, the storage space of SL811HST may not, in the design, be connected to external expansion memory and address latch.

When the SL811HST is operating in Host mode, start the process of a USB access equipment as follows:

1. Detecting access external USB device.
2. Detection of high speed equipment and set the corresponding register.
3. Read the USB device descriptor.
4. Initialization of the USB equipment, communication by requirements, and access equipment.

The microcontroller through the register controls the operation of SL811HST. The SL811HST register is divided into two parts, each part of the 5 register. For the part of USB control register (control USB transactions and data stream); another part is the general control register (control and global state information, other operating display). The microcontroller through the 8 bidirectional data line D1-D7, chip select signal lines nCS, read nRD, write nWR input signal line and an address line A0, visit SL811HST. SL811HST can be used as an external programmable I/O port or mapped to memory space access.

4 Software design of U disk read and write the host

SL811HST as a USB host, read and write USB software design of the equipment is divided into two parts: one is the driver as the host SL811HST read U disk, a part is the system call driver to complete the application to read and write U disk.

1. Driver design of the USB host

   Read U disk directly, as to realize the external mass storage device or embedded system, so the technology is the core of the realization of USB-HOST technology. Due to the agreement of many, the USB driver is also more complicated. This paper describes only the Host U disk read and write the required function module, initialization module, the enumeration module, data transmission module.

   Initialization module is arranged USB host Host/Slave work mode, interrupt enable, full speed/low speed mode, hardware and USB reset. Enumeration module is referred to the host in the detection of U disk is inserted, between the host and the USB operation. Through the enumeration obtained with U disk operation address, can also get U disk endpoint descriptor and various parameters, thus the enumeration is all USB host must have the function, the enumeration success, not only can prove the hardware system is correct, read/write operation is based.

   To access the SL811HST, microcontroller is divided into two stages: write the address and write/read data. SL811HST supports automatic address increasing mode, so only a single address should be set, then the data read or write stage, the internal address pointer automatically to the next data.

   <Algorithm>Void SL811write(byte a,byte d)

   ```
   {
     outportb(SL811_ADDR,a);
     outportb(SL811_ADDR+1,d);
   }
   BYTE SL811Read(BYTE a)
   {
     Outportb(SL811_ADDR,a);
     return(inportb(SL811_ADDR+1));
   }
   ```

   For the buffer read and write like this, no longer.

2. Application design

   When the system detects the inserted U disk, the U disk read and write process is shown in Figure 3.

Read U disk system work in the command/response mode, namely the first by a meter microcontroller commands, SL811HST and U disk in according to the order of the corresponding treatment, returns the associated response to the users of the system, the command is completed. This process can be repeated, so as to realize the whole system works.

USB bus contains four basic transfer types: control transfer, interrupt transfer, number of transmission, and synchronous transmission. The use of the system is the number of transmission. U disk device is inserted into a USB, USB HOST equipment for search, and equipment requirements to provide the corresponding descriptor. The descriptor in the USB HOST, to complete the equipment configuration, to identify Mass Storage equipment Bulk Only, and then enters the Bulk Only transmission mode.

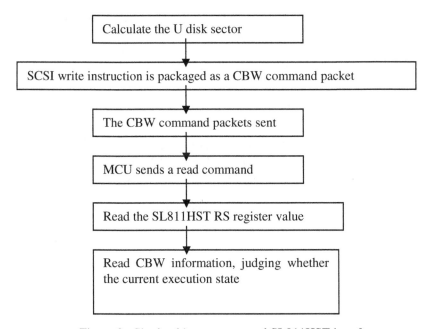

Figure 3: Single-chip computer and SL811HST interface.

In this mode, there are three types of data transfer between the USB and the equipment, namely CBW, CSW, and general data. CBW is from USB HOST sent to the device command, SCSI command set. U disk SCSI command from CBW is the corresponding command. After the completion of a command, to reflect the current state of the CSW command to Host, according to CSW to decide whether to send a CBW or data. Host requires USB equipment command for transmitting data, then need to specific data out, then sends a CSW, to enable the Host to the next step.

Note that, for the first time before the test, U disk must be formatted, because different manufacturers format parameter is not the same, may lead to abnormal reading and writing. In general, formatted in Win98 under the most thoroughly, therefore, the first time when debugging, should first disk in U 98 format. The U disk operating mainly includes the establishment of file, sequential write file, random read files, delete files. U disk operation before the first is to calculate the U disk sector address, then the microcontroller through the CBW commands to operate on the U disk data block. This design document in the U disk, the real-time clock to calls other modules, creates a new file name in time, and writes the data to facilitate future query.

5   Conclusions

Through the USB main control chip SL811HST to realize the U disk and other USB memory read and write, greatly facilitates the automatic testing system of data storage, therefore, has good application prospect.

This system used in portable intelligent flowmeter in the research and development, greatly facilitate the work for the workers of the measured data preservation. In addition, when the meter is connected with the host through RS232 interface, it can work in the Slave mode, as a USB device interface. Based on this convenient, it will be used for other system need large amounts of data storage.

References

[1] Changfei Tong, *C8051F Series Development Dnd C Language Programming*. Beihang University, BeiJing, pp. 52–142, 2005.
[2] Yicheng Liu, *USB Interface Technology of USB Data Format*. Petroleum Instrument, BeiJing, pp. 13–27, 2002.
[3] ZhaoMo Gu, Tsinghua, Analysis and application of USB bus structure. *High Performance Computing Technology*, **8(2)**, pp. 16–25, 2003.

A method of 3D recovery of human skeleton from monocular

Jianhao Ding[1], Zhijie Lin[2], Hongbiao Xie[3]
[1]*School of Media and Design, Hangzhou Dianzi University, Hangzhou, 310018, China*
[2]*Zhejiang University of Science and Technology, Hangzhou, 310018, China*
[3]*Infomation Engineering School, Hangzhou Dianzi University, Hangzhou, 310018, China*

Abstract

Human motion contains a wealth of information about actions and plays an important role in applications of interactive games, computer animation, and sports analysis. In this paper, we propose an automatic approach to estimate the relative 3D coordinates of skeleton joints from monocular video sequences by extracting postures and tracking joints. The relative 3D coordinates were estimated by scaled-orthogonal projection model. We utilized Kalman filter to track multiple frames postures. Comparing to the traditional methods, the advantages of proposed method include fewer constraints, without knowing the parameters of camera model and easy to implement for posture reconstruction.
Keywords: scaled-orthographic projection, posture estimation, motion tracking

1 Introduction

Given the video image, how to restore the body posture information is the fundamental issues of video-based human motion reconstruction. In recent years, with the development of the motion capture technology, it has become an effective means of obtaining the real human motion data and has widely used in various areas. Since most motion capture equipment is expensive, only arranged in the particular indoor environment, it is still difficult for applications such as outdoor sports, formal dance, and complex motion in the actual circumstances.

While a large number of human motion video including television, sports, dance is an important source for posture reconstruction. If we can obtain valid information from these real human movements, it will open a large treasure trove of human motion data.

In recent years, the multi-camera vision system must face to match corresponding feature point because of the illumination and other restrictions influence. With the development of graphics and image processing technologies and computer vision technology, it is possible to record human motion using ordinary camera and extract appropriate human motion information. The monocular video is low cost, easy to use, fewer constraints, favored by the majority of researchers [1–4].

3D human skeleton is a non-rigid motion with high-dimensional joint space, self-occlusion, and the ambiguity from three-dimensional space onto a two-dimensional image plane. It remains a complicated issue to directly obtain accurate three-dimensional movement of the human body from a monocular video sequences currently. Many research methods proposed assumptions, or used known prior motion data, or were composed of appropriate user interaction to meet different applications. When restoring three-dimensional motion for the joint position of human body, most of the methods require manual calibration in the initial frame or use the length of human skeleton as a priori information to estimate the 3D pose. There are many methods of calculating the relative three-dimensional coordinates according to the two-dimensional joints. The approach [3] used scaled-orthogonal projection model to restore the body posture based on a fixed limb-length human body model. The method [5] utilized a fixed or manual mark anthropometric data to customize the average length of the human body model, and then used iterative estimation to restore the 3D human body.

2   Scaled-orthographic projection model

Most of the existing large number of video sources is obtained from monocular; therefore, we can not compute the calibration from a single unconditional view video so as to recover the human motion. Scaled-orthographic projection model is popularly used by many researchers [5,6]. In this paper, the 3D human pose is estimated based on this kind of camera model. Under perspective camera model, the relationship between the coordinates (u,v) in an image and the 3D coordinates (x_c, y_c, z_c) in the scene can be denoted as $u = f \cdot x_c / z_c$, $v = f \cdot y_c / z_c$. When the object distance to camera is enough far, the focus meets the condition of $\bar{Z} \tilde{\ } dz$ same as to $f / z_c \to 1$. The orthogonal projection can be expressed as $u = x_c$, $v = y_c$. Assuming proportional factor $s = f / \bar{Z}$, the relationship between (u,v) and (x,y,z) can be represented through homogeneous coordinate.

The assumption of the scale orthogonal projection model requires that the distance between the object and the camera is much larger than the object depth variation, which applies to lots of computer vision applications. In the monocular

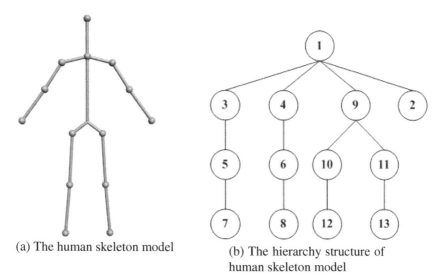

(a) The human skeleton model

(b) The hierarchy structure of
human skeleton model

Figure 1: 3D human skeleton model and hierarchy structure.

video of human motion data of this paper, the minimum distance from the camera
to human body is 4 m, much larger than the depth of the body's own changes.
Therefore, we use this model to restore the body's three-dimensional motion from
the monocular video.

3   3D human posture recovery

3.1 The representation of human body model

The human motion data recovered from monocular video is attached to the
abstract human body model. Currently researchers used many kinds of abstract
human body model. The more complex, the more similar to real body, the more
accurate recovery result, but the complexity and computation will be increased.

As shown in Figure 1(a), we represent human body as a skeleton stick model,
composed by 13 joints, including head, hand, foot, neck, wrist, knee, shoulder, and
trunk. In order to understand the articulated skeleton model more clearly, we use a
hierarchy diagram [7] to illustrate as shown in Figure 1(b). We take advantage of
vector $X = (l_i, p_i)$ to represent the skeleton model, where l_i and p_i denote the
length and the position of bone i, respectively, $i = 1, 2, \cdots, 13$. The motion of parent
joints can influence the children node associated with it, vice versa.

3.2 The 3D coordinates recovery of joints

We can obtain the two-dimensional coordinate values $\bar{X}_k = (u_k, v_k)$ of 13 joints
in the image through human skeleton extraction and initial joint position

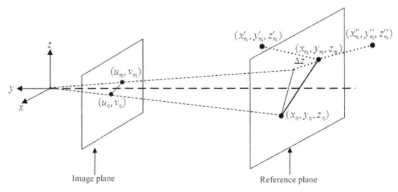

Figure 2: The projection of an articulated object *mn* under scaled-orthographic projection.

estimation. The process of three-dimensional coordinate recovery means using the known 2D coordinates and scaled-orthographic projection model to generate corresponding 3D coordinates $\tilde{X}_k = (x_k, y_k, z_k)$. Taking advantage of this model, the relationship between (x_k, y_k) and (u_k, v_k) can be formulated as: $x_k = u_k / s$, $y_k = v_k / s$, where u_k and v_k is known quantity. Therefore, the corresponding x_k and y_k can be calculated just depending on the appropriate scaling factor s, while the depth coordinate value is estimated by the body length information.

Figure 2 depicts the projection of three linked segments onto an image under perspective projection. The length of bone segment *mn* in the 3D space denoted as l_{mn} can be calculated as follows [8],

$$l_{mn}^2 = (x_m - x_n)^2 + (y_m - y_n)^2 + (z_m - z_n)^2 \tag{1}$$

Therefore, the relative depth of *mn* can be formulated as:

$$\Delta z = \pm \sqrt{l_{mn}^2 - ((u_m - u_n)^2 + (v_m - v_n)^2) / s^2} \tag{2}$$

In this equation, the relative depth value Δz can be regarded as the function of the scale factor s. Given the limb length d_{mn} of *mn* in the image, the l_{mn} can be expressed as $l_{mn} = d_{mn} / s$ through scaled-orthographic projection model. By Eq. (2), we can obtain:

$$\Delta z = \pm \sqrt{d_{mn}^2 - ((u_m - u_n)^2 + (v_m - v_n)^2)} / s \tag{3}$$

We can not determine the sign of Δz, that is to say there exist ambiguity. As shown in Figure 2, the distance from (x_m', y_m', z_m') to (x_m, y_m, z_m) is the same as the distance from (x_m'', y_m'', z_m''), whereas the sign is opposite, after projected in the image space. The sign of depth value Δz is determined by the position to the relative reference plane from these two joints. From the perspective of observers, the sign of Δz can be determined by the distance from the viewer points to the joints in image space. Therefore, by Eq. (3), there should be:

$$l_{mn}^2 - ((u_m - u_n)^2 + (v_m - v_n)^2)/s^2 \geq 0 \tag{4}$$

Through further simple transformation, the scale factor should satisfy the following inequality:

$$s \geq \sqrt{((u_m - u_n)^2 + (v_m - v_n)^2)}/l_{mn} \tag{5}$$

The minimum scale factor s of each segment chain of the skeleton model is calculated to meet the constraints, which satisfies inequality (5).

Toward the entire human body, the projection model corresponds to only a scaling factor, which should satisfy the inequality (5) of all 12 segments chains. Therefore, we estimate the 12 scale factors of the bone chain for the ith frame of a video sequence and take the maximum value as the initial estimate value of the scale factor s_i. Then according to any joint as a reference point, we can use Eq. (4) to obtain the relative three-dimensional coordinates of other joint. In this paper, the reference point $\bar{X}_{root} = (x_{root}, y_{root}, z_{root})$ is placed in the reference plane of $z_{root} = 0$. The relative depth values of other joints are estimated by hierarchy relationship so as to restore the 3D pose of the human body.

3.3 Multiple frame pose tracking

After establishing the 2D Kalman filter for each joint in the image in the monocular video, we can predict the two-dimensional position in the image respectively at the next time and restore the 3D coordinates using the scaled-orthographic projection model. If the three-dimensional coordinates are out of the range of human motion such as self-occlusion and lost the feature points, we use Kalman filters to track position. If the Kalman filters locate in the range of body movement, the algorithm will search new feature points around the predicted point. Otherwise, a feature point is calculated in accordance with linear interpolation. In the image space, the algorithm uses Eqs. (6) and (7) to predict the position and range for each joint in the next frame:

$$\hat{p}_{k+1} = p_k + v_k \cdot \Delta t + \frac{1}{2} a_k \cdot \Delta t^2 \tag{6}$$

$$\Delta p_{k+1} = \Delta p_k + \Delta v_k \cdot \Delta t + \frac{1}{2} \Delta a_k \cdot \Delta t^2 \tag{7}$$

where, the variable p_k, v_k and a_k represent the centroid coordinates of position, velocity, and acceleration of joints in the kth frame, respectively, $\hat{p}_{k+1}$ and Δp_{k+1} represent the prediction location coordinates and the searching scope of the matching target, Δv_k and Δa_k denote the predicting velocity and acceleration error of joints in the kth frame. The spatial location and range in three-dimensional space can also be predicted using formula (6) and (7) in the next frame.

4 Experiments

In the experiment, we use OpenGL and OpenCV to validate the algorithm. It is feasible to restore human movement joints in the three-dimensional coordinates from monocular video based on the scaled-orthographic projection model and the body own joint motion constraints. The resolution of test videos is 640×480, which captured by digital camera in the indoor and outdoor. Each section of human body in Figure 1(a) is recovered by calculating the scaling factor for the entire body. In monocular vision, the approach of 3D human body posture estimation based on scaled-orthographic projection model must compute the two-dimensional coordinates of the joints, length information (in pixels per unit length) of bones segment and the constraints on the relationship between bone segments. Limb length information can be directly obtained through the joint distance by the two-dimensional coordinate in the image. Their constraints relationship is restricted through a set of inequality of joints depth, in order to eliminating the depth ambiguity problem. The experiments give a joint skeleton posture model from any 3D perspective viewer. Figure 3 shows the recovery results of several frames of motion from more than 300 indoor and outdoor video sequences, wherein the next row is the abstract human skeleton motion recovery results corresponding to the actual video sequence frames at the upper row.

The experiments show that the whole restored movement is close to the actual body posture, but there exist a certain deviation. It is due to the Kalman filter tracking error and the cumulative result of illumination changes. In this experiment, the algorithm, when the number of frames exceeds 150, the tracking error is obvious. The upper posture recovery result of the abstract skeleton is deviated from the actual image in the last column in Figure 3. The closer joints from the root joint mean the smaller restored error. Obviously, the recovery result of the forearm joints is greater than the recovery error of upper arm, which is due to the recovery of the child joint influenced by the parent joints. For example, the recovery error of the calf joint is larger in the motion of lifting leg in the experimental results.

The scale factor of Taylor algorithm [3] is obtained by fixing the body height and the image height ratios. The algorithm accuracy is affected by the different body's proportions. The accuracy of the algorithm also depends on the scale factor s in the large extent, when the value of s is larger, the body posture tends to be "stretched" in the optical axis of the camera. In this paper, we estimate the scale of the non-fixed human skeleton model in the two-dimensional space.

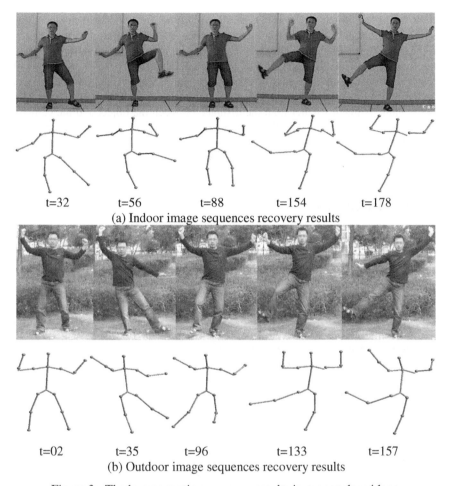

t=32   t=56   t=88   t=154   t=178
(a) Indoor image sequences recovery results

t=02   t=35   t=96   t=133   t=157
(b) Outdoor image sequences recovery results

Figure 3: The human motion recovery results in monocular videos.

Based on scaled-orthographic projection model and the inherent constraints relations of human body, the depth ambiguity between the joints can be eliminated partly. The accuracy of the algorithm consists of several aspects including the initial estimate of two-dimensional coordinates, the estimation accuracy of Δz and the ratio of each bone segment length.

5 Conclusion

In this work, we present the topic of recovering 3D models of humans from monocular video sequences. The problem is solved only assuming that the monocular video is captured in the more distant, without any special auxiliary equipment, while there are no special requirements on the background. We utilized the scaled orthographic projection model and the customized skeleton joint length of human body as the priori conditions. In two-dimensional image space, the human skeleton and joints are estimated as the initial position of each joint in the three-dimensional image space, so as to avoid manual initialization at the first frame. The advantage of using this model can satisfy the requirements of restoring the three-dimensional information of human body, without the camera calibration. However, this model is applicable to the situation which the target depth value is much smaller than the distance between the object and the camera. The other limitation is that the movement human must face to camera. It's suitable for the restoration of less precision interaction or entertainment. In the long sequence of human motion tracking, the results can be failed because of the tracking accumulated error.

Acknowledgments

The research work was supported by Foundation of Zhe'jiang Educational Committee under Grant No.Y201224034 and Y201223233.

References

[1] M. Andriluka, S. Roth, B. Schiele, Monocular 3D pose estimation and tracking by detection. In *Proc. of IEEE Conference on Computer Vision and Pattern Recognition*, pp. 623–630, 2010.

[2] Yi Ouyang, Sanyuan Zhang, Based on cluster tree human action recognition algorithm for monocular video. *Journal of Computational Information Systems*, **7(11)**, pp. 4082–4089, 2011.

[3] C.J. Taylor, Reconstruction of articulated objects from point correspondences in a single uncalibrated image. *Computer Vision and Image Understanding*, **80(3)**, pp. 349–363, 2000.

[4] B. Zou, S. Chen, C. Shi, U.M. Providence, Automatic reconstruction of 3D human motion pose from uncalibrated monocular video sequences based on markerless human motion tracking. *Pattern Recognition*, **42(1)**, pp. 1559–1571, 2009.

[5] Jian Chen, Wencheng Wang, Enhua Wu, Markerless human motion tracking from monocular videos. *Journal of Computer-Aided Design and Computer Graphics*, **17(9)**, pp. 2033–2039, 2005.

[6] Chenguang Liu, Peng Liu, Jiafeng Liu, Jianhua Huang, Xianglong Tang, 2D articulated pose tracking using particle filter with partitioned sampling and model constraints. *Journal of Intelligent and Robotic Systems*, **58(2)**, pp. 109–124, 2010.

[7] I. Karaulova, P. Hall, A. Marshall, A hierarchical model of dynamics for tracking people with a single video camera. In: *Proc. of British Machine Vision Conference*. Bristol, UK, pp. 352–361, 2000.

[8] B. Zou, S. Chen, X.N. Peng, C. Shi, Markerless 3D human motion tracking for monocular video sequences. *Journal of Computer-Aided Design and Computer Graphics*, **20(8)**, pp. 1047–1055, 2008.

HSV color space based pupil position locating method

Peng Cao, Qijie Zhao, Dawei Tu, Hui Shao
School of Mechatronics Engineering and Automation, Shanghai University, Shanghai, 200072, China

Abstract

Eye characteristics are significant information. They are widely applied in many fields, such as human–computer interaction, face recognition, and 3D face modeling from 2D images. Generally, the eye information researches are based on gray images. However, color images provide more information than gray images. In this paper, we compared several eye features in different color spaces, RGB, HIS, HSV. The results show that eye characteristics are most obvious in HSV color space. Then we proposed a pupil location method based on HSV color space. Firstly, pupil center was roughly located using extraction connected component of eye image in H channel. Then, pupil edge in HSV space was detected by means of Canny Algorithm. Finally, the extracted contour area was calculated by a minimum bounding rectangle. Experimental results indicated that the method can validly achieve pupil location quickly.
Keywords: contrastive research, HSV color space, pupil location

1 Introduction

With the development of technology, recognition and extraction of eye feature is becoming increasingly important, that is, the application of human–computer interaction, expression recognition, facial reconstruction are all based on them [1]. In recent years, many scholars have conducted a lot of researches on the eye feature extraction. The algorithms generally include the following categories.

The method based on gray scale comparison using the characteristic of the obvious gray scale contrasts of eyes [2, 3], detects eye position by integral projection. This algorithm is simple but has no strong commonality. Principal component analysis (PCA) [4] constructing feature space to extract characteristic parameters using the eye corner and eyelid feature points and so on, can position eye precisely, but the computational efficiency is low. Template-based method [5–7], establishing eye templates in advance, seek the targets matched with the templates in a specific area. Although it can get location and shape of an eye, the constraints to the images are too much and the function parameter equation is so complicated. Extraction method based on neural network [8] can well locate the eyes, but it is hard to precisely extract the features. Finally, the method based on Hough transform [9, 10] that eye image is mapped to the parameter space and the associated pixels are clustered by analytical form, has a high dependence on the parameter space.

Although there are many eye feature extraction algorithms, for a long time, researches are mainly based on gray scale image. According to human eye feature recognition, color images provide more abundant information. Pupil location method based on HSV color space has been proposed in this paper. The algorithm located pupil center roughly using the highlight information in H channel. Then, pupil edge of eye image in HSV space was detected by means of Canny Algorithm. Finally, the extracted contour area was calculated by a minimum bounding rectangle, that is, pupil location was achieved.

2 Eye feature research based on different color spaces

In practice, the color space proposed according to different purposes is multifarious. Around the eye feature in following paragraphs, several common color spaces are introduced and comparative research of the eye characteristics in the spaces are carried out.

2.1 Common color spaces

2.1.1 RGB color space

At present, most of the digital images are stored in RGB mode, and the RGB model is also one of the most important and common models in image processing. A variety of colors can be obtained by the superimposition of the 3 colors: red, green, and blue.

The coordinate system corresponds of the RGB color space is a cube shown in Figure 1. Red, green, and blue are located in the three vertices of the cube; black is fixed at the origin, and white is located at the peak of the farthest distance from the origin, moreover, gray level distributes along the line of two points, meanwhile, different colors locate the inside or outside of the cube, so we can use a vector to represent the 3D space.

Because of clear physical meaning of RGB space, we don't need to convert the space during image processing, but raw feel is insufficient, and the correlation of three components is quite high.

2.1.2 HSI color space

HSI model describes color from the visual system of people using the three elements of color tone (Hue), saturation (Saturation).

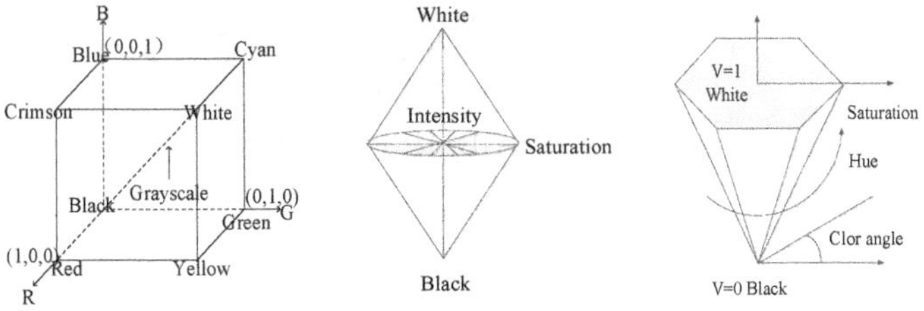

Figure 1: The model diagram of RGB, HSI, and HSV.

HSI color space can be described using a conical space model presented in Figure 1. Generally, the hue and saturation are referred as chroma used to represent the type and extent of the color. Meanwhile, the tapered cross section of the circle is chromatic circle, and the extension of tapered upward or downward is the brightness component.

2.1.3 HSV color space

HSV model is one of the color systems picking color from a palette or color wheel. HSV space contains hue, saturation, and value. The system is closer to people's color perception than the HSI.

HSV model can be described using a handstand hexagonal pyramid shown in Figure 1. Top surface is a hexagon, and from center to border represents the change of color saturation S; hue changes along the H direction; the center axis of hexagonal pyramid is presented by a V. And the top to the bottom of it represents a gray scale from black to white.

2.2 Contrastive reasearch about the eye feature in different color spaces

The digital image is usually saved as RGB model, so we need to make a color space transformation when the HSI and HSV model are used.

The formulas that RGB space converting to HIS space are presented as following:

$$H = \begin{cases} \theta, (B \le G) \\ 360 - \theta, (B > G) \end{cases} \quad (1)$$

$$\theta = \arccos \left\{ \frac{\frac{1}{2}\left[(R - B) + (R - G)\right]}{\left[(R - G)^2 + (R - G)(G - B)\right]^{1/2}} \right\}$$

$$S = 1 - \frac{3}{(R + G + B)}[\min(R, G, B)] \quad (2)$$

Figure 2: Eye image in RGB, HSI, and HSV color spaces.

$$I = \frac{1}{3}\left(R + G + B\right) \tag{3}$$

Then the formula between RGB and HSV is shown as below:

$$H = \begin{cases} \dfrac{G-B}{MAX-MIN} \times 60°, \left(R = MAX\right) \\ \left(2 + \dfrac{B - R}{MAX - MIN}\right) \times 60°, \left(G = MAX\right) \\ \left(4 + \dfrac{R - G}{MAX - MIN}\right) \times 60°, \left(B = MAX\right) \end{cases} \tag{4}$$

$$S = \frac{MAX - MIN}{MAX} \tag{5}$$

$$V = MAX \tag{6}$$

2.2.1 Comparison among the eye images in different color spaces

According to the above transformation formulas, eye images in different color spaces are presented in Figure 2.

The eye area contains eyelid, blephar, iris, and sclera. In the above three color spaces, eye appears in different features. Compared with RGB model, the four parts of an eye in HSI and HSV space has visible distinguish, especially in HSV. In image processing, such as extraction of eye edge or location and recognition of canthus, information can be obtained effectively. Besides, according to the processing algorithm of gray image, we can extract and locate the target easily.

2.2.2 Comparison among components of eye image in different color spaces

Because of eye lacking color information and the three components in HSI and HSV space are independent respectively, we could show the component of eye image in different color spaces to highlight some features. Figure 3 presents the components of eye images.

Seeing from each channel image in different color spaces, we find that there are obvious features in HSI and HSV space, for example, pupil shown in channel H presents highlight. When locating pupil center or region extraction, we could use extracting the connected components method to locate the highlight zone.

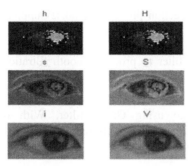

Figure 3: Three components of eye images in HIS and HSV spaces.

Figure 4: Pupil coarse positioning.   Figure 5: Detected pupil contour using Canny.

3   Pupil location method based on HSV color space

3.1 Pupil coarse location

Traditional pupil coarse location mainly uses integral projection. However, this method is susceptible to gesture and external environment. Moreover, there is so much noise in the projection drawing that the curve is irregular. So the location is always error. In this paper, pupil coarse location is achieved in the H channel of HSV space. Eye image of H channel presents highlight information in the pupil region and the comparison with background is obvious. Using extracting connected component method, we can effectively restrain the interference of eyelashes and the pupil coarse positioning accuracy is improved.

The connected component extraction is based on image pixel connectivity. Suppose S represents a subset of pixels in an image, if there is a passageway among all pixels of S, two pixels P and Q are regarded as connected. The path between pixel P and pixel Q refers to a particular pixel sequence (χ_0, y_0), (χ_1, y_1), $\cdots$, (χ_n, y_n), meanwhile, $(\chi_0, y_0) = (\chi_p, y_p)$, $(\chi_n, y_n) = (\chi_q, y_q)$. The eye image of H channel shows a large highlight connected region in pupil area, so the connected region center can be calculated. Figure 4 shows the coarse location of pupil center.

3.2 Extracting pupil edge using Canny operator

The image edge refers to a set of pixels that their gray level exist a step change or roof change. The frequently used detection operators are Roberts, Sobel, Log,

Canny, etc. In edge detection processing, noise suppression and edge accurate positioning can't be satisfied simultaneously. It's worth saying that Canny operator can keep a good balance between them. The basic idea of Canny is to select a certain Gauss filter to process smooth filtration, then edge points are calculated by maximum value of first-order differential. The basic process is as follows:

1. Smoothing image using Gauss filter. With one-dimensional Gauss function $H(x, y)$, we respectively remove the noise in rows and columns, getting smoothed image $G(x, y)$.

$$H\left(x, y\right) = \exp\left(-\frac{x^2 + y^2}{2\sigma^2}\right) \qquad (7)$$

$$G\left(x, y\right) = f\left(x, y\right) * H\left(x, y\right) \qquad (8)$$

2. Calculating the amplitude and direction of the gradient using a finite difference of first-order partial derivative.
    First-order differential template:

$$H_1 = \begin{vmatrix} -1 & -1 \\ 1 & 1 \end{vmatrix} \quad H_2 = \begin{vmatrix} 1 & -1 \\ 1 & -1 \end{vmatrix}$$

$$\phi_1\left(x, y\right) = f\left(x, y\right) * H_1\left(x, y\right) \quad \phi_2\left(x, y\right) = f\left(x, y\right) * H_2\left(x, y\right)$$

Amplitude:
$$\phi\left(x, y\right) = \sqrt{\phi_1^2\left(x, y\right) + \phi_2^2\left(x, y\right)}$$

Direction:
$$\theta_\phi = \tan^{-1}\frac{\phi_2\left(x, y\right)}{\phi_1\left(x, y\right)}$$

3. Processing non-maxima suppression for gradient amplitude. In order to finding out the edge, the local gradient maximum points must be preserved and non-maxima should be suppressed, that is, non-local maximum points are set zeros to obtain the refined edge.
4. Detecting and connecting edge using dual-threshold algorithm. We can get two edge images $N_1[i,j]$ and $N_2(i,j)$ using the double threshold T_1 and $T_2(T_1 < T_2)$. The dual-threshold method connects edge among $N_2(i,j)$ and collects edge points in the $N_1[i,j]$ until the contour is joined up. T_1 is used for finding out line segments and T_2 is served as searching faulted position in both directions along a segment.

There is obvious boundary line between pupil and iris in the HSV color space. After the processing of color changing into gray scale, image not only reserves the obvious eye characteristic of HSV color space, but can be disposed using the gray-scale image processing method. We obtain distinct pupil outline by Canny edge detection. Compared to the eye gray-scale processing, it reduces much noise interference. Then the accurate edge is refined by morphological processing methods. Figure 5 presents eye image of HSV color space after the processing of color changing into gray scale and the Canny detecting pupil contour.

3.3 Accurate location of pupil

Pupil contour, part of iris and eyelid contours can be gained after Canny detection. Taking the pupil coarse location center as reference point, we extract the smallest circular contour containing the point, reducing the interference of other non-pupil contour. Then using smallest circumscribed rectangular of the contour, we could compute pupil area size. Meanwhile, the pixels within the rectangle represent the pupil. The advantage of this method is that the extracted edge points can be disconnected and allows some false edge points to exist. According to the coarse location pupil center and the rectangular area, we can achieve pupil location.

4 Experimental results and analysis

According to the proposed pupil location algorithm, we set up an experimental system which mainly consists of 800 million pixels monocular camera, 2.5 GHZ, 4 GB memory, Win7 operating system, Dell PC. Using VC++6.0, combining with Matlab, Opencv, we have detected the proposed method. Different people were selected randomly from human being (yellow race). Then diverse backgrounds face pictures were shot in different indoor light or natural light conditions. Moreover, 250 eye images were extracted manually as a database.

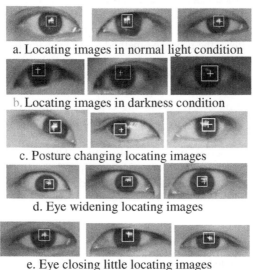

a. Locating images in normal light condition

b. Locating images in darkness condition

c. Posture changing locating images

d. Eye widening locating images

e. Eye closing little locating images

Figure 6: Pupil location of different people.

A total of 5 groups experimental images were collected, each group consisting of 10 people, and each person were taken 5 pictures. The collection condition was as follows: (1) the light is normal (daytime), moreover light is evenly spread on human face. In this condition, 50 images were collected. (2) 50 images were collected in illumination darker circumstances consisting of overcast and evening respectively 25 images. (3) Another 50 images were gained in posture changing cases, including head swing, eyes glancing up and down or saccade right and left. (4) The quantity images of eye widen and eye closing little was respectively 50. Using the database, experiment was carried out by the proposed method. Figure 6 shows some results of pupil location.

According to the experimental results, we found that pupil position could be located well in normal light condition. Even though posture changed, such as c condition and e eye closing little condition, the proposed method could locate pupil in a relative little scope. Moreover, the locating results of eye widened were optimal. However, it is worst to locate pupil in illumination darker circumstances. As we can see in Figure 6(b), the scope of pupil defined by the method was larger than the real area itself. In other words, the method was apt to cause greater error in this condition.

To sum up, the algorithm we proposed in this paper could achieve accurate location of the pupil. According to the obvious eye information in HSV color space, we could also reduce the amount of calculation, improving pupil location accuracy, obtaining certain robustness about the posture and pupil incomplete situation. Compared with traditional method of integral projection based on gray image and pupil location searching gray area, our method makes a quite improvement about computation speed and accuracy. Table 1 shows the contrast test results. Pupil location was achieved using gray projection and regional characteristics. The method calculated eye vertical axis value, and then obtained abscissa value through the regional characteristics. It was very susceptible to eyelashes and eyebrows. Therefore, it was easy to locate pupil in the eyebrows position. Compared with it, the proposed method using eye significant features in HSV color space could obtain a high accuracy and speed in locating pupil aspect. Average accuracy could reach approximately 94.6%. Average location time was about 4 s. Compared with document [3], which used eyebrows gray information to gain the rough position of eye, achieving coarse locating by calculating the lengthways gray, and then searching near the coarse point using a pupil filter to locate eye center, our method located pupil rough position through H channel, reducing the searching scope of precise location. Therefore, the speed of calculation was improved. But the area referred as pupil was rather larger than that of document [3]. Besides, the proposed method was always dependent on light.

5 Conclusions

In this paper, several eye features were compared in different color spaces. HSV color space carrying significant information was selected for proceeding feature recognition. Pupil location method was proposed based on HSV color space.

Table 1: Comparison Between the Proposed Method and Traditional Gray Image Location Algorithm.

Algorithm	Accuracy of Pupil Location (%)	Average Location Time(s)
The proposed method	94.6	approximately 4
Method in [11] document	89.7	approximately 6

Firstly, pupil center was located roughly by highlight information in H channel. In this way, we could restrain the interference of eyelashes, reducing the range of accurate location. Next, pupil edge in HSV model was detected by Canny algorithm. Finally, the extracted contour area was calculated by a minimum bounding rectangle, achieving pupil location. Compared with traditional eye location algorithm of gray image, our algorithm reduces the computational complexity, improving the processing speed and positioning accuracy, and also has a good robustness about the pupil incomplete situation. The disadvantage of this method is the pupil highlighted information in H channel is always depended on the illumination intensity. The coarse location will be effected. The problem will be improved in our future research.

References

[1] P. Cao, Q.J. Zhao, D.W. Tu, H. Shao, *Comparison of Eyes Characteristics in Different Color Spaces.* IHMSC, Hangzhou, 2013.
[2] J.X. Wu, Z.H. Zhou, Efficient face candidates selector for face detection. *Pattern Recognition,* **36(5)**, pp. 1175–1186, 2003.
[3] Y. Wu, Y. Yang, L.P. Wang, *An eye location algorithm based on the gray information and the pupil filter. Computer Engineering and Applications,* **33**, pp. 45–47, 2005.
[4] A. Pentland, B. Moghaddam, T. Starner, View-based and modular eigenspaces for face recognition. *Proc. IEEE Conference on Computer Vision and Pattern Recognition,* IEEE Press, pp. 84–91,1994.
[5] A.L. Yuille, P.W. Hallinan,D.S. Cohen, Feature extraction from faces using deformable templates. *International Journal of Computer Vision,* **8(2)**, pp. 99–111, 1992.
[6] K.M. Lam, H. Yan, Locating and extracting the covered eye in human face image. *Pattern Recognition,* **29(5)**, pp. 771–779, 1996.
[7] J.Y. Deng, Region-based template deformation and masking for eye-feature extraction and description. *Pattern Recognition,* **30(3)**, pp. 403–419, 1997.
[8] H. Rowley, A.S. Baluja, T. Kanade, Neural network-based face detection. *IEEE-PAMI,* **20(1)**, pp. 23–38, 1998.

[9] T. Kawaguchi, D. Hidaka, M. Rizon, Detection of eyes from human faces by hough transforms and separability filters. *Proc. IEEE Conference on Image Processing*, IEEE Press, pp. 49–52, 2000.

[10] Y.H. Li, S.N. Zhu, Hough transform for eye feature extraction. *Journal of Zhejiang University*, **42(7)**, pp. 1164–1168, 2008.

[11] Z. Fu, P.F. Wang, X.Q. Ma, Eye location arithmetic based on gray projection and region geometry characters. *Computer Knowledge and Technology*, **4(7)**, pp. 1706–1708, 2008.

The research and design of FPGA-based conversion interface of real-time HD video image

Shou-Liang Yang, Dong Zhang, Ling-Gang Zeng
Institute of Information Optoelectronics Technology and Application, Chongqing University of Arts and Sciences, Yongchuan Chongqing, China

Abstract

An FPGA-based conversion interface for real-time high-definition video images is proposed and realized in order to meet the demands of surveillance video image conversion for high speed, reliability, real time, and high definition. By using the Cyclone EP2C35F672C6 clips made by Altera Co. as the video image conversion interface chip, the Verilog HDL key codes are presented with the functions of video image format conversion, interlace converting to progression, conversion of color and space. The speed of video processing can be greatly enhanced by utilizing the concurrency and flexibility of programmable logic devices in the real-time processing of images. The experiment has proved that after the related debugging by the system, both the versatility and transposability are improved and the video images can be played more fluently.

Keywords: Video collection, video image format conversion, FPGA, VGA driving

1 Introduction

With the rapid development of digital video's transmission and processing technology, in video's real-time processing, the image data's higher handling capacity as well as the computational intensity call for the higher performance of image processing system. In the past, video surveillance application had limited channels, and people were less demanding for the image's quality and real-time performance.[1] Therefore, FPGA was seldom used. However,

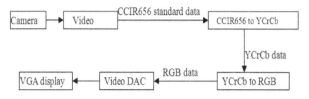

Fig.1: System scheme

DSP was less and less satisfactory as people's requirements for surveillance transformed from standard definition (SD) to high definition (HD), from single channel to eight channels, from nonreal time to real time, together with the functions of face recognition and motion estimation. FPGA's high degree of volume and flexibility can allow image's high degree of parallel processing, with higher speed than that of PC and digital signal processing chips 0]. Therefore, the intensive research into the FGPA-based conversion interface for real-time high-definition video images is greatly significant for the development of high-performance image processing products.

By using FPGA device as the digital processing chip of video images, this conversion interface can implement the transformation from interlace to progression and the conversion of colors and space. This paper focuses on the description of the system's hardware design, and the design of logical circuit within FPGA. It explains how the video images with the format of ITU BT.656 are displayed on the VGA displayer after the analog video signals output by cameras are decoded by ADV7181 TV decoding chip.

2 System scheme design

In this system, the CVBS composite analog video signals output by cameras are input into the video decoding chip ADV7181. After the decoding, they are transformed into ITU-R BT.656 standard data stream and then input into FPGA chip. The FPGA chip first implements the transformation from ITU-R BT. 656 to YCrCb, and then YCrCb to RGB color space until finally they are output to VGA interface through the video D/A converter. The system design is shown in Figure 1.

The conversion interface uses EP2C35F672 chip in Series Cyclone II produced by Altera Co. Ltd. as the video image conversion interface processing chip. The minimum system of FPGA is composed of EP2C35F672, a power circuit, a clock circuit, and EPCS16 configuration circuit, etc.

The video is collected by using ADV7181 decoding chip in ADI, which implements the A/D conversion for the CVBS composite analog video images. The real-time images are digitalized and processed by FPGA. The VGA display output device is ADV7123 chip produced by ADI Co., which implements the A/D conversion for the digital image data and transfers them onto the VGA interface displayer. Based on the industry standard sequence displayed on VGA, the level and frame synchronization signals are composite and the images are output and displayed.

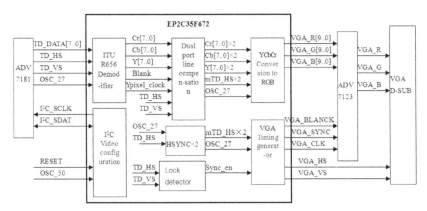

Fig.2: Video conversion interface

3 FPGA logical design

Through ADV7181 the analog video signals can output Standard CCIR656 YCrCb 4:2:2 standard digital video signals, and then are input into FPGA, which will complete the conversion interface of high-speed video images. The framework of the system is shown in Figure 2.

Two modules are included in the internal logical circuit of FPGA chip: I2C_AV_Config and TV_TO_VGA. The former is used to configure the TV decoder ADV7181; the latter is composed of itu_r656_decoder, double line buffer, HsyncX2, YcrCb2RGB and VGA_Timing_Generator etc.

3.1 itu_656_decoder module design

The module itu_656_decoder interpolates the YcrCb(4:4:2) data source gained by decoding TV decoding chip ADV7181, generates the YcrCb(4:4:4) signals, and at the same time generates the 13.5 MHz pixel clock and blanking signals.

By analyzing the FF 00 00 SAV/EAV in the output data stream of the camera and decoding it, one can gain the valid data YCrCb and field blanking signals. The camera outputs the video with the format CVBS, which first converts into YCrCb4:2:2 by ADV7181B, and then into YCrCb4:4:4 through itu_r656_decoder. Simultaneously, 13.5 MHz pixel clock and blanking signals are generated. As the data output from TV decoder are interlacedly scanned, weaving processing needs to be done to the data source, that is, convert the interlace signals to progressive signals. The key codes are:

```
always@(posedge iCLK_27 or negedge iRST_N)
    ……
    if(iSwap_CbCr)
    begin
        case(Cont[1:0])      //  Swap
        0:   Cb    <=  iTD_DATA;
```

```
1:    YCbCr  <=  {iTD_DATA,Cr};
2:    Cr      <=  iTD_DATA;
3:    YCbCr  <=  {iTD_DATA,Cb};
    endcase
    end
    else
  begin
    case(Cont[1:0])       //   Normal
    0:  Cb      <=  iTD_DATA;
    1:  YCbCr  <=  {iTD_DATA,Cb};
    2:  Cr      <=  iTD_DATA;
    3:  YCbCr  <=  {iTD_DATA,Cr};
    endcase
    end
```

3.2 Weaving processing interpolation module design

As the data output from the TV decoder are interlacedly scanned, weaving
processing needs to be done to the data source, that is, convert the interlaced
signals to progressive signals. The weaving processing is realized by using dual-
ported circuit buffer module and HsyncX2 module. The clock pixel is converted
from 13.5 to 27 MHz, and Signal Hsync decreases from 31.4 to 15.7 kHz. There
is a 1 KB dual-ported SRAM in the dual-ported circuit buffer module, which
doubles the YCrCb data (Y×2, Cr×2, Cb×2). The key codes are:

```
always@(posedge iCLK or negedge iRST_N)
  ......
  if(!iRST_N)
  begin
     mY <=  0;
     mCb     <=  0;
     mCr     <=  0;
  end
  else
  begin
     if(iX[0])
     {mY,mCr}  <=  iYCbCr;
     else
     {mY,mCb}  <=  iYCbCr;
           ......
```

3.3 The design of the YCbCr-to -RGB module

As both TV and CRT displayer display colors based on the RGB three primary
color composition, YCrCb has to be converted to RGB. The YCbCr-to-RGB
module is used to convert the YCbCr value to the corresponding RGB value

based on data effective signals provided by the de-interleaving module. The key codes are:

```
always@(posedge iCLK)
......
    if(X_OUT[19])
    oRed<=0;
    else if(X_OUT[18:0]>1023)
    oRed<=1023;
    else
    oRed<=X_OUT[9:0];
    if(Y_OUT[19])
    oGreen<=0;
    else if(Y_OUT[18:0]>1023)
    oGreen<=1023;
    else
    oGreen<=Y_OUT[9:0];
    if(Z_OUT[19])
    oBlue<=0;
    else if(Z_OUT[18:0]>1023)
    oBlue<=1023;
    else
    oBlue<=Z_OUT[9:0];
    {oDVAL,oDVAL_d}<={oDVAL_d,iDVAL};
        ......
```

Later on, the YCrCb-to RGB module sends the YCrCb×2 data to VGA displayer. The VGA timing generator generates individual VGA synchronous signals VGA_HS and VGA_VS, so that the output data can be shown on VGA displayer.

3.4 The design of the VGA timing generator

After the format of the image data are converted and the RGB format, which is suitable for VGA images, is gained, VGA controller is produced according to the VGA timing sequence. So the VGA line synchronous information HS and the field synchronous information VS are generated. At the same time, the 25 MHz clock is provided. All these are sent to decoding chip ADV7123 and output to VGA displayer through the video interface [9,10]. The key codes are:

```
always@(posedge iCLK or negedge iRST_N)
    ......
    if(H_Cont==H_FRONT-1)    //    Front porch end
    oVGA_HS  <=  1'b0;
    if(H_Cont==H_FRONT+H_SYNC-1) //    Sync pulse end
    oVGA_HS<=    1'b1;
```

Fig.3: VGA control Circuit simulation waveform

......
always@(posedge oVGA_HS or negedge iRST_N)
......
    if(V_Cont<V_TOTAL)
    V_Cont <=V_Cont+1'b1;
    else
    V_Cont <=0;
    if(V_Cont==V_FRONT-1)   //   Front porch end
    oVGA_VS <= 1'b0;
    if(V_Cont==V_FRONT+V_SYNC-1)//   Sync pulse end
    oVGA_VS <= 1'b1;
    ......

The VGA module's simulation result is shown in Figure 3.

4   Test results

The video image processing system is composed of three parts: collection, programmable logic, VGA display and output. The test is aimed to verify whether the video image conversion interface can realize the conversion from ITU-R BT.656 to RGB. The high-speed video images output by the camera are input into FPGA, and then transmitted to VGA display. After that, one can observe whether the video images are fluent and VGA display module is right. The test shows that the real-time images are fluent and have high quality. The playing effect is shown in Figure 4.

The video image processing system is composed of three parts: collection, programmable logic, VGA display and output. The test is aimed to verify whether the video image conversion interface can realize the conversion from ITU-R BT.656 to RGB. The high-speed video images output by the camera are input into FPGA, and then transmitted to VGA display. After that, one can observe whether the video images are fluent and VGA display module is right. The test shows that the real-time images are fluent and have high quality. The playing effect is shown in Figure 4.

5   Conclusion

This paper focuses on the high-speed video image conversion interface with the Altera EP2C35F672 FPGA chip and ADV7181 video decoding chip as the

Fig.4: Real Time HD video conversion test renderings

principal part. The experimental results show that the system, stable and reliable, can meet the demands of high-performance real-time image processing system. Moreover, by using the FPGA design, this system has a high degree of integration and flexibility. As users can also conduct system reconfiguration according to their own needs, this system is convenient and efficient to use. It is highly applicable in high-definition video monitoring.

References

[1]   Liu Song, Fu Yang, Guo Pei-yuan, Design of digital video monitoring system based on FPGA. *Video Engineering*, **3**, pp. 92–94, 2010.
[2]   Yang Qin, Zhou Yun-fei, Hu Yong-bing, Design of video image acquisition and display system based on FPGA. *Computer Engineering and Design*, **6**, pp. 1988–1992, 2013.

On generalized strong implicit vector quasi-equilibrium problems

Lin Zhu, Yali Zhao
College of Physics and Mathematics, Bohai University, Jinzhou, China

Abstract

In this paper, the solvability of a class of generalized strong implicit vector quasi-equilibrium problems with set-valued maps are introduced and studied. By using the continuous selection theorems and fixed point theorems, some existence theorems for generalized strong implicit vector quasi-equilibrium problems without any monotonicity assumption are obtained and the results presented here extend the corresponding results in this area.

Keywords: Generalized strong implicit vector quasi-equilibrium problem, continuous selection theorem, fixed point theorem, C-diagonally quasi-convexity

1 Introduction

Throughout this paper, unless specified otherwise, we always suppose that X and Y are nonempty subsets of two Hausdorff topological vector spaces, respectively, Z is another Hausdorff topological vector space and $C \subseteq Z$ is a closed convex cone with the apex at the origin 0 and $\operatorname{int} C \neq \varnothing$, where $\operatorname{int} C$ denotes the topological interior of C. Let $g : X \times X \to X$, $h : Y \times X \to Y$ be vector-valued maps and $K : X \to 2^X$, $S : Y \to 2^X$, $T : X \to 2^Y$ and $F : X \times Y \times X \to 2^Z$ be set-valued maps. We consider the following generalized strong implicit vector quasi-equilibrium problems (for short, GSIVQEP): find $\overline{x} \in X$, $\overline{y} \in T(\overline{x})$, $\overline{u} \in S(\overline{y})$ such that $\overline{x} \in K(\overline{x})$ and $F(g(\overline{x}, \overline{u}), h(\overline{y}, \overline{u}), x) \subseteq C$, $\forall x \in K(\overline{x})$.

By suitable choice of the maps F, g, h, K, S, T, we can also obtain many kinds of generalized quasi-equilibrium problems, generalized equilibrium problems and vector variational inequality problems as special cases of our GSIVQEP, for instance, see Ref. [4] and the references therein. So GSIVQEP is more general, which is one of our motivations to write the paper.

2 Preliminaries

Definition 2.1
Let X and Y be two topological spaces, $F : X \to 2^Y$ be a set-valued map.

(i) F is said to be upper semicontinuous (for short, u. s. c.) at $x \in X$ if, for each neighborhood V of $F(x)$, there is a neighborhood U of x such that for each $t \in U$, $F(t) \subset V$; F is said to be u. s. c. on X if it is u. s. c. at every $x \in X$.

(ii) F is said to be lower semicontinuous (for short, l. s. c.) at $x \in X$ if, for any $y \in F(x)$ and any neighborhood V of y, there is a neighborhood U of x such that for each $t \in U$, $F(t) \cap V \neq \varnothing$; F is said to be l. s. c. on X if it is l. s. c. at every $x \in X$. F is said to be continuous on X if it is at the same time u. s. c. and l. s. c. on X.

(iii) F is said to be closed if the graph $Gr(F) = \{(x, y) \in X \times Y : y \in F(x)\}$ is a closed subset of $X \times Y$.

(iv) F is said to be compact if the closure $\overline{F(X)}$ of its range $F(X)$ is a compact subset in Y.

Definition 2.2
Let X and Y be two topological spaces, $T : X \to 2^Y$ be a set-valued mapping. For each $y \in Y$, $T^{-1}(y) := \{x \in X : y \in T(x)\}$ is said to a lower section of T.

Definition 2.3
A nonempty topological space is said to be acyclic if, its reduction of any $\hat{C}$ each coherent group on rational numbers field is equal to zero.

In particular, each convex set, star-shaped set, and contractible set of the topological space are acyclic set.

Definition 2.4
Let X and Y be convex subsets of two Hausdorff topological vector spaces, Z be another Hausdorff topological vector space, and $C \subset Z$ be a nonempty subset, let $g : X \times Y \to X$, $h : Y \times X \to Y$ be vector-valued maps, let $F : X \times Y \times X \to 2^Z$ be set-valued map.

(i) F is said to be strongly I C-diagonally quasi-convex (for short, SIC-DQC) with respect to g, h, and the third variable if, for any finite subset $A = \{x_1, x_2, \cdots x_n\}$ of X, and for each $x \in CoA$ (where CoA denotes the convex hull of a set A), there exists an $x_i \in A$, such that $F(g(x,u),h(y,u),x_i) \subseteq C$, $\forall (y,u) \in Y \times X$.

(ii) F is said to be strongly II C -diagonally quasi-convex (for short, SIIC-DQC) with respect to g , h , and the third variable if, for any finite subset $A = \{x_1, x_2, \cdots x_n\}$ of X , and for each $x \in CoA$, there exists an $x_i \in A$ such that

$$F(g(x,u),h(y,u),x_i) \cap C \neq \varnothing , \ \forall (y,u) \in Y \times X .$$

Next, suppose that Z is a Hausdorff topological vector space, Z^* is the topology dual space of Z and C^* denotes the dual cone of the cone $C \subseteq Z$, that is $C^* = \{l \in Z^* : \langle l, x \rangle, \forall x \in C\}$. And suppose that C^* has $weak^*$ compact convex base B , that is, B is a $weak^*$ compact convex subset of C^* and such that $0 \notin B$ and $C^* = \bigcup_{t \geq 0} tB$. Define a function $\psi : Z \to R$ by

$$\psi(z) = \max_{\lambda \in B} \langle \lambda, z \rangle , \ \forall z \in Z .$$

Then ψ is sublinear (that is positively homogeneous, subadditive) and l. s. c. In order to obtain our results, the following lemmas and theorems are needed.

Lemma 2.1
Let B be a $weak^*$ compact convex base of C^* , for all $z \in Z$. Then

(i) $z \in C \Leftrightarrow \langle \lambda, z \rangle \geq 0$, $\forall \lambda \in C^*$;

(ii) $z \in C \Leftrightarrow \langle \lambda, z \rangle \geq 0$, $\forall \lambda \in B$.

Lemma 2.2
Let X be a topological space and Y be a convex subset of another topological vector space. Let $G : X \to 2^Y$ be a set-valued map and has an open lower section, then $F : X \to 2^Y$ defined as $F(x) = CoG(x)$ $(\forall x \in X)$ has an open lower section.

Lemma 2.3
Let X and Y be topological spaces. If set-valued maps $G, K : X \to 2^Y$ have an open lower section, respectively, then the set-valued map $\theta : X \to 2^Y$, be defined as $\theta(x) = G(x) \cap K(x)$ $(\forall x \in X)$ has an open lower section.

Theorem 2.1 (continuous selection theorem)
Let X be paracompact topological spaces and Y be another topological vector space. Assume a set-valued map $F : X \to 2^Y$ has a nonempty convex value and

has an open lower section, then F has a continuous selection, that is, there exists continuous map $f : X \to Y$ such that $f(x) \in F(x)$ $(\forall x \in X)$.

Theorem 2.2 (Browder fixed-point theorem)
Let X be a nonempty compact convex subset of Hausdorff topological vector space. The set-valued map $H : X \to 2^X$ has a nonempty convex value and an open lower section, then H has a fixed point in X.

Theorem 2.3 (Eilenberg–Montgomery fixed-point theorem)
Let X be a compact convex subset of locally convex Hausdorff topological vector space. Let a set-valued map $T : X \to 2^X$ is u. s. c. and has nonempty closed acyclic value, then T has a fixed point.

3 Main results

Theorem 3.1
Let X and Y be nonempty compact convex subsets of two locally convex Hausdorff topological vector spaces, respectively. And let Z be another Hausdorff topological vector space. Assume that $C \subseteq Z$ is a closed convex cone with the apex at the origin 0, C^* is the dual cone of C, and C^* has *weak* compact convex base B, $g : X \times X \to X$, $h : X \times X \to Y$ are two vector-valued maps, and $K : X \to 2^X$, $T : X \to 2^Y$ $S : Y \to 2^X$ and $F : X \times Y \times X \to 2^Z$ are four set-valued maps. Suppose that the following conditions are satisfied:

(i) K has an open lower section and for any $x \in X$, $K(x)$ is a nonempty convex set in X;

(ii) T is u. s. c. and for any $x \in X$, $T(x)$ is a nonempty closed acyclic set in Y;

(iii) S is u. s. c. and for any $y \in Y$, $S(y)$ is a nonempty closed acyclic set in X;

(iv) for any $(x, y, u) \in X \times Y \times X$, $F(g(x,u), h(y,u), x)$ is an nonempty compact set in Z and
   (a) for any $(u,v) \in X \times X$, the map $-F(g(\cdot,u).h(\cdot,u),v) : X \times Y \to 2^Z$ is l. s. c.;
   (b) for any $(y,u) \in Y \times X$, the map $F(g(\cdot,u), h(y,u), \cdot) : X \times X \to 2^Z$ is SIC-DQC.
   Then, GSIVQEP is solvable.

Proof. For any $(x,u,y,u) \in X \times X \times Y \times X$, let $\phi : X \times Y \times X \to R$ and $s : X \times Y \times X \to R$ be defined as follows:

$$\phi(g(x,u),h(y,u),v) = \min_{\lambda \in B} \min_{z \in F(g(x,u),h(y,u),v)} \langle \lambda, z \rangle$$

$$= \min_{\lambda \in B} \lambda \big[F(g(x,u),h(y,u),v) \big]$$

$$s(g(x,u),h(y,u),v) = -\phi(g(x,u),h(y,u),v)$$

$$= \max_{\lambda \in B} \max_{z \in F(g(x,u),h(y,u),v)} \langle \lambda, -z \rangle$$

$$= \max_{\lambda \in B} \lambda \big[-F(g(x,u),h(y,u),v) \big]$$

In order to obtain our desired result, it follows from Lemma 2.2 that we only need to show that there exist $\bar{x} \in X$, $\bar{y} \in Y$, and $\bar{u} \in S(\bar{y})$ such that $\bar{x} \in K(\bar{x})$ and

$$\phi(g(\bar{x},\bar{u}),h(\bar{y},\bar{u})v) \geq 0, \quad \forall v \in K(\bar{x}). \tag{3.1}$$

For this, we first prove that for all $v \in X$, $s(g(x,u),h(y,u),v)$ with respect to x and y is l. s. c. In fact, for each $r \in R$, let

$$L(r) = \big\{ (x,y) \in X \times Y : s(g(x,u),h(y,u),v) \leq r \big\}$$

$$= \big\{ (x,y) \in X \times Y : \max_{\lambda \in B} \lambda \big[-F(g(x,u),h(y,u),v) \big] \leq r \big\}$$

We claim that $L(r)$ is a closed subset in $X \times Y$. Let $\{(x_\alpha, y_\alpha)\} \subseteq L(r)$ be a net such that $(x_\alpha, y_\alpha) \rightarrow (x,y) \in X \times Y$, then for all α,

$$\max_{\lambda \in B} \lambda \big[-F(g(x_\alpha,u),h(y_\alpha,u),v) \big] \leq r \tag{3.2}$$

Since $-F(g(x,u),h(y,u),v)$ with respect to x, y is l.s.c., then by Lemma 2.1 (iii), for all $z \in -F(g(x,u),h(y,u),v)$,there exists a $\{z_\alpha\} \subseteq Z$ such that $z_\alpha \in -F(g(x_\alpha,u),h(y_\alpha,u),v)$ and $z_\alpha \rightarrow z$. Noting $\psi(z) = \max_{\lambda \in B} \langle \lambda, z \rangle$ $\psi(z) = \max_{\lambda \in B} \langle \lambda, z \rangle$ is l. s. c., we have

$$\max_{\lambda \in B} \langle \lambda, z \rangle \leq \min_\alpha \max_{\lambda \in B} \langle \lambda, z_\alpha \rangle$$

$$\leq \min_\alpha \max_{\lambda \in B} \lambda \big[-F(g(x_\alpha,u),h(y_\alpha,u),v) \big] \tag{3.3}$$

$$\leq r$$

implying $\max_{\lambda \in B} \langle \lambda, z \rangle$. By the arbitrary of z , we get

$$\max_{\lambda \in B} \lambda \left[-F(g(x,u), h(y,u), v) \right] \le r,$$

which means $(x, y) \in L(r)$, then $L(r)$ is closed. So, $s(g(x,u), h(y,u), v)$ with respect to x and y is l. s. c.

In order to finish the proof, we shall define the following two set-valued maps $P, G : X \times Y \times X \to 2^X$ as

$$P(x, y, u) = \{ v \in X : s(g(x,u), h(y,u), v) > 0 \},$$

$$G(x, y, u) = K(x) \bigcap CoP(x, y, u),$$

for all $(x, y, u) \in X \times Y \times X$, respectively. Then, for each $v \in X$,

$$P^{-1}(v) = \{ (x, y, u) \in X \times Y \times X : s(g(x,u), h(y,u), v) > 0 \}$$

is open set in X, implying P has an open lower section. It follows from Lemma 2.3 that the map CoP (where CoP denotes the convex hull of a set P) has an open lower section. Since K has an open lower section, in view of Lemma 2.4 that G has an open lower section.

Next, we show $\exists (\bar{x}, \bar{y}, \bar{u}) \in X \times T(\bar{x}) \times S(\bar{y})$ such that $\bar{x} \in K(\bar{x})$ and

$$G(\bar{x}, \bar{y}, \bar{u}) = \varnothing \tag{3.4}$$

Putting $U = \{ (x, y, u) \in X \times Y \times X : G(x, y, u) \neq \varnothing \}$.

(1) If $U = \varnothing$, then, $G(x, y, u) = \varnothing$ $(\forall (x, y, u) \in X \times Y \times X)$. Since X is a compact convex set and it follows Condition (i) from Theorem 2.2 that K has a fixed point, that is, there exists an $\bar{x} \in X$ such that $\bar{x} \in K(\bar{x})$. And it follows from Conditions (ii) and (iii) that $T(x) \neq \varnothing$ and $S(y) \neq \varnothing$. Then for any $\bar{y} \in T(\bar{x})$ and $\bar{u} \in S(\bar{y})$, we have $G(\bar{x}, \bar{y}, \bar{u}) = \varnothing$.

(2) If $U \neq \varnothing$, noting G has an open lower section, and $U = \bigcup_{w \in X} G^{-1}(w)$, thus U is a open set. Define a set-valued map $Q : X \times Y \times X \to 2^X$ as follows:

$$Q(x, y, u) := \begin{cases} G(x, y, u), & \forall (x, y, u) \in U, \\ K(x), & \forall (x, y, u) \in (X \times Y \times X) \setminus U. \end{cases}$$

Then, for any $w \in X$, $Q^{-1}(w) = G^{-1}(w) \bigcup (K^{-1}(w) \times Y)$ is a open set, implying that Q has an open lower section. Also noting that for any $(x, y, u) \in X \times Y \times X$,

$Q(x,y,u)$ is a nonempty convex set, then it follows from Theorem 2.1 that Q has a continuous selection $q: X \times Y \times X \to X$ such that $q(x,y,u) \in Q(x,y,u)$ $(\forall (x,y,u) \in X \times Y \times X)$. We also need to consider the following set-valued map $M: X \times Y \times X \to 2^{X \times Y \times X}$, defined as follows: $M(x,y,u) = (q(x,y,u), T(x), S(y))$, $\forall (x,y,u) \in X \times Y \times X$.

By Conditions (ii) and (iii), we get that the map M is nonempty closed acyclic. Since q is continuous, T and S are u. s. c. and nonempty closed acyclic, it follows from Lemma 2.1 (i) that M is closed. Noting $X \times Y \times X$ is compact, it follows from Lemma 2.1 (ii) that M is u. s. c. By using Theorem 2.3, we get that M has a fixed point $(\bar{x}, \bar{y}, \bar{u}) \in M(\bar{x}, \bar{y}, \bar{u})$. Moreover, $(\bar{x}, \bar{y}, \bar{u}) \notin U$. Indeed, suppose to the contrary that $(\bar{x}, \bar{y}, \bar{u}) \in U$, that is,

$$\bar{x} = h(x,y,u) \in H(\bar{x}, \bar{y}, \bar{u}) = G(\bar{x}, \bar{y}, \bar{u}) \subseteq CoP(\bar{x}, \bar{y}, \bar{u}),$$

implying $\bar{x} \in CoP(\bar{x}, \bar{y}, \bar{u})$ and there exist $x_1, x_2, \cdots x_n \in X$ and $x_i \in P(\bar{x}, \bar{y}, \bar{u})$ $(i = 1, 2, \cdots, n)$ and $t_i \geq 0$ and $\sum_{i=1}^{n} t_i = 1$ such that $\bar{x} = \sum_{i=1}^{n} t_i x_i$. Thus $s(g(\bar{x}, \bar{u}), h(\bar{y}, \bar{u}), x_i) > 0$, $i = 1, 2, \cdots, n$.

Then, $\min_{\lambda \in B} \lambda \left[F(g(\bar{x}, \bar{u}), h(\bar{y}, \bar{u}), x_i) \right] < 0$ $(i = 1, 2, \cdots, n)$. It follows from Lemma 2.2 that $F(g(\bar{x}, \bar{u}), h(\bar{y}, \bar{u}), x_i) \not\subset C$, $i = 1, 2, \cdots, n$, which contradicts Condition (iv) (b) and so $(\bar{x}, \bar{y}, \bar{u}) \notin U$. Thus, $\bar{x} \in K(\bar{x})$, $\bar{y} \in T(\bar{x})$, $\bar{u} \in S(\bar{y})$ and $G(\bar{x}, \bar{y}, \bar{u}) = \varnothing$, which implies that $K(\bar{x}) \cap CoP(\bar{x}, \bar{y}, \bar{u}) = \varnothing$ by Eq. (3.4). Specially, $K(\bar{x}) \cap P(\bar{x}, \bar{y}, \bar{u}) = \varnothing$, that is, for each $\bar{x} \in K(\bar{x})$ then $\bar{x} \notin P(\bar{x}, \bar{y}, \bar{u})$, so

$$s(g(\bar{x}, \bar{u}), h(\bar{y}, \bar{u}), x) \leq 0, \quad \forall x \in K(\bar{x}),$$

implying $\phi(g(\bar{x}, \bar{u}), h(\bar{y}, \bar{u}), x) \geq 0$ $(\forall x \in K(\bar{x}))$, completing the proof.

Theorem 3.2

Let X, Y, Z, C, B, and K be as in Theorem 3.1, $g: X \to X$ vector-valued map and the following conditions are satisfied:

(i) K has an open lower section and for any $x \in X$, $K(x)$ is a nonempty convex set in X;

(ii) for any $(x,y) \in X \times X$, $F(g(x), y): X \times X \to 2^Z$ is an nonempty compact set in Z and
   (a) for any $y \in X$, the map $-F(g(\cdot), y): X \to 2^Z$ is l. s. c.;
   (b) the map $F(g(\cdot), \cdot): X \times X \to 2^Z$ is SIC-DQC. Then,

there exists $\bar{x} \in X$ such that $\bar{x} \in K(\bar{x})$ and $F(g(\bar{x}), y) \subseteq C$, $\forall y \in K(\bar{x})$.

Proof. Let $Y = \{\bar{y}\}$ be single point set and let

$$T(x) = \{\bar{y}\}, \ \forall x \in X,$$
$$G(g(x,u), \bar{y}, y) = F(g(x), y), \ \forall x, y \in X$$

It is easy to check that all conditions of Theorem 3.1 are satisfied. Then it follows from Theorem 3.1 that the desired conclusion is immediately obtained.

Acknowledgments

The research work was supported by the National Natural Science Foundation of China under Grant No. 11371070.

References

[1] S.H. Wang, J.Y. Fu, On generalized strong vector quasi-equilibrium problems with set-valued maps. *Acta Analysis Functionalis Applicata*, **11(3)**, pp. 252–259, 2009.
[2] X H. Gong, Strong vector equilibrium problems. *Journal of Global Optimization*, **36**, pp. 339–349, 2006.
[3] Y.P. Fang, N.J. Huang, Strong vector variational inequalities in Banach spaces. *Applied Mathematics Letters*, **19**, pp. 362–368, 2006.
[4] E. Blum, W. Oettli, From optimization and variational inequalities to equilibrium problems. *Math Student*, **63**, pp. 123–145, 1994.

Coverage strategy in wireless sensor networks based on node scheduling

Huarui Wu[1,2,3], Li Zhu[1,2,3]
[1]Beijing Research Center for Information Technology in Agriculture, Beijing Academy of Agriculture and Forestry Sciences, Beijing, China
[2]National Engineering Research Center for Information Technology in Agriculture, Beijing, China
[3]Key Laboratories for Information Technology in Agriculture, Beijing, China

Abstract

Energy limited becomes a key and hot point problem of wireless sensor networks. This paper proposes a coverage strategy in wireless sensor networks, based on node scheduling. The strategy uses the relationship between energy consumption and coverage rate, combines with the Voronoi, which selected some redundant nodes and dispatched it. When the redundant nodes were in a sleeping state, the network energy consumption was reduced. Simulation results show that the strategy realize energy distributed evenly, effectively reduce the number of the nodes and network energy consumption, prolong the network lifetime.

Keywords: Wireless sensor networks, the network coverage rate, Voronoi, redundant node.

1 Introduction

In recent years, with the development of wireless communication and low power embedded technology, wireless sensor networks (WSN), which with low power consumption, low cost, and self-organization, are widely used in various fields, the finite energy [1–3] has become one of the key factors that restrict the performance of the network.

In order to improve the performance of WSN, and cover the requirements for monitoring area, the densely deployment is one of the most common method to improve the coverage rate [4]. But in this deployment strategy, there are large number of redundant nodes, and bring some energy consumption [5]. At present, most coverage control algorithm obtained the node geographic information, by means of external facilities, calculate the coverage relationship between nodes, and close down some nodes [6,7]. It is one of the current research issues that how to effective find redundant nodes of network, obtain the minimal set of nodes of the network, and execute node scheduling, under the conditions of content the network coverage.

In this paper, we proposed a coverage strategy in wireless sensor networks based on node scheduling. Without the node geographic information, the redundant nodes were analyzed; the redundant node sets were obtained and scheduled. This strategy is ultimately the purpose of reduce network energy consumption, and prolong the network survival life.

2 Discussed problems

The conference [8] presented a centralized algorithm, the nodes in the network are divided into several subsets, each subset can satisfy the network coverage requirements. Wang et al. [9] have proposed a node scheduling algorithm. It takes advantage of different coverage characteristics of various monitoring nodes to realize nodes scheduling. The algorithm only considers the network coverage, while ignoring the network connectivity. Tian and Georganas [10] proposed a distributed scheduling algorithm. The case that isn't taken into account, which may result in an excessive number of working nodes, causing unnecessary energy costs. Liu and Towslev [11] describe a model based on the mathematical relationship among network monitoring area, node sensing radius, coverage ratios, and the number of nodes. The working nodes are randomly selected and scheduled. However, this randomness is also a contributory factor for unstable network coverage. Wu et al. proposed a method of calculating the node redundancy. The node location information isn't involved in this method, but its own redundancy should be calculated. In such calculating process, the coverage of shared coverage area between adjacent nodes isn't considered, so there are plenty of redundant nodes. The above research are carried out by the node sensing radius under the condition of the network, but the node can be influenced by the external environmental factors, in actual operation process, the sensing radius will also change correspondingly. According to the previous research results, and aiming at the characteristics of nodes [12,13], we select the network nodes from the network coverage and energy consumption, which are to meet the network coverage requirements as little as possible, and in a certain extent to reduce the network overhead, and increase the network lifetime.

3 The lower solution based on interpolation

3.1 Network model

The WSN containing n nodes and these nodes are randomly deployed in a 2-D monitoring region A. Supposing the WSN has the following properties:

(i) Node communication radius R_c and the maximum perception radius meets relation: $R_c \geq 2R_s$.

(ii) Monitoring area boundary effect is neglected.

(iii) Node density is bigger, when all nodes in the network are active; the network coverage rate has exceeded 95%.

(iv) The accurate location information of nodes in the network is known.

3.2 Problem description

A large number of sensor nodes were randomly deployed in the monitoring area A, which belong to node set S. When the minimum coverage of monitoring area is η, that the monitoring area must exist a minimum work node set a. Through network node scheduling strategy, which can prolong the network lifetime, reduce network the monitoring cost.

Definition 1

Redundant node: Exist node Si, Sj in the monitoring area A, and $i \neq j$. If perception area of the node Si and Sj according to the relation: $\Omega1 \cap \Omega2 = \Omega1$, where $\Omega1$ is perception area of the node Sj in the monitoring area A, and $\Omega2$ is perception area of the node Si in the monitoring area A, then Sj is redundant node.

Definition 2

Node redundancy: Take any node Si in the monitoring area, in which neighbor node set is S_0, supposing the perception area of Si is φ, $\tau = \{\tau_1 \ldots \ldots \tau_n\}$ is the perception area set of S_0, Γ is node redundancy of Si.

$$\Gamma = \frac{(\varphi \cap \tau_1) \cup (\varphi \cap \tau_2) \ldots \ldots (\varphi \cap \tau_n)}{\varphi} = \frac{\sum_{i=1}^{n} (\varphi \cap \tau_i)}{\varphi} \tag{1}$$

Definition 3

Coverage rate: Coverage rate is the ratio of the effective coverage region to the monitoring region of all the operation nodes in monitoring region A at a certain time. It is an important indicator of network coverage performance measurement.

$$\eta = \frac{\sum_{i=1}^{n} \xi(i)}{A} \tag{2}$$

Definition 4

Neighbors set: For any node Si, its neighbor set is defined as:

$$\psi(i) = \{Sj \in S | d(Si, Sj) \le Ri + Rj, Si \in S, j \ne i\} \tag{3}$$

S is a node set which were deployed in monitoring area, d(Si,Sj) is euclidean distance between Si and Sj, Ri is the perception radius of Si, Rj is the perception radius of Sj.

Definition 5

Multiple coverage area: In monitoring region A, If there are some regional subsets $\Theta \subseteq A$, which was covered by at least two different nodes at the same times, Θ is multiple coverage area of area A.

4   Coverage strategy based on node scheduling

Wireless sensor network node scheduling coverage strategy, which needs to consider two questions: Nodes according to network situation judgment node properties, namely whether the node is the redundant nodes; How to scheduling the redundant nodes, which does not affect the quality of network coverage, can effectively prolong the network lifetime, and at the same time reduce unnecessary energy costs [12]. In order to solve an adverse effect on redundant nodes, this paper proposes a coverage strategy based on node scheduling, and select the redundant nodes. Redundant node set is identified depends on node working status and coverage rate, meanwhile, according to residual energy of redundant nodes, redundant nodes were scheduled. Not only can reduce the network energy costs but also can prolong the network lifetime.

Redundant nodes are one of the important factors affecting network quality of service. Accurately identified redundant nodes will enhance network performance. Supposing S is a completely coverage set of monitoring region M, take any node Si from S, Si will be removed from S, that is $Si \not\subset S$, the basic criterion is as below:

(i)   Check to see if the multiple coverage area exists in M.

(ii)   Find out the minimum coverage sets of M.

(iii) Network quality of service q must meet: $q \le \dfrac{(\bigcup\limits_{i=1}^{k} \Psi_i) \cap A}{A}$, monitoring area is A, Ψi is effective coverage area of nodes Si

(iv)   When the node Si is redundant node, Si is deleted from the node set S, Voronoi region vertex of neighbor nodes is still within coverage area.

Redundant node set C is defined on the above work, $C \subseteq S$. According to redundant nodes residual energy and current network coverage rate, redundant nodes were scheduled, the procedure is as follows:

Step 1: Identify the redundant node set and get the nodes residual energy.

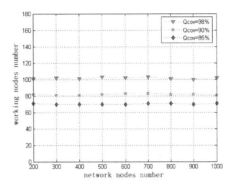

Figure 1: The network dynamic relationship.

Step 2: Delete the redundant nodes set S and the nodes associated side, get the new dual graph. Some problems need to consider in the process, when a redundant node dormancy, the adjacent redundant nodes also enter a dormant state. So coverage blind area will appear in WSN, which needs to combine the redundant nodes location and coverage area o make a choice, a node with small coverage area will enter dormant state.

Step 3: Looking for some redundant nodes, those nodes can be adjustable to dormant state. Due to the node redundancy expectations related to the number of neighbor nodes, some nodes with more neighbor nodes will be considered in priority. If the nodes have the same number of neighbor nodes, node vk will be set to sleep states and put it into Q, because residual energy of vk is the least.

Step 4: Repeat the above steps until all nodes were finished traversal, some nodes in Q can be set to sleep nodes, some nodes in $V-Q$ nodes constitute a balanced connected coverage set of region T.

5   Simulation analysis

This article passes the validity of the verification algorithm of emulation with strict experiment. The experiment uses the given settings: 120 sensor nodes randomly deployed in the .100×100m² . monitoring area. The node's maximum communication radius Rc=20 m, the perception radius can be varied, All sensor node have the same initial energy. In order to assess the proposed Balance Strategy on Energy and Coverage (BSEC) algorithm performance, in comparison with the Proposed Coverage Strategy of Wu (PCSW) algorithm [3], we find that it is more efficient.

Figure 1 reflects the dynamic relationship between network nodes number and working nodes number in monitoring area. Figure 1 shows that the working nodes number of algorithm BSEC is lower than that of PCSW, which further illustrates the working nodes number is intimately associated with network coverage rate, the algorithm has better scalability.

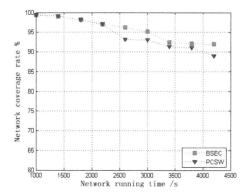

Figure 2: Network coverage rate in different time.

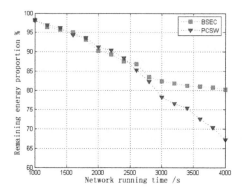

Figure 3: Network node energy in different time.

Figure 2 shows that the relationship between the network coverage rate and network lifetime. As can be seen from the figure, the two algorithms similar trends, but on the whole case, the proposed algorithm is perhaps a better balance of coverage rate and lifetime.

Network coverage rate is an important index for measuring the quality of network coverage. From Figure 3, it can be seen that node energy of BSEC algorithm more evenly distributed. The proposed algorithm scheduling for redundant nodes, making more uniform distribution of nodes, which can avoid some of the nodes premature mortality, reduces the energy cost of the network.

Figure 4 shows that BSEC algorithm is able to fully meet the monitoring requirements of network coverage. Actual coverage rate and expected coverage rate are very similar in BSEC algorithm. Therefore, BSEC algorithm meets the application requirements, select fewer working nodes, reduce the energy consumption of unnecessary network.

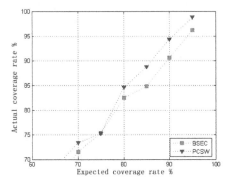

Figure 4: Network coverage rate.

6 Conclusion

For the characteristics of node random deployment, meanwhile, node perception area was easily affected by external environment. This paper discusses the coverage methods to realize node scheduling. The strategy finds out the redundant node set, which selects some nodes that meet the requirements of node redundancy, make the redundant nodes were asleep. When the network running for a period of time, the strategy according to the current network conditions to adjust the node working state, using fewer nodes ensure network running normally, and achieves anticipative aim. The experimental results show that BSEC algorithm can more accurate selection of redundant nodes than other algorithm, which guarantee the network connectivity, reduce the network energy consumption cost, achieve the goal of prolong the network lifetime.

Acknowledgments

This work was supported by Beijing Municipal Natural Science Foundation (4122034), the Natural Science Foundation of China (61271257), National Technology R&D Program (2013BAD15B04).

References

[1] F.V.C. Martins, E.G. Carrano, E.F. Wanner, et al., A hybrid multiobjective evolutionary approach for improving the performance of wireless sensor networks. *IEEE Sensors Journal*, **11(3)**, pp. 545–554, 2011.

[2] Nan Guo-fang, Chen Zhong-nan, Deployment algorithm of mobile sensing nodes based on evolutionary optimization. *Acya Electronica Sinica*, **40(5)**, pp. 1017–1021, 2012.

[3] J. Wu, S. Yang, Coverage issue in sensor networks with adjustable ranges. In: *International Conferences on Parallel Processing Workshops*, Montreal, Quebec, pp. 61–68, 2004.

[4] L. Liu, X. Zhang, H.D. Ma, Localization-oriented coverage in wireless camera sensor networks. *IEEE Transactions on Wireless Communications*, **10(2)**, pp. 484–494, 2011.

[5] P. Wang, S. Bohacek, Practical computation of optimal schedules in multihop wireless networks. *IEEE/ACM Transactions on Networking*, **19(2)**, pp. 305–318, 2011.

[6] G. Anastasi, M. Conti, M. Di Francesco, Energy conservation in wireless sensor networks: a survey. *Ad Hoc Networks*, **7(3)**, pp. 537–568, 2009.

[7] F.V.C. Martins, E.G. Carrano, E.F. Wanner, et al., A hybrid multiobjective evolutionary approach for improving the performance of wireless sensor networks. *IEEE Sensors Journal*, **11(3)**, pp. 545–554, 2011.

[8] S. Slijepcevic, M. Potkonjak, Power efficient organization of wireless sensor networks. In: *Proceedings of the International Conference on Communications*, Helsinki, pp. 472–476, 2001.

[9] D. Wang, B. Xie, D.P. Agrawal, Coverage and lifetime optimization of wireless sensor networks with Gaussian distribution. *IEEE Transactions on Mobile Computing*, **7(12)**, pp. 1444–1458, 2008.

[10] D. Tian, N.D. Georganas, A coverage-preserving node scheduling scheme for large wireless sensor networks. In: C.S. Raghavendra, K.M. Sivalingam (eds.), *Proceedings of the 1st ACM International Workshop on Wireless Sensor Networks and Applications*, Atlanta, pp. 32–41, 2002.

[11] B. Liu, D. Towslev, A study of the coverage of large-scale sensor networks. In: *Proceedings of the 2004 IEEE International Conference on Mobile Ad-Hoc and Sensor Systems*, Amsterdam, pp. 475–483, 2004.

[12] A. Chen, S. Kumar, T.H. Lai, Local barrier coverage in wireless sensor networks. *IEEE Transactions on Mobile Computing*, **9(4)**, pp. 491–504, 2010.

[13] Wen Jun, Jiang Jie, Dou Wen-Hua, Equitable direction optimizing and node scheduling for coverage in directional sensor networks. *Journal of Software*, **20(3)**, pp. 644–659, 2009.

Analysis on Henan electric power regional optical network improvement

Muwei Wang[1], Wenjun Liu[2], Yufang Yang[1]

[1]State Grid Henan Electric Power Information and Communication Company, Zhengzhou, China

[2]State Grid Henan Electric Power Company, Zhengzhou, China

Abstract

Currently regional optical network is far unable to meet IP-based service growth needs. To solve the problem, service properties and bandwidth requirement statistics are analyzed, and the technologies of SDH, MSTP, and PTN are compared. Finally, the program of "perfect existing SDH network and establish new PTN network" are suggested, which will prove to solve bottleneck of Henan electric power regional optical network and also save money.

Keywords: Electric power, regional optical network, data service, improvement, SDH, MSTP, PTN.

1 Introduction

Henan electric power regional optical network, established in about 2000, is an important support platform of regional electric power service collection and transmission. In recent years, due to the development of smart grid [1], information system and video requirement, data service grows rapidly [2]. Regional optical network has many new problems, such as simple network structure, low transmission capacity, aging equipments, and so on.

2 Present situation of regional optical network and existing problems

Henan electric power regional optical network consists of 18 region networks, relying on 220 kV and below power line cables. Most of the equipments are SDH, a small amount of MSTP. The bandwidth of backbone layer is 622 Mbit/s, access layer 155 Mbit/s. The network capacity usage tends to saturation, and five regions usage exceeds 75% of the region capacity. The proportion of ring network accounts less and the proportion of line network exceeds 68%. More than six manufacturers have stopped production, and over 31% of equipments work more than 7 years.

Therefore, the network can only satisfy the power production most needed services transmission requirements, such as dispatching telephone calls, power automation services, and unable to meet a large number of data transmission requirements. With the increasing development of new business, the regional optical network will restrict the power grid development [3].

3   Analyze of services and bandwidth

Currently, regional optical network mainly carries dispatching production services and management information services. Dispatching production services consist of dispatching calls, automation services, power telemeter, relay protection fault management, communication equipment monitor, power station video monitor, and so on. Management information services consist of office automation, management information system, office calls, video conference, marketing management, GIS, and so on.

The specific service category, property and transmission mode, are shown in Table 1 below.

In next 5 years, regional optical network will also increase with distribution grid services and regional dispatching data services, and cover all 110 kV and below power stations, power plants, sales offices, and users substations. According to the statistical bandwidth model, bandwidth requirement analyze of Zhengzhou region and Hebi region is shown in Table 2 below:

If all businesses are put into operation, bandwidth requirement of Zhengzhou region and Hebi region will increase 3–6 times, the proportion of IP service will increase 20% or more, the proportion of TDM service will decrease 20% or more, and IP service will account for more than 65% of total business.

As can be seen from the statistics, data service grows rapidly in recent years, of which proportion is increasing of the overall services. Currently, regional optical network is far unable to meet IP-based service growth needs.

4   The development and comparison of transmission technologies

For the rapid growth of IP-based service, transmission technology constantly evolves to meet the challenges. There are two important routes to transmit IP service. Route 1: SDH/MSTP, which is based on time slot switching technology and adds Ethernet interfaces to access IP service. Route 2: PTN, which is based on IP packet switching technology.

Table 1: Service Category, Properties and Transmission Mode.

Service Category	Service	Property	Transmission Mode
Dispatching production	Dispatching calls	Real-time voice	SDH,64 kbit/s
	Automation services	Real-time data	IP over SDH,2 Mbit/s
	Power telemeter	Nonreal-time data	
	Relay protection fault management	Real-time data	
	Communication equipment monitor	Real-time data	SDH,2 Mbit/s
	Relay protection	Real-time data	Fiber or SDH 2 Mbit/s
Management information	Office calls	Real-time voice	SDH,64 kbit/s
	Video conference	real-time video	SDH，8 Mbit/s
	GIS	Nonreal-time data	IP over SDH,2 Mbit/s
	Office automation		
	Management information system		
	Marketing management		

Table 2: Bandwidth Requirement Statistics.

Region	Total Bandwidth (bit/s)	Bandwidth Requirement This Year (Mbit/s)		Bandwidth Requirement 5 Years Later (Mbit/s)	
Zhengzhou	2x2.5G	3020		13830	
		TDM	IP	TDM	IP
		1856/61%	1164/39%	4495/33%	9335/67%
Hebi	622M	420		3615	
		TDM	IP	TDM	IP
		252/52%	232/48%	1141/32%	2274/68%

4.1 SDH/MSTP

In SDH, each service occupies fixed time slot. Even if no service is delivered in its time slot, the bandwidth is not released. SDH technology originated in the transmission of 64 kbit/s voice service (Figure 1).

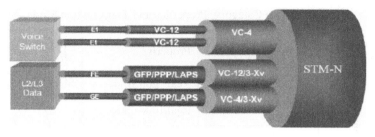

Figure 1: Model of SDH channels.

MSTP, which is the improvement of traditional SDH, adds a variety of services with different granularities in the SDH frame, provides multiprotocol access, aggregation, and transport capabilities, and is currently one of the most important ways to transmit service.

The advantage of MSTP is to handle Ethernet service. Earlier MSTP can transmit Ethernet service transparently, with guaranteed bandwidth and security, but the bandwidth utilization is low and the network flexibility is not good.

With the development of technology, MSTP gradually has Layer-2 switching capability to switch Ethernet-based data frame, providing greater network flexibility and low cost, suitable to access Ethernet service of the large number of users, but small volume of services and dynamic bandwidth.

MSTP has not changed the kernel that based on fixed time slot exchange, but merely enrich the service ports and realize Layer-2 switching capability. Therefore, for a large number of data services, MSTP cannot really meet the development of IP-based service growth needs [4].

4.2 PTN

PTN, proposed by ITU-T in 2004 and co-developed by ITU-T and IETF in 2008, is emerging with the rapid development of data service and increasingly high demand of growing bandwidth, IP business evolution, scheduling, flexibility, cost, quality, and so on [5].

Between IP service layer and underlying optical transmission layer, PTN technology adds a new layer, which is designed for IP packet traffic burst and statistical multiplexing transmission requirement. The core business of PTN, which supports a variety of interfaces, is to handle with IP packet service, not TDM service (Figure 2).

4.3 Comparison of PTN and SDH/MSTP

PTN is designed for the transmission of data service, mainly provides GE, FE interfaces, also can provide 2M or STM-N interfaces. The frame structure of MSTP is no longer STM-N or 2M, but IP packet. So for TDM service, SDH/MSTP is still the most suitable technology. Considering technology evolution, efficiency, construction cost, maintenance, management and application prospects, PTN is more cost-effective than SDH/MSTP [6].

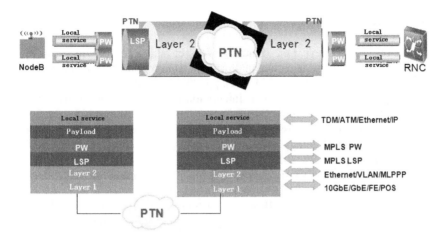

Figure 2: PTN protocol model.

5 Improvement program

Based on the analysis above, improvement idea of regional optical network can be suggested as follows: existing SDH network has to be perfected to transmit TDM services, and new PTN network has to be established to transmit data services. The idea enables SDH network and PTN network play their advantages according to different characteristics of services [7].

Keeping with this idea, improvement program are as follows:

"Perfect SDH network": perfect existing SDH network to cover all 35 kV and above power stations and county power companies to access all real-time services and optimize network topology.

"Establish PTN network": establish new PTN network to cover all 35 kV and above power stations, regional power companies, county power companies and sales offices to access all nonreal-time management information services and meet rapidly growing IP-based service needs.

Because Layer-2 isolation and time delay of PTN technology have not been tested in existing real power grid, it is inconclusive that safety isolation and relay protection delay are satisfied. Thus, SDH network transmits important and real-time service, and PTN network transmits less important and nonreal-time service.

With the power system reform and smart grid construction in recent years, there are increasing contradictions between low transmission bandwidth and rapidly growing IP-based service needs. The improvement program of "perfect SDH network and establish PTN network" will prove to be the key to solve bottleneck of Henan electric power regional optical network and also save money.

References

[1] Xiaotie Jia, Xueyi Lei, Yunfeng Wu, et al., PTN provides an ideal information communication platform for smart grid. *Telecommunications for Electric Power System*, **213(31)**, pp. 20–23, 2010.

[2] Rangjun Wu, Hongyan Chen, Integration of power system SDH network and PTN network. *China Hi-tech Enterprises*, **2011(28)**, pp. 123–124, 2011.

[3] Changjun Liu, Discussion on application of next generation optical transmission technology in electric power communication. *Technology Wind*, **2011(11)**, pp. 99–99, 2011.

[4] Qinjiang Wang, Electric power communication based on PTN. *Digital Communication World*, **2012(5)**, pp. 38–40, 2012.

[5] Xunming Yuan, Hao Zi, Research on transmission performance of packet transport network of electric power communication. *Telecommunications for Electric Power System*, **236(33)**, pp. 58–62, 2012.

[6] Yanhua Zhou, PTN technology provides an ideal information and communication platform for supporting smart grid. *Journal of Anhui Electrical Engineering Professional Technique College*, **2011(16)**, pp. 112–118, 2011.

[7] Ruzhen Li, Haiyang Wang, Xue Yang, et al., Planning and construction scheme of PTN network of Shandong electric power company. *Telecommunications for Electric Power System*, **224(32)**, pp. 12–17, 2011.

A data fusion algorithm based on self-adaptive weighted estimation in farmland WSN

Desheng Li[1], Huarui Wu[2,3,4], Feifei Li[2,3,4], Yisheng Miao[2,3,4]
[1]School of Science, Beijing University of Civil Engineering and Architecture, Beijing, China
[2]Beijing Research Center for Information Technology in Agriculture, Beijing Academy of Agriculture and Forestry Sciences, Beijing, China
[3]National Engineering Research Center for Information Technology in Agriculture, Beijing, China
[4]Key Laboratories for Information Technology in Agriculture, Beijing, China

Abstract

There are several uncertain factors in the farmland wireless sensor networks data collection, such as complex environment, sensor measurement error, and data missing in both time and space dimension. This paper proposed a self-adaptive weighted fusion scheme to improve the data accuracy of farmland wireless sensor networks. This paper calculated relative Euclidean distances as data weight of each multiple sampling data and picked out error data based on this data weight. After all the large error data had been excluded according to the data correlation degree, data fusion based on the data weight within the effective data is realized. Data fusion is more effective by introducing the weight mentioned above. Experiment shows that the self-adaptive weighted fusion scheme has a higher accuracy and efficiency than the existing methods.
Keywords: Wireless sensor networks, data fusion, relative distance, adaptive weighting.

1 Introduction

Crops are affected by environment conditions like light, temperature, humidity, etc. A large amount of data is collected in the farmland environment monitoring and real-time transmission is needed. Networks can achieve long-distance transmission of large amounts of data. Wireless sensor network developed in recent years has been applied in many fields because of its low cost, flexible network structure, and long data transmission distance. As the development of modern agriculture, the wireless sensor networks used in agriculture has attracted more and more attention.

Generally, sensor nodes have only capabilities of simple calculation, storage, wireless communication, and power supply. The researchers focus on data fusion to avoid the waste of communication bandwidth and energy as well as to improve the ability of information collection. The purpose of data fusion is to obtain more accurate and reliable value and to reduce the measurement error based on limited number of data. The data fusion algorithm directly affects the performance of sensor network.

2   Data fusion in agriculture

Currently, most researchers in data fusion are focus on the relationships of various functional elements on data fusion, and then give the best description and explanation to improve and expand the fusion model theory and methods. In fact, with the construction of large-scale systems, more and more functions are distributed into subsystems. Constructing a practical data fusion model is becoming more and more important. In recent years, large-scale agricultural cultivation base have been equipped with modern agricultural management mode. Automatic computer control has achieved in crop planting based on the high accuracy of sensor data collection. The researchers deploy a large number of sensor nodes in large-scale fields, by which they collect the information of crop conditions and environment parameters and then transfer the data to the terminal computer. In order to lower data transmission costs, redundant data need be removed by a processing algorithm before transfer to the control system. This method will reduce the production cost by eliminating the redundant data.

The traditional method usually considered measurement data as normal distribution. The traditional method uses a certain test method to choose outliers, and then determines the estimation of characteristic parameters based on processed data. However, multiple sets of experimental data analysis show that most of the distribution of data is not conformed to normal distribution but somewhere between uniform and normality. The traditional method also considered some outliers as useful data if they are not completely cleared. Hu and Liu [1] used the degree of mutual support between the data to exclude data with large errors. Duan et al. [2] used centralized and distributed parameter estimation to deal with multiple measurements data collected by the multisensor measurement system based on the method of least squares criterion. Liao et al. [3] proposed a weighing-estimation algorithm by inspected variance. This algorithm improved the precision efficiently, and it is appropriate for multisensors data acquisition systems. Qiu and Wu [4] used filter for target state estimation. It applied batch estimation to wireless sensor network data fusion. The method proposed a multisensor and multitarget batch estimation method, but it depends on the state–space model and the model directly affects the accuracy of the data fusion results.

This paper processes data by adaptive weighted algorithm and degree of mutual support between the data. This algorithm is mainly divided into two steps. Because of large random error in farmland environmental monitoring, the algorithm first excludes invalid data due to random errors. To avoid errors caused by data reduction, we estimate the relative true value by data before and after the data. Once useless data has been excluded according to the data correlation degree, data fusion within the effective data will be realized.

3 Data filtration

We first get n measured values of the physical characteristics by measuring device in one measure cycle, which are $x_1, x_2...x_n$. x_i does not strictly follow the normal distribution because of the calculation error, environmental noise, human disturbance, the accuracy of the measuring device, the characteristics of the test object, and some other factors. So there may be some data deviated from the exact values. We introduce a new evaluation method since we do not know the exact value and cannot directly eliminate the invalid data by the relative distance and other methods. Supposing that there is a set of collecting data $x_1,x_2...x_n$, first, we compare data by confidence distance measure. The sensor measurement model described by Gaussian density function is:

$$P_i(x) = \frac{1}{\sqrt{2\pi}\sigma_i} \exp\left[-\frac{1}{2\sigma_i^2}(x - x_i)^2\right] \tag{1}$$

where x_i represents the measure value of sensor i; σ_i^2 represents the variance.

In order to reflect the deviation between x_i and x_j we introduce the concept of distance measure confidence:

$$\begin{aligned}
d_{ij} &= 2\left|\int_{x_i}^{x_j} P_i(x/x_i)dx\right| \\
d_{ij} &= 2\left|\int_{x_j}^{x_i} P_j(x/x_j)dx\right|
\end{aligned} \tag{2}$$

Based on the Eq. (2), this algorithm defines a new confidence distance to prevent the inconsistency of confidence distance because of different sensor measurement accuracy.

$$d_{ij} = d_{ji} = \sqrt{2\left|\int_{x_i}^{x_j} P_i(x/x_i)dx\right| + 2\left|\int_{x_j}^{x_i} P_j(x/x_j)dx\right|} \tag{3}$$

d_{ij} is the confidence distance between sensor i and sensor j, which reflects the mutual support between the two sensors. For example, $d_{ij} = 0.8$ indicates that the measured value of sensor j is at 80% confidence range if we use the measured value of sensor i as the estimated value.

A larger d_{ij} indicates a greater likelihood of sensor measurements error; a smaller d_{ij} indicates a greater likelihood that these two sensors reflect the true value.

$$S_i = \sum_{j=1}^{n} d_{ij} \tag{4}$$

where S_i is the distance between the data x_i and all the other data. As can be seen from Eq. (4), the larger the value of S_i, the farther the distance among the data x_i and the other data, the more deviation from the exact value and the smaller the accuracy of data. Of course, for different data groups, the size of S_i may be different due to the size of the data itself, as well as various precision of measuring equipment, so we don't just simply set a fixed threshold. Now we provide a set of parameters associated with the array in order to filter valid data:

$$\begin{cases} x\_min = \min(x_1, x_2 \dots x_n) \\ x\_max = \max(x_1, x_2 \dots x_n) \end{cases} \tag{5}$$

where x_min indicates the minimum value of the data, while x_max means the maximum value of the data;

$$l = \frac{x\_max - x\_min}{2} \tag{6}$$

Parameter l is the half of the array range;

$$S = \frac{1}{n} \sum_{i=1}^{n} S_i \tag{7}$$

It is considered that x_k is a valid data if $x_i \in (S - l, S + l)$; otherwise, it is considered as an invalid data. After the invalid data removed, we get a new set of data $x_1, x_2, \cdots, x_{n-1}$. To maintain the diversity of data, we need to add an effective data to replace the invalid data x_k, the new x_k is: $x_k = \frac{x_{k-1} + x_{k+1}}{2}$ (where x_{k+1} and x_{k-1} are valid data; if $k = 1$, then $x_1 = x_2$; if $k = n$, then $x_n = x_{n-1}$). Since the array has been changed, so does S_i, we need to recalculate parameters according to Eqs. (1)–(7).

4 Adaptive weighted scheme

After the data filtration, we get a new set of data $x_1, x_n, \cdots, x_n$, although this set of data can be considered as valid data, they will have different error due to the environment and the equipment accuracy. The fusion results will be greatly improved if the coefficient proportion of the data fusion be determined by the error of the data. In the above steps, we have used the confidence measure S_i between the data and the other data to represent the error between the data and true value. From the definition of S_i, we find that the greater the value of S_i, the bigger the confidence distance measure between x_i and the other data, then the error of S_i will be bigger, so we can build the linkages between the weighting coefficient and S_i. The results calculated simply by averaging will have big errors if data have different accuracy.

Supposing that w_i is the weighting coefficients of the ith data, how to improve the calculation method of w_i is the research focus. This paper presents a new algorithm based on adaptive weighted average. The weighting coefficient for each measuring data is determined by the importance of this data in the data array. That means a high-accuracy data reduces to a big weighting coefficients, and a low-accuracy data reduces to a small weighting coefficients.

w_i is determined by the error of x_i. If x_i is nearby true value, w_i will have a bigger value, or w_i will have a smaller value. Since S_i is the parameter to expression the Euclidean distance between true value and w_i, we can measure S_i with w_i. But there is not a proportional relationship between w_i and S_i because that a bigger value of S_i indicates a lower accuracy of x_i, as well as a smaller value of w_i. For convenience of description, we build the relationships between w and S by intermediate variable r. That is:

$$r_i = \frac{1}{S_i}, \quad (i = 1, 2 \cdots n) \tag{8}$$

There exists a positive relationship between x and r. However, according to information-sharing principle, the amount of the information estimated by the optimal fusion can be equivalently decomposed into the amount of a number of measurement data, or, the information can be shared by a number of subsystems. The weighting coefficients needed to meet:

$$\sum_{i=1}^{n} w_i = 1, \quad (0 < w_i < 1) \tag{9}$$

The weighting factor has the practical significance only if it satisfies the Eq. (9). According to the requirements of the algorithm and the Eq. (9), w can be structured as follows:

$$w_i = \frac{\dfrac{1}{S_i}}{\displaystyle\sum_{j=1}^{n} \dfrac{1}{S_j}}, \quad (i = 1, 2 \cdots n) \tag{10}$$

Now w_i not only satisfies Eq. (9) but also meets the requirements of weighting coefficients, the higher the accuracy of x_i, the smaller the value of S_i, thus the greater the value of r_i, the greater the value of w_i and the higher accuracy of x. In summary, data fusion results can be calculated as follows:

$$x = \sum_{i=1}^{n} \frac{r_i}{\sum_{j=1}^{n} r_j} * x_i \tag{11}$$

5 Analysis of numerical experiments

This paper chooses 10 sets of temperature data to test the algorithm. The data is collected from 11:00 to 16:00 on September 5 in every 30 min in Xiaotangshan agricultural base of Beijing Research Center for Information Technology in Agriculture. According to the research requirement, we collected the accurate air temperature in each period. We have analyzed that the data measured in farmland environment has large random error. Furthermore, the sensors deployed in the large-scale farmland have low accuracy. In order to avoid the affects of the random error and the low accuracy of the sensor, researchers proposed an optimized method to collecting data, that is, sensors collect data multiple times in a short period of time, then transport the realistic data to the root after preprocessing the data. This will raise the accuracy of the data without increasing the amount of transferred data. The 10 sets of data are shown in Table 1 (we measured five times in each measure period):

Figure 1 shows the result of the two algorithms compared with the true value. As can be seen from Figure 1, - x-line and - o-line is nearly completely overlapped, which indicates that the results of proposed algorithm is close to the true value. - + - line and - x – line is only some overlap, such as 12:00, 13:30, 14:00, 15:30, that means the data measured at this four measurement time is

Table 1: Ten Sets of Data.

	Five Data Measured in Each Period					True Value
Array 1	34.3	34.4	34.9	35.2	34.5	34.5
Array 2	36.7	36.3	36.6	36.5	36.6	36.6
Array 3	36.2	36.3	36.2	34.4	36.3	36.2
Array 4	35.5	36.3	36.3	36.8	36.5	36.3
Array 5	36.9	37.0	37.0	36.9	36.3	36.9
Array 6	35.8	36.8	36.0	36.0	36.4	36.0
Array 7	36.2	36.1	36.0	37.3	36.2	36.2
Array 8	36.4	36.5	36.6	36.5	35.4	36.5
Array 9	33.9	33.9	33.9	33.7	34.0	33.9
Array 10	33.7	33.5	33.6	32.4	33.5	33.5

Table 2: Comparison Results of 10 Sets of Data.

	True Value	Algorithm of This Paper		Averaging Method	
		Results	Error	Mean	Error
Array 1	34.5	34.60	0.10	34.68	0.18
Array 2	36.6	36.56	0.04	36.54	0.06
Array 3	36.2	36.13	0.07	35.88	0.32
Array 4	36.3	36.34	0.04	36.27	0.03
Array 5	36.9	36.90	0	36.82	0.08
Array 6	36.0	36.14	0.14	36.20	0.20
Array 7	36.2	36.22	0.02	36.36	0.16
Array 8	36.5	36.42	0.08	36.28	0.22
Array 9	33.9	33.90	0	33.88	0.02
Array 10	33.5	33.48	0.02	33.34	0.16

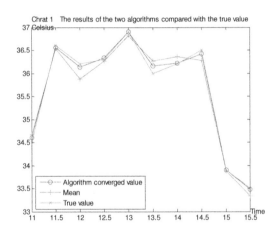

Figure 1: The results of the two algorithms compared with the true value.

different from the real values. Since the data is large and the difference among the data is small, the difference among three broken line in Figure 1 is not clear. Then we evaluate two methods through the error of two results. From Table 2, we can see that the error between the true value and the result of this algorithm is very small, in addition to the error of the array 1 is 0.1 and the error of the array 6 is 0.14, the error of other eight sets of data is less than 0.1. On the other hand, the error is relatively large if simply averaging the data, only four sets of data's error is less than 0.1, the errors of third set of data is as high as 0.32, in general, the result of this algorithm has a higher accuracy.

6 Conclusion

In view of the complex agricultural environmental conditions, large random errors in data monitoring as well as the data transmission limitation of farmland wireless sensor networks, this paper presents a new data fusion algorithm. First, this algorithm introduces confidence distance measure to calculate the confidence distance between each data and replaces invalid data which has larger error. Then we calculate weighting factor of each data based on confidence distance. By self-adaptive weighting parameter calculation, this algorithm improves the accuracy of data fusion. For agricultural environment, this data fusion algorithm meets the accuracy requirements, reduces redundant data transmission and reduces the cost of data transmission.

Acknowledgments

This work was supported by National Technology R&D Program (2012BAD52G01); Natural Science Foundation of China (61271257); Beijing Municipal Natural Science Foundation (4122034).

Reference

[1] Z.T. Hu, X.X. Liu, A practical data fusion algorithm. *Automation Instrumentation*, **26(8)**, pp. 7–9, 2005.
[2] Z.S. Duan, C.Z. Han, T.F. Tao, Multi-sensor parameter estimation data fusion based on least-squares criteria. *Computer Engineering and Applications*, **15(15)**, pp. 1–3, 2004.
[3] X.C. Liao, M. Qiu, H.R. Mai, The study on data fusion algorithms of multisensor based on parameter estimation. *Journal of Transducer Technology*, **20(1)**, pp. 193–197, 2007.
[4] S. Qiu, W. Wu, Survey of data fusion in wireless sensor network. *Journal of WuHan University of Technology*, **30(7)**, pp. 119–122, 2008.

Design of the Guided filter based on FPGA

Weijie Ren, Yan Piao
School of Electronics and Information Engineering, Changchun University of Science and Technology, Changchun, China

Abstract

The Guide filter as a filter tool had been applied to many image-processing applications since it emerged, and had made a very good effect. In this paper, we study the principle and method of designing the Guide filter by adopting pipeline technology, and then, the paper provides a bit more detail on the functional module design and the hardware implementation. Through the hardware emulation in platform of Quartus II and ModelSim-Altera 6.5e, the results show that the design of Guided filter based on FPGA possess advantages like fast operation speed and good real-time performance. It has important engineering application value.

Keywords: The Guided filter, FPGA, pipeline technology, real-time.

1 Introduction

The Guide filter is proposed based on a local linear model that the output is affected by the guidance image. The guidance image can be the image itself, may also be other images. Practice has proved that the Guided filter had good effects in image demising, detail smooth, feather, soft matting, and so on [1].

The filtering algorithm is more complex, and the computational cost is larger. All those deficiencies lead to a poor real-time performance and hinder its practical application. Considering the internal parallel algorithm module in an independence state, the hardware implementation can be a good way to deal with those problems which mentioned in above.

At present, most of the Guided filter literature is about the theory research and in the software algorithm simulation, and about its hardware implementation is very few. Parallel in software is parallel to the macro, on microscopic interleaved execution, and hardware in parallel is the true parallelism [2]. The FPGA is

WIT Transactions on Information and Communication Technologies, Vol. 61, © 2014 WIT Press
www.witpress.com, ISSN 1743-3517 (on-line)
doi:10.2495/MIIT130561

programmable devices based on look-up table structure. It has a large capacity of Block RAM resources, and the new configuration can be through the system to change the logic function. All characteristics of the FPGA provide the possibility for the Guided filter implementation in hardware.

2 Working principle and design idea

2.1 Working principle

First, we define the Guided filter and its kernel [1]. The key assumption of the Guided filter is a local linear model between the guidance I and the filter output q. We assume that q is a linear transform of I in a window w_k centred at the pixel k:

$$q_i = a_k I_i + b_k, \forall_i \in w_k \tag{1}$$

where (a_k, b_k) are some linear coefficients assumed to be constant in w_k . We use a square window of a radius r. This local linear model ensures that q has an edge only if I has an edge because $\nabla q = a \nabla I$. To minimize the difference between q and the filter input p, we minimize the following cost function in the window:

$$E(a_k, b_k) = \sum_{i \in w_k} ((a_k I_i + b_k - P_i)^2 + \varepsilon a_k^2) \tag{2}$$

Here ε is a regularization parameter preventing a_k from being too large. We will investigate its significance in Section 3.2.1. The solution to Eq. (2) can be given by linear regression:

$$a_k = \frac{\dfrac{1}{|w|} \sum_j I_i p_i - u_k \overline{p_k}}{\sigma_k^2 + \varepsilon} \tag{3}$$

$$b_k = \overline{p_k} - a_k u_k \tag{4}$$

Here, u_k and σ_k^2 are the mean and variance of I in w_k , $|w|$ is the number of pixels in w_k , and $\overline{p_k} = \dfrac{1}{|w|} \sum_{i \in w_k} p_i$ is the mean of p in w_k .

Next we apply the linear model to all local windows in the entire image. However, a pixel i is involved in all the windows w_k that contain i, so the value of q_i in Eq. (1) is not the same when it is computed in different windows. A simple strategy is to average all the possible values of q_i. So after computing (a_k, b_k) for all patches w_k in the image, we compute the filter output by:

$$q_i = \frac{1}{\mid w \mid} \sum_{k, i \in w_k} (a_k I_i + b_k) P_i \tag{5}$$

$$q_i = \overline{a_k} I_i + \overline{b_k} \tag{6}$$

where $\overline{a_i} = \sum_{i \in w_k} a_k$, $\overline{b_i} = \sum_{i \in w_k} b_k$.

With this modification ∇q is no longer scaling of ∇I, because the linear coefficients $(\overline{a_i, b_i})$ vary spatially. But since $(\overline{a_i, b_i})$ are the output of an average filter, their gradients should be much smaller than I near strong edges. In this situation we can still have $\nabla q \approx \overline{a} \nabla I$ meaning that abrupt intensity changes in I can be mostly maintained in q.

2.2 The idea of hardware design

To design the Guided filter based on FPGA would consider two main aspects.

(a) Simplified algorithm. The filtering algorithm contains a lot of battles, addition and subtraction operations, causing large amount of calculation, leading the running speed at a slow pace and hard to analysis or modification. How to optimize the algorithm and simplify the operation is an important content of study. In this paper, we set an addressing module to solve the problem of division which is a difficult problem in the design on FPGA. In addition, we design a state identification module for the signed number calculation. In this way, the optimization algorithm can improve the reliability and the running speed.

(b) The module design. How to design the system module that speed is fast, performance is reliable, and hardware resources occupancy is less which is an important part of the hardware implementation. In addition, the module must be designed corresponding to the filtering algorithm steps and can fast accurately complete its system function [3]. Based on the above requirements, we designed the module in pipeline design principles. On the premise of doesn't need a large number of additional hardware setup, the system improve the capacity of processing data in unit time.

3 Hardware design and realization

As shown in Figure 1, the Guide filter hardware system can be composed by the signal controller module, the mean filter module, the variable calculation module and the data buffer module.

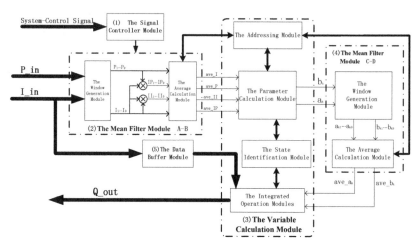

Figure 1: The design of Guided filter system structure.

3.1 Signal controller

The signal controller module composed by ranks of counter and comparator, is used for monitoring the system control signals real-timely. Through analyzing the state of system control signals, the module send instructions of Field signal or Line signal to the other module to ensure they work properly.

3.2 The mean filter module

In the design of the system, as shown in Figure 1, the mean filter module A to D have been used in Eqs. (2) and (4) two positions. According to the design idea of mean filter, the module is composed by the window generation module and the average calculation module. In module A–B also contains several multipliers and registers to solve the multiplication.

3.2.1 The window generation module
The window generation module used in this paper with a size of 3×3, was designed as shown in Figure 2, need to use 2 FIFO and 6 registers [4]. FIFO, First-In and First-Out, was quickly generated by the system, the depth is 1024 and the data width is 8 bits. Under the control of FIFO controller, P_in and I_in as the input data was written to and read from the FIFO, first the FIFO1, and then the FIFO2. When the data of line $(i-2)$ filled the FIFO1, and began to store into FIFO2, the data of line $(i-1)$ began to store into the FIFO1. According to the pipeline design principle, every data would be handled in this way [5].

Each line of the window will set two register as data buffer to cache the same column coordinate data. When the FIFO1 and the FIFO2 being full, and the data of line i is arrival, the data at the action of column cache would generate a window with a size of 3×3, and we would get 9 data.

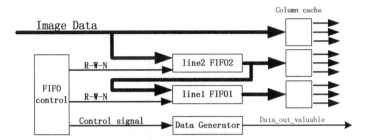

Figure 2: The principle of the window generation module.

3.2.2 Average calculation

The average calculation was divided into two-stage process, the summation and the division operation.

$$Ave=Sum/N \tag{7}$$

$$Sum = \sum_{i=1}^{N} I_i \tag{8}$$

As shown in formula (7) and (8): "Sum" is the SUM of all data values in the window of 3×3, "I_i" is the data in the window, "Ave" is the average, and N is 9. The calculation in formula (7) contains the binary division, and the algorithm will be explained in Section 2.3.1.

3.3 Variable calculation

The variable calculation module is composed by the parameter calculation module, the addressing module, the state identification module and the integrated operation modules. In the process of calculation, each module processes the data, respectively. Then for the different requirements, the module is called by another, and the data transmits through the module in the one to another. At the same time, the data of each module is always in calculation states. So the system can calculate the data in parallel at one time.

3.3.1 The addressing module

The realization of binary division on FPGA device is very complex [6], so usually the division is dealt by using an optimization algorithms that convert to multiplication—the dividend multiply by the reciprocal of the divisor [7]. The operation principle of the module is that when the divisor gave, we could calculate the reciprocal which is in the form of decimal, and the value is not more than 1, and then take the fractional portion in binary form, in the end, take the high 16 bits with the last digit of the integer part forming a 17-bit binary number as the reciprocal of divisor. In other words, the process of obtaining the reciprocal just likes once addressing in the FPGA device [8].

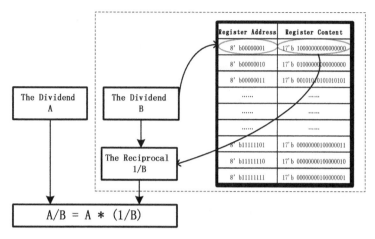

Figure 3: The schematic of the addressing module.

In whole design process of the Guided filter, although the divisor is not a fixed value, but its value always in a range of 0–255, so the optimization algorithm is feasible. Therefore, in the specific implementation process based on FPGA, we can set the divisor as the register address, and the reciprocal as the content of the register. The schematic is shown in Figure 3.

3.3.2 The state identification module

The design of signed binary number in FPGA device always affects the programmer debugging data. In order to improve the reliability of the system, this paper for signed binary arithmetic set state identification. By comparing the input data, the module can generate a state enable signal and make the parameter calculation module and the integrated computing modules work in proper status. As shown in Figure 4, in the calculation of "$n=A-B$" and "$m=n+k$", A, B is the input data and k is constant, the working process as follows:

3.4 Data buffer

As shown in Figure 1, the module of window generation that used in the position of Eqs. (2) and (4) would cause time delay. So in the design of the data buffer module, we used the FIFO generated by system as the line buffer, and the shift register for calculating delay module. As shown in Figure 5, we see that, I_in through the data buffer module by using four line buffers and two sets of register, finally output I_in_delay.

4 Simulation and verification

The FPGA device used in this paper is Altera Cyclone® IV 4CE115 with 114480 Les, 432 M9K memory blocks, 3888 Kbits embedded memory and four PLLs.

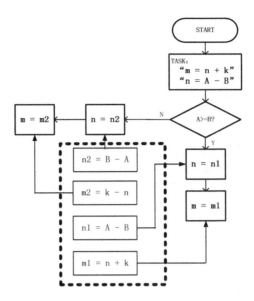

Figure 4: The state identification module working process.

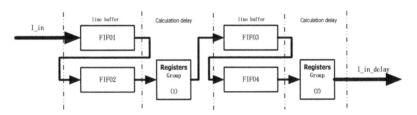

Figure 5: The data buffer module.

The simulation software is the ModelSim-Altera 6.5e. Through using Verilog under the platform of the Quartus II 11.0, the program would synthesize the function module. Then compiled and loaded the program into the ModelSim simulation—Altera 6.5e, we will get the simulation results shown in Figure 6: Under the action of system synchronous clock, P_in and I_in through the system and output q as the final result.

As shown in the Figure 6, for a period of time delay, I_in and P_in output 9 data in one time. The data that in the Figure 6 location of the yellow line: data P_in1 to P_in9:60, 62, 59, 58, 58, 57, 60, 60, 59; I_in1 to I_in9: 203, 204, 204, 206, 207, 207, 204, 204, 205; ave_P, ave_I is the average of the sum in the window, the data is 59, 205; the output q is 59.

5 Conclusion

This scheme adopted the pipeline technology and took the advantage of the FPGA, improved the efficiency of image processing and the capacity of

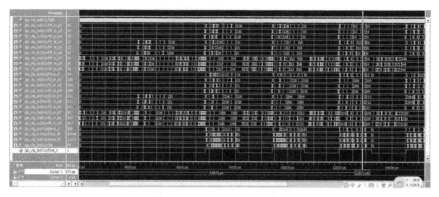

Figure 6: The simulation result of the system.

processing the data in unit time. Comparing with the software, the Guide filter based on the FPGA device can not only realize high-speed image processing but also the system hardware structure is simple, and the system is high integration and high reliability.

Acknowledgments

The research work was supported by Natural Science Foundation of Jilin Province under Grant (No. 201215142) and Scientific Development Projects of Jilin Province under Grant (No. 20130206012GX; No. 20110355).

References

[1] Kaiming He, Jian Sun, Guided image filtering. *Pattern Analysis and Machine Intelligence*, **35(6)**, pp. 1397–1409, 2012.
[2] Haibo Luo, Zelin Shi, Real-time large window-sized 2D median filter based on multi-phased grouping and sorting network. *Infrared and Laser Engineering*, **37(5)**, pp. 935–939, 2008.
[3] Minmin Huang, Yuan Lin, Design of 3-stage instruction pipeline 51 core. *Modern Electronic Technique*, **211(20)**, pp. 83–85, 2005.
[4] Yueli Hu, Huijie Ji, Research on image filtering algorithm and its FPGA implementation. *Computer Measurement & Control*, **16(11)**, pp. 1672–1675, 2008.
[5] Yuxin Wang, Yuanyuan He, FPGA-based algorithm of fast median filter. *Application Research of Computers*, **26(1)**, pp. 224–226, 2009.
[6] S.F. Obermann, M.J. Flynn, Division algorithms and transactions on computers, **46(8)**, pp. 833–854, 1997.
[7] Liucheng Wang, Yongcai Lin, Implementation of fast and high-precision division algorithm on FPGA. *Computer Engineering*, **37(10)**, pp. 240–242, 2011.
[8] Fei Wang, The implementation of division algorithm with fast and high-precision on FPGA. *Microcontroller & Embedded System*, **26(2)**, pp. 77–79, 2003.

"Safe City" dynamic monitoring system: a big data research

Jue Zhao[1], Sheng Zhang[2]
[1]*Computer and Information Engineering College, Hunan University of Commerce, Changsha, China*
[2]*School of Information Science and Engineering, Central South University, Changsha, China*

Abstract

There is a serious challenge to manage the ultra-large-scale, heterogeneous, rapid changing audio and video data set for the "Safe City" monitoring system construction. By using a specific city as an example, this paper describes system architecture about how to build the "Safe City" system in detail. It proposes to use distributed IP SAN to storage massive amounts of data. In addition, streaming media server and load balancing algorithm are used to distribute data quickly. A limited matrix channel allocation algorithm is designed for legacy analog data transmission. As a result, different legacy platforms can be integrated to the new system and analog and digital signals are treated as the same. In the end, we built a security framework with characteristics of mass access capability, scalability, wide compatibility, high transparency, ease of use, etc.

Keywords: Big data, Safe City, monitoring, distributed storage, load balancing, heterogeneous platform integration

1 Current situation

As China's economy has increased remarkably, it also brings lots of challenges on social issue. Indeed, the public safety issue has raised substantial attention which demands immediate actions. In order to answer the need proactively, it is necessary to promote the development of video surveillance system. On October 12, 2005, Ministry of Public Security launched a nationwide program for city security alarm and monitoring called "3111" project. Currently, organizations at Changsha, which participate the city safety emergence response collaboration

 WIT Transactions on Information and Communication Technologies, Vol. 61, © 2014 WIT Press
www.witpress.com, ISSN 1743-3517 (on-line)
doi:10.2495/MIIT130571

program, have implemented a large number of video surveillance systems separately without any information sharing. As a result, each of them acts as an isolated information island and can't work collaboratively to address urgent situations. In addition, the city has implemented 10 county security monitoring centers, 72 patrol offices, and more than 3878 security cameras. When it comes to the volume of data which gathered by this scheme, if all video clips are in D1 format, the daily data volume generated will be close to 80T (3878*2.0M*3600*24/8/1024/1024=79.88 TB).

Big data has become a buzz word among the high technology industry [1]. It is defined by three Vs in terms of volume, variety, and velocity. The "Big Data" concept emphasizes the dynamic, fast change, and unstructured data format [2]. These characteristics of "Big Data" perfectly match the information gathered from the video surveillance system. Therefore, this paper intends to contribute on how to manage the dynamic surveillance system from big data perspective.

Similar to most of city in China [3], with the increasing number of surveillance systems, the issues raise significantly: (i) the exponential data increase in different formats and frequencies; (ii) various standards and protocols in the existing surveillance systems make the systems can't "talk" to each other; (iii) data reliability and usability is low.

To address this situation, this paper proposes the solution to integrate the existing systems and upcoming systems in order to establish a universal platform, on which multilevel and multiorganization collaboration can be archived. The functions on the platform include, but not limited to, video information sharing and control, information storage, stream media service, real-time video selection.

The key issues to address are:

(i)   Storage, transaction and access of video data in high-volume, fast change frequency and unstructured format.
(ii) Increase the system reliability and usability.
(iii) Integration issues among systems/equipments with various standards and protocols.

2   System architecture

Based on the current organizational structure, the system is designed in three layers (shown in Figure 1):

Level 1 control centre: Municipal surveillance center.
Level 2 control centre: Branch office surveillance center.
Level 3 control centre: Patrol office surveillance access point.

Data transaction between the level 1 and level 2 data uses the core network, which is based on current network in police department. Data transaction between the level 2 and level 3 can use upgraded current network and network provided by ISPs. Level 2 provides the data source to level 1 and manages the information nodes from level 3. In additional, to access information nodes at the same level (only for level 2 and level 3), it requires the permission from upper level.

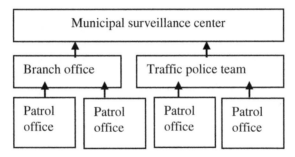

Figure 1: System structure.

3 Big data storage, distribution, and transit

3.1 High volume unstructured data storage

Currently, distributed data storage is a common practice to manage massive heterogeneous data, for example, CFS from MIT as well as GFS and HDFS from Google. In our city's surveillance system, it, mostly, includes large volume of heterogeneous data, such as video clips, picture, voice, etc. At the same time, it also stores index information for the heterogeneous data search and navigation, such as equipment, channel, time, and security information of the surveillance data. Based on this situation, the date storage model is a matrix, which is to use centralized data in headquarter and distributed data in each branch at the same time.

The headquarter storage network is IP SAN storage matrix based on iSCSi protocol, which is used to maintain video data concerned by the headquarter. Compared to the traditional DSA/NAS storage model, IPSAN inherits the IP network's openness, high capacity, high reliability, easy of manage, and extension. In addition, the capacity of the matrix can reach to infinity theoretically reaching to TB. This method has been widely used in data centers.

In the front end, the camera used for video collection includes the video coder which supports iSCSI protocol. As a result, the surveillance video will be packed and transited back to IP SAN disk array directly to reduce the workload on the streaming media server. On the other hand, branch office still keeps the surveillance video in its original format to reduce the burden on remote data transportation and make the local access easy and direct. The headquarter can extract the video data from branch level in its original formats and convert it to place in the centralized storage. The text and number information is managed and stored in the headquarter network center.

3.2 Massive heterogeneous data distribution

Center network server cluster includes streaming media server (storage server), database server, load balancing server, security server, etc. In order to handle data with three Vs and network security needs. Storage server is responsible for reliable and fast access video data transaction. Streaming media server is responsible for the distribution of video streaming and access. Database server is responsible for all video and video source information's query and positioning. Load balancing server response for rational resource allocation during large volume of data traffic. Security server is responsible for the implementation of security operations against each level and support special protection for confidential data.

Since each streaming server (storage server) has resource limitation on loading, when the traffic on the server exceeds a certain number, the server performance will be significantly impacted. It is not acceptable for real-time surveillance system. Therefore, the server cluster has load balancing server to allocate the system resource to for data processing. In this paper, a weighted formula is proposed to consider all the facts which can bring impact:

$$Fact_k(t) = \frac{Task_p * Process_k Weight_p}{Connect_k(t)Weight_C + Response_k(t)Weight_R}$$

$$Connect_k(t) = \begin{cases} \infty & Connect_k(t) > Connect\_Max_k \\ Connect_k(t) & Connect_k(t) \leq Connect\_Max_k \end{cases}$$

(1)

In the formula, $Fact_k(t)$ represents the kth server' response index at t moment. The bigger this number, the more possible for this server to handle the job at t moment. Process k represents the processing capacity of kth server. The value of this factor is based on third-party software. The simple way to estimate is to use the CPU frequency and memory of the server. Weight p represents the weighted factor of processing capacity; $Connect\_Max_k$ represents the threshold of upper connection limit for kth server; $Connect_k(t)$ represents the actual connection number at t moment for kth server. If $Connect_k(t)$ is larger than $Connect\_Max_k$, then the value of $Connect_k(t)$ is infinity and $Fact_k(t)$ is close to 0. Therefore, no more new task will be assigned. Otherwise, the less of the connection, the bigger value of $Fact_k(t)$. Then the server has higher chance to take a new task. $Weight_c$ is the weighted index for number of connections. $Response_k(t)$ represents the response time of the kth server at t moment. A simple way to calculate it is to user the value of Ping. The smaller the value of Ping, the bigger value of $Fact_k(t)$. As a result, the server has higher possibility to take new tasks. $Weight_r$ is the weighted factor for the value of Ping. $Task_p$ is the priority level. The higher level of task, the bigger number of $Fact_k(t)$.

3.3 Heterogeneous data transit

There are two types of data to be transited: digital signal and analog signal. The principle is to make data in module mode and hierarchical. In new systems, the digital signal is the main format and in legacy systems, the analog signal is the main format to transit in a mixed fashion.

3.3.1 Digital signal transit

According to the designed hierarchy, the whole platform links to two tiers of networks. In order to increase the reliability of the core network in the headquarter, two core switchers will be deployed. The equipments in the core level use duel-core star schema to build the network. The front-end cameras will connect the access switches through the encoder. It uses gigabit fibers to connect access switchers to core switchers. For the access tier network, it demands lots of investment on equipments (i.e., fibers), if it follows the star schema. Indeed, the bandwidth would not be used sufficiently. Therefore, Ethernet over PON (EPON) technology is accepted. Based on the surveillance spots, each access node leads several fibers to link several spots in a tree schema via a passive optical splitter.

3.3.2 Analog signal transit

Since there are many analog video conversion metrics in the original systems, it is important to handle these metrics in order to connect all dots in the network [4]. Then it raises a critical question that how to efficiently manage video information in a multilevel metrics in order to maximize the bandwidth usage of the only video data transaction channel?

The basic assumptions are here:

(i)   Treat all the branches as a node, and build a tree topology structure where the analog signal has no issue to choose the router.
(ii) Video control command is from the network gate based on priority of the equipment code.
(iii) When the connection channel is available, the higher level can command video in lower level.
(iv) When the lower level channel is occupied by the higher level, then the lower level has to find alternative channel.
(v)   Monitoring channel in lower level will be informed when the higher level will occupy its channel.
(v)   If video will be requested at the same level, then the request will be traced back to the shared higher level (shown in the formula 2).

In the formula, Out_i, In_i, $Width_i$ represent the ith output port, input port, and the width that lower level matrix can upload to the higher level. By using Hash Table, it finds the address automatically to match output. The In_i will match to In_i Mod $Width_i$. If In_i Mod $Width_i$ is local channel, then it could be stripped. If there is a conflict (this output port is requested by the higher level), then it will take the Linear Detection Method. The corresponding output is (In_i+di) Mod $Width_i$, $di=1,2,3,\ldots$ In_i' is the input port for the ith matrix's in the higher level. Therefore:

$$Out_i = \begin{cases} In_i \ Mod \ \text{Width}_i & \text{No higher occupancy} \\ (In_i + di) \ Mod \ \text{Width}_i, di = 1,2,3,.... & \text{occupancy} \end{cases}$$

$$In_i{}' = \sum_{i=1}^{n} \text{Width}_i + Out_i \qquad\qquad (2)$$

4 The integration of heterogeneous platforms and compatible

4.1 Heterogeneous platforms

Legacy system platform is mainly divided into four categories: pure digital platform, mix platform of analog and digital signal with SDK package, mix platform of analog and digital signal without SDK package, pure analog signal. Access method is displayed in Figure 2.

Pure digital platform: by using standardized network sharing platform, the various systems communicate with each other through the same standard protocol. By deploying Access Gateway at the branch office, the connection can be built for pure digital signals and the video resource at the branch office can be accessed. The branch office surveillance center can actively register to municipal surveillance center servers, and then central video resource database servers at municipal level organize the received resource directory. In this way, it can manage control authority and on the resource and achieve a unified centralized management.

Mix platform of analog and digital signals with SDK package: The legacy monitoring system opens their external SDK interface and then the new monitoring system can access resource in the legacy ones via the SDK interface. The access gateway defines the matrix port resources and converts control signal to archive the control on system matrix between layers. In addition, the access gateway is responsible for resource data server registration for the resource central control. Although this approach can achieve interoperability between systems, but there is no standard specification constraints, the interfaces are arbitrary and variability.

Mix platform of analog and digital signals without SDK package and pure analog signal: the legacy system outputs a number of analog signal images. Through the encoding server at the new platform, the analog signal can convert to digital. Then the new platform can manage the data resource at the legacy systems. This approach is simple to implement, and there is no security risk. The main disadvantage is the platform at upper level can only receive image transaction from the lower level and can't access and manage the resource directly.

4.2 Nondiscrimination treatment between analog and digital signals

Working against the actual needs, this solution innovatively assigns two attributes (digital and analog) to the same device. In this fashion, it satisfies the demand on video resource monitoring as well as the access flexibility from computer end. In

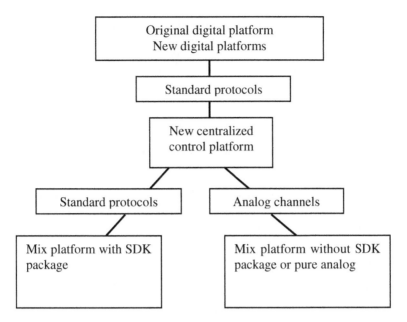

Figure 2: Access to heterogeneous platforms.

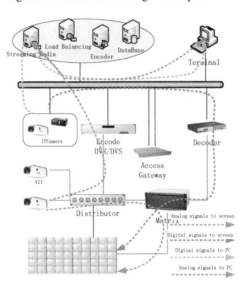

Figure 3: Nondiscrimination with analog signals and digital signals.

the solution, front camera has a unique number, which has two properties: one connects to a certain encoder (or directly to the switch) via distributor, and then it has a corresponding digital channel, including IP and port number; another property connects to the port of a matrix (or through a decoder to connect to the matrix), including the matrix number and port information at least. Thus, regardless of the camera is an analog signal or digital signal, which can be displayed and controlled on your desktop or on a large screen television. Through the encoder/decoder, analog signals and digital signals can be converted to each other as shown in Figure 3.

5 Conclusion

This paper discusses the key technologies and a solution proposal to build the dynamic monitoring system. It uses the project of "Safe City" as an example to discuss the specifics. The system has advantages in massive data volume capacity, flexible extendibility, wide compatibility, transparency, and ease of use. With this system, it will increase the capability of the law enforcement, e-government, and the government response to outbreaks significantly.

References

[1] Li Guojie, The scientific value in the study of the big data. *Communications of the CCF*, **8(9)**, pp. 16–20, 2012.
[2] Zhou Xiaofang, Lu Jiaheng, Li Cuiping, et al., A big data challenge from the perspective of data management. *Communications of the CCF*, **8(9)**, pp. 9–15, 2012.
[3] Hu Ruimin, Cao Xuesong, Chen Jun, et al., "Safe city" system construction principles and key technologies. *Security and Safety Technology Magazine*, **7**, pp. 3, 2007.
[4] Han Xue, Wang Xudong, Wen Wenkai, et al., Design and implementation of agent based on SNMP in video matrix router. *Journal of Dalian Maritime University*, **37(3)**, p. 89, 2011.

Definition and application of the flexible business object model

Chengzhong Song[1,2], Limin Shen, Peng Zheng[2], Qingda Zhang[2], Wenwen Jiang[2], Fang He[2], Xiaoming Han[2]
[1]*College of Information Science and Engineering of Yanshan University, Qinhuangdao, China*
[2]*Information Department of Qinhuangdao Shouqin Metal Materials Co. Ltd., Qinhuangdao, China*

Abstract

Aimed at the problem that the flexibility of end user is too low, the conception of flexible business object based on adaptive object model was proposed. The business function of specific domain was described through flexible business object model, user-level flexibility was achieved by flexible adjustment on the model. Moreover, the flexible business object model was formalizing described, and its support for flexibility was discussed. Finally, its implementation process based on domain engineering was given, and a modeling example for manufacturing execution system was provided to verify the practicability and effectiveness of the proposed method.

Keywords: Flexible information system, user-level flexibility, flexible business object model, adaptive object model.

1 Introduction

With the improvement of the social information level, information system has infiltrated most professions now. The request of information system has become to the active discovery and personalization from passive acceptance. This required that the information system can instantly satisfy the customers' needs change and diversity of requirements.

Flexible software [1] means that software can meet and adapt to user needs change in a certain range. It used "flexibility" to describe the software's ability to

WIT Transactions on Information and Communication Technologies, Vol. 61, © 2014 WIT Press
www.witpress.com, ISSN 1743-3517 (on-line)
doi:10.2495/MIIT130581

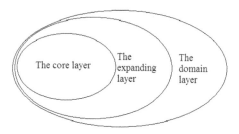

Figure 1: Flexible business object model's hierarchy.

adapt to changes. According to the different capability of software users, software flexibility has been divided into three levels: (1) flexibility for low-level users, it allows software provides simple operation to adjust the software's functionality (such as setting function parameters, customize queries, and so on), the operations did not require any programming knowledge; (2) flexibility for advanced users, it allows users to complete some complex key adjustments through the setting and software interface (such as initialization definition, business rules definitions, business process definitions, and so on), achieving this flexibility level needs more computer knowledge and domain knowledge; (3) flexibility for development users, it allowed users to make further adjustments to the software, add built-in behavior of the software, change the composition of the software (such as component replacement, objects adjustment, and so on), this flexibility required higher business knowledge and software capability.

2 The definition of flexible business object model

Flexible business object model describes the composition of business objects in specific areas [2], as well as the relationship between the business objects. It describes the realization of business use cases, it is an abstract of the way that business roles and business entities how to contact and collaboration to perform the business, allows advanced users (domain experts) dynamic adjust it to adapt to user needs change during the run time.

Flexible business object model is a self-described business object model, it is divided into three levels, the core layer, expanding layer and domain layer (Figure 1). The core layer reflects the core business functions of the field, is relatively stable. The expanding layer is the package of the domain change part, and provides interface of transformation, change, and expansion, this makes the business object model in the open state. The domain layer is the core layer and expanding layer's description for users, this layer shields the specific technical implementation of the model, domain experts only need to concern with the business logic of the application, without concern with the technology platform and implementation details.

Definition 1: The attributes set of the business object is a tetrad, $A=\{ID,N,T,V\}$. ID is the unique identification for the property. N is the attribute name, T is the type of the property, and V is the value of the property.

Definition 2: The behavior collection of business objects is a triple, $H=\{ID,N,T\}$, ID is the unique identification for behavior. N is the name of the behavior, T is the type of behavior after metadata explain.

Definition 3: The business object's relation collection is a tetrad, $R=\{ID,P,C,S\}$. ID is the unique identification for relation. P is the outflow object of relation, C is the inflow object of relation, S is the constraint condition of relation.

Definition 4: Flexible business object model is a six-tuple, FBOM=$\{BS,ES,TS,CS,VS,AS\}$, BS stands for basic information collection of the business object, ES stands for the stable information collection of business object, TS stands for volatile information collection of business object, CS stands for the context collection of the business applications, VS stands for the view collection of the business object, AS stands for adaptation operation collection of the business object.

Definition 5: The basis information collection is a tetrad, BS=$\{ID,ON,UN,UD\}$, it describes the basic properties related to the business object, ID is the unique identification for business object. ON stands for the name of the business object, the name is familiar for advanced users or domain experts, UN is the name of user who created the business object, UD reflects the last modified time of business object.

Definition 6: The stable information set is a triple, ES=$\{SA,SH,SR\}$. It describes the core businesses and functions in some given domains. This information is obtained after the domain analysis, it is a concentrated expression of domain knowledge, and it is relatively stable. SA is the common property collection of the business object in some given domains. SH is the common behavior collection of the business object in some given domains. SR is the common relation collection between business object in some given domains.

Definition 7: The variable information collection is a triple, TS=$\{DA,DH,DR\}$. It is the description of different understanding in certain business domains or different manifestations of the same understanding, it is optional information, sometimes need to be adjusted according to the needs of users while software running. DA stands for the set of business object attributes which changing possible, DH stands for the set of business object behaviors which changing possible, DR is the description of constraints or relation between different business object which changing possible.

Definition 8: Business application context collection CS=$\{c_i|i \in N\}$, it describes the specific environment and applicable scene of business object application, provides more convenience for user to select the business object. c_i is the description of ith business object application scenarios, N is the set of natural numbers.

Definition 9: Views collection, VS=$\{<a_i,v_i>|i \ N, a_i \in SA \cup DA\}$. Options: it describes the manifestations of business objects, business object associated with business roles by the view, a business object can have multiple views, different business roles control business object by views (Figure 2). According to the request of business object's composition and performance, it can be realized by

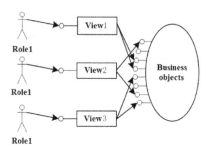

Figure 2: The relationship of business role, view and business objects.

the related representation. View simplified the representation of domain concepts; it is the interface of business objects and application. $<a_i, v_i>$ stand for the business object's specific attributes a_i which corresponds the view v_i. N is the set of natural numbers.

Definition 10: Adaptation operation collection AS is the process of existing business objects' configuration and use the existing business objects to generate new business object. Its purpose is to meet the new requirements and application context. Adaptation operation is the configuration of relationship between the business object attributes, behavior, views, and business objects.

According to the flexible software metric elements, the business object is relatively rigid; the controllable soft point is less. If we use flexible business object model for business modeling, business object attributes, the relationship between behavior and business objects can become soft point, setting the flexible points as Fa, Fb, Fr, the formula of softness is $K_i = S_{max}(i)/(1+F_{min}(i))$, refer to the flexible force soft distance parameter setting table, with the increase of business entities, software's compliance $A = \sum_{i=0}^{N} Ki$ will increase exponentially. So, flexible business object model is quite suitable for the development of flexible software.

3 The development process of flexible business object model

Depending on the applicable scope, the flexible business objects are divided into two categories: domain generic flexible business objects, domain dedicated flexible business objects. Depending on the field of object-oriented analysis method, the implementation steps of flexible business object model (Figure 3) are as follows:

Step 1: Definition of domain requirements. Making clear the domain business requirements, and giving the preliminary definition term for each professional ability, confirming the scope and boundaries of the domain, collecting information of the domain.
Step 2: Analysis of domain commonality. Making abstraction and refinement for specific domain business, determining the common needs of the domain.

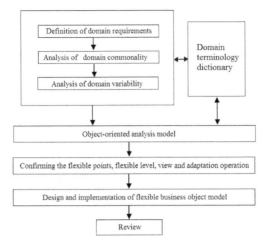

Figure 3: Implementation process of the flexible business object model.

Step 3: Analysis of domain variability. Identifying variable requirements, determining the type of the variable requirements (optional or multi-select one).

Step 4: Establishing object-oriented analysis model. On the basis of the existing business object model, using the results of the common variability analysis, making supplemental and modifying the business object model, using class diagrams, case diagrams, and other forms to express the business object model in specific domain.

Step 5: Design and implementation of flexible business object model. According to the results of the analysis in previous stages, with reference to the formal definition of flexible business object model, determining the soft point in the business model, flexible level, view of the business object, the business model adaptation operation, making design and implementation of the system's business object model.

Step 6: Review. After the steps above, systems analysts and domain experts will analyze and evaluate the business object model, if the evaluation is not passed, iterating steps above.

4 The application of flexible business object model in the steel enterprises

Because of the complex business processes in steel enterprises, complex network and system environment, as well as the uneven automation levels, manufacturing execution system (MES) is difficult to adapt to the change of enterprise, the steel enterprises had an urgent need for flexible MES which was scalable and reconfigurable, and had strong integration capabilities. Combined with the actual steel enterprise MES implementation experience, and taking the complex from

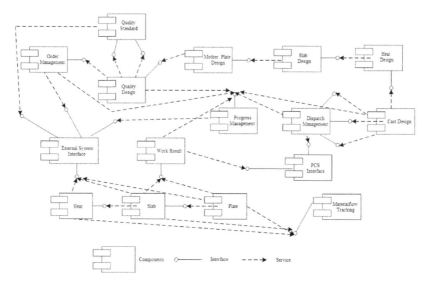

Figure 4: Flexible business object model of steel enterprises.

molten steel on workshops such as steelmaking, continuous casting, plate rolling as research object, based on a full business analysis, we designed a flexible business object model of steel enterprises as shown in the Figure 4.

1. External System Interface (ESI) module: Flexible interface provides the order process inquiry service and workshop production statistical data feedback service for ERP and other external systems, receives original sales order and quality standards data from ERP and other systems.

2. Order Management (OM) module: This module has functions like obtain new orders modify orders and cancel the order information by ESI interface, and stores the order data into the database.

3. Quality Standard (CS) module: This module gets quality parameters such as product chemical composition, mechanical properties, specifications, dimensional tolerances, and so on, and manufacturing standard information like manufacturing process route, metallurgical specifications through ESI interface, and stores these data into the database.

4. Quality Design (CD) module: It extracts quality standards information by CS interface, and extracts orders which have not been designed by OM interface, matches the orders with the corresponding quality parameters and manufacturing standards, then stores the design results into the database. In order to quality design process, it sets the order process to a corresponding state according to the design result.

5. Mother Plate Design (MPD) module: It obtains orders which have been designed completely through the interface provided by the CD, according to the order delivery, product type, specification, process constraints, equipment capacity status, and other factors, then designs the width and

thickness of the mother plate, and stores the design results into the database.

6. Slab Design (SD) module: It can get the MPD results by MPD interface, then designs the slab's width, thickness, length, weight, and other parameters, calculates the slab cutting time, then stores the SD results into the database.

7. Heat Design (HD) module: It can extract SD results via SD interface to design heat, calculates the processing time of the primary work stage such as converter, refining, casting, etc., binds slab number and heats in SD results, then stores the HD results into the database.

8. Cast Design (CAD) module: It can extract HD results via HD interface, then calculates the casting start time and casting end time take relevant process constraints into account, stores the cast design results into the database. It generates heat, slab, and plate operating instructions via the interface provides by DM, sets order process as the end planning state via the interface provides by PM.

9. Dispatch Manage (DM) module: Based on the constraint rule and combines with a human–machine interface, it can automatically adjust and determine the order's heat casting sequence, slab cutting sequence, steel plate rolling sequence, the PCS interface provided setSchedule function to issue the instructions directly to the PCS; then sets order process state as production process via the PM interface.

10. PCS Interface (PCSI) module: The getSchedule interface provides the services of obtaining MES operating instructions information for PCS and other process automation systems. The setPcsResult interface takes a passive approach to receive work result data from the PCS and other process automation systems.

11. Work Result (WR) module: It can obtain WR data via the getWorkResult interface provided by PCSI, and saves the data to database; according to WR return information via PM interface, it can update the order process in time.

12. Heat, Slab, Plate module: Most work stages of iron and steel enterprises from raw material input to product output, have both physical and chemical changes; however, according to the characteristics of material change, such as raw materials, semi-finished products, finished products, we can abstract entire logistics changes to heat to slab, slab to plate. So we can make the complex business processes simple and abstract by the components definition of the three material elements mentioned above.

13. Materialflow Tracking (MfT) module: Face to the rapid pace of production, we need to match and track the dynamic logistics and information flow online, make each process operator can grip work stage production status before and after instantaneously, reducing the loss of working time due to poor information.

14. Progress Management (PM) module: It can transfer the order process information to Supply Chain Management (SCM) system, Customer Relationship Management (CRM) system, and other external systems.

Based on these modules, MES can dynamically build a real business object model to complete business functions, business object, business object's properties and behaviors, the relationship between business objects have been reflected on the manipulation platform of the system with a user-friendly manner.

5 Conclusion

The intense changes of enterprise's external environment and the internal mechanism require software systems must adapted to various changes, therefore, how to improve the flexibility, especially the flexibility for advanced users and development level user has been a major problem to information systems. To solve this problem, this paper put forward the concept of flexible business objects based on the idea of adaptive object model, we can use flexible business object model for modeling, modify flexible business object model via software system manage platform, users do not need to care about the technical details and implementation platform, they can immediately respond to a variety of changes of business, this provides a new approach for the design of complex information systems. Finally, this paper gave the implementation process of the model with a domain engineering method then validated this model using flexible MES. The results showed that, the flexible business object model based on the AOM can significantly improve the user-oriented flexibility of software system.

References

[1] Shen Limin, Gao Chunyan, Li Feng, Quantitative analysis of software functional flexibility. *Journal of Chinese Computer Systems*, **29(1)**, pp. 61–65, 2003 (in Chinese).
[2] Cao Junwei, Fan Yushun, Concept, method and practice of flexible software system. *Computer Science*, **26(2)**, pp. 74–77, 1992 (in Chinese).

An efficient DNSSEC zone enumeration algorithm

Zheng Wang[1, 2], Liyuan Xiao[2], Rui Wang[2]
[1]*Computer Network Information Center, Chinese Academy of Sciences, Beijing, China*
[2]*China Organizational Name Administration Center, Beijing, China*

Abstract

Domain name system (DNS) security extensions (DNSSEC) is introduced as a set of extensions to DNS which provide data origin authentication, data integrity, and authenticated denial of existence. NSEC/NSEC3 record provides authenticated denial of existence for DNSSEC. Under both NSEC and NSEC3, the zone content is vulnerable to the zone enumeration attacks. A zone enumeration algorithm is proposed in this paper. The algorithm advances on one direction until the discovered fragments are defragged. A stack is dedicated for the defragment with advantage of time and space efficiency. Complexity analysis shows that compared with random DNS queries, the algorithm reduces the number of queries to N.

Keywords: DNS security extensions, authenticated denial of existence, zone enumeration.

1 Introduction

The domain name system (DNS) is one of the most critical components of the today's Internet, providing a link between human users and Internet locations by mapping host names to IP addresses. The early design of DNS protocols did not take security into a central consideration. As attacks against DNS have been identified to be more extensive and destructive in the these years, DNS security extensions (DNSSEC) is introduced as a set of extensions to DNS which provide data origin authentication, data integrity, and authenticated denial of existence.

To deny the existence of any resource record (RR) matching a query, the authenticated denial of existence is required. The initial RR type of DNSSEC is

WIT Transactions on Information and Communication Technologies, Vol. 61, © 2014 WIT Press
www.witpress.com, ISSN 1743-3517 (on-line)
doi:10.2495/MIIT130591

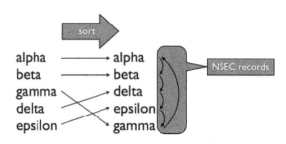

Figure 1: The NSEC chain.

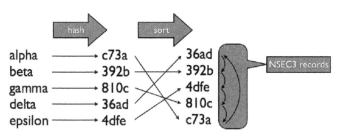

Figure 2: The NSEC3 chain.

NSEC. Every existing name, namely owner name, has a corresponding NSEC record, listing all of the existent RRs belonging to it. Each NSEC RR also contains the next existent owner name in the canonical order. In this way, an NSEC record states the range of names that do not exist. By signing this NSEC record by a corresponding RRSIG record, the DNSSEC validator can authenticate the nonexistence of a domain name. The NSEC chain is illustrated in Figure 1. Since the NSEC records essentially chain through an authoritative zone, the entire contents of the zone may be trivially enumerated by following NSEC records and making appropriate queries. To protect the privacy of a zone from zone enumeration attacks, NSEC3 is introduced to the DNSSEC specifications, providing hashed authenticated denial of existence. NSEC3 is almost equivalent to NSEC except that all owner names are cryptographically hashed and thereby their canonical order in NSEC3 is the hashed order. The NSEC3 chain is illustrated in Figure 2.

Under both NSEC and NSEC3, the zone content is vulnerable to the zone enumeration attacks. What makes NSEC3 more secure than NSEC is that the attacker must expend computational resources in a dictionary attack to learn the zone contents in clear text.

To launch the zone enumeration attacks, the attackers can send a selected set of queries and record the order of the owner names in the responses. While DNSSEC with NSEC requires N queries to enumerate a zone with N names, an attacker cannot deterministically choose which queries to send to obtain all the names in the canonical order. Therefore, the simple idea of retrieving the names continuously in the NSEC/NSEC3 chain is not practical. The central problem for the design of zone enumeration algorithm is how to maintain the known owner names and adaptively select the queries for the unknown owner names efficiently.

There have been some efforts for the DNSSEC-related measurement and evaluation. Yang et al. [1] provided the systematic examination of the design, deployment, and operational challenges encountered by DNSSEC over the years. Guette [2] proposed a new RR to automate the key rollover and avoid the inconsistency problem between the resolver key set and the name server key set. But few previous works address the zone enumeration issues faced by DNSSEC deployment.

A zone enumeration algorithm is proposed in this paper. It is optimized for maintaining the least necessary information for determining the next name to send and using only N queries to walk the zone.

2 The zone enumeration algorithm

Determining the next name to send is equivalent to select one name bracketed by its two neighboring names in the canonical order. The query for a name falling between r_s and r_n is denoted by $Q(r_s, r_n)$. While random query attempts for the unexplored name space can also traverse the zone, it is more efficient to enumerate names in one direction. This is because random query attempts usually result in a large number of name space fragments, and therefore the overwhelmingly lots of information maintained to record the known names.

In the proposed algorithm, the zone enumeration attempt to proceed in the direction of the canonical order. Note it is still possible that a fragment is encountered in the zone enumeration progress. Such fragment is called the residual space. The proposed algorithm tries to walk the residual space first before exploring the space ahead. So the already known space canonically after the residual space should be maintained by the algorithm. The walking of the residual space is likely to be recursively performed since more residual spaces may be found. It is not until the most recent residual space is found to neighbor the known space that this recursion is finalized. In that case, the residual space should be merged into the known space.

The zone enumeration algorithm, namely P-ENUM, follows the forward direction in the canonical order (Figure 3). Because the NSEC/NSEC3 chain is virtually a circle, the zone enumeration algorithm, namely R-ENUM, follows the reverse direction in the canonical order (Figure 5). The selection algorithm is shown in Figure 4. To efficiently handle the recursive walk of residual spaces, a stack is used. In the stack, PUSH(S, q) represents pushing the NSEC/NSEC3 RR q into the S stack, and POP(S) represents popping the S stack. The owner name and the next name of q are represented by q_s and q_n, respectively. The known NSEC/NSEC3 RR chain is recorded in R, whose head and tail are R_s and R_n, respectively. $L(R, q)$ represents merging the NSEC/NSEC3 RR q into R.

```
1. Input
2. A NSEC record of forward direction: R. (Rₛ < Rₙ)
3. Output
4. The entire zone linked by NSEC records
5. Algorithm  P-ENUM (R)
6. rₛ ← Rₙ
7. rₙ ← + ∞ /* */
8. While (true)
9.       q ← Q(rₛ, rₙ)
10.      If (qₛ = rₛ)
11.         R ← L(R, q)
12.         If (Rₛ > Rₙ) /* */
13.            R-ENUM (R)
14.         Elseif (Rₛ = Rₙ)
15.            Return (R)
16.         Elseif (Rₙ = rₙ)
17.            p ← POP(S)
18.            R ← L(R, p)
19.            If (Rₛ > Rₙ) /* */
20.               Return (R-ENUM (R))
21.            Elseif (Rₛ = Rₙ)
22.               Return (R)
23.            Else
24.                  rₛ ← Rₛ
25.         Else
26.            rₛ ← Rₙ
27.      Else
28.         If (S ≠ ∅)
29.            TS ← TOP(S)
30.            If (qₙ = TSₛ)
31.               PS ← POP(S)
32.               q ← L(q, PS)
33.            PUSH(S, q)
```

Figure 3: The pseudocode for P-ENUM.

```
1. Output
2. The entire zone linked by NSEC records
3. Algorithm  ENUM
4.    q ← Q(- ∞, + ∞)
5.    If (qₛ < qₙ)
6.       Return (P-ENUM (q))
7.    ELSE
8.       Return (R-ENUM (q))
```

Figure 4: The pseudocode for ENUM.

```
1. Input
2. A NSEC record of reverse direction: R. (R_s > R_n)
3. Output
4. The entire zone linked by NSEC records
5. Algorithm R-ENUM (R)
6. r_s ← R_n
7. r_n ← R_s /* */
8. While (true)
9.     q ← Q(r_s, r_n)
10.    If (q_s = r_s)
11.       R ← L(R, q)
12.       If (R_s = R_n) /* */
13.          Return (R)
14.       Elseif (R_n = r_n)
15.          p ← POP(S)
16.          R ← L(R, p)
17.          If (R_s = R_n) /* */
18.             Return (R)
19.       r_s ← R_n
20.    Else
21.       If (S ≠ ∅)
22.          TS ← TOP(S)
23.          If (q_n = TS_s)
24.             PS ← POP(S)
25.             q ← L(q, PS)
26.             PUSH(S, q)
```

Figure 5: The pseudocode for R-ENUM.

3 Complexity analysis

The number of DNS queries for DNS zone enumeration by the proposed algorithm is N. To compare with DNS zone enumeration by random DNS queries, we derive the number of DNS queries for DNS random queries. Here we define random DNS queries based on the assumption that the attacker does not keep the query attempts history to avoid duplicate queries for the already probed domain name space, and just sends random queries to explore the undiscovered domain name space.

Let the ith ($i=1, 2, \ldots, N$) discovered domain name space by random queries be h_i, and the overall domain name space be L. The probability distributions for the number of random queries for discovering h_i is derived as

$$p(t_i = n) = \left(\frac{\sum_{j=1}^{i-1} h_j}{L} \right)^{n-1} \left(1 - \frac{\sum_{j=1}^{i-1} h_j}{L} \right) \qquad i=1, 2, \ldots, N \qquad (1)$$

where t_i denotes the number of random queries for discovering h_i. We can derive the expectation of t_i as

$$E[t_i] = \frac{L}{L - \sum_{j=1}^{i-1} h_j} \quad i = 1, 2, ..., N \tag{2}$$

The number of DNS queries for DNS random queries can be approximated as

$$E = \sum_{i=1}^{N} E[t_i] \tag{3}$$

To simplify the analysis, we assume that each h_i is equal, $i=1, 2, ..., N$, or

$$h_1 = h_2 = ... = h_N \tag{4}$$

So the discovered domain name space is proportional to the number of emitted queries. Equation (2) can be rewritten as

$$E[t_i] = \frac{L}{L - i + 1} \quad i=1, 2, ..., N \tag{5}$$

We can transform Eq. (3) to a continuous model as

$$E \approx \sum_{i=1}^{N} \frac{L}{L - i}$$

$$\approx \int_{x=1}^{L-1} \frac{L}{L - x} dx \tag{6}$$

Equation (6) shows that the complexity of DNS zone enumeration by random DNS queries is $O[L\log(L)]$.

4 Conclusion

NSEC/NSEC3 record provides authenticated denial of existence for DNSSEC. Under both NSEC and NSEC3, while the zone content is vulnerable to the zone enumeration attacks. A zone enumeration algorithm is proposed in this paper. Compared with DNS zone enumeration by random DNS queries, it is optimized for maintaining the least necessary information for determining the next name to send and using only N queries to walk the zone.

Acknowledgments

This work was supported by the National Key Technology R&D Program of China under Grant No. 2012BAH16B00 and the National Science Foundation of China under Grant No. 61003239.

References

[1]   Hao Yang, Eric Osterweil, Dan Massey, et al., Deploying cryptography in Internet-scale systems: a case study on DNSSEC. *IEEE Transactions on Dependable and Secure Computing*, **8(5)**, pp. 656–669, 2011.
[2]   G. Guette, Automating trusted key rollover in DNSSEC. *Journal of Computer Security*, **17(6)**, pp. 839–854, 2009.

Effect of user participation on software project innovation performance

Ying Cao, Yu Gu
Department of Information Technology and Business Administration,
Dalian Neusoft University of Information, Dalian, China

Abstract

In this paper, we select 260 software projects in China mainland as research samples to analyze the effect of user participation on software project innovation performance based on factor analysis and regressive method. First of all, hypotheses are proposed based on the innovative features of software products. User participation consists of participation deepness and participation width. Then, we analyzed many samples and data. Furthermore, variables are explored based on those results. At last, all variables are studied by factor analysis and regressive method. The result shows that in the process of software products' innovation, user participation has positive effect to the innovation of software products. In addition, in the effect of user participation, knowledge integration has prominent effect to the innovation of software products. This indicates that in the R&D process of software product, we could use systematic knowledge integration to enhance the level of user participation in order to improve innovation performance of software products.

Keywords: Innovation performance, user participation, systematic knowledge integration, software products.

1 Introduction

Improve software product innovation performance is critical to the development of software industry, and users as an important source of innovation has received widespread attention of scholars and entrepreneurs. In software product development process, user resource integration, user value acquisition and the degree of interaction between the user and project must have user involvement. User participation become indispensable in software product development and it has an important impact on software products innovation. In recent years, with the rapid development of software industry, a number of valuable research samples has been accumulated which provides the foundation of empirical study on user participation in the software product innovation performance using and factor analysis and regression analysis method.

2   Related research review

Von Hippel first proposed user innovation which thought it is a kind of predictable way in the cooperation process between innovative user, manufacturer and suppliers [1]. Frey et al. [2] pointed out that user participation takes a very important part in industrial market. Lettl et al. [3] found that user participation has an impact in early stages of radical innovation, especially in medical equipment technology area, a lot of cases show that users' role of fundamental innovation inventor or co-developer. Chen and other researchers pointed out that advanced users have great value on acquiring needs information and accelerating develop process [4].

As the typical characteristics of intensive knowledge software companies, knowledge innovation is the key to innovation. In the process of enterprise internal and external knowledge acquisition and sharing and utilization, system knowledge integration plays a catalytic role in knowledge creation [5]. In the process of knowledge integration, organization's key mission is to provide scenarios and means, production and service activities have been completed based on organization's operation [6]. Yang and Wang have been working from the perspective of social network embeddedness to expound the knowledge sharing incentive mechanism in the process of virtual team strategy and platform construction [7]. Enberg figured out members' common contribution and social network is the key to knowledge integration project; members' previous work experience, knowledge integration experience and social capital have a direct impact on the level of collaboration, and thus play a decisive role in knowledge integration efficiency and scope [8].

Based on the above analysis, it indicates that more attention has been paid on software user participation innovation research, and foreign scholars have made a lot of progress on this field. However, researches in China are still in the phase of qualitative research, quantitative research is relatively weak, it is necessary to deepen this study. Therefore, this research focuses on the intermediary role of user participation on software project innovation performance and system integration of knowledge based on many field studies.

3   Research hypothesis

3.1   User innovation and software innovation performance

Software enterprise organization innovation is composed by the networks of users, suppliers, peer enterprises, and cooperative enterprises. Many surveys found, user is the key to the software product innovation. The wider user participation in the development process, the more opportunities for users' communication in develop process, and thus it establishes a broad knowledge base that helps software innovative project completion. In addition, users can arise some advices such as product design, coding, and testing; therefore, software companies can understand more thoroughly in development and testing process.

Hypothesis 1: User involvement width has a positive impact on software project innovation performance; the wider of extensive user involvement, the higher innovation performance of software project; conversely, the lower of innovation performance.

Hypothesis 2: User involvement depth has a positive impact on software project innovation performance, the deeper of extensive user involvement, the higher innovation performance of software project; conversely, the lower of innovation performance.

3.2 System knowledge integration capability and user participation

System knowledge integration is the process of integrating the external technical knowledge and enterprise's self-learning technology. It requires companies' ability of technology accumulation, broad technical vision, and the ability to integrate external technologies.

Hypothesis 3: Width of user participation has a positive effect on system knowledge integration ability. The wider of user participation, the stronger system integration knowledge, and vice versa.

Hypothesis 4: Depth of user participation has a positive effect on system knowledge integration ability. The deeper of user participation, the stronger system integration knowledge, and vice versa.

3.3 System knowledge integration capability and software performance

Zirpoli and Becker believed that knowledge integration provides foundation for new product development, and from the perspective of resource supply chain to study knowledge integration and innovation [9]. Researches on software projects found that system knowledge integration ability is shown in project feasibility analysis, requirement analysis, system design, detailed design, and realization process of corporate users of reusable components and the integration of industry knowledge and utilization ability.

Hypothesis 5: System integration ability has a positive effect on software project performance, the stronger of system knowledge integration, the better of software performance, and vice versa.

3.4 Intermediary role of system knowledge integration

Software project has many reusable legacy assets of previous ones; it can play a key role in development through improving development efficiency based on effective system knowledge integration.

Figure 1: Conceptual model.

Hypothesis 6: System knowledge integration in user involvement has a positive influence on product innovation as the intermediary role, user involvement degree can improve software performance by promoting systematic growth.

3.5 Conceptual model

This research focuses on software project innovation performance, system knowledge integration, open innovation, and user involvement innovation theory; furthermore, it also studies the width and depth of users' involvement directly affects software project performance. As Figure 1 shows the conceptual model, it first analyzes the effect of users' participation, then it analyzes system knowledge integration promotion, finally, it analyzes the users' participation's direct impact on software performance.

4 Questionnaire design and data collection

4.1 Sample selection

This study uses questionnaire to collect data with software industry such as Neusoft, Dalian Huaxin technology, Haihui software and other 18 companies based on 24 software projects in Dalian city as the pre-research in April 2011. Interviewers are those project development directors and then perfect the questionnaire using the pre-research result. The main way for this research include face-to-face interview, Internet questionnaire and 350 questionnaires issued and get 322 feedbacks, of which 260 valid questionnaires, the effective rate is 74.25%.

4.2 Variable measurement

4.2.1 Independent variable-user participation

Kaulio proposed two dimensions of innovation and user participation, Participation width refers to the user how much involved in the development phase; participate depth refers to the user's participation in every stage of the depth of involvement [10]. According to field investigation and document analysis, this study presents the extent of users to participate in project planning, user needs analysis involved in the project the extent of user participation in the project implementation level, degree of user participation in project maintenance, new products can bring great benefits for the user (including economic or reputation, etc.), the user frequency of communication with the project team, the project integrated user domain knowledge level, whether the user is often useful to put forward comments or ideas, the design of the project system users often make constructive ideas, project coding users frequently asked questions, the test users are often involved in the project more views, the user involved in the project time (less to less than 20% participation; less 20–40%; generally 40–60%; many as 60–80%; more than 80% or more), the user can valuable recommendations on the products (means a commercial value and operability), and the proposal is novel products made by the user or proposed new requirements in it is a pioneer in the industry, such as 14 questions items, from the depth and breadth of user involvement user participation in two dimensions measure in actual situation.

4.2.2 Dependent variable-software product performance

According to research and document analysis, this study presents the final software product reliability project, the project final software product ease of maintenance, project final software product's ease of use, user satisfaction with the project, the project final software product quality level, the project within budget, the project ultimately meet the functional requirements of the user level, the project completed within the scheduled time, and thus it improves the project development process organization's ability to acquire knowledge to improve the ability to control the resources of the project, the project development process to enhance the project team ability to communicate with the user, a total of 11 questions of, respectively, reflecting the performance of the software products of the project and software project process performance measurement of two dimensions.

4.2.3 Intermediary variable-system knowledge integration

System knowledge integration is the important principle to measure enterprise's ability of knowledge management. Software innovation derives from users' needs; developers design the project content and communicate with the user, then modify the project until meet users' standard. Therefore, system knowledge integration ability can improve the efficiency and effectiveness of users' participation.

5 Scale design

This article is to analyze the relevant literature through carding proposed initial questionnaire question, then depth interviews with industry veterans, according to the interview results to modify the questionnaire, and finally for an interview, after repeated changes to finalize the questionnaire title items in this way to ensure measurement validity and reliability (Table 1).

In this study, the depth of user participation, user involvement width two dimensions to measure the degree of user involvement, the scale mainly refer to the Kaulio [10] and other studies, based on the pre-survey and interviews corporate results, and its operational definition as Table 2 shows.

Table 1: Operational Definition of User Involvement.

Variables	Multi-Item
Width of user participation	(user-01) The degree of users to participate in the project plan (user-02) Users to participate in the project needs analysis (user-03) Users to participate in the project implementation (user-04) Users to participate in project maintenance (user-05) The benefit from the new product for the user (user-06) Frequency of users communicate with project team
Depth of user participation	(user-07) The project integrated user degree of domain knowledge (user-08) Frequency of users useful opinions or ideas (user-09) Project user constructive ideas in the design of system frequency (user-10) Project code user the problem of frequency is presented in the paper (user-11) The opinions of user participation frequency project tests (user-12) Users involved in the project time (participation for less than 20% and less 20–40%, average 40–60%, 60–80% more, more for more than 80%) (user-13) User valuable products, novel suggestion (refers to the commercial value and high manoeuvrability) (user-14) The user of the proposed new requirements of products and/or suggestions in their own industry advancement

Table 2: Operational Definition of Software Project Innovation Performance.

Variables	Multi-Items
Software product performance	(proj-01) The reliability of the final project software products (proj-02) Eventually the maintenance of software products (proj-03) Eventually the usability of software products (proj-04) User satisfaction of the project (proj-05) Final project software product quality level
Software project process	(proj-06) The project completed within

performance	budget
	(proj-07) The final project meets the user's functional requirements
	(proj-08) The project completed within the scheduled time
	(proj-09) Improve the project development process in the organization's ability to acquire knowledge
	(proj-10) To improve the ability to control of project resources
	(proj-11) Improved in the process of project development project teams ability to communicate with users

6 Conclusion

Currently, software companies are embedded into the rapid development of complex heterogeneous industry; user participation become important external software product innovation industries access to knowledge, which objectively requires the innovation process more widely available user's experience, knowledge, and technology. Chinese software companies need to focus on fostering knowledge systems integration capabilities, for the use of external technical ability in order to better improve the performance of our innovative software projects.

Acknowledgments

The research work was supported by National Natural Science Foundation of China under Grant No. 71002094.

References

[1] P.D. Morrison, J.H. Roberts, H. Von, Determinants of user innovation and innovation sharing in a local market. *Management Science*, **46(12)**, pp. 1513–1527, 2000.
[2] K. Frey, C. Luethje, S. Haag, Whom should firms attract to open innovation platforms? The role of knowledge diversity and motivation. *Long Range Planning*, **44(5–6)**, pp. 397–420, 2011.
[3] C. Lettl, C. Herstatt, H.G. Gemuenden, Users' contributions to radical innovation: evidence from four cases in the field of medical equipment technology. *R&D Management*, **36(3)**, pp. 251–272, 2006.
[4] Chen Yufen, Chen Jin, A study on the mechanism of open innovation promoting innovative performance. *Scientific Research Management*, **30(4)**, pp. 1–9, 2009.

[5]   C. Yang, J.H. Liu, J. Sun, Learning process, knowledge integration and strategic innovation: evidence from China. *Strategic Management*, **15(4)**, pp. 3–7, 2010.

[6]   I. Han, M. Eom, W.S. Shin, Multimedia case-based learning to enhance pre-service teachers' knowledge integration for teaching with technologies. *Teaching and Teacher Education*, **34**, pp. 122–129, 2013.

[7]   Yang Bin, Wang Xuedong, Research on knowledge sharing process in virtual teams based on the social network embedded perspective. *Information Science*, **27(12)**, pp. 1765–1769, 2009.

[8]   C. Enberg, Enabling knowledge integration in competitive R&D projects the management of conflicting logics. *International Journal of Project Management*, **30(7)**, pp. 771–780, 2012.

[9]   F. Zirpoli, M.C. Becker, The limits of design and engineering outsourcing: performance integration and the unfulfilled promises of modularity. *R&D Management*, **41(1)**, pp. 21–43, 2011.

[10] M.A. Kaulio, Customer, consumer and user involvement in product development: a framework and a review of selected methods. *Total Quality Management*, **9(1)**, pp. 141–149, 1998.

Application of Jacobi method in radar signal processing

Shiru Zhang, Haobin Shi
College of Communications and Information Engineering, Xi'an University of Science and Technology, Xi'an, Shaanxi, China

Abstract

There are two methods in radar signal processing by finding eigenvalues and corresponding eigenvectors, Jacobi method and combination of Household and QR (HQR) method. The two methods are investigated in-depth and verified in ADSP-TS201 chips. Conclusions are drawn from comparisons with conventional look-up table (LUT) method that the Jacobi method is the best choice in radar signal processing, which has the virtue of real time that cannot be in common LUT method, and has lower spatial complexity and higher precision than the HQR.
Keywords: Jacobi, radar signal processing, eigenvalue, eigenvector.

1 Introduction

Eigenvalues and eigenvectors are always used in radar signal processing [1–5]. Usually, we calculate the eigenvalues and the corresponding eigenvectors and store them in a file, and then search the corresponding values we need according to the matrix characteristics in that file in actual use. Sen [2] selected the eigenvector corresponding to the minimum eigenvalue of the covariance matrix as the filter weight-vector. This can obtain the optimal improvement factors of the filter [4]. Look-up table (LUT) method is another method [4,6], which estimates the required parameters in advance and stores them in the hardware, invokes them when needed.

LUT method has many advantages, such as reducing the calculations and simplifying the designs, but it cannot be real-time due to the parameter estimations in advance. Furthermore, when the estimated parameters do not match the actual ones, the optimal results will not be received, and the filter will have no optimal improvement factor. Press et al. [7] stated there are two methods to solve eigenvectors and eigenvalues, one is Jacobi method, which has long computing time but small space complexity, the other way is HQR method (combination of Household and QR), which has shorter computing time but great complexity and decreasing performance as the order of matrix increasing. In HQR, the real symmetric matrix is first simplified into a tridiagonal matrix by Household method, and then the eigenvalues and eigenvectors can be found via resolving the tridiagonal matrix by QR method.

This paper will compare these methods according the performance of the filters in radar signal processing. The superior performance of Jacobi method in solving eigenvalues and eigenvectors is obtained.

2 Related basics

Based on the problem of solving matrix, eigenvalues and corresponding eigenvectors in radar signal processing, we give an example. For a clutter which has a Gaussian spectral density, its normalized spectral density is Ref. [4]

$$S_c(f) = \frac{1}{\sqrt{2\pi\sigma_c^2}} \exp\left\{-\frac{(f - f_0)^2}{2\sigma_c^2}\right\} \tag{1}$$

where σ_c^2 is the frequency standard deviation, f_0 is the center of the spectrum. According to Wiener filtering theory, the correlation function of the clutter is

$$\begin{aligned} R_c(i,j) &= F^{-1}\left[S_c(f)\right] \\ &= \exp\left(-2\pi^2\sigma_c^2\tau_{ij}^2\right)\left(\cos 2\pi\tau_{ij}f_0 + j\sin 2\pi\tau_{ij}f_0\right) \end{aligned} \tag{2}$$

where $\tau_{ij} = t_i - t_j$ is the correlation time. Consequently, the covariance matrix of the clutter $R_c(i,j)$ is

$$R_c = \left\{ \begin{matrix} R_c(0,0) & R_c(0,1) & \cdots & R_c(0,M) \\ R_c(1,0) & R_c(1,1) & \cdots & R_c(1,M) \\ \cdots & \cdots & \cdots & \cdots \\ R_c(M,0) & R_c(M,1) & \cdots & R_c(M,M) \end{matrix} \right\} \tag{3}$$

From Eq. (2), we know that when the center of the clutter spectrum f_0 is zero, the covariance matrix R_c is a real symmetric matrix, and when it is not zero, the covariance matrix R_c is a Hermitian matrix.

In radar signal processing, when the eigenvector corresponding to the minimum eigenvalue of the covariance matrix is used as the filter coefficients, the system will reach its maximum noise suppression ratio.

We can change the $n \times n$ Hermitian matrix to a $2n \times 2n$ real symmetric matrix [7], so that the eigenvalues and eigenvectors of this Hermitian matrix can be achieved. If $C = A + iB$ is a Hermitian matrix, where A and B are real symmetric matrices, the $n \times n$ eigenvalue problem (4)

$$(A + iB) \cdot (u + iv) = \lambda(u + iv) \tag{4}$$

is equivalent to a $2n \times 2n$ real symmetric matrix problems (extended matrix), as in Eq. (5).

$$\begin{bmatrix} A & -B \\ B & A \end{bmatrix} \cdot \begin{bmatrix} u \\ v \end{bmatrix} = \lambda \begin{bmatrix} u \\ v \end{bmatrix} \tag{5}$$

Because C is a Hermitian matrix, we have $A^T = A$ and $B^T = B$, then $2n \times 2n$ matrix on the left side of Eq. (5) is a real symmetric matrix.

3 Experimental results

3.1 Jacobi method versus LUT method

All the simulations in this paper were conducted in MATLAB 8.0 environment. MATLAB function eig () is used to solve a Hermitian matrix for minimum. We first evaluate the minimum eigenvalues and eigenvectors in MATLAB, and then the Jacobi method is used to do the same thing on the ADSP-TS201, and finally the filter spectra were plotted in MATLAB.

The results of Jacobi method in real time and LUT method for the dynamic clutter filter coefficient are shown in Figures 1 and 2.

Figure 2 is the enlarged view of the block area in Figure 1. Obviously, Jacobi and LUT method have almost the same clutter suppression performance. However, Jacobi method has a real-time property and can be used in the extreme case when the LUT method fails. When the frequency between pulses or groups of pulses in the transmitter is varied, the correlation time of the covariance matrix changed to be unknown in advance, or when frequency standard deviation σ_c^2 does not match with the estimated value in advance, LUT method fails, but in this time, Jacobi method can be used to obtain the optimal filter coefficients and exhibit its excellence.

3.2 Jacobi method versus HQR method

In engineering the space complexity is $n*(n+1)$ (n is the dimension of the matrix) in Jacobi method and $2n*(n+1)$ in HQR method. When the absolute value of the diagonal elements is significantly greater than the nondiagonal elements, the time complexity of Jacobi method is lower. When the matrix

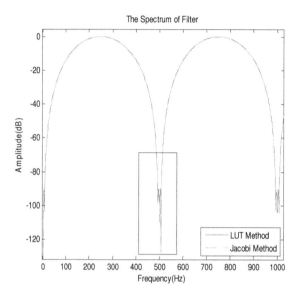

Figure 1: Performance of two methods.

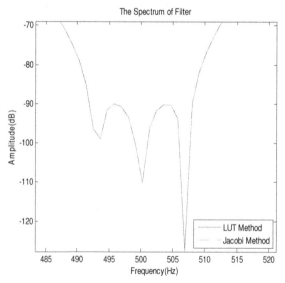

Figure 2: Details of the block area in Figure 1.

dimension is large, Jacobi method consumes more time than HQR method, while the performance of HQR method is getting worse.

We used ADSP-TS201 of ADI in solving radar clutter filters and compared the corresponding filter performance. The experimental results are as follows (the accuracy is 10^{-7}).

Table 1: Results Comparison for a Fourth-Order Real Symmetric Matrix.

	Eigenvalue	Eigenvector	Time Consuming (ms)
Jacobi	0.000031	[0.501042, −0.499188, −0.498846, 0.500920]	0.0182458
	3.980389	[0.499017, 0.500981, 0.500981, 0.499017]	
	−0.000000	[0.224274, −0.670427, 0.670683, −0.224531]	
	0.019581	[−0.670552, −0.224406, 0.224400, 0.670557]	
HQR	−0.000000	[0.223615, −0.669765, 0.671340, −0.225197]	0.0122792
	0.000031	[−0.501330 ,0.500076, 0.497957, −0.500631]	
	0.019580	[0.670557, 0.224403, −0.224410, −0.670550]	
	3.980388	[−0.499017, −0.500981, −0.50098, −0.499017]	

For the fourth-order real symmetric matrix as in Eq. (6), the results are shown in Table 1. As for the fourth-order Hermitian matrix as in Eq. (7), we first change it into an eighth-order real symmetric matrix, and then use the two methods mentioned above to get all the results in Table 2.

$$
\begin{bmatrix}
1.0000 & 0.9980 & 0.9921 & 0.9824 \\
0.9980 & 1.0000 & 0.9980 & 0.9921 \\
0.9921 & 0.9980 & 1.0000 & 0.9980 \\
0.9824 & 0.9921 & 0.9980 & 1.0000
\end{bmatrix}
\tag{6}
$$

$$
\begin{bmatrix}
1.0000 & 0.4984+0.8634\,i & -0.4940+0.8554\,i & -0.9726-0.0002\,i \\
0.4984-0.8634\,i & 1.0000 & 0.4984+0.8634\,i & -0.4940+0.8554\,i \\
-0.4940-0.8554\,i & 0.4984-0.8634\,i & 1.0000 & 0.4984+0.8634\,i \\
-0.9726+0.0002\,i & -0.4940-0.8554\,i & 0.4984-0.8634\,i & 1.0000
\end{bmatrix}
\tag{7}
$$

The two matrices mentioned above are the covariance matrices constructed in the solving process of a ground clutter filter and a moving clutter filter in X radar. The eigenvector corresponding to the minimum eigenvalue of the covariance

Table 2: Comparison of Eighth-Order Real Symmetric Matrix Results.

	Eigenvalue	Eigenvector	Time Consuming (ms)
Jacobi	0.000000	[−0.004211, −0.575287, 0.585227, −0.003196, −0.225456, 0.345474, 0.325714, −0.224176]	0.165569
HQR	0.000006	[−0.155625, 0.714366, 0.021664, −0.178698, 0.273466, 0.152418, −0.578830, 0.000000]	0.0339042

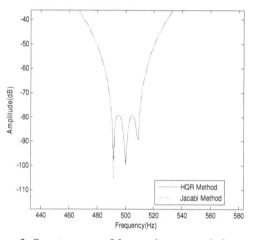

Figure 3: Spectrogram of four orders ground clutter filter.

matrix is the optimal filter coefficients. According to the two groups' coefficients, we can get the following spectrogram of the corresponding filters.

Comparing Tables 1 and 2, we can conclude that HQR method will consume less time than Jacobi method, especially in the eighth-order matrix. However, the more order, the poor performance. From Figures 3 and 4, when the matrix has lower order, the two methods have almost the same filter performance. When the matrix order is higher, such as eighth-order, HQR method got a 20 dB lower performance of clutter rejection than Jacobi method. And due to the poor accuracy three zeros decrease to two zeros. With the order number increasing, the performance difference will be greater.

From the experimental results, although Jacobi method exhibits almost the same performance with the traditional LUT method, it has a real-time property and can be used in some situation when the parameters are unknown and the desired table cannot be built in advance. By comparing the Jacobi method and HQR (combine of Household and QR method) method, the time complexity of

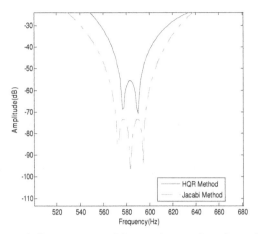

Figure 4: Spectrogram of four order moving clutter filter.

Jacobi is larger, but its space complexity is smaller than the HQR method. Also, the performance depends on the matrix order. When the matrix order is lower (less than or equal to 4), the above two methods have the same performances. However, when the order increases, Jacobi method has a greater performance than HQR method.

4 Conclusion

In radar signal processing or other specific engineering situations, eigenvalues and eigenvectors of a matrix are necessary to be solved. If the parameters of the matrix are known in advance, for example, in the feature vector method of radar clutter suppression method, its covariance matrix parameters, such as the correlation time between adjacent cycles, clutter Doppler spectral width, range of the clutter spectrum center, are known in advance, the best method is LUT method. When the parameters are unknown and the matrix order is lower than or equals to four, we can use HQR method. In the above situations, Jacobi method can always be used, but in other cases, for example, when the matrix parameters are unknown in advance or the order of matrix is lager, only Jacobi method is available.

References

[1] He Kun, Research and realization of radar clutter suppression method. *Journal of Xi'an University of Electronic Science and Technology*, **3**, pp. 8–10, 2006.
[2] Satyabrata Sen, OFDM Radar Space-Time Adaptive Processing by Exploiting Spatio-Temporal Sparsity. *IEEE Transactions on Signal Processing*, **1**, pp. 118–130, 2013.

[3]   Liu Tao, Gong Yaohuan, Wng Jie, et al, OTHR impulsive interference detection in strong clutter background. In: *International Conference on Communications, Circuits and Systems*, Milpitas, CA, pp. 410–413, 2009.

[4]   Song Jie, He You, Guan Jian, et al, A near adaptive MTI system for bimodal clutter suppression. *ACTA Armament ARII*, **30(5)**, pp 546–550, 2009 (in Chinese).

[5]   L. Pallotta, A. Aubry, A. De Maio, et al, Estimation of a structured covariance matrix with a condition number constraint for radar applications. In: *IEEE Transactions on Radar Conference*, Atlanta, GA, 7–11, pp. 0778–0783, 2012.

[6]   Y.M. Seddiq, S.A. Alshebeili, S.M. Alhumaidi, et al, FPGA-based implementation of a CFAR processor using Batcher's sort and LUT arithmetic. In: *4th International Workshop on Design and Test*, Riyadh, 15–17, pp. 1–6, 2009.

[7]   W.H. Press, B.P. Flannery, S.A. Teukolsky, et al, *Numerical Recipes in C: The Art of Scientific Computing—Second Edition*. Cambridge University Press, pp. 10–50, 1992.

The architecture of decision-making system of emergency operations

Julian Zhang

Computer Information Center, Beijing Institute of Fashion Technology, Beijing, China

Abstract

Based on the analysis of decision-making of emergency operations and the demand of information management, this paper presents the whole architecture of decision-making system of emergency operations and information integration. It also sets up the model of its information management through an example of "The Nation Public Health Emergency Surveillance Decision-Making System." It will provide the support to decision-making system of national emergency operations.

Keywords: Architecture, emergency, decision-making.

1 Introduction

The decision-making process is divided into four main stages: (1) survey on the environment, search the conditions and purpose of decision-making—intelligence activities; (2) create, develop, and analyze possible action plan—design activities; (3) select a special action plan from the available alternatives—choice activities; (4) decision implementation and review—examination activities. These four stages together, form a system of decision-making process. System policy is to choose the best of the development scenarios from the system analysis of alternatives. According to Simon's management theory, the basic decision-making processes are composed of the information acquisition, plan design, and plan choices. This paper analyzes emergency decision-making system, and sets up its technical architecture and application framework of the information integration. The national public health emergency decision-making system is used to establish and describe the emergency decision management model.

WIT Transactions on Information and Communication Technologies, Vol. 61, © 2014 WIT Press
www.witpress.com, ISSN 1743-3517 (on-line)
doi:10.2495/MIIT130621

2 The structure of emergency decision-making system

2.1 Information management demand about system architecture design

To resolve the problem of information management, the demand for emergency decision-making system is mainly reflected in the following: (A) real-time performance: it is required immediately to get the internal and external information, to store, and analyze information; (B) supporting large numbers of concurrent users to access and deal with information online: command center is a cross-sector service center and information from various units is also provided to the relevant unit. Therefore, the system must have massive data-processing capabilities to support On-Line Transaction Processing (OLTP) and On-Line Analysis Processing (OLAP); (C) cross-platform and departments: the characteristics of the original system are following the "divide and rule, relatively independent." The same institution may run a variety of systems and multiple networks, and currently running system is for specific features and services; (D) decision support and intelligence: command center must provide data analysis and decision support tools [1]. The system makes a situation and trend analysis according to the resources, social, economic, political, geographical, weather, and other information; (E) high reliability: command center system is the most important operating system, and its trouble-free operation is essential for critical moment and day-to-day functioning; (F) scalability: as the system is in operation, the accumulation of data and analysis standards will continue to expand both in information type and in size, the requirements for running the system reflect the diverse trends. In a development perspective, a system with a high degree of scalability is a living one.

2.2 The framework of the application system

An emergency decision-making system is divided into service systems, business systems, management systems, and decision support systems; management system includes the information services platform, data integration platform, emergency assessment platform, emergency consultation platform, emergency dispatching platforms, OLAP analysis platform; A business system includes emergency resource management, emergency expert system, emergency control systems, and emergency monitoring system; service system includes call centers and Web sites for information publishing, etc. The three systems connect to each other through the network. The application framework of an emergency decision-making system is shown in Figure 1.

3 Information integration and consolidation model

Based on the emergency decision-making system demand analysis, this paper presents the framework model of emergency decision-making system of information integration, as shown in Figure 2. The model is divided into three logical layers. The first layer is referred to as mapping layer, which makes it

Figure 1: The application framework of an emergency decision-making system.

possible for all system data resources open and information interchangeable between systems [2].

The second logical layer is referred to as information integrated layer. According to the business demand, this layer copies data from existing business system for migration to the decision-making centre. Data migration ways are both data replication and cross loader. Cross loader is used to move a large number of data which owe incremental differentiate easily; data replication is used to move large information with daily little variation. The information integrated layer realizes all the actual integration of system information, sets up the relation between the system user information and correspondence, forms a unified global user view, and expands the new user information in the original user information.

The third level is the data service layer, its service object is for the call center, top leaders and related research departments, and its primary interface is the standard SQL. The external data exchange is largely dictated by the XML implementation and in the future it will consider realizing integration with related external systems by adopting Web services.

Information integration is the process of sharing business application information through integrating business application system information.

Information integration creates value. Its overall strategy is to provide information integration solutions for emergency decision-making system based on different database systems, information management systems, and business application systems. Its technological core is for middleware and visualization process configuration management.

Integration involves data layer, system layer, and business layer:

(1) Data integration plan with communications middleware technology as the core.
(2) By data access middleware, realizing data consolidation of any heterogeneous database information.
(3) System integration plan with application middleware technology as the core.

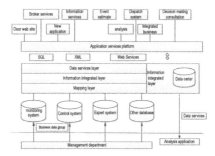

Figure 2: Framework model of emergency decision-making system of information integration.

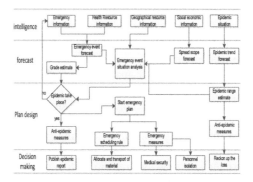

Figure 3: Overall structure of management process of national public health emergency decision-making system.

4 Emergency decision-making system management process

In a hierarchical view of science, and under the guidance of Simon's management idea of "information, design, choice," we take the national public health emergency decision-making system as an example, the overall structure of its management process shown in Figure 3. This model describes model architecture of the public health emergency decision-making and explains the "sensible" of emergency decision-making. "Sensible" of public health emergency decision-making describes public health emergency decision-making model architecture. When public health emergency decision-making system is carried out, we must adhere to the optimum utilization of resources and fully consider sharing resources between departments, and regional and social organizations coordination. According to the organizational structure of public health, public health emergency decision-making is a multicriteria decision-making model system. Public health emergency policy reveals quantitatively the mutual relations between the competition and conflict, and between objectives and systems. The multicriteria decision-making methods and related mathematical models are used to analyze the balance relation in public health, medical treatment, disease monitoring, and the various types of resource allocation. Meanwhile, the decision-maker's wishes are integrated into decision-making procedure through man–machine dialogue, this making the results reasonable.

5 Enterprise application integration model

5.1 Enterprise application integration model and implementation

At enterprise application integration (EAI) development process and the field, there are four modes: Point-to-Point, Hub-and-Spoke, Messaging Bus, and Enterprise Service Bus with BPM. The above four modes generated and applicators as technology development and with enterprise have further understanding of integration needs. They have their own advantages, disadvantages, and applicability, suiting for different business demands. The following will describe the four models separately.

At EAI field, point-to-point mode is the earliest one. It is to solve the separation of multiple systems of enterprise; unreliable data exchange which is necessary to carry out manually. Its guiding idea is that between any two of the required data exchange system (points) developed corresponding interface object. Extract the corresponding target data by these interface object from the data source system, to provide as a target application system. The characteristics of this model are clearly target of interface object, simplification of transmission of the data format, and the high transmission performance. But interface is complex, over coupling between applications, bad maintainability. And it is a data transmission rather than integration.

After point-to-point mode, the distribution device (star) mode is proposed. It is mainly to solve of the multi-interface and over coupling problem in point-to-point mode. It introduces DCS and adapter and the concept of have multiple systems access to the central device on the distribution through the adapter, thus for a designated system there is only one link interface in the entire architecture of EAI to outside systems. But its data redundancy is based on synchronized data rather than business-based applications; therefore, it is more tightly coupled and require a higher network.

Message Bus model aims at resolving the over coupling, connectivity, scalability problems. Its introductory asynchronous message mechanism have multiple systems connected to Message Bus through adapters and converters, all data and information are transferred in form of news. The message initiator is responsible for posting the news to the message bus, and news consumers (users) subscript for (monitor) specific news from the Message Bus, to achieve the Loose Coupling systems. Because of the Message Bus using of publish/subscribe technology implementation for respond to a message, system performance has declined in a certain degree, and cannot be achieved truly simultaneously, be unreliably to achieve global transaction between multiple systems.

5.2 XML format as the data exchange format standard

It is superior to the traditional EDI based on the standards XML as data exchange format. DTD models can be easily developed and applied. Adding new components and property will not affect the data processing applications. XML provides not only easy data transplanting but also a mechanism to display different view of data. For example, the formatted form can create HTML pages, and also can generate the database tables and insert data. By employed DOM, multiple applications can access an object of XML document.

XML offers Web-based application software strong functionality and flexibility; it supplies developers and users many benefits, such as more flexible query, the data show a various view, different sources of data integration, publishing data on Web, scalability, compression, and open standards.

Moreover, as a mechanism for portable data, the XML has a great expansion. XML format as document interaction has been widely received. It is easy to integrate collaboration in future operational systems and other external systems.

Web service is to create interoperable distributed applications of new platform. The main objective of Web service is cross-platform and interoperability. To achieve this goal, Web service is completely based on platform and software vendor's independence standards such as XML, XSD, etc.

Because Web service platform is a set of criterion, which defines how applications to achieve interoperability on the Internet, developers can employ any language, on any platform to Writing Web service, as long as the client can adopt Web service standards to inquiries and visits these services.

Web service is very useful in application cross-platform and cross-network communication. Web service is suitable for application integration, B2B integration, code and data reuse, as well as client and server communication.

5.3 Case in application

Existing applications and services integrated business logic into a service package by adapter and service to Pack applications and access to the Enterprise Service Bus. The Business system of emergency decision-making system sends decision-making data to Management Information System.

Through the certificate authorized query system users can access the emergency decision-making system to grasp the current real-time status of management system for public health data, or to integrate the corresponding analysis of the results of the information platform.

6   Conclusion

Construction of emergency decision-making system is the trend of the socio-economic development. Its theoretical base is Simon's management idea and the central nerve and soul to deal with emergency events. On the basis of the analysis of emergency decision-making solutions facing the major challenges and information management requirements, this article has proposed an emergency decision-making system framework which has some significance on national emergency decision-making system. The author had been in charge of the national public health emergency decision-making system design, and received Gold Award of 2004 National Ministry of health plan design, taken as a project of the preferred options. This structure model can be used for health, flood control, and enterprise emergency decision-making information system.

Acknowledgments

This work is partially supported by Beijing Municipal Education Commission Grant #KYJD02130208.

References

[1] Zhang Julian, Management information systems development and implementation. *Computer Application*, **1**, pp. 7–9, 2003.
[2] Fan Jingyan, Zhang Jujian, Jay, The whole structure and implementation techniques of enterprise application integration. *Telecommunications Technology*, **4**, pp. 36–40, 2005.

A decision support system for last train timetable optimization in urban rail transit network

Xi Jiang[1], Zhen Qu[2]
[1]State Key Lab of Rail Traffic Control and Safety, Beijing Jiaotong University, Beijing, China
[2]School of Civil Engineering, Tsinghua University, Beijing, China

Abstract

To improve the service level of traffic in the urban rail transit network, coordination of last train timetable on different lines should be taken into account in the operation. The decision support technology can play an important role in scheduling and rescheduling of the last train. The decision support problem of the last train timetable optimization was analyzed. An algorithm for the last train timetable evaluation and adjustment was presented to realize the decision support function. A decision support system for last train timetable optimization in urban rail transit network was designed and developed. An application example for Beijing metro given in this paper shows that the last train service can be improved, by using the decision support system to optimize the timetable.

Keywords: Urban rail transit, last train timetable, decision support system.

1 Introduction

Nowadays, with the city expanding, the rapidly growing traffic volume in city causes serious traffic congestion. Because of its advantages in safety, punctuality, and reliability, urban rail transit became an effective way to solve the traffic problems. In many big cities, to meet the growing demand for urban rail traffic, the transit systems have gradually developed into network-based systems from single-line-based systems. A network-based urban rail transit system improves service capabilities, on the other hand, faces more difficulties in the organization and management of urban rail transit, especially in the operation coordination on the

WIT Transactions on Information and Communication Technologies, Vol. 61, © 2014 WIT Press
www.witpress.com, ISSN 1743-3517 (on-line)
doi:10.2495/MIIT130631

whole network. In the last train period, the network accessibility differs from timetable to timetable on the lines. The operation coordination has important impact on travel convenience which achieved by transfer connection between lines in the network. Therefore, only when the last train timetables are coordinated, the last train service can be supplied better to meet the traffic demands on the rail transit network.

At home and abroad, scholars have worked a lot and obtained some research results on urban rail transit operation optimization problems. In Ref. [1], trains transfer models were constructed; route search algorithms with the target of shortest waiting time were studied in Ref. [2]; traffic assignment model based on route search was studied in Refs. [3,4]; in Ref. [5], a comprehensive evaluation method of urban rail transit network plan was studied. But in actual urban rail transit operation, decision support tools are needed for the administrators to optimize the last train timetable. Therefore, in this paper, the decision support problems of the last train timetable optimization are analyzed, the approach to construct the decision support system for last train timetable optimization in urban rail transit network is studied. A progressive method is used to schedule and reschedule the last train, combined with timetable evaluation and adjustment.

2 Analysis of computer-aided decision support problem

2.1 Decision support demands of last train timetable optimization

In actual operation of the urban rail transit, there are mainly two situations in which adjustments to the last train timetable are required. One type of adjustment is to adjust the original plan, aiming at improving the coordination of timetables on different lines. The other type is to make part adjustment to original timetable to solve the problem of huge amount of predictable passenger flow traffic.

As to the problem of urban rail transit operation plan, previous studies mainly focus on operation plan evaluation and operation plan optimization. Researchers usually construct the index system of evaluation and analysis, and use statistical methods to analyze and evaluate a given operational plan. Operation plan optimizing is to establish mathematical models with the objective of network operation coordination, and design algorithm to get the result. Generally speaking, previous research has some shortcomings in practical application. On one hand, the timetable coordination on urban rail transit network is a multiobjective optimization problem which consists of many complex factors, current research works on it are still in the theoretical stage; on the other hand, the macroscopic evaluation of the last train timetable cannot give sufficient guidance to operation optimization in actual work. Therefore, in the actual operation and management, application of previous research is limited. We combine two aspects of the problem to establish a decision support system, which provides computer-aided decision support functions for last train timetable coordination as follows:

(i) Given the last train timetable and the starting time, search routes from any original station to destination station, and output query results for routes at different moments from origination to destination.

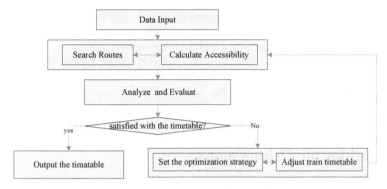

Figure 1: Multistage cycle progressive method.

(ii)   Given the last train timetable and traffic OD table, make passenger flow assignment on the network according to passenger travel choice rule, and calculate the overall satisfaction degree with traffic service in the period of last train time.

(iii)   Analyze the coordination of the last train timetable on network, according to passenger flow assignment and route search results.

(iv)   Adjust the last train timetable automatically, when optimization strategy and adjustment object was set by operator.

(v)   Analyze the coordination of the last train timetable on the network according to the route choice of passengers.

(v)   When managers want to change the last train timetable on certain lines for some reasons, adjust relevant timetable on lines automatically.

In this way, the coordinative optimization of the last train timetable can be gradually realized by adopting multistage cycle progressive method as shown in Figure 1, which includes the stage of route choice, network accessibility calculation, analysis and evaluation of timetable coordination, timetable optimization and adjustment, etc.

2.2 The main tasks of computer-aided decision support

To build a computer system and realize the computer–aided decision support process mentioned above, following research works are necessary:

(i)   Data Collection and process for decision making
    In this paper, decision support data includes passenger flow OD, rail transit passenger route choice rules, the original timetable of last train, train running parameters, and passenger movement parameters. The computer-aided decision support system should have functions as data collection, data process, data storage and data query, etc.

(ii)   Construction of the decision support model
    To adopt multistage cycle progressive method in last train timetable optimization, basic models needed to be constructed, which include the

route choice model, network accessibility calculation model, analysis and evaluation model for timetable coordination.

(iii) Human–computer interaction and decision support

With the network accessibility and network coordination, timetable of relevant last trains on the network can be calculated according to adjustment strategy set by the operator. Thus, an adjusted timetable is supplied for next stage of analysis and evaluation, and the progressive optimization is going on.

3 Algorithm for decision support

3.1 The last train passenger route choice

In this paper, a connected graph is used to describe the rail transit network. Stations on the network are defined as nodes; lines between two neighboring stations and transfers connection between two platforms are defined as arcs. Train running time, passenger walking time, or transfer waiting time is defined as weight of arc.

In urban rail transit system, many factors are taken into account in passenger route search, such as the travel time, transfer time, running distance, and comfort. Since we study passenger route choice behavior at the condition of last train time, we take the travel time as the main factor. The passenger travel time $T_{travel}^{o,d}$ from station o to station d, is the sum of $T_{trainrun}^{j}$ and T_{wait}^{i} is defined as the running time of train in section j on the route; $T_{trainrun}^{j}$ is defined as the dwell time of train at station j on the route; T_{walk}^{i} is defined as the walking time of passenger at transfer station i on the route; T_{wait}^{i} is defined as the waiting time of passenger at transfer station i on the route.

In the daytime, generally speaking, from each origination to destination, the rail transit network is accessible. But it is not the same at last train time. For the passengers who enter the urban rail transit system in the period of last train time, we can discuss the accessibility of the network in four different scenarios as follows:

The first scenario: Considering the original station and every transfer stations on the shortest route to the passenger's destination, if the passenger arrive the station earlier than the departure time of the last transfer train, for this passenger, the network with the last train timetable is accessible. This situation is called ASR (accessible with shortest route).

The second scenario: If the shortest route becomes inaccessible to the passenger who enters the urban rail transit system, and the passenger can reach one's destination on other routes, the network with the last train timetable is still accessible. This situation is called ADR (accessible with devious routes).

The third scenario: If the passenger arrives one's original station later than the departure time of the last train, the network with the last train timetable is inaccessible. This situation is called IAO (inaccessible from origination).

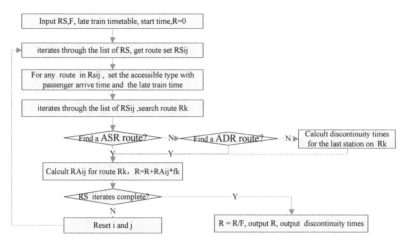

Figure 2: Algorithm process.

The fourth scenario: If the passenger arrives one's original station earlier than the departure time of the last train and arrive the transfer station later than the departure time of the last transfer train, network with the last train timetable is inaccessible. This situation is called IATS (inaccessible at transfer station).

3.2 Network accessibility calculation

Subject to last train time restrictions, the passenger's travel aim is to reach the destination or be as close to destination as possible. For a given last train operation plan, the reasonable judgment criterion is whether an accessible route can be searched in the period of late trains time and the proximity of the searched route to the shortest route in the daytime. Since there are four scenarios in accessibility analysis, in order to measure the overall influence of the last train timetable on passengers, we use relative accessibility rate R as the index to evaluate the coordination of last train timetable on different lines.

Given a traffic OD table, the Floyd route search algorithm with the last train timetable restriction is proposed to search route and calculate the relative accessibility rate of the network. Define RS as the searched feasible route set by using the Floyd algorithm; define $RS_{i,j}$ as route set from station i to station j; define $RA_{i,j}$ as the relative accessibility for passenger from station i to station j. Define F as the traffic volume of the network and f_k as the traffic on route k. The algorithm process is as shown in Figure 2.

We can calculate the relative accessibility rate $RA_{i,j}$ for passengers from station i to station j according to four different cases as follows. For the entire network, R is the weighted average of each $RA_{i,j}$.

Case ASR:

$$RA^{i,j} = 100\% \tag{1}$$

Case IAO:

$$RA^{i,j} = 0\% \tag{2}$$

Case ADR:

$$\tag{3}$$

is the travel time of the shortest route from station i to station j, $T^{i,j}_{\text{devious}}$ is the travel time of the devious route from station i to station j;

Case IATS:

$$RA^{i,j} = T^{i,j}_{transfer} \Big/ T^{i,j}_{\text{entire}} \tag{4}$$

$T^{i,j}_{transfer}$ is the travel time until passenger reach the last transfer station on the route from station i to station j, $T^{i,j}_{\text{entire}}$ is the travel time of the entire route from station i to station j.

4 Design and development of the decision support system

A last train timetable decision support system for urban rail transit network is designed and developed to achieve the decision support functions. The system can provide visualized route search results at the last train time, analyze the coordination of last train timetable on the network, and adjust relevant timetable for operation optimization according to the given adjustment strategy.

4.1 System structure and functions

The last train timetable decision support system is composed of the following five modules: network topology construction and visualization, data input and parameters management, route search and traffic flow assignment, coordination analysis and evaluation, and last train timetable adjustment. The system components and modules functions are shown in Figure 3.

4.2 Example for Beijing Metro

Taking Beijing Metro as an example, the decision support system can optimize the last train timetable by using the decision support function in the way of human–machine interaction.

4.2.1 Analysis and evaluation of timetable coordination

According to existing last train timetable, the relative accessibility rate curve of the network is as shown in Figure 4.

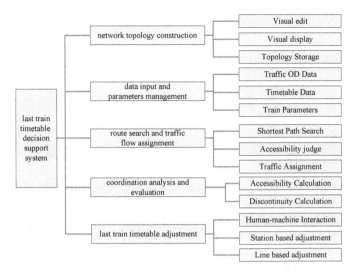

Figure 3: System components and functions.

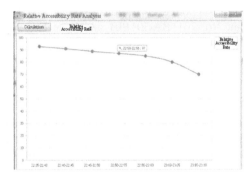

Figure 4: The relative accessibility rate curve.

4.2.2 The adjustment and optimization

Selecting line 2 as the object to study, according to the existing timetable, routes are searched for passengers whose origination stations are on the line 2.

After traffic flow assignment, the discontinuity times of stations are as shown in Figure 5. By postponing the late train to Huilongguan station on line 8 for 20 min, the discontinuity times of stations with new timetable is as shown in Figure 6, which means more passengers can be served by urban rail transit system in the period of last train time.

5 Conclusion

A decision support system for the late train timetable coordination optimization in urban rail transit network was constructed, which realizes the route search with constraint of the late train timetable, and calculation of coordination evaluation

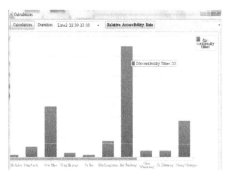 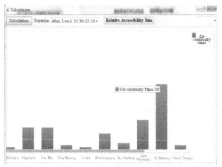

Figure 5: Existing discontinuity times.   Figure 6: New discontinuity times.

index. With human–machine interaction, late train timetable can be adjusted for optimization target.

Acknowledgments

The research work was supported by National Science and Technology Support Program under Grant No. 2011BAG01B01 and State Key Lab of Rail Traffic Control and Safety Foundation of Beijing JiaoTong University under Grant No. RCS2012ZT003.

References

[1] Xu Ruihua, Zhang Ming, Jiang Zhibin, Study on departure time domain of the first and last trains of urban mass transit network based on operation coordination. *Journal of the China Railway Society*, **30(2)**, pp. 7–11, 2008.

[2] Peng Yibing, Su Houqin, He Jinchuan, Study and implementation of algorithm for reachable multi-path transfer of rail transit's last trains. *Application Research of Computers*, **27(4)**, pp. 1373–1375, 2010.

[3] Xu Lin, He Shiwei, He Bisheng, et al., Study on urban rail transit capacity allocation based on k shortest path algorithm. *Logistics Technology*, **30(6)**, pp. 122–125, 2011.

[4] Si Bingfeng, Mao Baohua, Liu Zhili, Passenger flow assignment model and algorithm for urban railway traffic network under the condition of seamless transfer. *Journal of the China Railway Society*, **29(6)**, pp. 12–18, 2007.

[5] Zhang Yuzhao, Yan Yusong, Jiang Nan, et al., Research on the comprehensive evaluation of urban rail transit network plan with DEA method. *Journal of Railway Engineering Society*, **8**, pp. 96–99, 2010.

An anycast routing algorithm based on the combination of particle swarm optimization algorithm and genetic algorithm

Taoshen Li, Zhihui Ge, Qin Xiong
*School of Computer, Electronics and Information, Guangxi University
Nanning, China*

Abstract

The anycast routing problem (ARP) is a nonlinear combination optimization problem, which is proved to be an NP complete problem. An anycast routing algorithm which combines particle swarm optimization (PSO) and genetic algorithm (GA) is proposed to solve ARP with multiple quality of service constraints. This algorithm uses PSO algorithm as the main part of anycast routing algorithm, and its improved ideas are as follows: (1) using an update operator to make routing paths learn from each other and find the best path finally; (2) improving the convergence velocity extraordinarily by dynamically changing the inertia weight; (3) employing crossover operator and mutation operator of GA to make particles escape from local optimum and balance global and local search effectively. The experimental results show that algorithm can better express the advantages of PSO algorithm, and has faster convergence speed and can escape from local optimum.

Keywords: Anycast routing; particle swarm optimization; genetic algorithm; quality of service (QoS).

1   Introduction

Anycast is a new communication service defined in IPv6. In practice, anycast is a point-to-point flow of packets between a single client and the nearest destination server identified by an anycast address. The network of routers will then attempt to deliver the packet to the nearest server with the destination anycast address, which will then provide the desired anycast service [1]. With the wide application of anycast, anycast routing problem (ARP) has attracted much attention. Effective anycast routing algorithms are becoming important as the rapid expansion of the Internet leads to increased use of replicated servers and other anycast services. The ARP with multi-QoS (quality of service) constraints is known to be NP-complete problem [2]. So far, some heuristic algorithms have been used for solving ARP, such as genetic algorithm (GA) [3–5], ant colony algorithm [6], and so on [7].

The particle swarm optimization (PSO) is a parallel evolutionary computation technique developed by Kennedy and Eberhart [8] based on the social behavior metaphor. Though PSO is developed for continuous optimization problem initially, there have been some reported works focused on solving network routing [9]. In Ref. [10], the PSO-based anycast routing algorithm to optimize network resource and balance network load was proposed. Even though PSO algorithm has faster convergence speed in solving ARP problem, it does not possess the crossover and mutation processes used in GA and it finds the optimum solution by swarms following the best particle. Therefore, the PSO algorithm has slow convergence rate and is easily trapping in local optimum in later evolution period.

In this paper, based on PSO algorithm and GA algorithm, we propose a hybrid anycast routing algorithm to solve ARP problem with multi-QoS constraints. The paper is organized as follows. In the next section, we describe the formal definition of the anycast routing with multi-QoS constraints. Section 3 proposes an anycast routing algorithm based on the combination of PSO algorithm and GA algorithm. In Section 4, the computational simulation is made to illustrate the efficiency of the algorithm. Finally, we conclude our paper in Section 5.

2 Network models and problem notations

Generally, a network is defined as a directed graph $G=(V,E)$ with node set V and edges set E, and $|V|=n$, $|E|=m$, Edge $(i,j)\in E$ has three parameters, namely bandwidth capacity $b_{i,j}$, delay $d_{i,j}$ and cost $c_{i,j}$. For each edge (i,j), $b_{i,j}$ is known as the bandwidth capacity of the link from node i to node j, $d_{i,j}$ is the required delay when data pocket pass through the link, $pl_{i,j}$ is the packet loss rate and cost $c_{i,j}$ is the used cost of the link.

Given a graph $G=(V,E)$ and an anycast packet with anycast (destination) address A, let $G(A)=\{d_1,d_2,\ldots,\ d_q\}$ $(q<n)$ denote the group of designated recipients, $G_s(A)=\{s_1,\ s_2,\ldots,\ s_k\}$ $(k<n)$ denote the group of source hosts that may send packets with anycast address A. Each source node has a bandwidth requirement of B units, delay requirement of D units, package loss rate of PL units on each edge that it uses to send data to destination. The ARP is that of finding a set of paths $\{p_1,p_2,\ldots,\ p_k\}$ $(k<n)$ from each member of $G_s(A)$ to any member of $G(A)$. Each path p_i $(i=1,\ 2,\ldots,k)$ represents the path from the node s_i $\in G_s(A)$ to one of the member node of $G(A)$.

The functions of bandwidth, delay, package loss rate, and cost of a feasible path p can be formulated as follows:

$$\text{Bandwidth}(p) = \min b_{i,j} \quad i, j = 1,2,\cdots,n \qquad (1)$$

$$\text{Delay}(p) = \sum_{i=1}^{n} i \sum_{j=1}^{n} d_{i,j} \quad i,\, j = 1, 2, \cdots, n \tag{2}$$

$$\text{Ploss}(p) = \sum_{i=1}^{n} i \sum_{j=1}^{n} \text{pl}_{i,j} \quad i,\, j = 1, 2, \cdots, n \tag{3}$$

$$\text{Cost}(p) = \sum_{i=1}^{n} i \sum_{j=1}^{n} c_{i,j} \quad i,\, j = 1, 2, \cdots, n \tag{4}$$

The objective of QoS anycast routing algorithm is that select a feasible path which can meet the condition of bandwidth and delay constraints and its cost is minimum in all paths from $Gs(A)$ to $G(A)$. That is, selected path must simultaneous satisfy following conditions:

$$\text{Bandwidth}(p) \geq B \tag{5}$$

$$\text{Delay}(p) \leq D \tag{6}$$

$$\text{Ploss}(p) \leq \text{PL} \tag{7}$$

$$\min \sum_{i=1}^{k} \text{Cost}(p_i) \quad i = 1, 2, \cdots, k \tag{8}$$

3 Our algorithm

To solve ARP, we propose an anycast routing algorithm based on the combination of PSO algorithm and GA algorithm (PSOGA_AR). This algorithm uses PSO algorithm as the main part of anycast routing algorithm. When algorithm obtains local optimum, crossover operator, and mutation operator of GA algorithm are executed to make it escape from local optimum. PSO algorithm runs repeatedly until the existing conditions are satisfied.

3.1 Coding and initialization

Applying PSO in solving ARP problem, one key issue is how to encode anycast routing into a solution in the search space. Real number encoding is usually used by most applications in the continuous optimization problems. However, ARP is a combine optimization problem and real number encoding will make the coding and decoding process too complicated. In order to overcome the drawback of real number encoding, we use sequence coding. The path from source node to member of anycast group will be coded for a particle.

In algorithm, we use depth-first search algorithm of graph to generate initial particles directly. That is to say, we random find *Popsize* paths from source node to the anycast group as the initial population.

3.2 Adaptive inertia weight

The inertia weight ω is an important parameter in PSO algorithm, which is initialized typically in the range of [0,1]. It is regarded that a larger inertia weight facilitates global exploration and a smaller tends to facilitate local exploration to fine-tune the current search area. In order to enhance the balance of global and local search, we get the inertia weight as below:

$$\omega = (\omega_{max} - \omega_{min}) \times \exp(-\beta \times (t/T_{max})^2) + \omega_{min} \qquad (9)$$

where the value of β is determined by experience, empirically $\beta\sigma^2$ [15,20]. By using this adjustment strategy, the algorithm uses bigger inertia weight to increase global search ability in the early evolution stage. With increase in generations, inertia weight is decreased rapidly to improve local search ability and speed convergence up.

To guarantee algorithm convergence, the relationship among c_1, c_2, and ω needs to satisfy the following inequality:

$$\omega > (c_1 r_2 + c_2 r_2)/2 - 1 \qquad (10)$$

As r_1, r_2 are random numbers in the range [0,1], we take $c_1 = c_2 = 1.4962$, so $\omega > 0.4962$. Also, ω must satisfy $0 < \omega < 1$, so as to set $\omega_{max} = 0.95$, $\omega_{min} = 0.5$.

3.3 Update operator

The process of the update operator is described as follows:

```
Update_ operator （int gBest, int i）
{
Choose a subroute A in the best particle randomly;
    Choose the link clip B in one particle according to the first node and the
        final node of A, in which the first node and the final node of B is the
        same as A;
                        if (B does exist) {

    if(the fitness of A is bigger than B)
            replaces B with A; // update particle i
        else
            replaces A with B; // update best particle
        Delete duplicated nodes in the path.
    }
    else return;
}
```

3.4 Crossover operator

In later evolution stage of PSO algorithm, the convergence speed becomes significantly slower. At the same time, after the algorithm converges to a certain precision, it cannot optimize anymore. In order to maintain the algorithm diversity, improve search performance and avoid PSO algorithm plunged into local optimum, we introduce the crossover and mutation operator of GA algorithm to PSO algorithm. Because sequence coding is adopted, crossover operator can be carried out by the node. The process of the crossover operator is described as follows:

Step 1: Randomly selecting two particles in the group according to crossover probability P_c, and finding all the same nodes in them except the source node and the end node.
Step 2: Randomly choosing one common node as a cross-point, and then exchanging the part path of two particles at the back of the cross-point.
Step 3: Delete duplicated nodes in the two new particles.

3.5 Mutation operator

It had been discovered that particles among the swarm would tend to be aggregated at one or a few particular places as the PSO algorithm kept on running. In order to describe quantitatively the convergence status of the particle swarm, the variance of the population's fitness (σ^2) is introduced and defined as follows:

$$ \tag{11} $$

where n is the population size, and f_i is the ith particle's fitness value of objective function, while f_{avg} is average fitness of all particles. The parameter f is used to limit the value of σ^2, which can be determined as follows:

$$ f = \max\{1, \max|f_i - f_{avg}|\} \quad i \in [1, n] \tag{12} $$

The variable σ^2 reflects the degree of convergence among all particles. A smaller σ^2 indicates the more obvious trend that the particle swarm tends to be aggregated. If the algorithm is of premature convergence, the best position presently found by the whole swarm, namely *gBest* is out of question the local optimum. In that case, if some changes are to be made to adjust *gBest*, the particles may shift the direction and enter into other fields of search space. Therefore, when the premature convergence occurs, taking σ^2 as trigger condition, *gBest* can be updated by introducing mutation operator according to the following equation:

$$ gBest = gBest \times (1 + \tau \times 0.5) \tag{13} $$

where τ is random parameter between (0,1) to obey standard normal distribution.

3.6 Algorithm description

The PSOGA_AR algorithm is described as follows:

> *Input*: The network $G=(V,E)$, $G(A)$, $G_s(A)$, an anycast QoS request
> $R=(s,G(A),B,D,PL),r_1, r_2, c_1, c_2, \omega_{max}, \omega_{min}$,
>> set the population size is *Popsize*, the maximum number of generations
>> as *Maxgen*.
> *Output*: an optimal routing path that satisfied with the QoS request R: *gBest*
> {
>> Initialization(); // Initialize population
>> generation=0; *gBset*=0;
>> Delete the paths which do not satisfy with the bandwidth constrains;
>> // Calculate the fitness value of all particles;
>> for (i=0; i<*Popsize*; i++) {
>>> X[i]=initial position of ith particle; V[i]=initial speed of ith particle;
>>> if (X[i] better than *gBset*) *gBset*=X[i];
>> }
>> Choose *Popsize* particles by selection operator;
>> while(generation <*Maxgen*) {
>>> if (*Number* $\leqslant$ *threshold*) {
>>>> for （i=; i<*Popsize*; i++） {
>>>>> Update the position(X[i]) and speed (V[i]) of each particle;
>>>>> Calculate the fitness value of ith particle;
>>>>> if(the fitness of ith particle superior to *pBest*) *pBest*=X[i];
>>>>> if(the fitness of ith particle superior to *gBest*) *gBest*=X[i];
>>>>> else Update operator for particle i and the best particle;
>>>> } }
>>> else {
>>>> Crossover operator;
>>>> Mutation operator;
>>> }
>>> Calculate group fitness variance σ^2 using formulas (11) and (12);
>>> if (algorithm satisfies convergence condition) break;
>>> Update *gBest* according to formula (13);
>> }
>> Output *gBest*. // That is optimal path.
> }

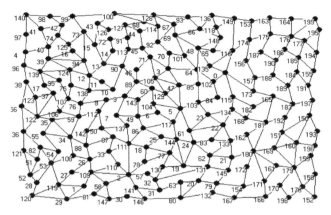

Figure 1: Network topological diagram.

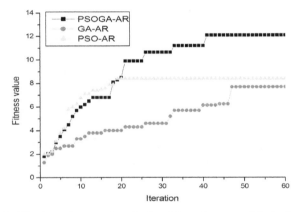

Figure 2: The best fitness of each algorithm changes with the iterations.

4 The algorithm performance analysis

In order to evaluate performance of routing algorithm, we create random network graph with 200 nodes as shown in Figure 1. In Figure 1, the each link delay takes a value in [5–10] at random, each bandwidth takes a value in [25–60], each cost takes a value in [3–15], and each package loss rate takes a value in [1–4].

Assume $PopSize$=30, $Maxgen$=40, c_1=c_2=1.4962, r_1=r_2=0.5, λ=0.4, ω_{max}=0.95, ω_{min}=0.5, δ=10^{-4}, σ_d^2=1; f_c=0.6, f_d=0.3, f_{pl}=0.1. Suppose a QoS routing request is R=(S,$G(A)$,30,80, 30), where $G(A)$={198,100,124,122,29,188}, S={103,83}.

In experiment, we have compared the PSOGA_AR algorithm with the GA-based anycast routing algorithm (GA-AR) [3] and the PSO-based anycast routing algorithm (PSO_AR) [10] by analyzing the best fitness of each algorithm changes with the iterations and their routing time.

Figure 2 shows the evolutionary situation of the optimal particle's fitness value of three algorithms with the iterations. Experimental result indicates that the

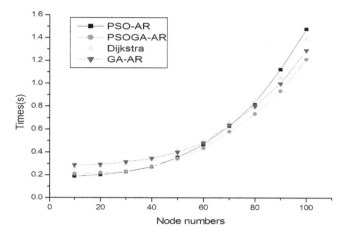

Figure 3: Routing time comparison among PSOGA-AR and other algorithms.

PSOGA_AR algorithm not only has faster convergence than GA-AR algorithm but also can overcome the disadvantage of PSO algorithm to jump out of the local optimum.

Figure 3 gives the run time comparison results of finding an optimal path among classical Dijkstra's algorithm, GA-AR algorithm, PSO-AR algorithm and PSOGA-AR algorithm in the way of anycast communication. We conduct simulation experiments on 10–100 nodes, respectively, and then compare various performance parameters under the same simulation condition. Obviously, the run times of PSOGA-AR algorithm to find an optimal path is fewer than other three algorithms.

5 Conclusion

In the proposed algorithm, an updated operator is used to solve the problem, in which the routing paths can learn from other better paths, and a dynamical method is applied to computing inertia weight to improve the convergence velocity extraordinarily. When algorithm plunged into local optimum, the crossover operator and mutation operator of GA are employed to make particles escape from local optimum and maintain particle's diversity. The experimental results show that the algorithm is a feasible and effective. It not only converges fast but also can escape from the local optimum and search the global optimum finally.

Acknowledgments

The research work was supported by National Natural Science Foundation of China under Grant No. 61363067.

References

[1] X.N. Wang, A scheme for solving anycast scalability in IPv6. *International Journal of Network Management*, **18(8)**, pp. 315–322, 2008.

[2] W.J. Jia, D. Xuan, W. Zhao, Integrated routing algorithms for anycast messages. *IEEE Communications Magazine*, **38(1)**, pp. 48–53, 2000.

[3] T.S. Li, S.Q. Chen, Y. Chen, et al., Research on anycast routing algorithm with multiple QoS parameters constraint. *Journal of Communication and Computer*, **2(4)**, pp. 54–60, 2005.

[4] E.R. Silva, P.R. Guardieiro, An efficient genetic algorithm for anycast routing in delay/disruption tolerant networks. *IEEE Communications Letters*, **14(4)**, pp. 315–317, 2010.

[5] Chun Zhu, Min Jin, An anycast routing algorithm based on genetic algorithm. *WSEAS Transactions on Computers*, **8(1)**, pp. 113–122, 2009.

[6] M. Xiao, T.S. Li, An efficient ant colony algorithm for QoS anycast routing. In: *Proceedings of 4th International Conference on Computer Science and Education*, IEEE Computer Society, Nanning, China, pp. 135–138, 2009.

[7] K. Walkowiak, Heuristic algorithm for anycast flow assignment in connection-oriented networks. In: *Proceedings of 5th International Conference on Computational Science*, LNCS, Springer-Verlag, Atlanta, GA, pp. 1092–1095, 2005.

[8] J. Kennedy, R.C. Eberhart, Particle swarm optimization. In: *Proceedings of IEEE Conference on Neural Networks*, IEEE, Piscataway, NJ, pp. 1942–1948, 1995.

[9] J. Wang, X. Wang, M. Huang, An intelligent QoS multicast routing algorithm under inaccurate information. In: *International Conference of Computational Intelligence and Security*, IEEE Computer Society, Guangzhou, China, pp. 1073–1077, 2006.

[10] M. Yang, T.S. Li, An RDO-PSO algorithm for anycast routing with multi-QoS constraints. In: *Proceedings of 4th International Conference on Computer Science and Education*, IEEE Computer Society, Nanning, China, pp. 376–379, 2009.

An algorithm of inspecting airline luggage dimension based on cube-fitting

Qingji Gao, Taiwen Li, Qijun Luo
Robotics Institute, Civil Aviation University of China, Tianjin, 300300, China

Abstract

The automatic inspecting of luggage dimension is one of the problems in the self-service baggage check-in system. To solve this problem, a laser scanning system of luggage dimension measurement was constructed and an algorithm of checking airline luggage dimension based on cube-fitting was proposed. In the preprocess, the background and noise information was filtered out from the point cloud which was captured by scanning the luggage contour. Then the point cloud was projected to the horizontal plane, and its minimum bounding rectangle is obtained through the searching method of rotating point cloud based on its center. Secondly, the point cloud was projected to the perpendicular line and was segmented by an adaptive threshold. The height of luggage handles and baggage tags was cut, while the actual height was left. Finally, many measuring experiments of different baggage were repeated many times to verify the affection of this algorithm.

Keywords: check-in system, cube-fitting, MBR, adaptive threshold.

1   Introduction

With the promotion and application of civil self-service, 21% of travelers have used self-service up to 2012 in China. It saves about one hundred million yuan for the civil aviation every year and greatly reduces the passengers' check-in time while waiting in line. However, passengers with baggage still need to queue for the baggage handling. The self bag drop system is an automated system which is developed to solve the problem. Automatically checking whether the airline luggage dimension meets the Civil Aviation Authority (CAA) and airlines requirements is the key issues of the system which must be solved.

WIT Transactions on Information and Communication Technologies, Vol. 61, © 2014 WIT Press
www.witpress.com, ISSN 1743-3517 (on-line)
doi:10.2495/MIIT130661

The CAA published the article 37 about baggage handling (domestic): the size of signal handling baggage can not exceed $L_{max} \times W_{max} \times H_{max}$. If the baggage exceeds the above provisions, it cannot be handled unless the carrier permits. However, it can not be processed in self bag drop system, so the traveler must go to the artificial baggage counter.

Stereo vision and laser ranging are used to inspect airline luggage dimension. As the laser ranging is more stable than stereo vision which is easily affected by the external environment, so this paper intends to adopt a 2D laser range finder to inspect airline baggage dimension. Reference [1] adopted line fitting in segment to recognize obstacles and creates a flat map; reference [2] applied a 2D laser scanner to dynamically measure metro rail gauge. They all belong to Mobile Laser Ranging, but did not give the 3D model.

This paper is proposed by using laser rangefinder to scan moving baggage and obtain the surface position information of the luggage. Theoretical analysis and experimental results are proposed based on single- and two-plane laser system layout. Firstly, the point cloud data is projected to cube horizontal plane and longitudinal direction. The method of minimum bounding rectangle (MBR) is applied to obtain baggage length and width, and baggage's height is got through the method of adaptive threshold and normal distribution. Bags can be classified based on length, width, and height (LWH), which give the inspection results of baggage's specification. This method is provided with the feature of high accuracy, good stability, strong practicability, and can rapidly inspect whether various airline luggage dimensions meet the requirement of self bag drop system.

2 System structure and principles

Self bag drop equipment is shown in Figure 1. Left is luggage channel section, and the right is check-in system. The luggage channel section is comprised by the baggage drop zone, the scanning area and the detection zone. The baggage drop zone is outside the entrance, baggage scanning area is between the entrance and the shelter blinds, and the luggage detection zone is within the blocking curtain. Baggage passes through these three areas in a proper sequence. A 2D laser is installed above the baggage scanning area. Baggage's surface will be scanned in every cycle when it gets into the scanning area. After the baggage is completely in the detection zone, the 3D laser data of the baggage outer surface is got.

Figure 1: Self bag drop equipment.

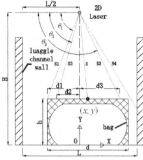

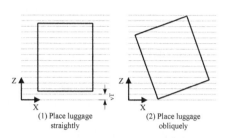

Figure 2: Single-planar laser installation diagram.

Figure 3: Laser scanning diagram for the luggage surface which placing straightly and obliquely.

2.1 Installation of single planar laser

The planar laser detection system layout consists of single- and multi-planar laser systems. In order to reduce the detection blind, the laser in single-plane laser system (single laser system for short in the following) is installed in the luggage channel above H, and can evenly cover the luggage channel, shown in Figure 2. The luggage channel's width is L, and the laser scanning cycle is T. The point below the laser on the belt is as the origin, the cross-section of horizontal is assumed as X direction, the longitudinal is Y direction, and the belt forward direction is Z direction. In Figure 2, some key laser beams like S_1–S_4 are drawn. The angles of S_1–S_4 to X direction are respectively θ_1, θ_2, θ_3, and θ_4. S_1 laser beam exactly hits the baggage's outer edges. S_2 is the next laser beam of S_1. S_3 is the last laser beam beating on the baggage. S_4 is the next laser beam of S_3.

There is a point (x,y) on the luggage surface. The distance that the laser measures to the point is S, while the angle of this laser beam is θ, then:

$$\begin{cases} x = -S\cos\theta \\ y = H - S\sin\theta \\ z = \int v\,dt \end{cases} \qquad (1)$$

Among them, v is the belt surface moving speed and t is the time of the baggage in scanning zone. Baggage edge points which constitute baggage boundary line are extracted from the laser point cloud data, and then calculate length and width. The convex-hull on the luggage surface, such as handle, will not record to the effective height of the luggage which needs an appropriate method to filter.

2.2 Error analysis for signal laser system

Error analysis includes length, width, and height error analysis. The length measurement error primarily depends on the laser scanning cycle time and the moving speed of the belt. Two cases of the placing mode of the luggage are supposed: first is straight, i.e., $\phi \approx 0$. The luggage lateral direction and belt moving direction are substantially parallel, as shown in Figure 3(1). The red lines are laser scanning lines in the picture, and the black rectangle is baggage surface profile; second is oblique, i.e., $|\phi| >> 0$. There is a larger angle between the luggage lateral direction and belt moving direction, as shown in Figure 3(2).

Two-dimensional laser scans once every period of T, while the baggage moves a distance of $vT \times T$. If the luggage is placed straightly, front and rear edges of the luggage may not be scanned. The maximum error is $2 \bullet vT$ in this situation. Although the forefront and final end of oblique luggage may not be detected, four sides of it can be scanned. By the fitting of minimum bounding rectangle, the measurement error will be smaller.

Width measurement error mainly depends on laser rangefinder's angular resolution $\Delta\theta$. On the same height, the distance Δd between the adjacent laser beams is larger when closing to luggage channel wall. So the measurement error is larger. As shown in Figure 3, the luggage height is h, width is d. If the laser beam of S_3 just hits the edge of the baggage, there are:

$$
\begin{cases}
\theta_3 = \dfrac{\pi}{2} + \arctan\left(\dfrac{d-d_1}{H-h}\right) \\
d_2 = (H-h)/\tan\theta_2 \\
d_3 = -(H-h)\tan\theta_3
\end{cases}
\tag{2}
$$

So the maximum measurement error of width is:

$$
\Delta d_{max} = d - d_2 - d_3 = d - \frac{(H-h)}{\tan(\theta_1 + \Delta\theta)} + (H-h)\tan(\theta_1 + n\Delta\theta)
\tag{3}
$$

The measurement error of height depends on the detecting accuracy of the laser. If the surface of a luggage is absolutely smooth, the height is $y \in [h - Er, h + Er]$, where Er is the detecting accuracy of the laser. So the height laser data satisfies the normal distribution [6]. If not flat, the highest point will also meet the normal distribution. Then the maximum error is height Er.

2.3 Installation of dual planar laser

The paper only studies the dual planer laser system (following is referred to dual laser system) in multi-planar laser system. In order to reduce the measurement error of width and length in the single laser system and improve the accuracy of height measurement, a dual laser system is designed. This system integrates the characteristic of small measurement error for oblique luggage in single laser system. Two laser rangefinders are installed vertically to scan, and the angles to X axis are separately α and β, shown in Figure 4. Because the left

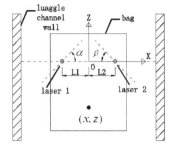

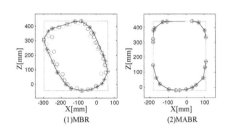

Figure 4: Installation of dual planar laser top view.

Figure 5: Method of minimum bounding rectangle.

and right laser respectively inspect left and right luggage channel, so it will reduce the measurement error of luggage width.

In laser 1 system, there is a point (x,z) on the luggage surface, so:

$$\begin{cases} x_1 = -S_1 \cos\theta_1 \cos\alpha - L_1 \\ y_1 = H - S_1 \sin\theta_1 \\ z_1 = \int v\,dt_1 + S_1 \cos\theta_1 \sin\alpha \end{cases} \quad (4)$$

In laser 2 system, there are:

$$\begin{cases} x_2 = -S_2 \cos\theta_2 \cos\beta + L_2 \\ y_2 = H - S_2 \sin\theta_2 \\ z_2 = \int v\,dt_2 - S_2 \cos\theta_2 \sin\beta \end{cases} \quad (5)$$

Firstly, two groups of laser data must be matched and coincided to get the full range of laser point cloud data of the baggage. Secondly, the edge point of the data will be found out like the single laser system to calculate the length and width. Meanwhile, the height data is the superposition from two laser data, so it is more stable and reliable.

3 Cube-fitting of laser point cloud

Airline luggage dimension is inspected with the maximum size, so this paper adopts the maximum size for luggage cube-fitting to get the minimum enclosing cube from the 3D laser data. In order to reduce the computational complexity, cube-fitting is transformed to the horizontal plane and longitudinal fitting. The method of minimum area bounding rectangle is used in horizontal plane.

There are many noises in laser point cloud data, so irrelevant data with the luggage needs to be filtered out firstly. The coordinates of the point cloud data are transformed according to Eq. (1). And finally the leftmost and rightmost points in each group are as the left and right boundary points of the luggage. If it is a dual laser system, coordinates are converted by Eqs. (4) and (5).

3.1 Measuring length and width with the method of minimum bounding rectangle

The maximum length and width dimensions of the luggage can be settled by the method of minimum bounding rectangle. Its idea is as follows:

Step 1: Seek out boundary points of the maximum convex polygon and make them as the new boundary points.
Step 2: With the coordinate origin as the center, rotate the coordinate system in fixed order and save the rotation.
Step 3: Calculate and save the area and number of minimum bounding rectangle. The number is correspondence with the rotation angle.
Step 4: Compare the area resulting from minimum bounding rectangle, where the smallest area bounding rectangle is the minimum area bounding rectangle.

There are some boundary points of a soft luggage in dual laser system, as shown in Figure 5(1) after coinciding two laser's data. Among them, the pink dot is the laser 1 data, the blue dot is the laser 2 data, and the red bounding rectangle is the minimum bounding rectangle. In order to reduce the computational complexity of the software, the maximum convex polygon is calculated firstly to obtain the new boundary points. The solution of minimum bounding rectangle is based on them. Obviously, the minimum bounding rectangle in left picture is not the minimum area bounding rectangle. So the way of rotating the coordinate system is employed in searching for the minimum bounding rectangle area. The result of MBR is shown in Figure 5(2).

3.2 Height measurement with adaptive threshold method

Baggage surfaces have different shapes such as flat, oblique, circular. Data distribution Θ of height direction differs from bag to bag. If the surface of baggage is absolutely smooth, the height data obeys normal distribution with standard deviation Er due to laser measurement error. For oblique and circle luggage, the height data of the highest point also meets this distribution. In this paper, the measurement error of laser rangefinder Er is 10 mm in [0, 1000 mm].

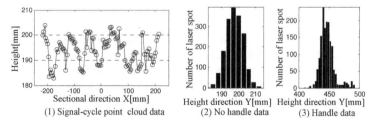

(1) Signal-cycle point cloud data   (2) No handle data   (3) Handle data

Figure 6: Laser height data of a flat baggage surface.

The height data from scanning a flat baggage surface by the laser rangefinder in a single cycle is shown in Figure 6(1). The statistical distribution of laser data for the luggage surface is shown in Figure 6(2), where the vertical axis is the number of the laser spot and the data obeys $N(195.3489\ 5.4502^2)$ normal distribution. And the actual baggage height of h is 195 mm. The measurement error is small.

Laser data of luggage surface will appear the interference data of convex-hull which needs to be filtered. The luggage handle data is choosed instead of it. When baggage keeps upright and the handle is at the highest point, the laser data is shown in Figure 6(3). There is another peak. The size of a general baggage handle is as the threshold. After filtering the handle data by the method of threshold the laser data obeys $N(446.6188\ 14.5562^2)$ normal distribution. The actual baggage height of h is 440 mm and the error is within 10 mm.

Due to the uncertainty of convex-hull's size and position, the value of the threshold needs to adaptively adjust. The strategy is as follows:

Step 1: Judge that convex-hull is in the distribution of baggage height data Θ.
Step 2: If there is no convex-hull, take maximum of Θ as the threshold τ. On the contrary, search Θ from big to small to seek out the right side of normal distribution in effective height and set it as τ.
Step 3: Data that less than τ is the luggage data and the other data is convex-hull which must be filtered.
Step 4: The highest valid value of baggage is acquired according to normal distribution principle of the laser data.

4 Results and analysis of experiments

4.1 Experiments of the measurement for luggage length and width

There is a conventional luggage of length $540 \times$ width $440 \times$ height 195 mm^3 taken as the measurement object. Experiments of length and width measurement are done contrastively based on single and dual laser systems and measurements are shown in Figure 7. The angle between luggage side and the Z direction is assumed as ϕ. The placement of $\phi = 0$ and $\phi = 30°$ are different. Obviously, the error of $\phi = 0$ is larger than that of $\phi = 30°$ in single laser system. But the error is very small when the baggage is placed obliquely and is less than 10 mm with arbitrary placing in dual laser system.

4.2 Experiment of the measurement of luggage height

In dual laser system, 10 groups of height data on four different shapes of luggage measured by normal distribution are shown in Figure 8. Among them, bag 1, bag 2, and bag 3 are white, black, and brown baggages. Their surfaces are flat. Bag 4 is a soft luggage and the handle of bags 3 and 4 are manually set on the above. Every average error is less than 10 mm from the table and the color has little affection on errors. The algorithm won't be affected by placing mode and placing

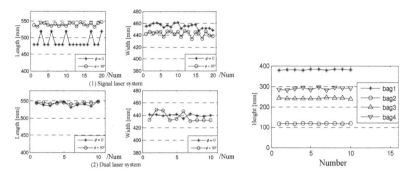

Figure 7: Measurement of length and width in single and dual laser systems.

Figure 8: Measurement of luggage height.

angle because point cloud data of the luggage surface is solved by statistical analysis. And the convex-hull data of luggage surface can be effectively eliminated and the height measurement is more real and effective.

5 Conclusions

The algorithm of checking airline luggage based on the cube-fitting is proposed in this paper. Theoretical analysis and experimental results are given with the system layout of single- and dual-plane laser. Firstly, the cube-fitting is projected to cube horizontal plane and longitudinal direction. The method of minimum bounding rectangle is used in horizontal plane for obtaining the outermost boundary of luggage. The maximum effective height of the luggage is got in longitudinal direction through the adaptive threshold method and the normal distribution method. The algorithm is efficient and has a fast response. It can stably and quickly inspect whether the dimension of various airline luggage meets the requirements of the bag drop system.

Acknowledgments

The research work was supported by Tianjin science and technology plan key projects under Grant No. 12JCZDJC34200.

References

[1] Mohammad Norouzi, Mostafa Yaghobi, Mohammad Rezai Siboni, Mahdi Jadaliha, Recursive line extraction algorithm from 2d laser scanner applied to navigation a mobile robot. *International Conference on Robotics and Biomimetics*, **3**, pp. 2127–2132, 2008.

[2] Qiang Yang, Jianhui Lin, Track gauge dynamic measurement based on 2D laser displacement sensor. *International Conference on Mechanic Automation and Control Engineering*, **4(4)**, pp. 5473–5476, 2011.

Discussion on problems existed in the electronic bidding information system and countermeasures

Xiaopeng Xie[1], Yunyi Li[2] and Lun Gao[3]
[1]*The Department of Bidding Office, Chongqing University of Science and Technology, Chongqing, China*
[2]*The Department of Continuing Education, Chongqing University of Science and Technology, Chongqing, China*
[3]*The Department of Research, Chongqing University of Science and Technology, Chongqing, China*

Abstract

Electronization of procurement operating link for bidding is one of the necessary core contents for electronization by government procurement. This paper analyzes the current situation for construction of electronic bidding system, analyzes five existing problems and discusses the specific thought for construction of electronic bidding system in the whole flow.

Keywords: electronic bidding, information system, countermeasure.

1 Introduction

Within recent years, along with issue and implementation of such relevant laws as Bidding and Tendering Law and Government Procurement Law, although the bidding and procurement work is standardized and mature increasingly, such obvious problems as low efficiency, complex procedure, region limitation, and resource wasting exist. In order to comply with the bidding electronization tendency, the governmental competent authorities and bidding execution authorities have performed some active attempts on the basis of traditional work and have achieved better effect to get wide attention from society and better evaluation. The starting of electronic bidding system in our country is later, in order to realize the electronization in the whole process of bidding, tendering, bid opening, and evaluation of bid, the rudiment has not been formed currently. Meanwhile, on the aspect of legal force for electronic documents, the effective means and corresponding system guarantee still lack, in addition, such bottleneck and puzzles as popularization and application as well as deepening construction are facing [1, 2].

2 Advantage of electronic bidding

The electronic bidding is a kind of coordinative working mode to conduct the bidding business based on the support of network information technology. The characteristics of real time and openness of internet break the regional difference and space limitation and save plenty of time and economic cost for people; meanwhile, the information is communicated timely to enhance the transparency of bidding process and accelerate the integral progress of bidding activity. The electronic bidding also solidifies the system design and flow standard through information technology means so as to desire to standardize the operating procedure, avoid the execution deviation, and reduce the project risk.

2.1 Eliminate the space–time barrier and build the uniform bidding market

An important purpose of bidding system is to establish the market order with fair competition and obtain the optimal economic efficiency through sufficient competition among bidders so as to realize the reasonable allocation of resources, build uniform open bidding market with orderly bidding. Due to openness of market, while breaking the physical space–time barrier, the electronic bidding platform enhances the information transparency, the bidder can obtain the tendering information through the network and participate in the bidding activity so as to improve the work efficiency and reduce the cost. The electronic bidding sufficiently reflects the fair, public, and just competition principle and restraint the occurrence of regional protectionism, industrial monopoly, and administrative intervention actions executed by each local government and local department.

2.2 Reduce the rent-seeking space and build sunny bidding environment

Through utilizing the network information technology, the electronic bidding electronizes and digitizes the bidding links so as to realize the resource sharing and standardize the operation so that the transaction behavior of bidding realizes the transformation from dispersion, concealing and disorder to concentration, openness and standardization so as to avoid producing the possibility of rent seeking due to asymmetric information. The platformization business operation is performed through serving the network as the carrier for electronic bidding so as to reduce the space of flexible operation; meanwhile, various operations remain the trace and log to be more beneficial for supervision and inspection after events and maximally realize the sunny trading.

2.3 Accumulate the basic tendering information and establish the tendering resource information base

In the traditional bidding activity, the bidding data can only be managed through such modes as manual registration and re-logging. Not only due to repeated laboring but also due to desynchronized data updating and poor data relevancy, the human resources are wasted as well as the business and management are detached. Relevant information and data are acquired by the electronic bidding platform directly from the business flow, close data relevancy and strong linkage effect. The preciseness of bidding process ensures the reliability of data information and forms the bidding information through accumulation for a period of time to be beneficial for analyzing and summarizing the tendering procurement work by the tendering authority and improve the business management level as well as provide the effective data support for governmental supervision department to grasp the industrial developing current situation and tendency in real time and scientifically perform the macroeconomic decision-making.

3 Analysis on construction difficulties for electronic bidding system

The application for most electronic bidding system mainly concentrates on the issue for bidding announcement currently, the on-line downloading is realized partially for bidding documents, meanwhile, a small part of tendering authorities realize the electronic auxiliary bid evaluation. The structuring compilation for bidding documents and tendering documents in the core of bidding work as well as automatic relevancy comparison for contents of these two documents in the process of review still lack the perfect electronization scheme. Such problems as network safety and legal effect for electronic bidding are also difficulties during construction.

3.1 Excessive simplification or complex operation for bidding documents

The compilation of bidding documents is a critical work on the stage of bidding. In the bidding document, the organization form of whole bidding, responding mode of tendering as well as principle and method for bid evaluation and bid determining are specified, which is the basis of orderly developing the whole bidding procurement activity. Currently, the compilation of bidding documents covers such two modes: firstly, Word file is directly uploaded onto the system. After the file compiling personnel from tendering authority completes the compilation for tendering file through such Word processing software, the tendering document is served as integrity to upload onto the system and convert it into document with unchangeable version, the bidder may download and read it via remote network, while reviewing, the expert may also directly read it. This kind of operation mode is simpler for the compiling personnel; however, since the tendering document is not processed via structuralization, the application and mode aren't different from the ones of paper document. Meanwhile, in order to realize the electronization of review process, the review clauses and scoring standard should also be reset in the bid evaluation system, not only the labor is repeated but also the error omission inconsistent with tendering document are also easily caused. Secondly, the mode that the tendering documents are separated and reassembled via structuralization. The file compiling personnel from tendering authority logs the contents of tendering document into the compiling system of tendering file item by item, various parameters and clauses required in the process of bid evaluation are assembled by the system to automatically generate the electronic bidding document after all contents are completed by filling in decomposition. In order to ensure that the output format of tendering document is standardized and complete, the file compiling personnel is required to set one by one and log-in the title, style, numbering, and contents in each part of tendering document, the operation is more complicated, generally, the professional technicians are required for assistance. Although this kind of mode realizes the structuralization of document, however, due to excessive complicated operation, the operation efficiency is reduced not to be beneficial for popularization.

3.2 Insufficient standardization for documenting of bidding documents

The documenting of bidding documents is an important link to respond the requirement of tendering document, show the strength and achievements of bidder, and decide the success and failure of tendering documents. Since many bidders lack the bidding experiences, the bidding is deemed as the ineffective bidding generally because the bidding documents don't respond the corresponding critical clauses so as to cause the waste of bidding cost and reduce the bidding competitiveness. While standardizing the bidding work, the electronic bidding system also faces the difficulties that must be overcome. There are two main kinds of mode to compile the electronic bidding documents currently, firstly, mode of only maintaining the technical parameters on bidding. Based on the product parameters and scope required to be filled and reported in the bidding system and in combination with own product characteristics, the bidder shall perform the response one by one, and the system automatically generates the corresponding form. This kind of mode is applicable for competitive items of products regarding supply of goods in the agreement to solve the classification and review problem on technology and price for over thousand kinds of bidding products, however, for commercial part, it is still required to compile the paper files. Although this kind of method improves the efficiency to some extent, however, the commercial part of bidding document can't be standardized; meanwhile, paper documents exist massively so as not reach the purpose of saving the cost. Secondly, the mode that the attachment is uploaded to splice the bidding documents; Based commercial on the format of bidding document specified by the bidding document, the bidder fills in the response contents for corresponding commercial part, and the technical documents shall be served as the attachment and uploaded onto the corresponding location in the system in form of picture or document, finally, these two parts are spliced as the electronic bidding document. This kind of mode may better standardize the file documenting of bidder and can't produce incomplete response phenomenon basically. However, there are obvious shortcomings simultaneously, firstly, the format of edition files assembled and spliced by many attachments is disorder comparatively not to benefit the integral reading and printing output; secondly, due to difference of own condition of bidder and personnel quality, the uploaded pictures are excessively huge or unclear; thirdly, redundant attachments cause that the time of generating the electronic files and inducing into bidding system is much longer. Above problems easily cause inconsistent electronic document and paper document, meanwhile, if there are many bidders, the inducing speed of electronic bidding documents may affect the speed of bid opening.

3.3 Safety problem restricts the development of electronic bidding

As a kind of network information system, non-ignored safety potential risk and problems exist in the electronic bidding system are easy to be assaulted by cracker and virus so as to cause such serious consequence as information stealing, changing and deleting and bring about the harm to bidding work as well as affect the smooth operation of project. How to ensure the safety, truth, reliability, and confidentiality of information in the electronic bidding system is a facing challenge to popularize the electronization bidding. Meanwhile, in the existing relevant bidding laws and regulations, there are not definite legal force and safety requirements on electronic bidding document.

4 Construction thoughts for electronic bidding system in the whole flow

The electronic bidding system should realize the electronization, programming and standardization management for the whole flow from compiling of bidding document, issue of tendering announcement, on-line downloading for bidding document to bid opening and bid evaluation so as to provide an integration operating platform.

4.1 Optimize and simplify the work procedure

The compilation for tendering documents is divided into such four steps as introduction of general template, importing of technical documents, parameter requirement setting, and assembling for generated files. Firstly, based on the types and characteristics of tendering project, a pre-set general framework template is selected, this template may be maintained and managed by the dedicated person designated by the tendering authority, including the framework of bidding document and partial general contents, in addition, partial non-editable and unmodified contents may be set. Secondly, for complicated technical documents and contents those are inadvisable to be formatted, the file compiling personnel firstly compiles them properly via Word processing software and then imports them into the system as well as converts into version files via virtual printing. Thirdly, pertaining to contents required to be applied in the successive links, the planning and setting are performed via the system to generate the edition files. Finally, above three parts are automatically assembled as electronic tendering documents. This kind of compilation mode realizes the structuralization of critical contents in the tendering document so as to complete the planning and setting for successive bidding and link of bid evaluation as well as eliminates unnecessary repeative operation. Meanwhile, through deepening application of template, not only the efficiency is improved but also the process is standardized.

4.2 Standardize the compilation of bidding documents and improve the bidding efficiency

The compilation of bidding documents is divided into compilation for commercial documents, filling and reporting for technical parameters, unloading for technical response documents as well as setting for corresponding scoring items. Firstly, through Word processing software inlaid into the compilation system of bidding documents, fill in the contents of commercial part. Secondly, based on the bidding format specified in the electronic tendering documents, fill in and report the technical parameters and response contents. Thirdly, upload the technical response documents inadvisable to be logged in formatting into the system and convert them as edition files via virtual printing. Finally, set the corresponding relationship between contents of bidding documents and each scoring item in the tendering document to be consulted and reviewed by the review expert. After completing the above various operations, the system automatically integrates and generates the electronic bidding documents. This kind of mode maximally simplifies bidder's operation and realizes the automatic relevancy comparison of contents for tendering documents and bidding documents so as to improve the efficiency and standardization degree for bidding and tendering operation.

4.3 Full electronization in the processing of bid opening reflects "three justice" principle

Bid opening is an important link to reflect the openness of bidding and tendering, mainly including such functions as check-in of bidder, bid announcement, and automatic generation of opening meeting. Firstly, prior to deadline of bidding, the operator should import the bidding data package and perform the electronic check-in in the system. Secondly, after commencing the bid opening, the system automatically shifts onto the bid opening interface and log in such relevant information on bidding price in the system. For items with supply of goods in the agreement, the system realizes the bid announcement in the modes of showing such relevant information as product price and configuration. Thirdly, extract the project information and automatically generate the host address of bid opening meeting based on the template and standardize the operation of tendering authority on some extent.

4.4 Express and correct review by electronic bid evaluation for system

Bid evaluation is a link that the review expert reviews and rates the bidding documents as well as recommends the successful bidder candidates based on the tendering documents and the detailed rules and regulations of scoring, the function realization for this part is not so complicated, mainly, the interface should be simple and easy to be understood so as to facilitate the operation by expert. Firstly, the expert may consult the corresponding contents in the electronic bidding documents and may mark in the system. Secondly, after completing the scoring, the system may automatically perform the automatic summarization and calculate the scoring and ranking condition in combination with the price scoring. Thirdly, extract relevant project information and coordinate the template to automatically generate the bid evaluation report. Through system scoring, the error rate for expert scoring and summarization are reduced greatly via system scoring, the work for operator from bidding authority is simplified. Meanwhile, the paper document is not required to be consulted any longer so as to avoid ineffective bidding caused by such problem as unclear contents in the bidding document.

4.5 Application of digital certificate technology so as to ensure the information safety

The healthy development of electronic bidding requires the guarantee by legal regulations and safety means. Based on Electronic Signature Law, integrate the digital certificate in the electronic bidding system and realize the identity authentication of users in the process of realizing the bidding and tendering, electronic signature of data information as well as data encryption so as to ensure the determinacy of user identity, confidentiality, integration, tamper-proofing, and non-repudiation of information transmission so as to ensure that the responsibility is clear and distinct as well as traceable in the process of bidding and tendering so as to effectively solve the legal force problem for electronic bidding and tendering behavior.

References

[1] Gao Yan, Tendering procurement and bid evaluation method. *Petrochemical Engineering Economics*, **3(4)**, pp. 52–54, 2012.
[2] Wu Yufeng, Liu Yan, Difference and advantage between e-commerce procurement and traditional procurement. *Digital Chemicals*, **4(4)**, pp. 73–75, 2011.

Design of FSK modulation system based on virtual instrument

Xiaoqi Yin
Huaiyin Institute of Technology, Huai'an Jiangsu, 223003, China

Abstract

Based on analyzing the modulation and demodulation principle for 4FSK signal, this paper discusses a modulation solution for 4FSK signal based on LabVIEW. In the simulating process, the system is combined of many modules, such as control gate, bandpass filter, dimension converter, sampling, and decision. Every modulation and demodulation submodules can be called each other, and all of them form the communication software package. The module diagram and simulation results of the 4FSK system are given, and it indicate the proposed FSK modulation system diagram is effective and feasible.

Keywords: FSK, virtual instrument, LabVIEW, modulation, subVI, simulation.

1 Introduction

FSK (Frequency-shift keying) is a kind of digital modulation technique which is widely used in the transmission of information. It uses discrete values of baseband digital signal to control the carrier frequency characteristics and transmit information and has good anti-noise and anti-decay properties [1, 2]. In the time of digital communications, the signal is transmitted on the data line, such as the telephone line, network cable, fiber or wireless medium, the main use of FSK modulation method, which converts the binary data into an FSK signal for transmission.

LabVIEW is a kind of development software based on virtual instrument technology, instead of programming language, it uses graphical mode to program and fundamentally updates the instrument concept. In this paper, it is used the design of subVI module based on LabVIEW, and each module in the modulation and demodulation process has been designed of a corresponding subVI, such as control gate, bandpass filtering, signal conversion, sampling, and judgment, all of them form the software package, then the digital communication system can be established. It introduces the principle of 4FSK modulation and the structure of every module, every modulation and demodulation modules can be called each other, and all of them form the communication software package. The module diagram and simulation results of the 4FSK system are given.

2 FSK modulation and demodulation

In the process of binary digital modulation, if the sinusoidal carrier frequency change with binary baseband signal at f_1 and f_2, then it forms binary frequency shift keying signal (2FSK signal). Binary frequency shift keying signal can be considered as two different carrier signal superimposed on the binary amplitude shift keying [3, 4]. If the symbol "1" corresponds to the carrier frequency f_1, symbol "0" corresponds to the carrier frequency f_2, the binary frequency shift keying signal in time domain expression is:

$$e_{2FSK}(t) = \left[\sum_n a_n g(t-nT_S)\right]\cos(\omega_1 t + \phi_n) + \left[\sum_n b_n g(t-nT_S)\right]\cos(\omega_2 t + \theta_n) \qquad (1)$$

wherein, $a_n = \begin{cases} 0, & \text{Transmission probability } P \\ 1, & \text{Transmission probability} 1-P \end{cases}$, $g(t) = \begin{cases} 1, & 0 \le t \le T_s \\ 0, & \text{others} \end{cases}$,

$b_n = \overline{a}_n$ is the inverse relationship, ϕ_n, θ_n represents initial phases of the nth element.

The binary frequency shift keying signals can be generated by analog FM circuit or digital keying circuit [5]. Binary frequency shift keying signals can be demodulated in many ways, such as analog frequency decision method, digital detection method, non-coherent demodulation methods, and coherent demodulation method [6].

Because the coefficient of bandwidth utilization is low, the binary digital modulation system has limitations in practical application. In order to improve the coefficient of bandwidth utilization, we usually use multi-level digital modulation system [7]. In this article, the input binary digital signal is transformed to four-level baseband signal in MFSK (4FSK) system, selected different carrier frequency by the gate circuit, obtained 4FSK modulated signals by the adder and transmitted on the channel added with Gaussian white noise, then filtered by the bandpass filter to obtain the signal on a certain frequency, after multiplying and low-pass filtering, the final demodulated signal can be obtained from sampling and judgment module.

3 Design of 4FSK modulation system

3.1 4FSK modulation module

4FSK modulation module is designed to make the binary sequence into four-level baseband signal, and select a carrier with certain frequency to pass from four gates. The four-channel signals would be added and converted to one-dimension array, then we can obtain 4FSK modulated signal.

3.1.1 Control gate circuit

In the control gate circuit subroutine, one element of the input sequence is compared with the determination value at t time, if they are same, the output is a cycle carrier wave, otherwise the output is the signal with amplitude "0."

3.1.2 Dimension converter of signal array

In the two-dimensional array into a one-dimensional array subroutine, each time what you enter the outer loop is a two-dimensional array, and that of the inner loop is an element, every input element and the output controls will be built into a new one-dimensional array by using local variables which should be set to "0" before running every time.

3.1.3 Bandpass filtering

In the bandpass filter subroutine, a certain frequency carrier signal can pass through a bandpass filter. The sample rate is regarded as unit "1," and the sum of the rate and carrier frequency will be added or subtracted with a numeric constant as the higher or lower cutoff frequency.

3.1.4 Sampling and judgment

In the sampling and judgment subroutine, the output is two binary numbers of every comparison. Since the modulation process of 4FSK require four gate circuit to determine the frequency by four control gate circuit, the four gate circuits are different, and the difference is that judgment No. 1 outputs "00" if the sampling value is greater than the judgment value, judgment No. 2 outputs "01" if the sampling value is greater than the judgment value, judgment No. 3 outputs "10" if the sampling value is greater than the judgment value, judgment No. 4 outputs "11" if the sampling value is greater than the judgment value respectively.

3.2 4FSK demodulation module

In the 4FSK demodulation module, the received 4FSK modulated signal is multiplied by four by coherent carrier, after bandpass filtering, the corresponding frequency signal can be obtained, and then by four sampling decider after sampling and judgment to get four two-dimensional array, at last, the two-dimensional array would be transformed into one-dimensional array to recover the binary sequence.

3.3 4FSK modulation system

The input sequence would be transformed into modulated signal by 4FSK modulation, which would be transmitted in the Gaussian white noise channel, then the demodulated signal the same as input signal would be obtained at the

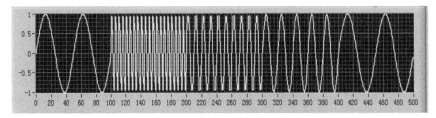

Figure 1: 4FSK modulation signal.

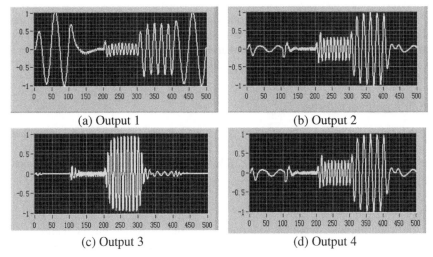

(a) Output 1   (b) Output 2

(c) Output 3   (d) Output 4

Figure 2: 4FSK demodulation signal.

output terminal, thereby completing the information received without error. Figure 1 shows the front panel of 4FSK modulation signal, which has been modulated by the carrier frequency 20 Hz, 50 Hz, 100 Hz, 200 Hz, and the sampling rate is 1 kHz.

When the input sequence is 0011100100, the input sequence would be modulated by the 4FSK modulation system, transmission in the Gaussian white noise channel, and then four-channel waveforms would be obtained after demodulation and filtering module. Four-channel waveforms from four bandpass filters are shown in Figure 2. As we can see from the figure, after demodulation and filtering, outputs obtained are consistent with the input sequence 0011100100, and they are on the setting frequency band.

4   Conclusion design of 4FSK modulation system

In this paper, 4FSK modulation system is designed based on LabVIEW, it includes each subroutine modules and the top-level module. Based on the modulation and demodulation principle, each module has been established the corresponding sub-VI, that is control gate, bandpass filtering, signal conversion, sampling and judgment. According to the characteristics of modulation 4FSK, it has been completed all sub-module design and parameter settings, the simulation waveforms has verified the reasonableness of 4FSK modulation design and its functionality.

Acknowledgments

The research work was supported by National Spark Program under Grant No. 2012GA690304 and Huai'an Municipal Science and Technology Support Program under Grant No. HAS2012046.

References

[1] Hao Chi, Xihua Zou, and Jianping Yao, Analytical models for phase-modulation-based microwave photonic systems with phase modulation to intensity modulation conversion using a dispersive device. *Lightwave Technologyy*, **27(5)**, pp. 511–521, 2009.

[2] R. Mahapatra, A.S. Dhar, andD. Datta, On feasibility of a multiplier-less phase-shifting scheme for digital phase modulation and its VLSI implementation. *International Journal of Electronics*, **94(1/2)**, pp. 171–181, 2007.

[3] Meng Wusheng, Zhu Jianbo, and Huang Hong, Data acquisition system based on LabVIEW. *Electronic Measurement Technology*, **31(11)**, pp. 63–65, 2008.

[4] Sun Yumei, Design and realization of an FSK modem based on FPGA. *Electronic Science and Technology*, **22(5)**, pp. 38–39, 2009.

[5] Li Shuang-Li, Sheng Li-Yuan, and Chen Jia-Lin, Differential detection demodulator of 2FSK based on fractional delay filters. *Computer Simulation*, **28(7)**, pp. 138–141, 2011.

[6] Che Ren-Xin, Ji Yong-Gang, Design and implementation of a digital phase modulation system based on FPGA. *Journal of Dalian Jiaotong University*, **30(2)**, pp. 89–92, 2009.

[7] Li Xiaofeng, Design of multi-channel and multi-parameter virtual instrument based on LabVIEW. *Computer & Digital Engineering*, 2008, **36(3)**, pp. 148–150, 2011.

A study on collective model-based floating population missing data simulation

Zheng Wang[1,2], Yingjie Wang[1]
[1]Institute of Geographic Sciences and Natural Resources Research, CAS, Beijing
[2]Graduate University of Chinese Academy of Sciences, Beijing.

Abstract

The floating population refers to the temporary migration of people without changing their household registration locations. The floating population has a big influence on the economic development, social stability, and environmental protection, and the changes of floating population lead to many chain reactions on social and economic problems. Therefore, studying how the number of floating population change is of great significance. The most important basis of study on Chinese floating population is the previous national census data. However, Chinese census conducted every 10 years, which causes a long interval period between each census without data. In 10 years, the society and country can have great changes, so as the floating population. In order to solve the problem of missing data, this paper collected the previous census and sampling survey data, and the statistics of the population survey data published by the Ministry of Public Security to simulate the floating population change. The neural network model and linear regression model, related with the exponential curve model, were used in regression simulation of the floating population in each province of China. On this basis, this paper built comprehensive models of each province in China to simulate the number of floating population per year between two censuses. Using the survey data of Beijing Bureau of statistics, this paper carried on the test of precision. The test result shows that: the analog value of the collective model is very close to the true value and the effect of the simulation is very ideal.

Key Words: floating population, missing data, collective model, neural network model, linear regression model, exponential curve model.

WIT Transactions on Information and Communication Technologies, Vol. 61, © 2014 WIT Press
www.witpress.com, ISSN 1743-3517 (on-line)
doi:10.2495/MIIT130691

1 Introduction

The floating population refers to the temporary migration whose household registration is not changed, including the temporary population and non-transient population [1]. The most important basis of study on Chinese floating population is the previous national census data. However, Chinese census conducted every 10 years, and the society and country had great changes, so as the floating population. The missing data in the year of no census brings lots of inconvenient to the research of floating population.

Existing scholars have done a lot of research on the floating population problem. The floating population of foreign scholars started earlier. Ravenstein [2] proposed seven regular migration theories. The American sociologist Zipf [3] proposed the gravity model. The American scholar Lee Everett [4] proposed a "push-pull theory." Yale University John C. H. Fei and Gustav Ranis [5] proposed Lewis-Fei-Ranis population flow model. The US development economist Michael P. Todaro [6] proposed a "Todaro migration model."

Chinese scholars also have done a lot of research for the floating population. The foreign scholars' theory could not reflect the actual situation in China. Most Chinese scholars study confined to a certain area and their perspectives are single. And since the time of some research is prematurely, the result of the study is unable to explain the changes of floating population in recent years. Although some studies have data models, most of the models are used to predict the future and could not do well simulate of the missing data in the census interval year.

To solve the problem of missing data of the floating population, this study selected the neuron model, linear regression model, and exponential curve model. And according to the different of R2 value, integrated the three methods and establish a comprehensive model.

2 Data sources and processing

2.1 Census and sample survey data

Since the founding of our country, national census has been conducted respectively in 1954, 1964, 1982, 1990, 2000, and 2010. In addition, the sample survey data of the floating population is also important. The 1% sample survey of national population has been carried out three times, in 1987, 1995, and 2005, respectively.

Since the statistical caliber of the inter-provincial floating population in the census after 1990 is identical, the data in the census after 1990 can be used together. This paper selects and analyzes the national census data in 2000, 2010, and the 1% sample survey data in 1995, 2005. There is not any statistical caliber difference existed in these four times' statistical data.

2.2 Other data

In addition to census and survey data, this study collected Ministry of Public Security statistics of the "Republic of China National sub-county demographic

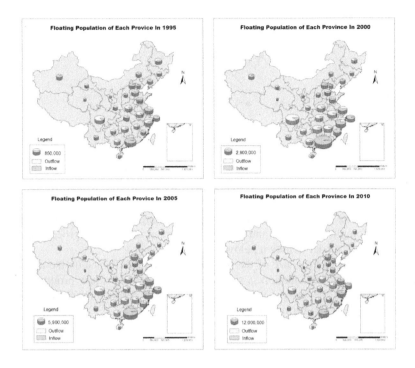

Figure 1: Floating population of each region in 1995, 2000, 2005, and 2010.

data (1992–2000)," by which we could calculate the inflow and outflow of population. The calculation result are in high degree of consistency with the census and survey data of the National Bureau, and it can be put together for data modeling and data analysis. The thematic map of floating population data in each year was shown in Figure 1.

3 Data simulation method

3.1 Model introduction

The characteristic of the floating population data of this article is that: the large span of the calculate year, so many years of missing data, the small amount of the total sample, and the very uneven distribution. So, the general time series analysis and modeling methods can't be applied. Coupled with a lot of impact factor of floating population and the complex variation, using a single model for data analysis would not reflect the actual situation well.

3.1.1 Neural network model

Neural network model (Figure 2) is capable of overcoming the small sample size, the uneven distribution of statistical data and other difficulties. It is suitable for

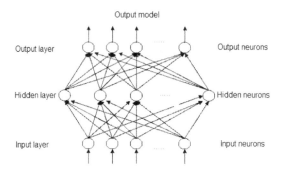

Figure 2: Neural network model.

China's floating population data simulations. Using neurons, we can build a variety of complex topology, and parallel distributed information processing. The neural network model is shown below.

Weights represent the size of the previous degree of influence on the next one. The neuron model calculation is that, after calculated the inner product of the input vector and the weight vector, we get a scalar result through a nonlinear transfer function. The formula is below:

$$t = fWA + B \qquad (1)$$

wherein W is the weight vector, A^I is the transpose of the input vector, B is the bias, and f is the transfer function.

3.1.2 Linear regression model and exponential curve model

The main factor causing population movements is from economic momentum. The exponential curve model is always used by economic growth simulation. So this paper attempts to use exponential curve model to simulate the floating population data. The solving equations is shown as Eq. (2).

$$y = \frac{e^{a+bx} + c}{d} \qquad (2)$$

The multiple linear regression models are applicable for the change in posture problems which can't be determined in advance. So, this paper also attempts to use the multiple linear regression models to simulate the floating population data. Using different data repeatedly, we can get the fittest linear model for floating population. The linear regression model is respectively shown as Eq. (3).

$$y = a_0 + a_1 x + a_2 x^2 + \dots + a_n x^n \qquad (3)$$

There are many ways to solve the exponential curve model and the linear regression model problem. In this study, the available data is limited. The method

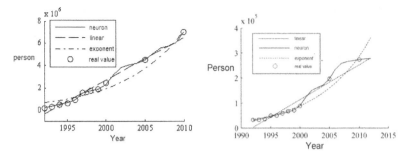

Figure 3: Float-in population and float-out population in Beijing.

of least squares analysis does not need too much supporting from the sample data, so it can solve the fitted model more accurately.

3.1.3 Integrated model

Using the three methods above to simulate the floating population data, we can obtain three types of analog values. Based on the different sizes of R2 value of three analog values, we can integrate the three models to get the analog value of the floating population. The formula is following.

$$P_s = \frac{R2_l}{R2_l + R2_e + R2_n} P_l + \frac{R2_e}{R2_l + R2_e + R2_n} P_e + \frac{R2_n}{R2_l + R2_e + R2_n} P_n$$

wherein, P_s, P_l, P_e, P. were the analog value of integrated model, linear regression model, exponential curve model, and neuron model, respectively, $R2_l$, $R2_e$, $R2_n$ are the R2 value size of the linear regression model, exponential curve model, and neuron model, respectively.

3.2 Simulation result

Taking Beijing as an example, the results of the simulation are shown in Figure 3.

It can be seen through the simulation results that population regardless of inflow or outflow is increasing year by year. In the simulation results of the floating-in population, the three models are fitting the results well, and as can be seen from the R2, the integrated model is better than any other of the three models.

4 Data simulation results and discussion

Bureau of Statistics of Beijing has published the floating population data from 2006 to 2009. By analyzing the absolute error and relative error, we can verify the simulation results, and analyze the simulation of the integrated model.

Table 1: Simulation Result of Floating-In Population in Beijing (unit: person).

Year	Statistics	Analog Value	Absolute Error	Relative Error
2006	3834000	3677038	156961	0.040939
2007	4197000	4517996	320995	0.076482
2008	4651000	4965643	314643	0.067651
2009	5092000	5487797	395796	0.077729

As can be seen from Table 1, the relative errors between the analog value and the statistical value are less than 8%. The error of the data in 2006 is 4.09%, which is very close to the true value. With being proven, effect of the data simulation is very good overall.

Summary

This article uses the integrated model method which is based on neurons models, exponential curve models, and linear regression models to simulate the inflow and outflow population of various regions in China for the first time. After the inspection, we can find that the analog value is closer to the true value and the effect of the simulation is very satisfactory. The integrated model can be used to solve the problem that the data of floating population in the census interval year are missing.

References

[1] Y.F. Li, Q. Lu, and C.H. Zhou, The prediction of Beijing floating population in 2010. *Geographical Research*, **25(1)**, pp. 133–135, 2006.
[2] E.G. Ravenstein, The laws of migration. *Journal of the Royal Statistical Society*, **48(2)**, pp. 167–235, 1885.
[3] G.K. Zipf, The P1P2/D hypothesis on the intercity movement of persons. *American Sociological Review*, **11(6)**, pp. 677–686, 1946.
[4] E.S. Lee, A theory of migration. *Demography*, **3(1)**, pp. 47–57, 1966.
[5] G. Ranis and J.C.H. Fei, A theory of economic development. *The American Economic Review*, **51(4)**, pp. 533–558, 1961.
[6] J.R. Harris and M.P. Todaro, Migration, unemployment and development: a two-sector analysis. *Economic Journal*, **60(1)**, pp. 126–142, 1970.

A schema matching method for the semantic integration of spatial data

Qiang Wang[1,2], Huarui Wu[1,3], Huaji Zhu[1,3]
[1]Beijing Research Center for Information Technology in Agriculture,
Beijing Academy of Agriculture and Forestry Sciences, Beijing, 100097
[2]School of Surveying and Land Information Engineering, Henan
Polytechnic University, Jiaozuo, 454000
[3]China National Engineering Research Center for Information
Technology in Agriculture, Beijing, 100097

Abstract

How to integrate and reuse of existing spatial data resources has become the key condition to enhance spatial data value and reduce duplication spatial database. Through the analysis of the differences of spatial data semantic level, we propose the schema matching method to integrate spatial data based on geometry type, feature classes, attributes. This paper designs the semantic similarity calculation method in the process of schema matching, provides the calculation formula of schema similarity. At last, we choose the data of the first national land survey and the second national land survey as instance to verify the semantic integration method.

Keywords: spatial data, semantic integration, schema matching similarity calculate.

1 Introduction

Spatial data because of the complexity of its own data model, data structure, data semantics, etc., compared to the general transaction management is much more difficult to integrate. Traditional spatial data integration methods focus on grammatical level of data integration, solve the problem of heterogeneous logic model and data structure [1], such as data conversion, data interoperability, direct access to the data model. For the same concept of different understanding and expression, and use the same term to describe different concept, resulting in the difference of data semantic level. The semantic differences of spatial data mainly reflected on the model and instance, such as generalization, naming differences and dimension differences, expression [2].

The so-called schema matching refers to from two (or more) models to determine the related elements semantically corresponding relation, and declare the specific process of mapping [3]. Based on GeoDatabase model that widely used in Geographic Information System, a typical GIS model generally contains three kinds of model elements, geometry type, feature classes, and attributes [4]. Geometry type refers to the space entity point, line, surface. Feature classes are those that have the same spatial representation (such as point, line, or surface) set and the common elements of a common set of properties listed in the same. Attributes refer to the semantic characteristics of spatial entities. According to the different levels of schema elements, schema matching between the spatial data type mainly includes three types geometry type matching, feature classes matching, and attributes matching.

2 Integration process

This paper presents a multi-source data integration method that with the schema matching of geometry type, feature classes, and attributes. This method is mainly composed of five processing steps. (1) Clearing the source data type and data structure, determine the target data to be integrated, carrying on geometry type matching (point to point, line to line, surface to surface). (2) Identifying relevant feature classes and calculating names similarities to match the feature classes. (3) Using examples to validate the matches, to statistical summary attributes to feature class, comparing common examples of value and property, verifying features matching is correct. (4) To determine the relevant attributes and calculating the attribute similarity of name, type, value to matching feature class. (5) To determine the relationship between schemas and checking schema matching relations is correct.

3 Method

We know the geometry type, feature classes, and attributes are the keys to determine the matching relation of spatial data integration. The geometry type matching is relatively simple, according to the common spatial data organization form, only the same geometry types of data exist corresponding relation. Feature classes and attributes schema matching relationship were achieved by computing semantic similarity, including the name similarity, instance similarity, types of similarity, similarity of attribute values. The validation after schema matching is mainly data instance summary statistics, the same instance of the attribute value contrast and a small amount of manual intervention. Comparison of corresponding feature classes of the same number of fields, statistical value of the property of the corresponding maximum, minimum, average, and other statistical information, all instances of a attribute will be sorted in ascending or descending order to find the corresponding instance can verify whether the correct matching relationship established.

3.1 Geometry type matching

Currently common GIS spatial data, such as the ArcGIS SHP format data, MapGIS of WT, WL, WP format data, the data are organized by three forms points, lines, and surfaces. Point is used to define the small discrete location geographical elements can't be expressed by a line or surface, such as location, telephone poles, and the water level. Points can also be said address location, GPS coordinates, or peak. Line represents the geographic objects that shape and position are too narrow to be expressed as a zone (e.g., street centerlines and rivers). Also used line to indicate the element that has length but not area, such as contours and borders, surface having a plurality of edges, expressed shape and position of the similar feature type (such as state, county, parcels, soil type, and land use area). If two feature classes match, they must match the geometry model that there exists a point–point, line–line, surface–surface matching relationship. Geometry type matching is a prerequisite feature classes matches.

3.2 Feature classes matching

Step 1: (Names Matching): Implementation feature classes focused on matching the names of the feature classes matching. "If the names of the two elements are identical, then there is a match between them," it is most often used in applications matching methods. Feature classes names are usually composed of the sentence by the word. Statement refers to two statements similarity degree of similarity. Similarity reaches a set threshold, they think these two statements are similar [5,6].

Let statement $S1$, $S2$ can be cut into m and n words, $S1 = \{c_1, c_2, \ldots, c_m\}$, $S2 = \{c'_1, c'_2, \ldots, c'_n\}$, then $S1$, $S2$ of the similarity can be calculated by the following equation:

$$Sim(S1, S2) = \sum_{i=1}^{m} w_i Sim(c_i, c'_j) \tag{1}$$

Among them, $Sim(c_i, c'_j)$ is the biggest similarity matching of the word c_i. w_i is weight $w_1 + w_2 + \ldots + w_m = 1$.

Word similarity $Sim(c_i, c'_j)$ can be combined with HowNet common sense knowledge base for calculation [8]. In HowNet, righteousness is the smallest unit of semantic description concept, a concept has more than one meaning. Concept is a relationship of mesh, the most important relations is the up and down relations. To calculate the similarity between words concept can take advantage of the up and down tree hierarchy in the composition of a relationship. When two

Table 1: Feature Class A (Road Town Land Use Information Land Patch in 1996).

Class Name	Class Code	Patch Number	Patch Area	Deduction Area
Village	203	5	32325.92	90.82
Dry land	114	91	10900.9	75.31
Forest land	131	34	2252.4	0
River water	321	11	15544.59	131.65
Pond water	154	23	5256.9	55.96
Highway land	262	103	59580.15	0

phases at the same time, the original path distance of righteousness node of the deeper level, the higher the similarity [9]. Consider the level of depth node "dp," two original righteousness p_1, p_2 similarity calculation formula is:

$$Sim(p_1, p_2) = [a \times \min(dpp_1, dpp_2)] / [d + a \times \min(dpp_1, dpp_2)] \qquad (2)$$

Among them a is to adjust parameters, d is path distance in the hierarchy.

Concept contains more than one meaning in the original, each just the function of the original is not the same. Considering the influence of the different, set different weighting factor, the concept c_1, c_1' similarity can be calculated:

$$Sim(c_1, c_1') = \sum_{i=1}^{m} w_i Sim(p_i, p_j') \qquad (3)$$

Among them describe the two concepts is a collection of righteousness $c_1 = \{p_1, p_2, ..., p_m\}$, $c_1' = \{p_1', p_2', ..., p_n',\}$, $Sim(p_i, p_j')$ is the biggest similarity matching of the original righteousness p_i. $w_i = d_i / \sum_{i=1}^{n} d_i$, $d_i = \min(dpp_1, dpp_2)$.

Step 2: (Instance to verify the match): The data instance can often provide important semantic clue for schema matching task. You can match by the same properties statistical number field, and the content of the same attributes of statistical information to determine whether the element class match. Such as the feature class A and B in Tables 1 and 2, the same name attribute fields in a total of 10, different attribute fields have 5 (Tables 1, 2 only to enumerate some attributes).

For the same name attributes, if the data type for the numerical type, such as patch number, patch area, deduction of area, its statistical summary information including maximum, minimum, average, standard deviation, elements of class A, B numeric attributes were calculated by the same examples in this four statistics on the value, see Table 3. Set difference threshold, statistic difference is smaller than the threshold corresponding attribute matching.

Table 2: Feature Class B (Road Town Second Survey Planar Land Investigation Data).

Class Name	Class Coding	Patch Number	Patch Area	Deduction Area
Dry land	013	42	36850.18	101.33
Orchard	021	8	1590.01	62.42
Paddy field	011	95	7331.71	59.48
Pond water	114	18	8812.31	34.17
Highway land	102	7	30621.84	0
Village	203	14	11621.41	49.68

Table 3: Data Instance to Verity Feature Class Matching.

Attribute	Maximum	Minimum	Average	Standard Deviation
A. Patch code	103	5	44.5	36.15
A. Patch area	59580.15	2252.4	20976.81	19781.79
A. Deduction area	131.65	0	58.96	40.93
B. Patch code	95	7	30.7	31.04
B. Patch area	36850.18	1590.01	16137.91	9278.06
B. Deduction area	101.33	0	51.18	30.64

For string attributes, specific semantic attribute with attribute content matches. If the attribute field elements A, B are famous for "ownership units," its attribute values are "XX Township village of XX" form, can be initially determined the attribute matching relationship exists; at the same time the attribute values to be enumerated statistics, such as "class name" attribute, elements of class A to class "called" = {village, dry land, forest land, river, pond, the highway land}, elements of class B "class name" = {village, dry land, paddy field, orchard, pond, the highway land}, range from the two attribute values contained in the national standard classification of land given.

3.3 Attributes matching

If the two feature classes match, then their attributes also have matching relationship of part or all. The attribute name matching is the attribute matching the most important, most of the same name attribute has a direct correspondence between factors and the type of attribute, content and attribute matching considerations.

Step 1: (Names Matching): The name of the difference is mainly reflected in the ways of expression, such as "encoding," "code" is the same meaning; in addition, the use of the English translation of Chinese names, acronyms is a common method for naming attributes. Similarly calculation for attribute name first words that constitute semantic expansion. Attribute name A and B after word semantics for expansion are: $A' = \{A'_1, A'_2, ..., A'_m\}$, $B' = \{B'_1, B'_2, ..., B'_n\}$, calculating the attribute name A, B similarity $NSim(A, B)$:

$$NSim(A, B) = \sum_{i=1}^{m} w_i Sim(A'_i, B'_j) \qquad (4)$$

Among them $Sim(A'_i, B'_j)$ indicate the word i in A' the largest similarity match for B', w_i is weight.

Step 2: (Types Matching): The same general has the same properties. But this does not mean that property is not different types of correspondence, such as floating point attribute and double attribute may be stored in the area of data accuracy, the "char" attribute type attribute and "string" type can represent stores English character data; data of date type common can use string say, can also use the date attribute storage special. Based on the consideration of different type of attribute may exists corresponding relation, the type of attribute matching similarity:

$$SSim(A, B) = \begin{cases} 1, & S(A) = S(B) \\ a, & S(A) \neq S(B), S(A), S(B) \in R \\ 0, & S(A) \neq S(B), S(A), S(B) \notin R \end{cases} \qquad (5)$$

Among them $S(A)$, $S(B)$ are attribute types. $a \in (0,1)$. R are pre-defined rules, indicate a set that A,B have different types but exist a corresponding relationship.

Step 3: (Values Matching): Due to the application background, data reference source, the data storage standard of different, the source data and target data describing the same space entity state will have different attribute values. Considering factors influence on the attribute value matching, these differences are attributes of the attribute value matching:

$$VSim(A, B) = \sum_{i=1}^{n} Sim(\alpha_i, \beta_i) / n \qquad (6)$$

Among them $Sim(\alpha_i, \beta_i)$ is the similarity for the ith corresponding factor. Similar to the attribute name, type, and attribute values weighted sum of similarity, with similar properties can be integrated similarity:

$$Sim(A, B) = w_n NSim(A, B) + w_s SSim(A, B) + w_v VSim(A, B) \qquad (7)$$

w_n, w_s, w_v are weights, $w_n + w_s + w_v = 1$.

Table 4: Attribute Similarity Calculation.

Attribute Name	Class Name	Class Code	Patch Code	Feature Code	Ownership Nature	Ownership Name
Attribute Similarity	0.9	0.89	0.85	0.55	0.35	0.92
Attribute Name	Patch Area	Deduction Area	Located Units	Changing Index	Changing Time	Space Objects
Attribute Similarity	0.86	0.86	0.92	0	0.85	0

4 Experiment

In this paper, the experimental data is selected Hainan QiongHaiShi Road Town, a harmonic two land use data. First two layer elements (classes) name initially determined the similarity of the match, then calculate the number of the same name as the attribute fields and relevant statistical information corresponding to the attribute of the same name as the field to verify the matching of the element class. Determined by the attribute similarity calculation for matching the properties. Feature class name "Road Town land use information land patch in 1996" shared to {"1996," "Road Town," "land," "use," "information," "land patch"}. The name "Road Town second survey planar land investigation data" can be segmentation for {"Road Town," "second survey," "planar land," "investigation," "data"}, within the GIS professional data a time period in 1996 for the land, to patches are generally planar, combined with HowNet words database, has name similarity for both:

$$0.15 \times 0.9 + 0.15 \times 1 + 0.2 \times 1 + 0.1 \times 0.15 + 0.1 \times 1 + 0.3 \times 0.8 = 0.84;$$

Instance matching is shown in Tables 1 and 2 authentication methods.

Attribute "class code" and "class code" type as string type, and attribute value assignment rules are different, its attribute similarity as:

$$0.5 \times (0.5 \times 1 + 0.5 \times 0.8) + 0.2 \times 1 + 0.3 \times 0.8 = 0.89 .$$

Can calculate all attributes in the source data and target data corresponding to the attribute of the similarity in Table 4.

Set a threshold value is 0.5, there is a matching relationship similarity is greater than the threshold value of the attribute, is in the process of data integration model of matching relationship graph (partial attributes) in Figure 1.

5 Conclusions

With the enormous growth through geographical spatial data, the data integration of use is more and more important. Schema not only rely on the semantic

Shape: polygon

Road Town second survey planar land investigation data

Class name	Dry land	Orchard	Village
Class code	013	021	203
Approval Number	Null	Null	Null
Patch area	36850.18	1590.01	11621.41
Deduction coefficient	1	1	0.5

Geometry type Matching

Feature Classes Matching

Attributes Matching

Shape: polygon

Road Town land use information Land patch in 1996

Class name	Forest land	Dry land	Village
Class code	131	114	203
Patch area	2252.4	10900.9	32325.3
Ridge coefficient	0.5	1	0.5
Space Objects	Null	Null	Null

Figure 1: The geometric data integration, feature classes, attributes matching.

similarity of professional knowledge and expert experience and general scientific knowledge, but also because of the specific application. Increasing applications of machine learning ability, and through the concrete application of the automatic learning of knowledge matching process, perfecting the system of semantic dictionary to improve the accuracy of semantic similarity is very necessary, can be used as a further work to study; and schema matching was applied to other spatial data model, such as grid model, abstracts the available models and semantic, so as to realize data integration can also be used as a research direction.

Acknowledgments

This paper is supported by a grant from the National Science and Technology Support Program (No. 2012BAJ23B04).

References

[1] G.F. Song, Seamless integration of multi-source spatial data research. *Progress In Geography*, **19(2)**, pp. 111–112, 2000.

[2] Y.H. Wang, Y.H. Niu, and Y. Lin, Semantic differences into account fundamental geographic information database update client implementation model. *Geography and Geo-Information Science*, **27(1)**, pp. 1–6, 2011.

[3] Z. Zhang, H.Y. Che, and P.F. Shi, Describe the framework and pattern matching algorithm model. *Pattern Recognition and Artificial Intelligence*, **19(6)**, pp. 716–717, 2006.

[4] C. Quix, L. Ragia, L. Cai, and T. Gan, Matching Schemas for Geographical Information Systems Using Semantic Information. Proceeding of Workshop on Semantic-Based Geographical Information Systems (SeBGIS), OTM Confederated International Workshops, Montpellier, France, LNCS 4278, Springer-Verlag, pp. 1566–1575, 2006.

[5] C. Zheng, Q.S. Xia, and C.N. Sun, Based ingredients sentence similarity computing. *Computer Technology and Development*, **22(12)**, pp. 101–102, 2012.

[6] S.C. Yang, An improved sentence similarity computing model. *Journal of University of Electronic Science and Technology of China*, **35(6)**, pp. 956–959, 2006.

[7] A.P. Xu and F.L. Bian, GIS Chinese dictionary query system design and segmentation research. *Geomatics and Information Science of Wuhan University*, **31(4)**, pp. 348–351, 2006.

[8] Q. Liu and S.J. Li, *Based on the "Text" Lexical Semantic Similarity Calculation*. Chinese Computational Linguistics, Taiwan, 2002.

[9] Y.J. Wu, Y. Chen, and F.A. Shang, A new similarity calculation based ontology mapping algorithm. *Application Research of Computers*, **26(3)**, pp. 870–872, 2009.

A collaborative evolutionary bi-objective portfolio selection model with DE-ACO algorithm

Yaping Yu, Yuelin Gao, Ji Li
Institute of Information and System Science, Beifang University of Nationalities, Yinchuan, 750021, China

Abstract

The constraint of quantity and investment limit is introduced into Markowitz mean-variance (M-V) model, we establish a mean semi-absolute deviation bi-objective portfolio selection model and design a bi-objective optimization algorithm with difference-ant colony coordination evolution algorithm (DE-ACO) for empirical analysis. Numerical experiments show that model is reasonable and the DE-ACO algorithm is effective.

Keywords: bi-objective portfolio optimization, number of assets, investment limit, differential evolution, ant colony optimization, cooperative coevolution.

1 Introduction

Markowitz's theory hold that investors hope the risk of investment is minimum in certain benefits conditions, or in certain risk conditions, can obtain great return [1]. However, in the real market, the application value of M-V model is limited, a growing number of researchers take into account the limitations of some real conditions on the basis of M-V model, such as cardinality constraints, quantity constraints, the minimum transaction costs and transaction volume constraints [2,3]. In addition, they also put forward the new method for measurement of risk, such as Harlow proposed using the LPMn measure risk [4] and CVaR [5]. These new constraints and the risk measure make it more difficult to use a deterministic method to solve the portfolio problem. And a heuristic algorithm has become the inevitable choice to solve the problem of optimization method because of its uncertainty. In recent years, the algorithm of solving the model has been widely

WIT Transactions on Information and Communication Technologies, Vol. 61, © 2014 WIT Press
www.witpress.com, ISSN 1743-3517 (on-line)
doi:10.2495/MIIT130711

used and promoted with the development of the optimization algorithm. Chang, Meade improved the M-V model and took into account cardinality constraints using genetic algorithm, simulated annealing and tabu search hybrid algorithm to solve the efficient frontier of the model [6]. Schaerf simulated securities investment situation by individual investors, joined cardinality constraint and investment restrictions and compared the local search of tabu search algorithm with other algorithms [7]. Armananzas and Lozano solved the problem of portfolio using three different heuristic algorithm and depicted efficient frontiers of five kinds of stock index [8]. On the basis of the base and transaction volume constraints, K.P. refined securities investment category, designed the multi-objective optimization algorithm based on the NSGA-II and gave efficient frontiers under different base [9]. Deng put forward an improved particle swarm optimization for solving the Cardinality Constraints Markowitz Portfolio Optimization problem [10].

Based on the Markowitz mean-variance model, we propose a mean semi-absolute deviation bi-objective portfolio selection model. Differential evolution algorithm [11] (DE) and ant colony optimization algorithm [12] (ACO) are two kinds of new optimization algorithm. Their efficiency, global optimization, and easy implementation have become a common concern of the academia. In this paper, we use the two algorithm, design the difference-ant colony coordination evolution algorithm (DE-ACO) and apply China's securities market for empirical analysis.

2   Models for portfolio optimization

In order to make the Markowitz portfolio model to get better application in practice, risk measuring more reasonable and better reflect the public's expectations, many researchers improved the method of risk measurement, they put forward the semi-variance, absolute deviation, the semi-variance absolute deviation, maximum absolute deviation, VaR (value at risk) and CVaR. But in the absence of constraints, risk quantification methods such as lower deviation or absolute deviation can be converted into linear programming problem, which through deterministic method such as simplex method can solve. Therefore, this kind of risk quantitative research is relatively small. In this paper, we restrict the number of assets and investment, using the maximum negative deviation to evaluate risk. This is because the real distribution of yield is not affirmatory, the maximum negative deviation measurement method enlarge the risk to a certain extent, which perfectly reflects cautious psychological of conservative investors.

We consider a portfolio selection problem with n assets. r_{it} be the return of each asset on the T period, $t = 1, 2, \cdots, T$, $i = 1, 2, \cdots, n$. Let x_i, $i = 1, 2, \cdots, n$ be the weight of assets i, i be the return of the portfolio,

$$\max\{E(\sum_{i=1}^{n} x_i \delta_i r_{it}) - \sum_{i=1}^{n} x_i \delta_i r_{it}, t = 1, 2, \cdots, T\}$$ be the risk of the portfolio. $\delta_i = \{0, 1\}$,

$\delta_i = 1$ if any of assets i $(i = 1, 2, \cdots, n)$ is held in the portfolio, 0 otherwise. K_1, K_2 are respectively lower bound and upper bound of the number of investment assets, l_i and u_i are the minimum and maximum assets investment in assets i, respectively.

Portfolio selection model as follows:

$$
\begin{cases}
\min \ \max\{E(\sum_{i=1}^{n} x_i \delta_i r_{it}) - \sum_{i=1}^{n} x_i \delta_i r_{it}, t = 1, 2, \cdots, T\} \\[2mm]
\max \ \sum_{i=1}^{n} x_i E(r_i) \\[2mm]
s.t. \ \sum_{i=1}^{n} x_i = 1, \ x_i \geq 0 \\[2mm]
K_1 \leq \sum_{i=1}^{n} \delta_i \leq K_2 \\[2mm]
\delta_i l_i \leq x_i \leq \delta_i l u_i
\end{cases}
\tag{1}
$$

3 DE-ACO coordination evolution algorithm

It is generally believed that the portfolio selection problem is a complex mathematical programming problem. Because of the complexity of the problem, the traditional optimization algorithms cannot be applied. Thus we use differential evolution algorithm and ant colony optimization algorithm to solve portfolio selection.

3.1 Differential evolution

Differential evolution algorithm (DE) was first introduced by Rainer Storn and Kenneth Price in 1995. It was based on real number encoding, random search in continuous space. The main characteristic of DE algorithm is simple, the convergence speed is quicker than the Genetic Algorithm, Particle Swarm Optimization, stronger stability, is suitable for solving complex optimization problems. Initial population of the differential algorithm randomly generated and evolution population operate through operator such as variation, crossover, and selection of every individual in a population. Individual difference algorithm is composed of real value vector, evolutionary operation is as follows:

(i)   Variation operation: Classical differential evolutionary algorithm uses DE/rand/1 variation policy, the variation on difference vector between the parent individuals. x_i^t is the current evolutionary individual, i is the ith individual in current population, T is the current evolutionary iteration. Three individuals x_{r1}^t, x_{r2}^t and x_{r3}^t $(r1 \neq r2 \neq r3 \neq i)$ are randomly selected from the current population, and $x_{r2}^t - x_{r3}^t$ is vector difference between the parent individuals, the scaling factor F and individual $r1$ merge to get new individual u_i^{t+1} :

$$v_i^{t+1} = x_{r1}^t + F(x_{r2}^t - x_{r3}^t) \qquad (2)$$

where $F \in [0,2]$ is a fixed number, called the scale factor, used to control the degree to which the influence of the new individual difference vector.

ii) Crossover operation: DE crosses through the mutated vector and the target vector, increases the diversity of population. v_i^{t+1} is called mutated individuals with the current individual x_i^t crossover operation as follows, to generate new individuals u_i^{t+1} :

$$u_{ij}^{t+1} = \begin{cases} v_{ij}^{t+1}, & \text{if } rand(0,1) \leq CR \text{ or } j = jrand \\ x_{ij}^t, & \text{otherwise} \end{cases} \qquad (3)$$

where $CR \in [0,1]$ is the crossover probability, which is uniformly distributed random numbers, it determines the ratio of the new individual u_i^{t+1} instead of variation individual v_i^{t+1} with the current individual x_i^t. Obviously, the greater CR, the selection probability of mutation individual u_i^{t+1} will be larger. $jrand = rand(1,D)$ is a random integer, it can guarantee u_i^{t+1} is different from v_i^{t+1} .

iii) Selection operator: DE strategy through "greed" selection to produce new individual:

$$x_i^{t+1} = \begin{cases} u_i^{t+1}, & \text{if } f(u_i^{t+1}) < f(x_i^t) \\ x_i^t, & \text{otherwise} \end{cases} \qquad (4)$$

where $f(x)$ is the fitness function, differential evolution select the best fitness of the individual as a child, it has the elite reserved strategy, and can guarantee the convergence of the optimal solution.

3.2 Ant colony optimization

Ant colony optimization (ACO) was first introduced by Dorigo in the 1990s. After a large number of studies, people have found that ants transfer information through the pheromone between individuals, and work together to complete a series of complex task. In the process of movement, the ants can leave pheromone on the path to it passes through, and can sense its presence, distinguish its strength, so as to guide their behavior. As a result, an ant colony collective behavior shows a positive feedback phenomenon that the more ants path through, the greater the probability of others choose this path, it is through the communication between ants to reach the purpose of searching for food.

m is the number of ants, each ant has the following characteristics: Variables are the legacy number of pheromone according to city distance and connection, choose the next city at a certain probability. $\tau_{ij}(t)$ is pheromone intensity of the edge $e(i, j)$ at moment t. It is assumed that the ant takes legal course, in other words the ant not allowed visited the city once again unless complete it through travel around, the ant left pheromone at each edge after completion of travel. Let $\tau_{ij}(0) = C$, which means the initial moment of each path is equal to the amount of information, where C is a constant, the ant $k(k = 1, 2, \cdots, m)$ determines direction of forward motion according to the path information, $p_{ij}(k)$ is the probability of the kth ant moving from position i to position j at time t.

$$p_{ij}^{t} = \begin{cases} \dfrac{\tau_{ij}^{\alpha}(t) \cdot \eta_{ij}^{\beta}(t)}{\sum\limits_{s \in allowed_k} \tau_{ij}^{\alpha}(t) \cdot \eta_{ij}^{\beta}(t)}, & if\ j \in allowed_k \\ \\ 0, & otherwise \end{cases} \tag{5}$$

where $allowed_k = \{0, 1, \cdots, n-1\} - tabu_k$ is the next city that ant k is allowed through, $tabu_k(k = 1, 2, \cdots, m)$ is the city that ant k passed at present, $tabu_k$ adjust dynamically with the evolution process. η_{ij} means the visibility of the edge (i, j), in general, $\eta_{ij} = \dfrac{1}{d_{ij}}$, d_{ij} is the distance between i and j, respectively, α and β are the relative importance of pheromone and heuristic factor, ρ is the track persistence. The legacy of information taper off. Ants complete a cycle after moment n, every path make adjustment according to the following information:

$$\tau_{ij}(t+n) = \rho\tau_{ij}(t) + \Delta\tau_{ij} \tag{6}$$

$$\Delta\tau_{ij} = \sum_{k=1}^{n} \Delta\tau_{ij}^{k} \tag{7}$$

where $\Delta\tau_{ij}^{k}$ is the kth ant left pheromone on the path ij, $\Delta\tau_{ij}$ is incremental information of path ij at the end of this cycle.

3.3 DE-ACO coordination evolutionary algorithm

In this paper, we designed the difference and the collaborative evolution of ant colony algorithm (DE-ACO) to solve the portfolio selection model. The design of the DE -ACO algorithm steps as follows:

Step 1: (Initialization parameters): generate the population size of N, D_C and D_I are dimensions (D_C is continuous dimension, D_I is integer dimension), the maximum iteration is T_{max}.

Step 2: (Initialization population): randomly generate initial population of XC, according to the current XC_i, to guide and update the discrete solutions XI_i, calculate the objective function f_i, evolution generations $T = 1$.

Step 3: Find out non-dominated solutions of the current group and stored in external files, copy the current Pareto solutions.
Step 4: (Termination condition): If the stopping conditions are met, go to step 6, if not, go to step 5.
Step 5: Enter the iteration, the operation for individuals in the population as following:
Step 5.1: Update real part variables by Eqs. (2) and (3); update the integer part by Eqs. (4), (5), (6), and (7).
Step 5.2: The selection of variables to Pareto after overall cooperative coevolution X, update with the current solutions in the external file and copy X.
Step 6: When it meets the maximum number of iterations, the iteration algorithm is terminated, retain the final overall variables and output results.

4 Numerical experiments and the results

In order to illustrate the effect of limited number of assets to the portfolio and judge whether the selection of number of securities for portfolio is obviously different or not, this paper selects 24 stocks from different industries and different circulation: fluoride (000247), byd (002594), the agricultural development (002299), jiangsu wuzhong (600200), dongfang electric (600875), taiyuan corundum (000795), baotou steel shares (600010). Data is original week closing price from January 6, 2012 to October 29, 2012, getting 41 observation data, which means $T = 41$ (return in terms of logarithmic return). For the above data, we use DE-ACO algorithm to solve and get the Pareto optimal solution set. The Pareto frontier is shown in Figures 1–4.

From Figures 1–3, when the number of alternative assets is less ($K = 8$), whether limit number of assets or not is no effect to the Pareto frontier; when the number of securities stock pool increases ($K = 16$), Pareto frontier in the number of assets limiting circumstances focuses on area where earnings significantly increased. Despite depicting the Pareto frontier is not complete after limited number of assets, enough to meet the psychological needs of the investors. When the number of securities stock pool increases again ($K = 16$), the superiority of not limit the number of assets appears, but applies mainly to the lower risk cases. The Pareto frontier after limited number of assets under three different number of securities conditions as shown in Figure 4, it is clear that the portfolio is more and more excellent after the number of assets was extended, which show clearly that decentralizing the asset allocation can reduce risk effectively.

Based on the above analysis, in the case of limited number of assets, when the risk is fixed, investors do not too much loss, on the other hand, even can help investors to save energy to do technical analysis and to catch the opportunity, thus obtain additional gains to some extent.

5 Conclusions

In this paper, based on the current actual situation of stock market, we put forward the semi-variance the absolute deviation of bi-objective portfolio

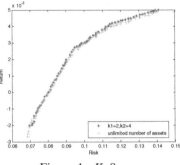

Figure 1: *K*=8.

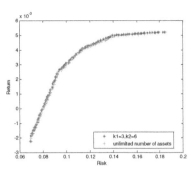

Figure 2: *K*=16.

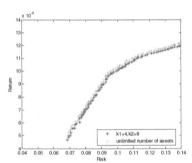

Figure 3   *K*=24.

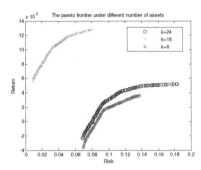

Figure 4: Compare of different number of securities.

selection model, and for this model we design a difference-ant colony coordination evolution algorithm (DE-ACO), compare the Pareto frontier for different number of assets and whether limited investment or not. Empirical analysis shows that the number of optional assets is relatively small, whether limited number of assets or not is no effect to the Pareto frontier. With the increase of number of alternative assets, limiting number of assets will have a certain effect on the profit of investors and shows that decentralizing the asset allocation can reduce the risk of investors may face greatly, also illustrates the feasibility of the DE-ACO algorithm for solving multi-objective portfolio model.

Acknowledgments

The work is supported by the Foundations of National Natural Science China under Grant No. 60962006, the National Social Science Fund project funding under Grant No. 07XJY038 and the research projects of State Ethnic Affairs Commission under Grant No.12BFZ005.

References

[1] H.M. Markowitz, Portfolio selection. *Journal of Finance*, **7(1)**, pp. 77–91, 1952.

[2] H. Konno, H. Yamazaki, Mean-absolute deviation portfolio optimization model and its application to Tokyo stock market. *Management Science*, **37(5)**, pp.519–531, 1991.

[3] H. Konno, H. Shirakawa, H. Yamazaki, A mean-absolute deviation-skewness portfolio optimization model. *Annals of Operations Research*, **45(1)**, pp. 205–220, 1993.

[4] W.V. Harlow, Asset allocation in a downside-rise framework. *Financial Analyst's Journal*, **47(5)**, pp. 28–40, 1991.

[5] R.T. Rockafellar, Stanislav Uryasev, Optimization of conditional value-at-risk. *Journal of Risk*, **2**, p. 175, 2000.

[6] T.J. Chang, N. Meade, J.E. Beasley, Y.M. Sharaiha, Heuristics for cardinality constrained portfolio optimization. *Computers & Operations Research*, **27(13)**, pp. 1271–1302, 2000.

[7] A. Schaerf, Local search techniques for constrained portfolio selection problems. *Computational Economics*, **20(3)**, pp. 177–190, 2002.

[8] R. Armananzas, J.A. Lozano, A multi-objective approach to the portfolio optimization problem. Congress on Evolutionary Computation, CEC 2005, Edinburgh, UK, pp. 1388–1395, 2005.

[9] K.P. Anagnostopoulos, G. Mamanis, A portfolio optimization model with three objectives and discrete variables. *Computers and Operations Research*, **37(7)**, pp. 1285–1297, 2010.

[10] Guang-Feng Deng, Woo-Tsong Lin, Chih-Chung Lo, Markowitz-based portfolio selection with cardinality constraints using improved particle swarm optimization. *Expert Systems with Applications*, **39(4)**, pp. 4558–4566, 2012.

[11] R. Storn, K. Price, Differential evolution—a simple and efficient adaptive scheme for global optimization over continuous spaces. *Journal of Global Optimization*, **11(4)**, pp. 344–359, 1997.

[12] M. Dorigo, V. Maniezzo, A. Colorni, The ant system: Optimization by a colony of cooperative agents. *IEEE Transactions on Systems, Man and Cybernetics, PART B*, **26(1)**, pp. 29–41, 1996.

A multi-objective cultural algorithm based on particle swarm optimization with crowding entropy

Junhua Liu, Yuelin Gao

Institute of Information & System Science, Beifang University of Nationalities, Yinchuan, 750021, China

Abstract

The mutation strategy of particle swarm optimization is integrated into the cultural algorithm to enhance the diversity and uniformity of the distribution of the Pareto solutions, using elitist strategy updates external elitist archive to improve the convergence accuracy, adopting crowding entropy strategy, and global optimal particle selection strategy to maintain external file. So a multi-objective cultural algorithm based on particle swarm optimization (MO-CA-PSO) is proposed. The results show that the proposed MO-CA-PSO is not only having higher accuracy of convergence but also getting a more uniform distribution of Pareto solutions.

Keywords: multi-objective optimization problems, cultural algorithm, particle swarm optimization, elitist archive, crowding entropy.

1 Introduction

In this paper, the following multi-objective optimization problem (MOP) was researched:

$$\begin{cases} \min\ F(x) = [f_1(x), f_2(x), \ldots, f_k(x)]^T \\ \text{s.t.}\ \ x = (x_1, x_2, \ldots x_n) \in X \subseteq R^n \end{cases} \tag{1}$$

where x is an n-dimensional decision variable, X is decision space, $F(x)$ is the objective function. On the basic concepts of multi-objective optimization problems is seen from reference [1]. Multi-objective optimization has been widely studied in the field of science and engineering. Unlike the single objective optimization, there are more than one objective that need to be fulfilled simultaneously, where two or more are conflicting, so it can not only access the optimal concurrently, but also get a set of solutions which conform to the concept of Pareto optimal set. This paper combines the advantages of multi-level structure of the cultural algorithm with the characteristics of rapid convergence of particle swarm optimization algorithm, using elitist strategy updates external elitist archive to improve the convergence accuracy and adopting crowding entropy strategy to maintain external file, which aims to promote the diversity and uniform distribution of Pareto solutions. So a multi-objective cultural algorithm based on particle swarm optimization (MO-CA-PSO) is proposed. Through representative multi-objective benchmark problems, the results show that MO-CA-PSO is not only having higher accuracy of convergence but also getting a more uniform distribution of Pareto solutions.

2 The description of particle swarm optimization and cultural algorithm

2.1 Particle swarm optimization (PSO)

Assume that in the D dimensional search space, the ith particle's position is denoted as $x_i = (x_{i1}, x_{i2}, \cdots, x_{iD})$, and $x_{id} \in [l_d, u_d]$, $d \in [1, D]$, u_d, l_d are respectively upper and lower limits. The ith particle's velocity is denoted as $v_i = (v_{i1}, v_{i2}, \cdots, v_{iD})$, the best position found so far in the search process $P_i = (P_{i,1}, P_{i,2}, \cdots, P_{i,D})$, the best position found in the whole population $P_g = (P_{g,1}, P_{g,2}, \cdots, P_{g,D})$. The velocity and position of every particle are updated iteratively according to the following equations:

$$v_{i,j}(t+1) = w \cdot v_{i,j}(t) + c1 \cdot r1 \cdot [P_{i,j} - x_{i,j}(t)] + c2 \cdot r2 \cdot [P_{g,j} - x_{i,j}(t)] \quad (2)$$

$$x_{i,j}(t+1) = x_{i,j}(t) + v_{i,j}(t+1), j = 1, 2, ..., D. \quad (3)$$

where $c1$ and $c2$ are learning factors, representing the cognitive weight and social weight, $r1$ and $r2$ are two random numbers generated by an uniform distribution in the interval [0,1]. w is a inertia weight and is a very important parameter on affecting the performance of the algorithm. When w is smaller, the algorithm has strong local search ability, on the contrary, the algorithm tends to global search. Typically, w is initialized to 0.9, followed by making it with the number of iterations increasing linearly decreased to 0.4. The linear change is determined by the following formula [2]:

$$w = w_{max} - t(w_{max} - w_{min}) / T_{max} \quad (4)$$

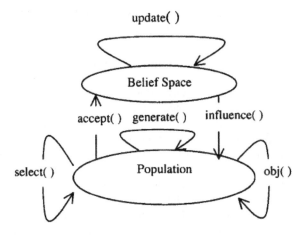

Figure 1: Cultural algorithm framework.

where T_{max} is a maximum number of iterations and t is the current number of iterations.

2.2 Cultural algorithm (CA)

Culture algorithm (CA) [3–5] is made up of two parts, which are population space and belief space. As can be seen from Figure 1, two spaces have an independent evolution based on the evolutionary operation and evaluation function of each operation. At the same time, the two spaces are linked together through a set of communication protocols that are composed of accept function and influence function. Individuals in the population space form individual experience during the evolution and deliver the individual experience to the belief space by accept function. In the belief space, individual experiences are processed more optimal by certain conduct rules to form group experiences, then update the existing group experiences and new individual experiences with the update function. In addition, influence function can take advantage of the belief space's experiences and knowledge which can solve the problems in the population space to guide the evolution of the population space efficiently and enhance the efficiency of the evolution of the population space. Object() in the population space is the objective function (fitness function), aims to evaluate the individual fitness value of population space. Generate function is to generate the next generation of individuals based on individual behavior rules and father's individual parameters, and select function according to the rules from the newly generated individuals selects a part of individuals as the next generation of the individual's parents to the next round of iterations until the termination condition is satisfied.

3 Multi-objective cultural based on particle swarm optimization algorithm with crowding entropy

3.1 Using crowding entropy to maintain the external archive

Similar to the general multi-objective PSO algorithm, the internal population space produces a set of nondominated solutions in every generation, during the algorithm running, we use the external archive (EA) to store the nondominated solutions produced from each generation. Commonly we use the method of maintaining EA from MOEA. But during the algorithm running, with the iteration proceeding, the scale of the EA is gradually increased. When its size reaches a certain number, we should limit it, otherwise, it will greatly increase the computational complexity. When the size is controlled, due to no precedence relations between the individuals of the archive, the individual density information has become the main basis of screening. In this paper, crowding entropy is used to maintain the external elite archive, aiming to increase the diversity of nondominated solutions and enhance the uniformity of the Pareto optimal solution.

In MO-CA-PSO algorithm, external elite archive is used to store nondominated solutions of internal population evolutionary generated, here we cite the crowding entropy in the literature [6] to maintain the external elite archive.

For the ith individual, we set:

$$E_{ij} = -[pl_{ij}\log_2(pl_{ij}) + pu_{ij}\log_2(pu_{ij})]$$

$$pl_{ij} = dl_{ij}/c_{ij} \, , \; pu_{ij} = du_{ij}/c_{ij} \, , \; c_{ij} = dl_{ij} + du_{ij}$$

The crowding entropy is defined as the following:

$$CE_i = \sum_{j=1}^{k}(c_{ij}E_{ij})/(f_j^{\max} - f_j^{\min}). \tag{5}$$

For the jth objective function, dl_{ij} and du_{ij} are the minimum and maximum distance of the ith solution to its two neighbors. The parameters $f_j^{\max}$ and $f_j^{\min}$ are the maximum and minimum values of the jth objective function, and k is the number of objective functions.

In the process of external file maintenance, if its size does not reach the scale of the external archive, nondominated solutions that are generated newly will be compared with the individual in the EA, when met the requirements, it is added to the external elite archive. If its size reaches the scale, the individual that has the minimum crowding entropy is removed one by one from the EA, until the required scale is met. The most prominent advantage of this maintenance procedure is that the individual has the minimum crowding entropy is deleted one by one, which avoid deleting more than one individual, so enhance the uniformity of the Pareto optimal solutions and increase the diversity of solutions.

3.2 Global optimal particle selection

In the MO problem, due to different choice of the optimal particle will lead to the final search results completely different, and then the finalized indicators of Pareto optimal solution will be greatly affected. Therefore, for MO-CA-PSO, another important issue needed to solve is the global optimal particle selection. The usual approach is to use the concept of Pareto dominance, consider all the nondominated solutions in external elite archive and determine a "leadership" from it. And the "leadership" can guide the evolution of the particle swarm to the dispersion area of Pareto front, which can ensure its distribution uniformity. Here, we use the optimal particle selection strategy learn from the literature [7].

(1) If crowding entropy of all individuals in the Pareto set are infinite, and that contain only a small number of boundary individuals, the algorithm will select one as a gbest randomly.

(2) If there is an individual in the Pareto set, whose crowding entropy is not infinite, the algorithm will use the roulette wheel method to select gbest, that is to say, having greater probability to select individual which has a bigger crowding entropy as gbest, which is calculated as:

$$p(x_i) = CE_i \Big/ \sum_{i=1}^{M} CE_i$$

(6)

Here, CE_i is the crowding entropy of the ith individual, M is the size of the Pareto solutions for the current generated, $p(x_i)$ is the probability of being selected for the ith individual. If individual crowding entropy is infinite which will cause the roulette wheel choice failure, so it is needed to redefine the crowding entropy of boundary individuals whose original crowding entropy is infinite. It is defined to be a median of remaining individuals crowding entropy which are obtained by removing the individuals whose crowding entropy are infinite.

The experimental results show that Pareto front is obtained by using this method has an relatively good uniformity at last.

3.3 MO-CA-PSO algorithm description

Step 1: Let algorithm parameters, such as the internal and external population size, maximum number of iterations, the inertia weight value and so on.

Step 2: Initialize the internal population space, at the same time set the upper and lower limits of speed and position, calculate fitness function value of the internal population space particles. Store the nondominated solutions to external elite archive of the belief space and calculate the crowding entropy.

Step 3: Update the particle swarm's gbest based on crowding entropy.

Step 4: According to formula (2) and (3), update the speed and position of particles in the internal population, meanwhile, dispose them according to the upper and lower limits. In addition, calculate fitness function value of each particle and update the particles' self best value based on the nondomination relationship.

Step 5: Adopt the external elite archive policy to update the external file by means of the accepting function.

Step 6: If condition is met, do the influence operation.

Step 7: Judge whether the maximum number of iterations is arrived. If it reaches, output the external elite individual as the Pareto optimal solution set. Otherwise, the number of iterations plus 1 and return to Step 3 and proceed.

Where condition as the judgment rules determines whether do an influence operation, here we set every 20 generations do an influence operation. If the condition is met, five elite individuals selected from the belief space will replace the corresponding numbers of individuals in the internal population space, according to the relations of domination.

4 Test results and performance analysis

To demonstrate the competitiveness of MO-CA-PSO algorithm, it is compared with three multi-objective evolutionary algorithms that are representative of the state of the art: MOPSO, NSGA-II, and SPEA2. Four commonly recognized benchmark functions ZDT1-ZDT3 and ZDT6 are adopted. Two performance metrics [6], namely the generational distance (GD) and the diversity metrics (Δ), which measure the closeness of the Pareto solutions identified by MO-CA-PSO to the true Pareto solutions in the objective space and diversity of Pareto solutions along the Pareto front, respectively. To compare and analyze the performance of the four algorithms conveniently, using the following unified parameters: internal population size is 100, external population size is 100, the maximum number of iterations is 500, inertia weight of the MO-CA-PSO algorithm: w_{max}=1.2, W_{min}=0.4, learning factor: $c1$=$c2$= 2.0, maximum speed v_{max} and minimum speed v_{min} in particle's flight is respectively 0.1 times of the upper and lower position. In NSGA-II, η_c=20, η_m=20, *Poolize*=100, *Toursize*=2. MO-CA-PSO and NSGA-II are operated independently at 10 times. The generational distance and diversity metrics of four algorithms to each test function's statistical results are in Tables 1 and 2. The comparisons of four test functions' Pareto front by MO-CA-PSO and NSGA-II are given respectively through Figures 2–5.

Can be seen from Tables 1 and 2, MO-CA-PSO algorithm is superior in convergence and uniformity than MOPSO algorithm. In the convergence index (GD), MO-CA-PSO algorithm is better than SPEA2; for the four test functions, in addition to the ZDT3 results are slightly worse than NSGA-II, others are all better than NSGA-II. In the diversity index Δ, MO-CA-PSO algorithm is better than the other three algorithms. From Figures 2–5, we can see that the Pareto front

Table 1: Generational Distance Statistics Results of four Test Functions of Four Kinds of Algorithm (GD).

Functions	GD	NSGA-II	SPEA2	MOPSO	MOCA-PSO
ZDT1	mean	1.3437e-3	8.6104e-3	1.8564e-1	1.1188e-3
	std	1.4078e-4	2.5973e-3	7.7429e-2	1.2256e-8
ZDT2	mean	9.8112e-4	2.4766e-2	5.2428e-1	7.3862e-4
	std	6.4138e-4	1.6083e-2	2.9699e-1	1.0196e-4
ZDT3	mean	2.4783e-3	9.7165e-3	4.3418e-1	4.1134e-3
	std	1.2746e-4	5.2305e-3	6.4880e-2	7.2226e-4
ZDT6	mean	7.5818e-2	1.9309e-2	5.2135e-2	2.1579e-3
	std	6.0797e-3	1.3994e-3	2.4963e-2	1.8710e-5

Table 2: Diversity Metrics Statistics Results of four Test Functions of Four Kinds of Algorithm (Δ).

Functions	Δ	NSGA-II	SPEA2	MOPSO	MOCA-PSO
ZDT1	mean	5.0429e-1	2.9644e-1	2.93805-1	1.81769e-1
	std	3.9251e-2	1.0850e-1	1.6956e-2	1.9711e-4
ZDT2	mean	4.8775e-1	5.0517e-1	2.88026e-1	1.88302e-1
	std	2.7686e-2	1.8356e-1	1.7580e-2	1.6694e-2
ZDT3	mean	5.9025e-1	5.0310e-1	6.17796e-1	4.71455e-1
	std	3.0439e-2	9.7283e-2	3.5019e-2	1.9389e-3
ZDT6	mean	4.8611e-1	2.4861e-1	1.12325e-0	2.56971e-1
	std	3.6054e-2	4.9667e-2	1.7311e-1	7.4849e-2

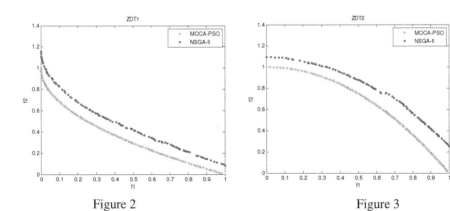

Figure 2   Figure 3

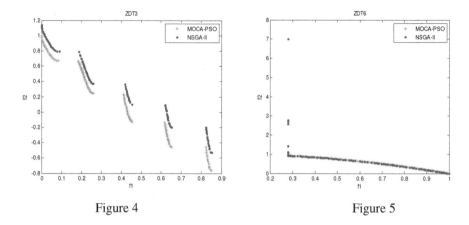

Figure 4   Figure 5

generated by MO-CA-PSO algorithm is all lower than NSGA-II, and the degree of homogeneity is also better than the latter.

5   Conclusion

MO-CA-PSO relies on the advantage of dual evolution and dual promotion in the cultural algorithm, uses particle swarm as its internal population space. Through the accepting function, the dominant elite individual will be contributed to the external elite archive of belief space, then uses the crowding entropy to maintain the external archiving, and promotes the efficient guidance by influence operation to the internal population evolution adequately, to adapt to the characteristics of Pareto optimal solutions in the MO problem, thereby enhances the effectiveness of the algorithm. Compared with the other three typical MO algorithms, test results show that the new proposed algorithm on convergence and uniformity of Pareto optimal solution set is better than others.

Acknowledgments

The research work was supported by National Natural Science Foundation of China under Grant No. 60962006 and the research projects of State Ethnic Affairs Commission under Grant No.12BFZ005.

References

[1]   K. Deb, Multi-Objective Optimization Using Evolutionary Algorithms, Chichester, Wiley, pp. 13–46, 2001.
[2]   Y. Shi, R.C. Eberhart, Empirical study of particle swarm optimization, Proceedings of Congress on Evolutionary Computation, IEEE Service Center, Piscataway, 1951–1957, 1999.

[3] C.A. Coello, R.L. Becerra, A cultural algorithm for constrained optimization. Computer Science, **2313**, pp. 98–107, 2002.

[4] R.G. Robert, An introduce to cultural algorithms, Proceedings of the 3rd Annual Conference Evolution Programming, Word Scientific Publishing, Singapore, pp. 131–136, 1994.

[5] Xidong-Jin, Robert G. Reynolds, Using Knowledge-Based Evolutionary Computation to Solve Nonlinear Constraint Optimization Problem: A Cultural Algorithm Approach, Congress on Evolutionary Computation, [s.n.], Washington, DC, pp. 1672–1678, 1999.

[6] Yao Nan Wang, Liang Hong Wu, Xiao Fang Yuan, Multi-objective self-adaptive differential evolution with elitist archive and crowding entropy-based diversity measure. Soft Compute, pp. 193–209, 2010.

[7] Liqin Liu, Xueliang Zhang, Liming Xie, et al., Dynamic aggregation distance-based multi-target culture particle swarm optimization algorithm and its application. Agricultural Machinery, **41(3)**, pp. 189–194, 2010.

The operation and maintenance management flow and system for cloud data center

Hong Jun Zhan[1], Wei Zhang[2,3]
[1]Transportation Management College, Dalian Martime University,
Dalian City, Liaoning Province, 116026, China
[2]School of Computer Science, Beijing Information Science and
Technology University, Beijing, 100101, China
[3]Beijing Key Laboratory of Internet Culture and Digital Dissemination
Research, Beijing Information Science and Technology University,
Beijing, 100101, China

Abstract

The cloud computing data center mainly consists of numerous computers, network equipments, storage devices, power supply equipments, and many business systems serving for various departments in diverse purposes. The challenges encountered in the problem and knowledge management of IT (Information Technology) greatly restrain the reliability of cloud computing services. So, the idea of this paper was to realize the integrated operation and maintenance services especially problem and knowledge services. That is, this research aimed to provide an integrated solution to improve the IT management level comprehensively and standardize IT problem and knowledge environmental management. Also, the value and profit resulting from the IT resource input can be maximized.

Keywords: ITIL, problem management, knowledge management, cloud data center.

1 Introduction

The paper stems from the actual business requirement. At present, the enterprise contains a number of computers, network equipments, storage equipments, power equipments, and so on. It also includes many business systems, such as the official documents system, the website system, the network system, real-time communication system, mail system, mobile office system, communication system, monitoring system, backup system, video system, desktop systems for different departments, and different purpose. These IT resources need daily operation and maintenance to guarantee their efficiency. With the deepening of the information construction, IT resources are in the face of increasing pressure of operation and maintenance. So standard and efficient operation and maintenance process, operation and maintenance work, operation and maintenance management, operation and maintenance performance evaluation has become the key to ensure that IT resources efficient.

The main contents of the system include: the construction of the operation and maintenance service management system to monitor system; providing a variety of statistical analysis reports; displaying the entire contents of system monitoring results and statistics with friendly graphical interface; and, the integrated operation and maintenance monitoring system realize the automation of management, comprehensive monitor analysis, scientific decision-making and fundamentally improve the business management level. From the specific function modules, the system supports the service desk management, incident management, request management, configuration management, change management, release management, knowledge management, problem management, and so on.

2 Related work

ITIL [1] operations and maintenance service is that the supplier provides the maintenance for meeting the operations and maintenance of the demand sides. It includes the maintenance services of infrastructural facilities, the maintenance services of operation system, and system maintenance and operation support service. In this paper, well-known IT outsourcing service provider based on ITIL and methodologies have been studied, such as BMC's BSM model [2], CA's ESM [3] methodology, the IT operations and maintenance product of Shen Zhou Tai Yue [4]. And also, through reading a lot of correlative papers about IT Service Management, we get understanding of IT service management model which as the theory of ITIL operations and maintenance service system for the banks.

BMC is one of the internationally principal providers of the IT service software. It shows complete product line and it manages well in centralized monitoring, the service processes, and the network management. The BSM model in BMC is the IT management product that is most suitable for the ITIL architecture in this industry. As the largest management software company in the world, CA is an internationally dominating provider of the ITSM software. The IT service process management in CA works on the open management platform based on the workflow. This platform shows the ability to flexibly customize the workflow. Thus, it can rapidly adapt to changes and the ITSM execution efficiency is improved by automating processes. As one of the principal IT service software providers in China, Ultrapower [4] is skilled in centralized monitoring of network management and processes. It shows high capacity to integrate the advantages of the existing software and then conduct the second-time research and development. It has held a significant share in Chinese IT management market. For example, China Mobile, China Unicom, and China Telecom are very successful in some provinces.

3   The model based on ITIL for cloud data center

The functional description: all the created events are displayed and many management operations like searching and changing can be undertaken. The system should show the functions of event starting and event handling, specifically including problem and knowledge management workflow.

Shown in Figure 1, the aim of the problem management process is mainly to record the problems that have occurred and have been already solved; also, it can provide basis for the solutions to future problems. The problem management facilitates the preservation of related problems, the emergency plan, and solutions.

Shown in Figure 2, in the knowledge management process, knowledge and information are collected, analyzed, saved, and shared. Its principal goal is to improve the quality of management decisions by providing reliable and secure knowledge and information.

The system adopts industry standard, uses the ITIL theory and best practices map out an overall plan from techniques, process, and staff and construct the IT operation and maintenance systems. The system takes an event-oriented service process management as a main line, provides several roles such as front-line staff, second staff, problem administrators, and knowledge administrators, and designs several business processes of different roles. Furthermore, this system designs the relevant database based on business process requirements and demonstrates the main interface after the realization of the system. The paper the detailed design the problem treatment process, the knowledge process, and so on. According to business process required event table, the event log table, watch, watch problems table, knowledge table are designed, and the paper shows the problem management processing, knowledge management processing, statistical analysis, and the main interface.

4   Realization and test of the system

According to the standard in this industry together with the ITIL theory and the best practice, the complete system for IT system monitoring is established, by taking technologies, processes, and staff into account comprehensively.

The system widely used J2EE multilayer architecture, it is an enterprise' middleware platform to connect a variety of resources and applications spreading

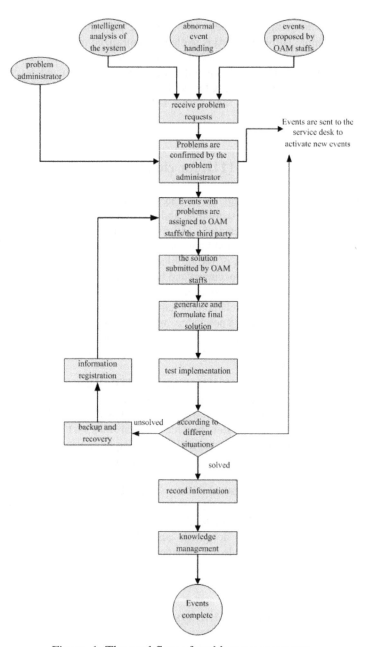

Figure 1: The workflow of problem management.

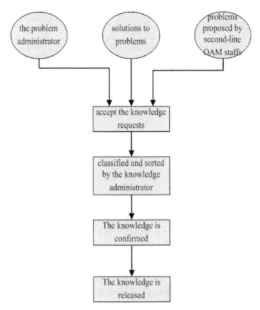

Figure 2: The workflow of knowledge management.

on the network link, which providing a range of application components and a run-time environment for the construction, management and operation of the enterprise' business application. The framework has been designed as a 3-tiered architecture, including data collecting layer, business logic layer, and data shown layer. And, the data collecting layer includes topology, configuration, performance, alarms, business acquisition, and preprocessing; the business logic layer includes the management system and service management; the data shown layer realize the information dissemination, system monitoring view, the business monitoring view and comprehensive reports through the operation and maintenance portal.

All the business functions that are required are included in the system and fully realized. The system shows stable functions and high operating efficiency. Figure 3 shows the interface image of the function problem and knowledge management workflow. The analysis on the test results indicates that the severe functional errors in the system have already been modified and the rest errors show no influence on the normal operation of the system. So, functionally, the system requirements are mostly satisfied. According to the test results of the system performance, it can be inferred that this system can allow 200 users to simultaneously conduct the concurrent operations, such as the on-line operation and order submission. No abnormal situation is presented and the system shows good stability. This is consistent with the expected performance result. In conclusion, the system fully satisfies functional, performance, and user interface requirements. Thus, the expected goals in system usability, stability, security, and extensibility are achieved.

Figure 3: The user interface of the system.

5 Conclusions

The aim of this paper is to manage problem and knowledge management service processes of the overall IT equipments and business systems for data center. The corresponding specific managements are presented as follows. The management system of asset and problem and knowledge management process services should be established to realize the comprehensive problem and knowledge management monitoring. Various statistical forms ought to be supplied and monitoring results and statistical contents of the integrated system are presented fully and clearly in graphs. Finally, the comprehensive problem and knowledge management monitoring system is formed to improve IT management level radically and standardize IT environmental management. Moreover, the value and profit resulting from the IT resource input can also be maximized.

This paper shows the testing process and results. The system applies manual tests by integrating tests and applications. And this system tests the system functions by functional testing, interface testing, and threshold testing, analyze the faults of the original system and revise and improve it. Testing and application results show that the system can meet the business needs. The implementation of the system realizes the whole operation and maintenance services to the "comprehensive, integrated, standard, and automation control" for bank. It is to provide a set of overall solutions to improve the management level, regulate IT environment use, the maximum of the IT resources for the investment of the value and benefits generated.

Acknowledgments

The research work was supported by the Beijing Excellent Talent Training Project (2012D005007000009), General Program of Science and Technology Development Project of Beijing Municipal Education Commission (KM201110772014), and the Opening Project of Beijing Key Laboratory of Internet Culture and Digital Dissemination Research. We like to thank anonymous reviewers for their valuable comments.

References

[1] Connor, John Source, What is ITIL? *Software World*, **37(5)**, pp. 3–5, 2006.
[2] Wen Qiong Shu, BMC: the leader of the BSM. *Communications World*, **40**, 2006.
[3] Qiang Yao, IT Service Management In Details (No.6 ESM Methodology). *Software Engineer*, **09**, pp. 25–28, 2004.
[4] Wang Xin, Shen Zhou Tai Yue Eight ITIL Productions. *Network Security Technology & Application*, **10**, pp. 36–40, 2007.

Mathematical model establishment of Konjak industry output structure and development bottleneck analysis in Pengshui, Chongqing

Liyu Chen[1], Si Liu[2], Ludi Zhao[3], Ying Yu,[4] Hanzhao Yuan[5]
[1]College of Mathematics and Computer Science, Ningxia University, China
[2]Department of Chemical and Biological Engineering, Zhejiang University, China
[3]College of Public Administration, Zhejiang University, China
[4]College of Economics, Zhejiang University, China
[5]College of Humanities, Zhejiang University, China

Abstract

Konjak industry has become the second pillar industry in Pengshui economy, but its development hit bottleneck for many reasons. This paper aims to study current situation of Konjak industry development of each link in Pengshui, Chongqing. Structural mathematical model is set and appropriate variables are chosen. Through the analysis, four structural factors are considered vital, namely technical factor like planting technology, political factor like governmental supervision and intervention to purchase link, economic factor, and labor link. Based on selected significant factors, this paper expects to offer proposals directed at some theoretical breakthrough of Pengshui Konjak industry development bottleneck.

Keywords: Konjak development, Pengshui Mathematical models, bottlenecks.

1 Introduction

Peng autonomous county is core field to develop Konjak efficient agricultural base in Wuling mountainous areas. After years of development, Peng Konjak is beginning to take shapes in the emerging industry and the Ministry of Agriculture has put Pengshui Konjak industry development into the twelfth five-year plan.

WIT Transactions on Information and Communication Technologies, Vol. 61, © 2014 WIT Press
www.witpress.com, ISSN 1743-3517 (on-line)
doi:10.2495/MIIT130741

Table 1: Main Crops Yield and Output Statistics in Pengshui in Year 2011.

Crop Type \ Index	Planting Acreage (mu)	Specific Yield (kg/mu)	Output/mu (yuan)	Net Income per year/mu (yuan)
Rice	563895	359.8	1151.36	835
Flue-cured tobacco	134000	130	3100	1600
Armorphophallus Konjak	13000	840	5292	3292

Remarks: average price of main production of taro and commercial Konjak is 6.3 yuan per kg.

But Konjak processing section in Peng is quite weak with a long road of industrialization. This paper aims to analyze from several aspects.

2 Industry status quo analysis

2.1 Feasibility analysis

Konjak is the only found main economic crop that can provide lots of glucan-mannan chitosan's, which is soluble dietary fiber. According to nutritious study, modern civilization disease prevalence is mainly caused by lack of dietary fiber intake. Since perception of Konjak health care function becomes more and more wide, demand for relative products is increasing incredibly. Because of glucan-mannan glycan unique physical and chemical properties, Konjak is widely used in chemical industry, papermaking textile, petrochemical cosmetic additives, and other fields of aeronautics and astronautics [1,2].

2.2 The status quo of industry development condition

2.2.1 Natural conditions

According to statistical yearbook, common cultivated land area is 92000 hm^2 and forestland area is 188000 hm^2 in Pengshui, which provides space for planting in much mountainous forest located lower and middle [3–5]. Most suitable soil for Konjak planting is characterized as deep loose texture, good rich organic matter content, and drainage of lightweight sandy loam. Peng mountain soil fertility level is above average as a whole, which not only meets the requirements of crops' growth, but also yields higher than other crops accounting for obvious price advantage (Table 1).

2.2.2 Locational conditions

Pengshui is located in the southeast of Chongqing. Yuhuai railway, Yuxiang highway and 319 national highways pass through the county. It is a land transportation hub and supplies distribution center of Chongqing, Hubei, Hunan, and Guizhou. Locational advantages laid a good logistics platform for industry.

2.3 Present situation of Konjak industry development

Mainly farmers and enterprises plant Konjak. Industry association organizes experts exert technical guidance in the field. Under the guidance of government, leading enterprises divide areas in their finished products processing. Now Pengshui Konjak industry has initially formed a industry chain of "government + leading enterprises + industry cooperative + peasants." Government formulates and implements preferential policies to perfect industry chain and contact group allocation to participate in industrial operation platform. The State Council has certificated Pengshui Konjak as a geographical indication mark for industry and commerce.

2.3.1 The status quo of taro cultivation

The planting base construction cannot keep the pace with market demand. Although a variety of testing seeds are introduced, varieties that put in circulation are single. Localization breeding process is slow so that could not meet local supply of high quality.

2.3.2 Technology development

In 2011, Pengshui started to cooperate with colleges and universities and successively introduced white Konjak, bulbil Konjak varieties, etc. However, technical problems still mainly hinders Konjak industry development. First, popularization of taro storage stays difficult. Current storage methods do not adapt to large scale and easily lead to lesion. Second, disease treatment is tough, especially the southern blight of soft rot. Researchers lay much importance on prevention because once infected, the disease is incurable.

2.3.3 Peasants' planting enthusiasm

Konjak growth conditions are harsh. They are easily affected by meteorological disasters with growing risks. Influenced by objective factors such as cost and risk, the peasants' planting enthusiasm about Konjak is inferior to expectations according to our investigations. Driving effect of large planting leading role is not obvious, either.

2.3.4 Preferential policies

Pengshui government executes protective price policies for Konjak. Subsidy policy is divided into six aspects. 1. Land subsidies. 2. Economical cooperation subsidies. 3. Direct grain subsidy. 4. Refunds of returning farmland to forest. 5. Loan discount for taro. 6. Agricultural insurance.

3   Mathematical model establishment of Konjak industry development

Here we set <comp: P, f, n, i, A italics--global>

$$P = f(X_1, X_2, \ldots X_n, A_i) \tag{1}$$

We set P as total output, X_i as factors of separate independent output variables, A as fixed factors including soil composition and so on.

To differentiate formula （1）

$$dP = \sum_{i=1}^{n} \frac{\partial P}{\partial X_i} \, dX_i + \frac{\partial P}{\partial A} \, dA \tag{2}$$

$$dP = \sum_{i=1}^{n} \frac{X_i}{Y} \frac{\partial Y}{\partial X_i} \frac{dX_i}{X_i} + \frac{A}{Y} \frac{\partial Y}{\partial A} \frac{dA}{A} \tag{3}$$

$\dfrac{\partial Y}{\partial X_i} \dfrac{X_i}{Y}$ is variable structure factor of flexibility, considered as α_i, $\dfrac{A}{Y} \dfrac{\partial Y}{\partial A} \dfrac{dA}{A}$ is

contribution of fixed factors for Konjak output growth, considered as α_0

So formula above can become

$$\frac{dP}{P} = \sum_{i=1}^{n} \alpha_i \frac{dx_i}{x_i} + \alpha_0 \tag{4}$$

Depict the primitive function

$$\log P = \alpha_0 + \sum_{i=1}^{n} \alpha_0 \log x_i + \sigma_x \tag{5}$$

σ_x is set as random disturbance and error.

Finally substitute into appropriate variable values and draw output value and fluctuate trends.

4   Equation factorial right variables and bottleneck of output growth promotion analysis

We extract appropriate quantitative variables from classic influencing factors and sort them in order so as to connect independent variables to structural factors of the differential equation for establishing reasonable assignment relations.

4.1 Technical factor X_1

Konjak needs strict growth and storage conditions. Although Konjak industry association led by Pengshui government generalizes planting technology in its utmost, many technical problems still remains unresolved and become important variable in equation.

4.1.1 Planting technology X1a

Due to the rigid growth condition, diseases and insect pests easily damage Konjak. Up to now, Pengshui is still in desperate need of effective insect pest control and cure techniques.

4.1.2 Storage technology X_{1b}

Konjak cannot be piled up and needs strict temperature and humidity conditions to store. The current storage technology stays at low level, which hinders production increase.

4.2 Political factors X_2

Konjak industry development is a systematic engineering, needing cooperations from government departments, enterprises, and peasants at all levels. As a prerequisite, mechanism necessary is the guarantee of its successive work. With policy execution, supervision and so on, government behaviors will be important in efficiency of development.

4.2.1 Supervision mechanism X_{2a}

To protect interests of farmers, support of local governments toward Konjak industry is comparatively stronger. But without thorough supervision mechanism, it is prone that special fund is not used as planned. It poses a threat to capital chain of industry development and public trust. At the same time, effect of policy implementation does not get timely feedback. Thus, when and how to subsidies is not expected and controlled in farming process exactly.

4.2.2 Intervention to purchase link X_{2b}

Government organizes excavation and necessarily primary processing, and then sells primo products to unified enterprise. Validity of such operation mode is questionable under background of market economy. Moderate intervention from officials can put forward the market normalization, avoid vicious competition aroused by information asymmetry to protect interests of stakeholders to a certain extent. But authorities tend to appear deviation in self-positioning, which provides a certain space for rent-seeking.

What is more, since the government plays a pivotal role in the purchase link, the government might have the tendency to abuse its power and even corrupt, which is the major concern of the local people. Hence, it is crucial to enhance the government's credibility, so that people could have more faith in the industry as well as the government policies.

4.3 Economic factor X_3

Konjak, as the second pillar industry, has just started in 2008. Attractiveness of it is insufficient now that economic benefit is not widely recognized. First of all, for many farmers, Konjak cultivation means big investment risk compared to relatively mature flue-cured tobacco industry. Secondly, price fluctuation weakens risk-adverse farmers' confidence. Moreover, as a result of infancy industrialization, there is a lot of blank space in sales links. Immature industrial chain leads to its low market competitiveness.

4.4 Labor link X_4

More and younger adults in Pengshui choose to go out to work. Thus the left-behind in village are basically children and elderly labor, not up to much production. As a result, the ratio of labor can't meet the needs of the development of industry.

5 Further discussion and future step

Given a suitable structural output equation for Pengshui Konjak industry, the research focus changed. First of all, how to determine the impact of these selected factors is elastic. This requires greater amounts of data, including economic contribution rate of planting and storage technology development in X_1, mechanism change in quantitative study in X_2, benchmark comparison in flue-cured tobacco industry in X_3, the rate of change of labor force and the unit of output in X_4. Secondly, due to a lack of empirical research, the validity of the model is difficult to verify. At the same time, variables in the subsequent trial may change in the error feedback study. So the choices of variables also need more powerful support.

6 Corresponding structural politics recommendations and conclusions

(1) Coordinate each work in Pengshui Konjak industrialization, to avoid the problem of inefficient execution of steering group to a certain extent.

(2) Strengthen policy implement feedback mechanism and timely understanding of Konjak dynamic market development to formulate reasonable development planning.

(3) Reduce capital subsidies in intermediate link to ensure that the funds can be effective in the production and sales link.

(4) Seek higher level technical support. Improve the efficiency of special funds use and strengthen scientific research funding examine.

(5) Establish brand awareness and build characteristic industry brand. Extend the industry chain. Develop high value-added services of tourism such as ecological sightseeing leisure.

(6) Optimizing investment environment. Rural financial institutions at all levels must complete financial support in industry investment.

(7) Cultivate leading enterprises to build promoting carrier. Establish unified industry standards and avoid vicious competition in the process of development through division of production.

References

[1] Konjac research centre of Southwest University, Government of Pengshui County, *Pengshui Autonomous County Konjac Industry Development Planning* （2012–2020）, 2012.

[2] Document No [2012]231 of the People's Government of Pengshui, *Informing about doing Konjac purchase work in 2012 from government office of Pengshui.*

[3] Document No [2012]232 of the People's Government of Pengshui, *Informing about promoting Konjac industry development in 2013 from government office of Pengshui.*

[4] Headquarters office of Konjac industrialization in Pengshui Autonomous County, *Compilation of data in Pengshui Konjac industrialization,* 2012.

[5] Ling Zhao, *Empirical Analysis of Relationships between Agricultural Industrial Structure Adjustment and Agricultural Economic Growth-Take Chongqing as an Example*, Public Forum, 10, pp. 78–79, 2009.

[6] Kun DEng, Empirical analysis of relationships between agricultural industrial structure adjustment and agricultural economic growth-take Sichuan province as an example. *Guangdong Agricultural Sciences*, **09**, pp. 193–197, 2011.

Accelerating continuous range queries processing in location based networks on GPUs

Wei Liao, Zhimin Yuan, Jiasheng Wang, Zhiming Zhang
*Department of Information Security, Naval University of Engineering,
Wuhan, 430033, China*

Abstract

Continuous range queries on moving objects are an important problem in different fields such as LBSN and database area. To evaluate massive concurrent queries toward mobile objects in spatial networks, we present a multi-staged framework MSF to improve the parallelism with multi-threaded technology, which departs the query processing into three simultaneous stages for continuous range queries processing. Further, in-memory spatial network adjacent matrix, shortest path matrix and moving objects hash table structures are introduced to describe road network topology and store mobile objects. Based on above structures, the GPU-RQ algorithm and GPU-QU algorithm are proposed to improve the efficiency of the initial range queries computing and queries updating. Experimental evaluation shows that GPU-RQ algorithm and GPU-QU algorithm achieve a performance improvement about 1 to 2 order magnitude over its GPU brute-force algorithm in almost all conditions.

Keywords: range queries, moving objects, GPU, multi-thread, MSF framework.

1 Introduction

With the rapid development of smart mobile phones and satellite-assisted positioning systems, location-based services (LBS), popular in many-especially urban-areas, such as road-side assistance, highway patrol, and location-aware advertisement, has gained many attentions in the past few years. Recently, online social network (OSN) services, typically facebook and twitter, also have become a very important web service that provides Internet-based platforms for users to interact with their friends. Nowadays we have been seeing a convergence of LBS and OSN as two of the most important mobile services. And a new kind of social

WIT Transactions on Information and Communication Technologies, Vol. 61, © 2014 WIT Press
www.witpress.com, ISSN 1743-3517 (on-line)
doi:10.2495/MIIT130751

networks, called location-based social network (LBSN), is becoming increasingly popular and hundreds of millions of users are active in a daily life [1].

Graphics processing units (GPUs) have over a decade been used for general-purpose computation, called GPU computing. Compared to the CPU, modern graphics architectures provide tremendous memory bandwidth and computational horsepower. This performance gap has its roots in the physical per-core restraints and architectural differences in between. The CPU is in essence a serial Von Neumann processor and is highly optimized to execute a series of complex logical operations. GPUs were growing greatly in performance due to its massive parallelism. In fact, with many lightweight parallel cores, GPUs can often provide substantial computational power to accelerate general purpose applications at a much lower equipment cost and much higher energy efficiency. Parallelism appears to be a practical way of increasing performance, and there are many applications that display embarrassingly parallel workloads that are perfectly suited for GPUs. Actually, massive concurrent continuous range queries exhibit natural parallelism. However, to cope with such computing-extensive applications, it is a practical way for modern database systems to use GPU stream computing model for parallelism to improve the throughout.

In this paper, we aim to develop a scalable and practical query processing multi-staged framework for spatial queries on mobile objects and implement the continuous range queries computing algorithm on GPUs for LBSN services.

The rest of the paper is sectioned as follows. First, we give a short overview of GPU accelerated algorithms in Section 2. Then we describe the multi-staged framework for continuous queries processing and the data structures in Section 3. And range query algorithm on GPUs named GPU-RQ algorithm and GPU-QU are detailed for the initial queries computing and updating in Section 4. Then we experimentally evaluate the GPU-RQ algorithm and GPU-QU algorithm through various simulations in Section 5. Finally, we conclude this paper in Section 6.

2 Related work

GPUs provide a natural way of study for spatial queries computing in a massively parallel computational environment. Most works have been done to accelerate kNN computing on GPUs for static points in Euclidean space. The first CUDA implementation of kNN computing is the "brute force" kNN searching algorithm [2], which speed increase by up to one or two orders of magnitude depending on the data compared to CPU-based implementations. Further, Jia Pan [3] uses locality sensitive hashing and cuckoo hashing to construct an efficient kNN algorithm that has linear space and time complexity. Heap-based kNN algorithm [4] builds in parallel a heap with the current k smaller elements instead of sorting the vector of query distances, thus outperforms parallel quick sort-based implementation. Lawrence Cayton [5] proposes a novel data structure RBC which provides significant speedups over the GPU-based brute force approach. GPU-based parallel LSH algorithm [6] uses the parallel RP-tree algorithm and Bi-level LSH algorithm to perform approximate k-nearest neighbor computation in high-dimensional spaces. Gleb Beliakov [7] replaces the sort operation in classic

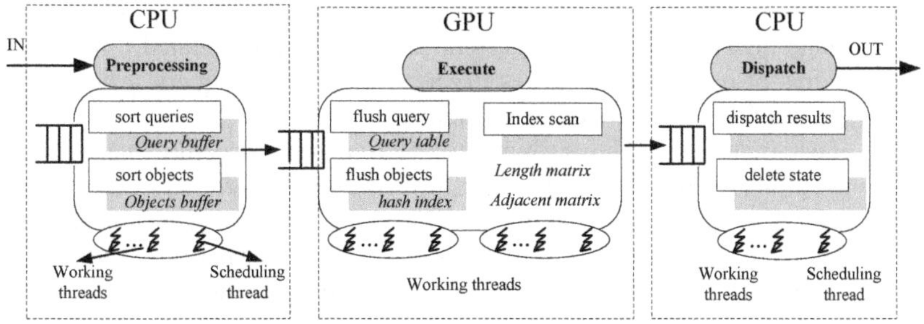

Figure 1: Processing of MSF framework.

kNN algorithm with calculating the order statistics and makes the kNN method not only more efficient, but also increases its stability with respect to the order in which the data is presented to the algorithm. Marta Fort [8] presents a GPU-based algorithm for computing discrete distance functions on road networks by computing discrete order-k Network Voronoi diagrams and for approximately solving kNN queries and Aggregate kNN queries. Ricardo [9] first evaluates the GPU-based range queries processing algorithms including list of Clusters and SSS-index on static objects. However, to our best knowledge, few researches have been conducted on the range queries computing for mobile objects on GPUs.

3 Processing architecture and data structures

The GPU-based continuous queries processing system utilizes a multi-staged framework (MSF) to support on-demand simultaneous pipelining. MSF executes queries following the stream model. As shown in Figure 1, the processing of continuous queries are divided into three stages: preprocessing stage at CPU host, executing stage on GPU device, and dispatching stage at CPU host. Each stage communicates by memory copying between the CPU host and the GPU device, and the outputs of former stage become the inputs of latter stage.

The MSF framework mainly consists of the following data structures:

(1) Query Buffer, QB. The query buffer is used to cache the incoming updating, inserting, and deleting continuous queries. The form is as $<QID, Qloc, r, EdgeId>$, where QID identifies a query q, $Qloc$ is the current location of q at updated time, r is the radius of q, $EdgeId$ identify the network edge that query q lies in. And QB is a CPU host memory structure.

(2) Object Buffer, OB. The object buffer is used to buffer the incoming updating, inserting, and deleting mobile objects. The form is as $< OID, Oloc, EdgeId >$, where OID is the identifier of an object, and $Oloc$ is the new position of this object, $EdgeId$ identify the network edge that mobile object o lies in. And OB is a CPU host memory structure.

(3) Query Table, QT. The query table is a linear structure storing the incoming continuous queries, which is represented as the form $<QID$,

Qloc, r, EdgeId >. And *QID* represents the identifier of a continuous range query *q*, *Qloc* is the current location of *q* at updated time, *r* is the radius of *q*, *EdgeId* identifies the network edge that query *q* lies in. And *QT* is a GPU device memory structure.

(4) Hash Index, *HI*. The hash index HI is a hash structure managing the positions of mobile objects. The form is as < *EdgeId*, *list<O_{inf}>>*, where *EdgeId* is the identifier of an edge, *list<O_{inf}>* is the list of objects lies in this edge. And *O_{inf}* has the form *<OID, Oloc >*, where *OID* identifies a moving object, and *Oloc* represents the current position of this object. *HI* is a GPU device memory structure.

(5) Adjacent Matrix, *AM*. The adjacent matrix *AM* is a matrix $N \times N$ used to describe the topology of spatial road network, the element . $AM\left[i, j\right] \in AM$ .represents the initial node of the shortest path from node v_i to v_j. Obviously, if node v_i is adjacent to node v_j, then $AM\left[i, j\right] = v_j$, the adjacent matrix *AM* contains the adjacent information between every edge, so we can judge which two edges are adjacent. And with the adjacent matrix *AM* we can obtain the shortest path between any two edges. And *AM* is a GPU device memory structure.

(6) Length Matrix, *LM*. The weight matrix *LM* is a matrix $N \times N$ used to describe the shortest path length of spatial road network. The element $LM\left[i, j\right] \in LM$ represents the length of the shortest path from node v_i to v_j. Obviously, if node v_i is adjacent to node v_j, then $LM\lfloor i, j\rfloor$ represent the weight of edge connect node v_i and node v_j. And *LM* is a GPU device memory structure.

4 Range query algorithms on GPU

Based on the above in-memory data structures, we propose a GPU-based initial range query processing algorithm (GPU-RQ) that utilizes the network expending strategy to search the within-range objects under the MSF framework.

Algorithm 1 details the GPU kernel executing steps for GPU-RQ algorithm in executing stage. The algorithm firstly initializes the searching queue *H*, see Line 1. The algorithm obtains the edge *e* that the query *q* lies in, pushes *e* into the searching queue *H*, and constructs a spanning tree of query *q* (*line 2*). Then from the top of the queue our algorithm fetches an edge *e* and pushes its adjacent edges to searching queue *H* in order of the shortest path length to the query *q* (*line 3*). For each edge *c*, the algorithm computes the shortest path length *dist(q,c)* between query *q* and current edge *c*. If the *dist(q,c)* is less than *r*, then this edge *c* is added into heap *H* and spanning tree *q.tree* (*line 4–6*). When we get the heap *H*, then the algorithm searches all the edges in *H* and computes the objects within query range *r* (*line 8–14*), if the edge *te* is not the leaf edge of *q.tree*, then all the objects lie in query range *r* (*line 9, 10*), or else the distance between each object in edge *te* and *q* must be computed (*line 11–13*). Until the queue *H* is empty, then the algorithm is finished (*line 14*). Note that, when pushing edges adjacent to current edge into the queue H, the edges that have already been pushed into the queue or been processed must be skipped to avoid revisiting.

Algorithm 1: GPU-Based Range Query Processing Algorithm (GPU-RQ)

1. Initialize the empty heap H;
2. Get the edge e that contains q,enheap e into H, let e be root of $q.tree$
3. Search each edge c going from e according to its shortest distance dist(q,c) from q ;
4.   For current edge c,
5.   if dist$(q,c)<r$, enheap c into H, and add c to $q.tree$
6.   else skip c
7. Get next edge in H as e if have and return to step3
8. While $H \neq \phi$, get the top edge te in H,let v is the farther node of te
9.   if $dist(q,v)<r$
10.   push all the objects in edge te to $q.result$
11.   else for each object o in te, Compute the distance between q and o
12.   if dist$(q,o)<r$, push this object o into $q.result$
13.   else skip o
14.   If the heap $H=\phi$, then return

Algorithm 2 details the GPU kernel executing steps of one query updating for GPU-QU algorithm in executing stage. The algorithm firstly pushes all the leaf edges of spanning tree $q.tree$ into searching queue H (*line 1*). Then from the top of the queue H our algorithm fetches an edge e(*line 2*). If this edge lies outside the query range of q, then this edge is enheaped and the spanning tree is cut (*line 3*). Else all the adjacent edges are pushed into H and simultaneously added into spanning tree (*line 4*).when all the edges in H is visited, we can get the final queue. For each edge te in H, if te lies within the query range r, then all the objects are pushed into the results of q (*line 6, 7*), else the objects on edge te must be computed whether falling into the range of query q (*line 8–10*).

Algorithm 2: GPU-Based Query Updating Algorithm (GPU-QU)

1. Push all leaf edges of $q.tree$ into the heap H
2. For each edge e in H
3.   If dist$(q,e)>r$, cut e from the $q.tree$ and enheap the adjacent edge into H
4.   Else search each edge c going from e; enheap c into H, and add c to $q.tree$
5. While $H \neq \phi$, get the top edge te in H,let v is the farther node of te
6.   if $dist(q,v)<r$
7.   push all the objects in edge te to $q.result$
8.   else for each object o in te, Compute the distance between q and o
9.   if dist$(q,o)<r$, push this object o into $q.result$
10.   else skip o
11. If the heap $H=\phi$, then return

Table 1: Parameters.

Parameters	Default	Value Range
Number of objects (N)	100K	50—250 K
Range of query	500	100–1000
Number of queries(qN)	5K	1K, 3K, 5K, 7K, 10K

Table 2: Environment Parameters.

Parameters	CPU Xeon E1230	Parameters	GPU Tesla C2050
Processors	3.2 GHz*4	CUDA kernel	448
Data cache	L3 8 MB	DRAM	3 GB

5 Experiments and analysis

We evaluate the performance of GPU-RQ algorithm and GPU-QU algorithm under MSF framework using the Network-based Generator of Moving Objects to generate simulated moving objects. The input is the road map of Oldenburg (a Germany city) which has 6105 road nodes and 7035 road segments. The generator output 100–250K objects in each segment of the road networks. Initially each object randomly chooses a destination and moves. When the object reaches its destination, an update is reported by randomly selecting the next destination. When we normalize the data space to 10000×10000, the default velocity of objects is equal to 20 per timestamp. At each timestamp about 0.8% moving objects update their velocities. The queries are produced by choosing some objects and issuing a continuous range queries. Table 1 summarizes the parameters used. In each experimental setting, we vary a single parameter and keep the others as default values. The hardware environment is shown in Table 2. The experiments evaluate the performance of queries with mean time of GPU cost (in milliseconds).

Figure 2(a) measures the effect of cardinality N (range from 50 to 250K) on the query processing performance when fixed $r=1000$, $qN=5K$. GPU-QU algorithm outperforms the GPU-RQ algorithm and improves about one to two order magnitude over the GPU brute-force algorithm. For GPU-QU algorithm utilizes adjacent matrix and the spanning tree to recompute the results, while GPU-RQ algorithm must search the shortest path length matrix to compute the initial results, thus reducing the cost of shortest path length matrix scanning. The GPU brute-force algorithm need to search from the root edge with expanding strategy and compute the shortest path online, so spending more GPU time than GPU-QU algorithm and GPU-RQ algorithm. We can find that the cost of GPU time increases slowly with N, for the variety of N doesn't affect the number of searched edges and only increase the shortest length computing cost of moving objects.

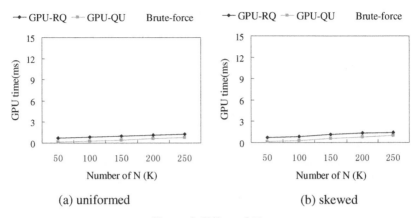

(a) uniformed

(b) skewed

Figure 2: Effect of *N*.

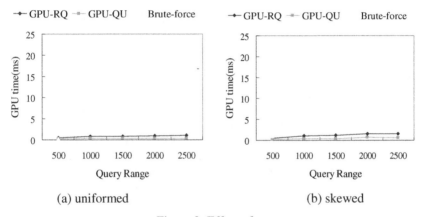

(a) uniformed

(b) skewed

Figure 3: Effect of *r*.

On the other hand, Figure 2(b) shows the performance of the three algorithms on skewed mobile objects, which are almost the same as on uniformed. So we can conclude that the performance of GPU-QU algorithm and GPU-RQ algorithm mainly affected by the query range and the number of queries.

Figure 3 illustrates the effect of query range *r* (range from 500 to 2500) on the query processing performance when fixed *N*=100K and *qN*=5K. As shown, GPU-QU algorithm still outperforms the GPU-RQ algorithm and GPU brute-force algorithm almost in all conditions. When the *r* increases, the performance of GPU brute-force algorithm degrades greatly, while the cost of GPU-QU algorithm and GPU-RQ algorithm increase slightly. For when the query range increases, the GPU brute-force algorithm need search more edges and the cost of shortest path computing increases greatly. The GPU-QU algorithm and GPU-RQ algorithm only search the shortest path length matrix once to find all the edges that lie in the searching range in all conditions, thus exhibit a steady performance. On the skewed condition, as shown in Figure 3(b), the three algorithms exhibit a similar performance as in uniformed condition.

6　Conclusions

In this paper, we introduce the multi-staged framework (MSF) exploiting pipeline strategy to improve the parallelism on GPUs. Based on adjacent matrix and shortest path length matrix, two GPU-based algorithms: GPU-RQ algorithm and GPU-QU algorithm for initial query computing and incremental updating, which use threaded workload parallelism to improve the throughout and performance are proposed. Experimental evaluations show that GPU-RQ and GPU-QU algorithms outperforms brute-force algorithm in almost all conditions.

Acknowledgments

This paper is supported by Chinese National Science of Foundation (61100042) and College National Science of Foundation (HGDYDJJ11008).

References

[1]　A. Madan, M. Cebrian, D. Lazer, and A. Pentland, Social sensing for epidemiological behaviour change. *Proceedings　of the 12th ACM International Conference on Ubiquitous Computing*, ACM, Copenhagen, Denmark, pp.291-300, 2010.

[2]　Vincent Garcia and Frank Nielsen, Searching high-dimensional neighbours: CPU-based tailored data-structures versus GPU-based brute-force method. *Proceedings of IEEE Conference on Computer Vision/Computer Graphics Collaboration Techniques and Applications (MIRAGE)*, Springer, Rocquencourt, France, pp. 425–436, 2009.

[3]　Jia Pan, Christian Lauterbach, and Dinesh Manocha, Efficient nearest-neighbour computation for GPU-based motion planning. *Proceedings of International Conference on Intelligent Robots and Systems (IROS)*. IEEE, Taipei, pp. 2243–2248, 2010.

[4]　R.J. Barrientos, J.I. Gómez, and C. Tenllado, Heap based k-Nearest neighbour search on GPUs. *Congreso Espanol de Informática (CEDI)*, IEEE, Valencia , pp. 559–566, 2010.

[5]　C., Lawrence, A nearest neighbour data structure for graphics hardware. *Proceedings of the 1st International Workshop on Accelerating Data Management Systems Using Modern Processor and Storage Architectures (ADMS)*, VLDB, Singapore, pp. 7–12, 2010.

[6]　J. Pan, D. Manocha, Fast GPU-based locality sensitive hashing for k-nearest neighbour computation. *Proc. of the 19th ACM SIGSPATIAL Int. Conf. on Advances in Geographic Information Systems,* ACM, Chicago, pp. 211–220, 2011.

[7] G. Beliakov, G. Li, Improving the speed and stability of the k-nearest neighbours method. *Pattern Recognition Letters*, **33(10)**, pp. 1296–1301, 2012.

[8] M. Fort, J.A. Sellarès, GPU-based computation of distance functions on road networks with applications. *Proceedings of the 24th ACM Symposium on Applied Computing,* ACM, Hawaii, pp. 1320–1324, 2009.

[9] J. Ricardo, J. Barrientos, I. Gomez, Range query processing in a multi-GPU environment. *Proceedings of the IEEE 10th International Symposium on Parallel and Distributed Processing with Applications (ISPA),* IEEE, Madrid, Spain, pp. 419–426, 2012.

An improved frequency offset estimation algorithm for OFDM system in inter-symbol interference environment

Hang Liu, Feng Zheng, Yun Tang
Department of Telecommunication, Beijing University of Posts and Telecommunications, Beijing, 100876, China

Abstract

Long-term evolution (LTE) communication system is developing rapidly in recent years. Its down link using the orthogonal frequency division multiplexing (OFDM) technology for data transmission. OFDM system can make the spectrum utilization significantly improved. However, because of the system structure, OFDM symbol is sensitive to frequency offset. Even little frequency offset can easily bring inter-carrier interference (ICI). The existing frequency offset estimation algorithm has been matured in common channel environment. This paper presents a frequency offset estimation algorithm which can solve the problem of estimation in inter-symbol interference environment. This algorithm is based on the SC algorithm. In the fifth section of this paper, the simulation results show that the improving algorithm has better performance than SC algorithm.

Keywords: LTE system, OFDM system, frequency offset estimation, frequency offset compensation, SC improving, inter-symbol interference, multipath channel.

1 Introduction

Compared with the traditional channel bandwidth which W is divided into N since the band of frequency division, orthogonal frequency division multiplexing (OFDM) has higher band utilization. In order to ensure that each band does not overlap, the original frequency division multiplexing technology need to be protected at all since the band is inserted between every interval. In the OFDM system, frequency selective channel bandwidth is divided into overlapping

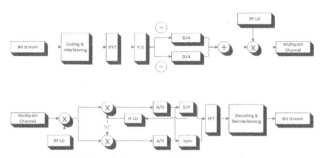

Figure 1: Block diagram of OFDM receiver and transmitter.

channel but not orthogonal frequency selective narrow-band channel. This avoids the need to use to separate carrier protection bandwidth. So it makes OFDM system has higher spectrum efficiency. Because the channel in OFDM system in the receiver can completely separate, reducing the complexity of the receiver, so that the OFDM is attractive in high speed mobile data transmission, such as long-term evolution (LTE) downlink link [1,2].

In order to improve the performance of OFDM system in mobile environment, frequency offset estimation and compensation are pretty significant parts. For frequency offset estimation in the OFDM system [3], there are quite a few classic algorithms previously [4]. In the literature [5] Moose introduces a kind of maximum likelihood estimate method, which takes advantage of the two continuous symbols that are the same to each other. The scope of its maximum normalized frequency offset estimation is times the sub-carrier spacing. ML proposes an efficient iterative algorithm for joint frequency synchronization and channel estimation algorithm [6]. This method's ML estimator MSEs are tightly close to CRBs at large SNRs with a good tracking range. SC algorithm presents a method that uses the training sequence for frequency offset estimation and it is the prototype of the algorithm in this paper. SC using the particular transmission way, it makes first half sequence is same with second half sequence in the transmission section. And it makes two same parts do relevant operation at the receiving section and calculates the frequency offset.

2 OFDM principles and the influence of frequency offset

2.1 OFDM principles

Consider an OFDM system with N subcarriers. The signal is generated at baseband by taking the inverse fast Fourier transform (IFFT) after quadrature amplitude modulated (QAM) or phase-shift keyed (PSK) $x_k = Re_k + jIm_k$ (Figure 1). In the figure, the block P/S represents a parallel-to-serial converter. An OFDM symbol has a useful period T and preceding each symbol is a cyclic prefix of length N_{cp}, which is longer than the maximum channel spread L for eliminating the interference between adjacent OFDM symbols (ISI), an N_{cp} points cyclic prefix is inserted at the beginning of each OFDM symbol [6]. The frequencies of

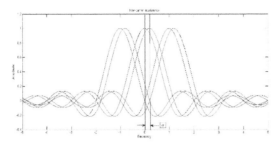

Figure 2: The loss of orthogonality caused by frequency offset.

the complex exponentials are $f_k = k/T$, and the useful part for $2N + 1$ subcarrier is given by [7]: $u(t) = \sum_{k=lN}^{N} x_k \exp(j2\pi f_k t)$, $0|t|T$.

The baseband signal is quadrature modulated, up-converted to the radio frequency (RF) and transmitted through the channel.

At the receiver, the signal is down-converted to an intermediate frequency (IF), and quadrature demodulated. The block S/P . A carrier frequency offset of Δf causes a phase rotation of $2\pi t\Delta f$. If uncorrected this causes both a rotation of the constellation and a spread of the constellation points similar to additive white Gaussian noise (AWGN). A symbol-timing error will have little effect as long as all the samples taken are within the length of the cyclically-extended OFDM symbol [8].

2.2 The influence of carrier frequency offset

As mentioned above, frequency offset will bring about ICI in the OFDM system (Figure 2). There are two reasons lead to the carrier frequency offset generally in OFDM systems. One is the oscillator of transmitter and the receiver has frequency deviation, it leads to the subcarrier frequency offset. Second, there is Doppler frequency offset when the relative speed exits between the terminal and the base station. And nonlinear channel leads to phase noise. The carrier frequency offset is divided into integer frequency offset and decimal frequency offset. Carrier phase offset generally does not change the signal amplitude, so it would not bring the signal noise ratio (SNR) loss.

The signal of time-domain in receiver is:

$$r(k) = [\sum_{m=0}^{N-1} X_m H_m e^{j2\pi mk/N}]e^{j2\pi mk/N} + n(k) = \sum_{m=0}^{N-1} X_m H_m e^{j2\pi(m+\tau)k/N} + n(k)$$

The H_m said channel transfer function, the τ play the part of normalized clutter frequency offset, and the $n(k)$ said additive white Gaussian noise sampling.

After demodulation the data of frequency-domain can be expressed as:

$$Y(n) = \sum_{k=0}^{N-1} r(k)e^{-j2\pi nk/N}$$

$$= X_n H_n \frac{\sin(\pi\tau)}{\sin(\frac{\pi\tau}{N})} e^{j\pi\tau(N-1)/N} + \sum_{m=0,m\neq n}^{N-1} X_m H_m \frac{\sin\left[\pi(m+\tau-n)\right]}{\sin\left[\frac{\pi(m+\tau-n)}{N}\right]} e^{j2\pi(m+\tau-n)(N-1)/N} + w(n)$$

It can be seen from the above equation that the carrier frequency offset will lead to a drop in signal amplitude and inter-carrier interference, and it can make serious loss of the system performance. The subcarrier that needs demodulation arithmetic was not at its peak sampling, it caused the signal amplitude reduced. And adjacent subcarrier sampled without the zeros points leads to the inter-carrier interference.

The formula:

$$X_n H_n e^{j\pi\tau(N-1)/N} \sin(\pi\tau) \,/\, \sin\left(\frac{\pi\tau}{N}\right)$$

According to the useful signal demodulation results.
Its amplitude and phase of the attenuation degree is:

$$H_n e^{j\pi\tau(N-1)/N} \sin(\pi\tau) \,/\, \sin\left(\frac{\pi\tau}{N}\right)$$

And 3.4 said the output inter-carrier interference after demodulation.

$$\sum_{m=0,m\neq n}^{N-1} X_m H_m e^{j2\pi(m+\tau-n)(N-1)/N} \sin\left[\pi(m+\tau-n)\right]/\sin\left[\frac{\pi(m+\tau-n)}{N}\right]$$

The $w(n)$ is the plural data of additive white Gaussian noise (AWGN). It can be seen that when N is kept constant, with the increase of carrier frequency offset, inter-carrier interference is increasing in the system. And when τ is kept constant, with the subcarrier's number increasing, it also leads to the occurrence of the phenomenon.

3 The principle of algorithm

3.1 SC algorithm

SC algorithm using system model as shown in Figure 3.

In Figure 3, the C_i is the training sequence, it's produced by the PN sequence by QPSK and the U_n is training symbol, it's obtained by training sequence after IFFT transformation. The $H(t)$ is the impact of time multipath channel accordingly. The $N(t)$ is the additive white Gaussian noise (AWGN). The $s(t)$ is

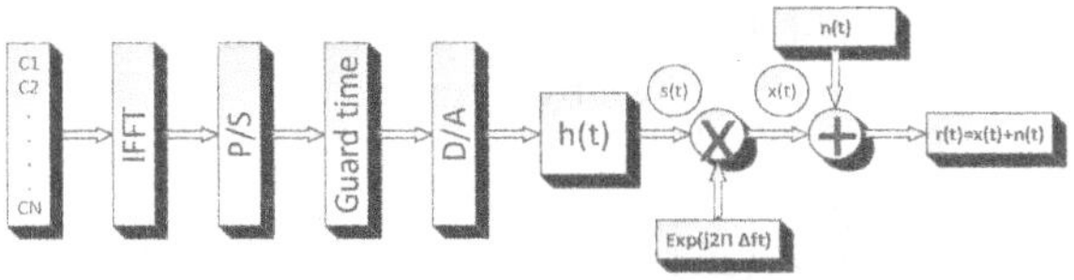

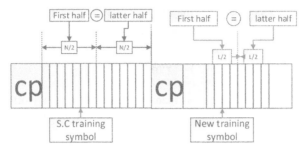

Figure 3: SC system model.

First half $\boxed{=}$ latter half   First half $=$ latter half

$N/2$ $N/2$ $L/2$ $L/2$

cp   cp

S.C training symbol   New training symbol

Figure 4: SC and the new training sequence model.

an ideal training symbol after channel and the Δf is the carrier frequency offset. The data N is the length of inverse fast Fourier transform (IFFT). If we assume that $s(k)$ is the result of sampling $s(t)$, we can get the formula:

$$r(k) = s(k)\exp(j2\pi k\Delta fT / N) + n(k)$$

Assuming that   , the training sequence can get L points after IFFT transformation with length of L. These sampling points constitute the first half of the training symbol, and the second part is the same as the first. Just like the Figure 4.

After the training sequence passed through the ideal channel, theoretically, the first half and the second half of the symbols should be same in time-domain. In the frequency-domain, we can pass on even number of the subcarrier sequence with a pseudo-random sequence and odd number of subcarrier does not send data for achieving the previous purpose. In the simulation experiments, training symbol can be realized by sending QPSK constellations point at every even number subcarrier. It can also come true through the training symbol does IFFT with average length repetitively. The training symbols can be used to estimate decimal frequency offset between adjacent subcarrier. From above we can know that the first half of the training symbol and the second is same, so except the phase deviation caused by the frequency offset the received signal's first half and second should also be same in time-domain. At the receiving end, we can make the two parts of the signal do correlation operation. After the correlation operation we can remove the influence of channel and get an approximate phase value. Assuming that the symbol of the starting position is accurate and the results of the phase are approximately equal, then the range of the accumulation is large enough. The sum of the product of every pair sample values that get from the related operations could be shown by formula:

$$P(d) = \sum_{m=0}^{L-1} r^*(d+m)r(d+m+L) = |P(d)| e^{j2\varphi}$$

The main difference between the two halves of the training symbol will be a phase difference of   It can be estimated by:

$$\varphi = angle(p(d))$$

Suppose can be guaranteed less than   , then the frequency offset estimation should be :Otherwise, the frequency offset estimation results should be: where   is an integer.

3.2 The improved algorithm based on the SC

Under the environment of the mobile channel, OFDM system will be affected by a variety of interference. When the cyclic prefix (CP) length is much less than the number of multipath, there will be a significant inter-symbol interference. In this condition, the frequency offset estimation which calculated by the classic SC algorithm will have the very big deviation. In order to improve the accuracy of frequency estimation under such a special circumstance, this paper proposes an improving method that changes the training signal of classic SC algorithm. In the new training signal, I shorten the length of training sequence that makes correlation operation. By cutting off both sides redundant parts which suffered serious attenuation, we can effectively avoid the inter-symbol interference. But if there is no ISI, we have to give away some accuracy of frequency offset estimation.

The improved algorithm principle is Figure 4. This method will reduce the length of related calculation sequence, it uses L/4 length to do the correlation operation that is L/2 in old algorithm. Due to the data that is used for the correlation is decreased, the accuracy of frequency offset estimation will be reduced in normal channel, and this will lead to lower bit error rate (BER). But when the system is suffering the ISI, this method of frequency offset estimation will maintain a relatively stable estimation accuracy.

4 Simulation results and analysis

Simulation parameters: Length of OFDM symbol: 1024 bits; Number of guard interval (Ng): 0:1:6; Signal to noise ratio (SNR): 10:10:80; Fd: random decimal within 0–0.25, generated by the random function; Multipath number: 6; Fading channel of multipath (dB): 0, -6, -10, -14, -20, -26; Delay of time from path 1 to path 6: 0, 2, 4, 6, 8, 10; Channel: AWGN, multipath and frequency offset.

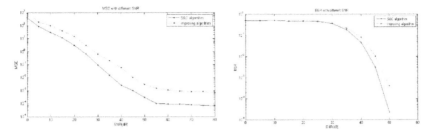

Figure 5: MSE of two algorithms with different SNR.

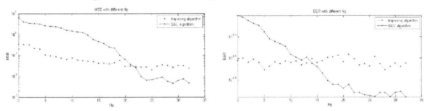

Figure 6: MSE and BER with different Ng.

In the absence of the ISI, from Figure 5, the property of MSE gradually gets better with the increase of SNR. Obviously, the SC algorithm performance is better than the improving algorithm in all SNR.

It just confirms the previous inference. Individually watching the MSE drawing Figure 5 (front), the curve of MSE declines nearly flat after 55 dB of SNR. And the BER is also approaching zero after 50 dB of SNR as Figure 5 (behind). Thus, the 40 dB of SNR is the best choice that we could observe the pros and cons of the two kinds of schemes.

By reducing the Ng length to control the degree of the ISI in this simulation as shown in Figure 6. From Figure 6, we can see that SC algorithm's MSE has been getting better with the increase of Ng, and the improving algorithm has been almost flat. The map also presents that in poor condition, where Ng is within 22, the performance of SC algorithm is worse than improving algorithm.

The BER's graph also confirms the previous phenomenon. The only difference is that the intersection of the two curves is coming early (Ng=14). This may be due to other distractions in the channel.

5   Conclusions and applications

SC algorithm has better performance in frequency offset estimation without ISI. It just can be used in an ideal situation that the ISI is completely avoided. The improving algorithm this paper presents has better performance when the CP is too short to eliminate the ISI.

In the presence of interference of the known channel environment, we can use the improving algorithm to estimate frequency offset. Another application, frequency offset estimation module can be made into an adaptive system. This adaptive system can adjust the sequence length of frequency offset estimation for adapting the changing channels.

Acknowledgments

I would like to express my gratitude to all those who helped me during the writing of this paper: The fundamental research funds for the central universities under grand No. 470527 and the science research project of Shanxi provincial department of education No.11JK1016.

References

[1] Stefania Sesia and Issam Toufik, *LTE-The UMTS Long Term Evolution: From Theory to Practice.* Posts and Telecom Press, Beijing, pp. 89–111, 2012.

[2] B. Le Floch, R. Halbert-lassalle, and D. Castelain, Digital sound broadcasting to mobile receivers. *IEEE Transactions on Consumer Electronics*, **35**, pp. 493–503, 1989.

[3] Maohua Ran, Jianguo Huang, and Marine Eng, OFDM carrier offset estimation based on signal phase matching principle, *IEEE Youth Conference on Computing and Telecommunication, 2009.* YC-ICT'09., Beijing, pp. 66–69, 2009.

[4] T.M. Schmidl and D.C. Cox, Fellow, robust frequency and timing synchronization for OFDM. *IEEE*, **45**, pp. 1613–1616, 1997.

[5] P.H. Moose, A technique for orthogonal frequency division multiplexing frequency offset correction. *IEEE Transactions on Communication*, **42**, pp. 2908–2914, 1994.

[6] Yi Sun and R.Y. Yen, An efficient iterative algorithm for joint frequency synchronization and channel estimation in OFDM Systems, 3rd IEEE *International Symposium on Microwave, Antenna, Propagation and EMC Technologies for Wireless Communication*, Beijing, pp. 430–435, 2009.

[7] Anastasios Stamoulis, Suhas N. Diggavi, and Naofal Al-Dhahir, Intercarrier interference in MIMO OFDM. *IEEE Transactions on Signal Processing,* **50**, pp. 2451–2464, 2002.

[8] Linglong Dai and Zhaocheng Wang, Time-frequency training OFDM with high spectral efficiency and reliable performance in high speed environments, *IEEE Global Telecommunications Conference*, Houston, TX, pp. 1–5, 2011.

The relational database theory and Web service technology

Jianxiao Liu[1], Jian Wang[2], Feng Liu[1], Xiaoxia Li[1], Fang Wu[3]
[1]College of Science, Huazhong Agricultural University, Wuhan, 430072, China
[2]State Key Lab of Software Engineering, Wuhan University, Wuhan, 430072, China
[3]Digital Department of Library, Huazhong Agricultural University, Wuhan, 430072, China

Abstract

Cloud computing is a new kind of internet technology, and all the resources are appeared in the form of Web service in the cloud. Users can find the services to meet their needs according to their different requests, including atomic and composite services. Service computing is a new research direction around Web service discovery, clustering, selection, composition, QoS, management, and so on. At present, the existing research work has been used to solve one of the aspects about service computing technology, but there is not a universal method to solve all these problems. In this paper, we use the relational database (RDB) theory into Web service technology research. On the basis of storing service information, we take advantage of the relational database theories (such as join, select, project, aggregate function, view, procedure, grant, and trigger) to realize Web service selection, clustering, composition, recommendation, evolution, access control, and so on. The service function and QoS information are mainly considered in the work.

Keywords: cloud computing, service computing, Web Service, RDB.

1 Introduction

Cloud computing [1] is a new kind of internet technology which is based on the traditional computing and network technology. All resources are appeared in the form of Web services in the cloud computing era, users can select the desired services and then assemble them to meet their needs better. In order to help users to select the services that meet their needs in the cloud, a new research direction, Service-Oriented Computing (SOC), is emerged. SOC is also called service computing [2]. It is a new computing paradigm and it has a profound impact in academic and industry. The coverage of service computing involves the entire life cycle of services, including service creation, implementation, clustering, discovery, composition, selection, recommendation, optimization [3,4], and so on.

The domestic and foreign scholars have conducted a lot of research work and made a series of achievement around service computing technology. For example, they use the user-centric, formal-based, QoS-based and some other methods to realize service composition. The traditional clustering method is usually used to cluster services from respects of service interface, function, semantic, and so on. The collaborative filtering, personalized QoS-aware, context-awareness, and some other methods are used to realize service recommendation. The existing research work has used different approaches to solve one of the service technologies. But there is not a common method that can solve all these problems. Through analyzing the intrinsic relation between the RDB theory and Web services technology, this paper uses RDB theory to realize services clustering, selection, composition, recommendation, access control, and so on. This approach can help to enhance the efficiency of service technology. The main work is given in the following.

(1) The self-join in RDB is used to join service information tables. It helps to enhance service clustering efficiency.
(2) The relational database operation (select, project, aggregate function, etc.) is used to obtain service information and realize service selection in high efficiency.
(3) Web service composition approach and repository are implemented through join, nested query, and view in RDB.
(4) The procedure is used to realize service recommendation. The grant mechanism is used for service access control. And trigger is used to update services information in time.

2 Web service information storage

Web service can be defined as a triple $ws=\{WSName, Input, Output\}$, and *WSName* represents the name of *ws*. *Input* and *Output* represent the input and output set of *ws*. Relational model is an important kind of data model at present, and RDB uses relational model to organize data. The data structure of each relation is a standardized two-dimensional table. *Input(i_id, pid, ws_id)*, *Output(o_id, pid, ws_id)*, *Para(pid, pname)*, *Service(ws_id, name, price, time, availability, ...)*. Input stores the input information and Output stores the output information of service. Para is the parameter information table. Service stores the name and QoS information, including price, time, availability, and so on.

3   Web service selection

SQL Statements is the core operation to query data in database, and the basic relational algebra structure [5] of SQL statement is shown as follows:

$$\pi_{A_1, A_2, \dots, A_n} (\sigma_p (r_1 \times r_2 \times \dots \times r_m))$$

Join is also called θ join, it selects tuples that satisfy certain conditions among properties from the Cartesian product of two relations. $R \bowtie_{A\theta B} S = \{ \widehat{t_r t_s} \mid t_r \in R \land t_s \in S \land t_r[A] \theta t_s[B] \}$

When to find services according to user's requests, we can use SQL statement to select service directly from service information tables. For example, when to select name and time of services whose input is *p2*. The *Service, Input, Para* are joined firstly, then the service information can be got using the operation of select and project.

$$\pi_{name, time} (\sigma_{pname='p2'} (Service \times Input \times Para))$$

The aggregate function in SQL is used to strength the retrieval function, and it includes the following functions: *COUNT(), SUM(), AVG(), MAX(), MIN()*, and so on. Users usually have QoS request information, such as the services whose price is the cheapest or the response time is the fastest. The statement of selecting *ws_id, WSName* of services whose price is the cheapest is shown as follows:

Select *ws_id*, name From Service, where price = (Select MIN(price) From Service);

The group by statement is used to group the query result according to the value of one or more property, and the equivalent values are divided into the same group. When to select services, users can group the services according to input, output, and QoS using group by statement. This can help to enhance service finding efficiency.

The order by statement is used to sort the query result in accordance with one or more attribute columns in ascending or descending order. When to select Web services, services will be sorted according to the order of one or more QoS values using order by statement. This facilitates user to choose services which can meet their QoS requirements. For example, order by price can be used to sort services according to price. This helps users to select services with proper QoS values.

4   Web service selection clustering

Web service clustering refers to group the Web services which realize same function and have same interface into service clusters. The services in the same service cluster have different QoS values.

Self-Join means joining a table with itself, and it selects the tuples which meet certain conditions among properties. The Input and Ouput tables will be joined using self-Join operation, and this helps to cluster services with similar function. It includes the following steps:

(1) $JoinIN \leftarrow Input_1 \bowtie_{Input1.pid@Input2.pid} Input_2,$ $JoinOUT \leftarrow Output_1 \bowtie_{Output1.pid@Output2.pid} Output_2$

(2) It constructs IO matching matrix according to *JoinIN* and *JoinOUT*.

$$v_{IO} = \begin{bmatrix} v_{11} & v_{12} & \cdots & v_{1n} \\ v_{21} & v_{22} & \cdots & v_{2n} \\ \cdots & \cdots & \cdots & \cdots \\ v_{n1} & v_{n2} & \cdots & v_{nn} \end{bmatrix}$$

(3) The elements which are not equal to 0 in v_{IO} have symmetry feature. $v_{ij}=0 \Rightarrow v_{ji}=0$, $v_{ij}!=0 \Rightarrow v_{ji}!=0$. When v_{ij} of *Input* is not equal to 0, the corresponding v_{ij} of *Output* will be judged further. This helps to speed up the service clustering.

After clustering services, a column named *ClusterID* will be added into Service table. It is used to annotate the cluster the services belong to *Service(ws_id, WSName, ClusterID, price, time, availability)*. Services whose *ServiceType* are same will be stored into the same service cluster. And these services realize similar function but have different QoS values.

5 Web service composition

5.1 Join

Service composition refers to orchestrate one or more services to form the composite service that can offer a value-added service [6]. At present, the research work about service composition mainly concentrates on service interface (*Input* and *Output*). The join operation in RDB theory is repeatedly used to join the *Output* and *Input* table. The matching tuples will be extracted to realize service composition in high efficiency. This process includes the following steps:

(1) Use $WSJoin \leftarrow Output \bowtie_{Output.pid@Input.pid} Input$ to join *Output* and *Input* tables.

(2) For each tuple in *WSJoin*, services of specific *ws_id* will be combined further. Supposing the service of *Output.ws_id* is ws_i and the service of *Input.ws_id* is ws_j, the output of ws_i is matched with the input of ws_j. The composition relations between ws_i and ws_j will be expressed as $ws_i \rightarrow ws_j$.

(3) *TInput* $\leftarrow$ $\pi_{i\_id,pid,ws\_id}(\text{WSJoin})$,*TOutput* $\leftarrow$

$\pi_{o\_id,pid,ws\_id}(\text{TInput} \times Output)$.

(4) Return to step (1) and join *TOutput* and *Input*. The composite services can be obtained through the repeat judging.

5.2 Nested query

A SELECT-FROM-WHERE statement is called a query block in SQL. A query block can be nested into the statement of WHERE and HAVING of another query block. This kind of query is called nested query.

Service matching, selection, and composition can be realized through nested query of RDB. We can get services which has composition relations with ws_i through the following steps:

(1) $ws_i.output \leftarrow \pi_{pname}(\sigma_{name=ws_i.WSName}(Service \times Output \times Para))$

(2) $tinput \leftarrow \pi_{pname}(Service \times Input \times Para)$

(3) Find *ws_id* of specific service using nested query IN, and $ws_i.output \subseteq$ *tinput*.

Or

(1) $ws_i.input \leftarrow \pi_{pname}(\sigma_{name=ws_i.WSName}(Service \times Input \times Para))$

(2) $toutput \leftarrow \pi_{pname}(Service \times Output \times Para)$

(3) Find *ws_id* of specific service using nested query IN, and $ws_i.input \subseteq$ *toutput*.

In the above statement, we can find services which has composition relations with ws_i from the following two aspects: (1) find the service whose input is matching with the output of ws_i; (2) find the service whose output is matching with the input of ws_i. Using the above two approaches, we can find services which have combination relations with ws_i.

5.3 View

View is a virtual table that does not necessarily exists in a physical form. View is defined in terms of base tables directly or indirectly. The composite services are the abstract services and they are formed through the combination of services that are stored in tables. In consideration of the intrinsic relation between view and composite service, we will store the composite service into view. According to the user's given input and output information, we can get composite service information from the view directly. And the efficiency will be enhanced. The composite service is composed of one or more atomic service, so the number of view columns is determined by the number of atomic services in particular composite service.

For example, given the composite service whose input is p_i and output is p_j. The SQL statement of storing the composite service into view is shown as follows:

Create View CAs

Select A.Input, A.name, B.name, B.Output From Service A, Service B, Input, Output Where A.Input='p_i' and B.Output='p_j' and A.Output=B.Input

The composite service can be stored using view through above statement. In addition, view can be defined on the basis of the existing view further. This helps to realize combining atomic service and composite services, combining composite service and composite service. Then the large granularity service will be formed.

6 Web service recommendation and management

6.1 Procedure

Some Web services are usually invoked by users together. These services are often the public services which can meet multiple user's requirements. For example, reserving ticket and credit card payment service, users often have to pay by credit card after booking ticket. Therefore, we can bundle the two services together. They will be recommended to users for invocation directly when users have proposed the requests. The procedure in RDB can be used to bundle these services together, and thus to invoke them repeatedly and enhance efficiency. For example, the procedure statement of bundling BookTicket and CreditCard service is shown as follows:

```
<algorithm>Create Procedure TicketCreditInvoke (data, startplace, destination)
AS Begin
    Select* from Service, Input where Input={data, startplace, destination};
    Select* from Service Where name=CreditCard;
End
```

The BookTicket and CreditCard service can be bundled together through above statement. When BookTicket is selected and invoked, Call Procedure TicketCreditInvoke('2012-12-9', 'Wuhan','Beijing') will be used to select BookTicket and CreditCard service at the same time. And the CreditCard service will also be recommended to users, and this can enhance efficiency.

6.2 Grant

In cloud computing, different tenants will order different services, as well as different tenant's administrator will assign different services to their users. The implementation of all these functions needs to assign different services access permissions for different users. Then users who have different permissions will have different privileges of using these services, such as selecting, adding, updating, and deleting services. We can take advantage of the grant and revoke mechanisms in RDB to define the access permissions of services for different users.

For example, the SQL statement of grant selection permissions of Service to U1, U2 is shown as follows:

Grant SelectON Table ServiceTO U1, U2

We can also use revoke to recover user's rights. This helps to manage the using services privileges for users flexibly.

In addition, we can create role for a group of users who have the same privileges. Using role to manage the database permissions can simplify the authorization process. Firstly, we use create role to create particular role, then we use grant to authorize to roles, then users will be authorized directly through specific role. Through these steps, it can implement service authorization more flexible and convenient.

6.3 Trigger

With the dynamic changing of application environment and user's requirements, services information will be changed accordingly. Then it needs to update the service information in the tables of RDB. When a Web service is not accessible (availability is 0), it needs to delete this service and the view that is formed on the basis of the service. When the QoS is changing, it needs to sort the services further. Trigger in RDB can be used to implement the above function. Supposing the availability of one service is 0, we need to delete the service and the corresponding view. The SQL statement of creating trigger that can realize the above function is shown as follows:

```
<algorithm>Create Trigger UpdateService After Update ON Service FOR
EACH ROW
  AS BEGIN
    IF(new.availability=0) THEN
      Select ws_id From Service Where availability=0
    Delete From service Where availability=0
      Delete From View where v_id= ws_id
    END IFEND
```

7 Related work

The research work about combining RDB and Web services concentrates on two aspects. The first one refers to the interaction between RDB and Web services. For example, the data in RDB is appeared in the form of Web services for invocation, and the RDB invoke Web services directly using some modes [7,8].

The second one concentrates on applying RDB theory into Web service technology, such as Web service aggregation, composition, matching, operation union, and so on. Feuerlicht has proposed a method for service aggregation that uses relational operations over interface parameters to assemble services from low granularity atomic service operations. Cui proposes an approach to aggregate Web services for end-user-doable construction of GridDoc application. This method uses the operations in RDB to filter the service output and tuples, such as select, project, union, join, and so on. Chenthati et al. propose an RDBMS schema for storing messages and the sequence of communications. The FSM is used to model the business flow and the corresponding Web service matching algorithm is proposed based on the table being designed. The above methods mainly store the Web service and ontology information, and they use operations (such as union, join, project, and so on) in RDB to select the required information. The specific function can be implemented and the service selection efficiency will be enhanced.

There are a lot of research work about Web service composition, selection, clustering, recommendation, management, and so on. These research methods are all used to solve one of the aspects about service technologies. Due to the limited spaces, we will not elaborate them in detail. And there is not an universal approach that can solve all these problems. The paper introduces how to use relational database theory to solve all the related technologies about Web service.

8 Conclusions

In the era of service-oriented software engineering, the research work about service computing includes service registration, clustering, selection, composition, recommendation, management, control, and so on. While there does not exist a universal method or theory that can solve all these problems. Based on the intrinsic relation between the Web service technology and the RDB theory, the RDB theory is used into the service computing technology in this paper. It realizes Web service clustering, selection, composition, recommendation, evolution, and so on using RDB theory. The functions can be easily realized and the efficiency can be enhanced.

As to the future research work, we plan to use ontology to annotate service information. And it helps to realize Web service technology from the semantic level. We will develop prototype system to support the idea of using RDB theory to implement Web service technology.

Acknowledgments

This research is supported by the State Key Laboratory of Software Engineering, Wuhan University, under Grant No.SKLSE2012-09-24, the Fundamental Research Funds for the Central Universities under grant No.2013QC020, the Huazhong Agricultural University New Doctoral Scientific Research Projects under grant No.52902-0900206081, 52902-0900206084.

References

[1] N.R. Michael, Building an open cloud. *Science*, **324**, pp. 1656–1657, 2009.
[2] J. Lin, A conceptual model for negotiating in service-oriented environments. *Information Processing Letters*, **108**, pp. 192–203, 2008.
[3] B.L. Tim, H. Wendy, H. James, S. Nigel, J.W. Daniel, Creating a science of the Web. *Science*, **313**, pp. 769–771, 2006.
[4] I. Foster, Service-oriented science. *Science*, **308**, pp. 814–817, 2005.
[5] S. Wang and S.X. Sa, *Introduction to Database Systems*, Higher Education Press, pp. 52–183, 2006 (in Chinese).
[6] M. Brahim, B. Athman, K.E. Ahmed, Composing web services on the semantic web. *The VLDB Journal*, **12**, pp. 333–351, 2003.
[7] H. Zhu, F. Guo, and Y.C. Feng, DM database management system web service research. *Chinese Computer Science*, **34(3)**, pp. 87–89, 2007 (in Chinese).
[8] Z.D. Wu, G.D. Xu, Z. Yu, X. Yi, E.H. Chen, Y.C. Zhang, Executing SQL queries over encrypted character strings in the database-as-service model. *Knowledge-Based Systems*, **35**, pp. 332–348, 2012.

The study of survive hierarchical topology control scenario design based on wireless sensor networks technical

Cong Chen
Department of Computer and Science, Wuzhou University, China

Abstract

WSN as a new information gathering and processing techniques, with the low-power communications technology, sensor technology, MEMS technology, and the rapid development of embedded systems technology, in today's society of information technology, economic, and social progress increasingly play more important role. Any information technology development to a certain stage, will produce and survivability, security and other related issues, in view of the special nature WSN, which can be the basis of survival is survivable topology control study, it is hoped the network topology designed to extend the network life and early death in the individual nodes continue to provide critical services, when fault/intrusion tolerance ability to reach the limit, and can be returned to work with renewable technologies. In this paper, energy saving and renewable technologies for WSN topology were studied and analyzed, put forward their own solutions. This paper summarizes the survivability of WSN. In any unfavorable conditions-based WSN system services should have the ability to continue to meet users' needs. This paper analyzes the characteristics of the wireless sensor network, the network management as the center, from the network management architecture, network topology control and network management protocol three aspects of wireless sensor network management were studied.

Keywords: WDN, Internet, MEMS, scenario.

1 Introduction

Things wireless sensor networks as one of the core enabling technologies is to achieve the perception of physical contact between the foundation, we can say without WSN, networking and the Internet is no essential difference [1]. With the development of computer, multimedia, and network technology, mankind entered the information society. Information resource has become the great driving force of social development, information, and knowledge plays a more and more important role in modern society. WSN basic idea originated in the 1970s, the US Defense Advanced Research Institute. In 1978, funding from Carnegie Mellon University conducted a distributed sensor network research projects, research is mainly based on wireless communication capabilities of sensor nodes S organizational networks [2]. Essentially WSN is a lot number of sensor nodes distributed in a region, through wireless communication from the tissue to form a multi-hop network system, which can complete the data collection from the insects, quantification, processing, integration, and transmission [3].

With the continuous development of WSN technology and applications, and its survivability and related safety issues continue to be exposed. Unlike five network applications begin to start, build basic platform, and then continue to patch security vulnerabilities development model, WSN nodes because of information processing, storage capacity is weak, limited energy and large-scale department bitter characteristics, makes it impossible to take the matter network mode, so how to solve the problem of survivability of WSN is very urgent [4].

Since a single node limited energy, their hardware failure, or even human vandalism will result in the premature death of nodes, thus splitting the connected network topology, and finally result in network paralysis thin [5]. The network topology often regenerate not only a waste of resources, but also because of the random distribution of nodes can not guarantee the connectivity of the new network, affecting network survivability. Thus, survival topology study aimed to design an individual node does not work, still maintain system function network topology, in the event of more serious problems, there are certain renewable capacity in the network lifetime as long as possible At the same time, continue to provide critical services to users [6].

This article is based on WSN own characteristics (no global identity, many communication, network dynamics and strong, data redundancy, limited resources and energy) is different from the traditional wireless network, the topology of WSN viable core set: meet coverage, connectivity is provided; make routing based favor transmission and processing of data; eliminate signal interference, efficient communication; node energy consumption work life spring extend the network; certain tolerance/intrusion tolerant capability to ensure network services; can achieve large-scale arrangement, the network structure renewable.

2 The related theory of wireless sensor network

2.1 Overview and basic architecture of the WSN

WSN is a set of sensors to form ad-hoc mode wireless network, the purpose of collaboration and awareness, collection and processing of network coverage perceive objects, and publish to the management node. WSN basic entity object

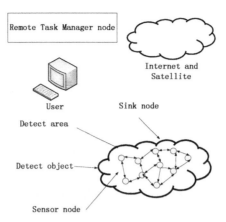

Figure 1: The general structure form of WSN.

Table 1: Contrast the Reaction System at Different Times.

	First type can survive system	Reactive survivable systems
System design	Need to redesign the system, the system is designed with sufficient redundancy	No need to redesign the system
Intrusion Detection	Intrusion detection, and give relevant responses	No intrusion detection, and give relevant responses
Response mechanism	Such as intrusion exists, periodically re-invasion according to specific	Take the appropriate construction technology system survivability

includes four categories: monitoring objectives, sensor nodes, sink node, and management node [7,8]. The general structure form of WSN is shown in Figure 1.

2.2 Survivability technical classification

Survivable systems at different times according to the technical defenses fall into two categories: the first type of error should be shielded system (the system when subjected to tapping out, no impact is difficult to present) and the reactive attack response system (through improved monitoring system, speed up the reaction time, thereby attack the system can continue to operate in case). Both the difference between the impact on the system was shown in Table 1.

Current WSN renewable technologies to fault/intrusion tolerance as the research focus, described as "work sick." But a "sick work" system that can tolerate many times the next attack, soon be invaded because of the death of each

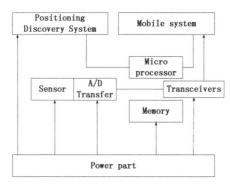

Figure 2: Sensor node structure.

subnet and ultimately unable to provide critical services users. Therefore, since the regeneration technology was born, and WSN as a new field of study, the Ministry of the large number of random nodes self-organize into a network, when some node fails, the remaining nodes can be re self-organized into a network, you can also re-deployed randomly some nodes, forming a new, faster WSN, just like humans, like procreation, death constantly born, continue to complete the system critical services.

2.3 WSN topology control and survivability

Management node is perceived by the recipient of information and applications, from a broad perspective, the management node can be a person, it can be a computer or other device. Such as military commander carried by an aircraft or a mobile computer can be used as the management node. A WSN, the management node, can have one or more than one management node can also be a multiple of WSN users.

Management node has two operating modes: one is active, that is actively managed node WSN query or the perception of the information collected; another is responsive, that passive management node receives information published by WSN, generally, the more responsive applications.

In summary, WSN is the targeted source of information for the application, and the network is through the target heat, infrared, sonar, radar, and seismic wave signals, to obtain temperature, noise, movement direction and speed target attribute, users want to accomplish in order to achieve the purpose of including environmental monitoring, event monitoring, targeting, and target tracking.

As the basic unit of WSN, sensor nodes constitute the basic platform of WSN nodes and WSN technology development are closely linked, directly determines the overall network performance. Mainly by the power sensor nodes, a sensor unit, a processor unit, and a wireless communication unit such as functional units, the basic structure as shown in Figure 2.

Flat network topology, the node of a circle, set the coordinates (x_1, y_1), the radius is R, i.e., sensing radius, the so-called perceived quality level is to be perceived. For example, we believe that as long as R is the radius of the circle is, all events are node points to the probability of a perception, that all points within the circle of the perceived quality is a relative of a point outside the circle is the perceived quality 0. Assuming any point coordinate plane (x_2, y_2), and the distance of the node

The perceived quality of $C(x, y)$, such as the mathematical expression:

The perception model probability, the sensing range II of the node A, point B, is monitored with a probability of P $(0 < P < 1)$, the probability P sensing the formula:

3 Node-based energy balance of algorithm design and implementation of family

3.1 Network management architecture of WSN

WSN centralized network management, network management, or only a few server acts as a manager Sink node, the other nodes without network management capabilities, the network manager and agent management information through the inquiry and response between a process of interaction manager collect information on all network nodes, enabling the management node controls the entire network. Centralized network management architecture shown in Figure 3.

Distributed architecture requires a network with multiple management nodes, each node manages its own subnet management through information exchange between nodes to complete the network management tasks. Each node has per subnet management even their own local management information to analyze and process only some of the results are reported to the management node, and the

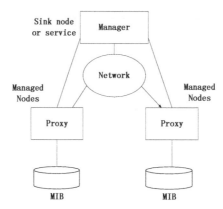

Figure 3: Centralized network management architecture.

use of such a network management system management structure size can be adjusted as required has strong adaptability and reliability.

Hierarchical architecture combines both centralized and distributed architecture advantages, set in the network will be a number of middle management node management tasks scattered, each intermediate node is responsible for its management of all nodes within the scope of management to gather information and sent to upper management node while upper management node receives an order, but at the same level no communication between the management node.

3.2 The family balancing algorithm based on the energy consumption of nodes

In this paper, the more in energy optimization and LEACFI clan head election BEOCS clustering algorithm similar to the process, and taking into account the scale of LEACH algorithm does not consider the randomness of the cluster, so that each member node residual energy are different, and each node equal probability of being selected as cluster head, so that the remaining nodes can deter less likely to become family heads, causing the node premature death. Therefore, in the process of joining node clusters remaining. The percentage of total energy was shown in Figure 4.

3.3 Algorithm design and implementation

The definition of LEACH wheel circular select cluster head nodes, the end of the cycle, a new round of cluster reconstruction. Because each wheel and reconstruction of consumption is very large, how to prolong the working period after clustering is the key. At the same time, taking into account the cluster head node task (receiving and forwarding data, data fusion, the nodes in cluster management), energy consumption is far more than the ordinary nodes, thus extend the work cycle race can easily lead to the cluster head node premature

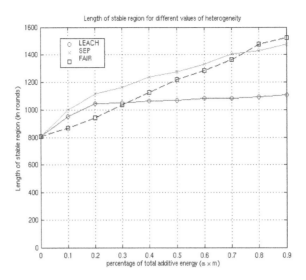

Figure 4: The percentage of total energy.

death, reduce the network lifetime. In view of the algorithm based on information management mechanism, the reasonable cluster, so that all nodes load balance.

Firstly, the cluster head energy optimization selection mechanism based on the cluster head selection, clustering process, group head node receives feedback message to add their own all the nodes, then according to the number of member nodes by TDMA for all nodes allocated time slot, and a random decide which nodes become deputy group head, temporarily replace the complete vine head node itself task.

4 Conclusion

In view of the particularity of WSN, which can be the basis of survival is survivable topology control study, it is hoped the design out of the network topology to extend the network lifetime, in the premature death of individual nodes to continue to provide critical services, when fault/ intrusion tolerance ability to reach limit, and can be returned to work with renewable technologies. Then WSN existing static network model and hybrid network model put forward their key technologies, and to mixed network coverage holes made known effective coverage of the mobile node based coverage holes patched program, both in theory and simulation verify its effectiveness and improve the WSN network topology survivability. In this paper, energy saving and renewable technologies for WSN topology were studied and analyzed, put forward their own solutions.

References

[1] M.M. Eusuff and K.E. Lansey, Optimization of water distribution network design using the shuffled frog leaping algorithm. *Water Resources Planning and Management*, **129(3)**, pp. 210–225, 2003.

[2] B. Amiri, M. Fathian, and A. Maroosi, Application of shuffled frog leaping algorithm on clustering. *The International Journal of Advanced Manufacturing Technology*, **45(1/2)**, pp.199–209, 2009.

[3] Luo Xue-Hui, Yang Ye, and Li Xia, Modified shuffled frog-leaping algorithm to solve traveling salesman problem. *Journal on Communications*, **30(7)**, pp. 130–135, 2009.

[4] R.V. Alireza and H.M. Ali, Solving a bicriteria permutation flow shop problem using shuffled frog-leaping algorithm. *Soft Computing*, **12(5)**, pp. 435–452, 2008.

[5] E. Elbeltai, T. Hegazy, and D. Grierson, A modified shuffled frog-leaping optimization algorithm applications to project management. *Structure and Infrastructure Engineering*, **3(1)**, pp. 53–60, 2007.

[6] Zhang Xiaodan, Hu Feng, and Zhao Li, Improved shuffled frog leaping algorithm based on molecular dynamics simulations. *Journal of Data Acquisition & Processing*, **27(3)**, pp. 327–332, 2012.

[7] Gg Yu, Wang Xueping, and Liang Jing, Improved shuffled frog leaping algorithm. *Journal of Computer Applications*, **32(1)**, pp. 234–237, 2012.

[8] A. Rahimi-Vahed and A.H. Mirzaei, A hybrid multi-objective shuffled frog-leaping algorithm for a mixed model assembly line sequencing problem. *Computers and Industrial Engineering*, **53(4)**, pp. 642–666, 2007.

The application of internet of things technology in pharmaceutical cold chain logistics

Qiang Wen[1], Qitao Chen[2]
[1]Law School, Yibin University, Yibin, 644000, China
[2]Books Information Centre, Yibin Vocational and Technical College, Yibin, 644003, China

Abstract

This article introduces pharmaceutical logistics and pharmaceutical cold chain logistics and drugs transportation problems, also tells the internet of things, we researched IOT technology and cold chain logistics, it contains radio frequency identification technology, video surveillance technology, sensor technology, mobile GIS technology. Cold chain logistics contains government regulators, consumers, and cold chain related businesses. And then, we analyze the advantages and disadvantages of IOT technology application in cold chain logistics and introduction of the application reference model, it consists of application layer, network layer, information perception layer. At last, we get the application reference model of internet of things technology in pharmaceutical cold chain logistics.

Keywords: internet of things, pharmaceutical, cold chain logistics, application and model.

1 Introduction

Drug is a special product, the cold chain is one of the more specific drugs part. Cold chain pharmaceutical refers to medicines storage, transportation chilled, frozen temperature requirements. Pharmaceutical logistics and other commodity logistics' distinction as follows [2]: Firstly, the logistics for pharmaceutical drug needs safety requirements, followed by pharmaceutical logistics costs account for a larger proportion of the total cost of drugs. Most medicines for cold chain storage and transportation process are needed in strictly limited, one important thing is to maintain an uninterrupted cold, constant temperature, the majority of pharmaceutical cold chain temperature requirement is 2–8°C. Quality and efficacy dependent on the temperature range, the current GSP requirements of the refrigerating temperature is 2–10°C. According to the China Association of Pharmaceutical [4] Commerce statistics shows that cold medicines accounted for 25% of total pharmaceutical sales, cold medicines, and cold chain logistics market is huge [1]. Pharmaceutical cold chain logistics refers to pharmaceutical manufacturing enterprises, trading enterprises, logistics enterprises, and the use of units using a dedicated facilities to make cold medicines finished products from the manufacturer to the library using, the unit temperature is always controlled drugs within the provisions of the logistics process [7]. Because drugs are closely related with the national health, the state has introduced the corresponding specification, but still there are many pharmaceutical logistics problems [3]. Drug safety incidents occur frequently, but complicated procedures leading pharmaceutical logistics chain logistics costs remain high.

Internet of things was firstly proposed in 1999, at that time also called sensor network. With the continuous development of sensor technology, internet of things began to enter people's lives have entered the innovation intensive and industrial revitalization, networking and therefore subject to many countries and enterprises attach great importance [5]. Networking technology in the pharmaceutical cold chain logistics in the application and development are mainly in Europe and other developed countries. Japanese cold medicines supply chain system has taken shape, management is very mature, upstream suppliers of goods and distributors can achieve information sharing, and RFID technology is widely used in the pharmaceutical logistics industry, so that the logistics center to achieve a standardized, coupled with a high degree of automation of storage and selection of equipment, easy operation, and powerful management of warehouses, cold medicines to ensure high efficiency of logistics operations while reducing logistics costs [6].

For pharmaceutical logistics characteristics and problems, the use of networking technology to build a real-time monitoring pharmaceutical logistics information models and applications, can be traced to achieve logistics information can be shared, transparent areas to ensure optimal drug safety and logistics costs.

2 IOT technology and cold chain logistics research

2.1 Key technology of things internet of things

Internet of things through the existing system, such as sensor network system (Figure 3) based on the integration, through further research, organic geochemical point into the surface, forming their own applications for industry reference model. The key technology can contain as follows.

2.1.1 Radio frequency identification technology

RFID (radio frequency identification) technology is the use of radio frequency signals, spatial coupling, and transmission characteristics of the non-contact

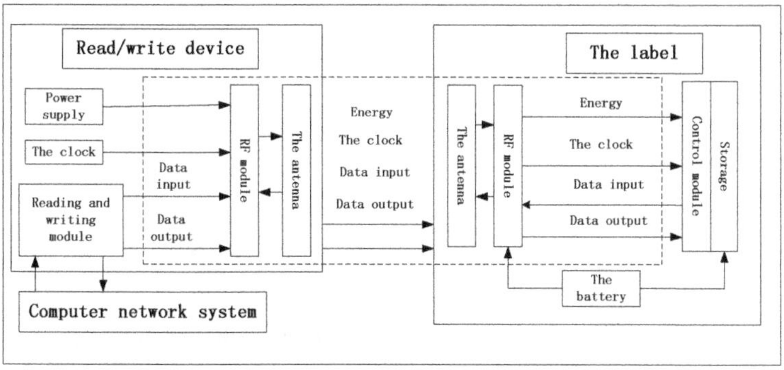

Figure 1: PFID technology working principle.

bidirectional communication, to achieve unique stationary or moving objects, effective and automatic identification and data exchange for an automatic identification technology. In this network, the system can automatically and in real-time identification of objects, locate, track, and trigger the execution of the corresponding event. Frequency identification system consists of three basic components, namely electronic tags, reader, and antenna. The basic working principle is shown in Figure 1.

2.1.2 Video surveillance technology

Real-time video surveillance and video playback are two important and fundamental tasks, its essence is the video source on the multimedia data to the video receiver. Real-time video surveillance required to complete real-time video transmission, with strong real-time requirements; currently solve such problems is a good way to use streaming and streaming technology. Another video processing technology difficulty lies in video compression technology. Video compression by reducing and removing redundant video data mode, to achieve effective transmit and store digital video files purposes. Compression, transmission, decompression, and the time required to display the file called latency. Under the same processing power, more advanced compression algorithm, the delay is longer. Video compression technique is shown in Figure 2.

2.1.3 Mobile GIS technology

Mobile GIS is mainly based on mobile computing environments, the limited processing capacity of mobile terminal conditions, to provide moving, distributed, with the case of mobile geographic information services, GIS (Geographic Information System), which combines GIS, GPS, (GSM/GPRS/CDMA/3G) shown in Figure 4.

2.2 Cold chain logistics research

Cold chain logistics is specialized logistics market today, is a very important symbol, as a branch of professional logistics, and is a continuous progress in

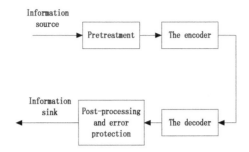

Figure 2: The principle of video compression technology.

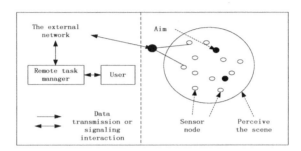

Figure 3: Sensor network technology.

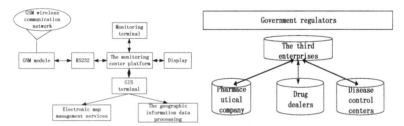

Figure 4: Mobile GIS map.   Figure 5: Cold chain logistics architecture.

science and technology as well as the continuous development of refrigeration technology in the context of established logistics. It is the product from the production, transportation to the consumer throughout the process is carried out under a low temperature condition. Therefore, cold chain logistics and general logistics, compared with a temperature regulation and control links, cold chain logistics primarily targeted for the perishable food, medicines, and other short-term logistics. In the cold chain logistics and transport process, consumers or retailers have special requirements for certain products, such as want to know more information about the product, or whether the product has been in the cold chain specific temperature range.

At present, although the lack of a country has integrated cold chain logistics standards in the regulations, there are large institutional gaps, but for pharmaceutical cold chain logistics, pharmaceuticals field of transport and

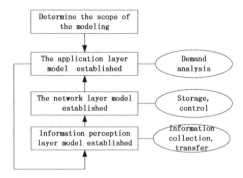

Figure 6: Cold chain logistics value chain.

Figure 7: The overall modeling steps.

logistics management regulations are more complete. It is difficult to effectively control the temperature, and thus the lack of a very strong security monitoring design, which also led to the refrigerated transport management when there is a certain risk, the use of networking technology to right in the refrigerated cold chain logistics and tracking retrospectively. Cold chain logistics structure model shown in Figure 5. Cold chain logistics development is a systems engineering, advanced facilities and technology is a basic condition, only the facilities supporting the convergence of technology, organization, and coordination of all aspects of the logistics chain in order to ensure food constantly (Figure 6).

3   The model and application of pharmaceutical cold chain logistics based on IOT

3.1 The advantages and disadvantages of IOT technology application in cold chain logistics

There is a common logistics, information flow and capital flow as the flow of goods along with constantly flowing stream changes, especially in cold chain logistics. The internet of things technology, improve enterprise management level and operational efficiency, pharmaceutical cold chain enterprises can effectively supervise all aspects of the corresponding use of appropriate, the cold chain pharmaceuticals in the environment should be some circulation. The advantages are: (1) It can improve the efficiency of information collection. To achieve the perception of bulk commodities information collection, replace the tedious manual entry, to achieve high efficiency in information collection. (2) Feedback efficiency can be improved. Sensor technology converged mobile node and the fixed node for various types of sensor nodes to achieve the object information and information about the environment in which the dynamic perception. Mobile GIS technology can be observed in pharmaceutical cold chain trajectory, for historical data analysis. (3) Cold chain process can be transparent. Real-time tracking, cold chain process can be transparent for businesses and consumers.

Although the internet of things technology in the pharmaceutical cold chain logistics get a lot of applications, there are many advantages, however, the existing networking technology in the pharmaceutical cold chain logistics application also disadvantages: (1) Information security issues. (2) Standard uniform with the problem of varying individual needs. (3) Associated with the pharmaceutical cold chain enterprises docking problems existing ERP. (4) Cost problems. (5) There is no mature application mode of internet of things.

3.2 The introduction of the application reference model

For the cold chain logistics industry, the industry structure and business processes has been relatively mature, we assume the premise that the process of defining the scope and modeling is reasonable rather technical thing. The model is able to achieve another premise is composed of the supply chain and is established between corporate marketing alliance formed to improve efficiency, collaboration and win–win economic base, along with the flow of goods, their software and hardware devices are interoperable information sharing. Things network layer theory principles, transmitted from the network deployment data storage solutions and information transmission network to create a network-layer security model. From a realistic generalized logical sequence of information system development model, the overall modeling steps shown in Figure 7.

The actual division of complex mixed cold chain enterprises, retail enterprises may have their own distribution centers even a source of raw material production and processing enterprises can carry out the logistics and distribution. In addition to the distribution of third-party logistics center possession and transport were also gradual to the processing and other areas of development, it is difficult to find a common one. Cold chain drug logistics structure model is shown in Figure 8.

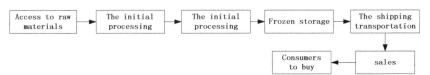

Figure 8: Cold chain drug logistics chain structure model.

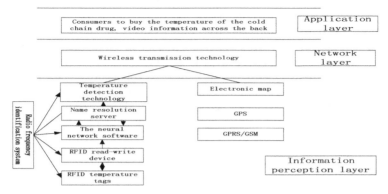

Figure 9: Application reference model.

3.3 Application reference model

According to the demand-driven principles, we start from the organizational analysis, the first system in which organizations define their relationship how to step into a targeted analysis of their needs. System in this organization reflects the level of corporate management and task allocation relationship is the enterprise decision-making task execution and production operations and other activities of the carrier. Their application reference model is shown in Figure 9.

Information transfer objective is to be achieved in the process of commodity circulation of information sharing, information can only be shared more to play its utility. Information sharing and transfer not only within the enterprise, it is the cold chain related businesses and end users to share and transfer. Things technology in the pharmaceutical cold chain logistics in the application object element is the cold chain drugs in the circulation process all kinds of information and its main constituents can be summarized as: government regulators, consumers and cold chain related businesses.

Combined with the specific circumstances of pharmaceutical cold chain logistics, coding principles presented in this paper are as follows: One thing one code; One library one code; One car one code; One device one code; One corporate one code; Introducing checksum. After the interaction between the system platform convergences, internet of things can be better applied to the pharmaceutical cold chain logistics.

4 Conclusions

To visualize pharmaceutical cold chain logistics, monitoring and traceability must exist and more mature things combined application of key technologies. Numerous and complex networking technology, this article summarizes the various techniques of things, select the radio frequency identification technology, video surveillance technology, sensor technology, and mobile GIS technology combine both the use of advanced networking technologies and cost minimization, but also meet the needs of users, can achieve a good visual monitoring, operation, and traceability.

Internet of things are building this technology in the pharmaceutical cold chain logistics application reference model of three layers to achieve, cold chain related business and consumer demand for third-party applications application layer starting to build the use of sensing technology to collect the information needed to monitor and trace information perception layer, the use of transmission and storage networking technology to build the network layer of cold chain logistics application mode.

Acknowledgements

The work was supported by Sichuan province philosophy social sciences key research base, system science and enterprise development research center funded project results, project number: 2012Xq12C10.

References

[1] D. Lee and J. Park, RFID-based traceability in the supply chain. *Industrial Management & Data Systems*, **108(6)**, pp. 713–725, 2005.

[2] Wanghua Bing, Heda Jun, and Wei Feng, RFID-based tracking and tracing platform can research and design. *Micro Calculation Information*, **24(29)**, pp. 199–201, 2008.

[3] M.W.A. Steen, ODP enterprise viewpoint specification. *Computer Standards and Interface*, **22(3)**, pp. 165–189, 2000.

[4] A. Amaral Leonardo, P. Hessel Fabiano, and A. Bezerra Eduardo, eCloudRFID—A mobile software framework architecture for pervasive RFID-based applications. *Journal of Network and Computer Applications*, **34(3)**, pp. 972–979, 2011.

[5] Zipursky Simona, Boualam Liliane, and Cheikh Dah Ould, Assessing the potency of oral polio vaccine kept outside of the cold chain during a national immunization campaign in Chad. *Vaccin*, **29(2)**, pp. 34–35, 2011.

[6] Nagy Zoltan, Electrochemistry on the intense. *Journal of Solid State Electrochemistry*, pp. 7–8, 2011.

[7] M.L. Chuang and W.H. Shaw, How RFID will impact supply chain networks, *2005 IEEE International Engineering Management Conference*, pp. 11–13, 2008.

Design and application of 3D virtual sports system based on Kinect Skeletal Tracking

Xiao-Yan L.E., Jun-Ya DAI, Hai-Bin Zheng
School of Computer Technology, Beijing Institute of Technology, ZhuHai, ZhuHai 519085, GuangDong, China

Abstract

The 3D virtual sports project bases on human Skeletal Tracking of Kinect and combines unity3D engine. We use Kinect sensor to capture image depth of field data, and deal with the data by skeletal tracking technology. Then, according to the 3D coordinates of various joints to calculate and determine the displacement movement, rotation angle, intensity, and speed. In basketball, for example, described in detail the design and implementation process of 3D virtual sports. Experimental results show that the 3D virtual sports used this method can control physical interact easily, naturally, and effectively.
Keywords: Kinect, Unity3D, skeletal tracking, virtual sports.

1 Introduction

With the continuous innovation and development of computer graphics, virtual reality and artificial intelligence, as well as sensors, microprocessors, and other input and output devices, a new generation of reality-based human–computer interaction (reality-based interaction, RBI) technology appears. The mechanical processing, urban planning, industrial control, digital entertainment, education, and other fields of applications have been extended since the birth of RBI. People are becoming easier to interact with machine, more naturally, even without wearing or holding any peripherals. Somatosensory interaction is a human–computer interaction technology that allows user to operate without the aid of any peripheral. It mainly take use of body movements, gestures, voice, and others that already possess the knowledge and skills in real life to directly interact with human. Microsoft launched a set named Kinect, which combines image recognition, video capture, voice control, and other technology. Without any

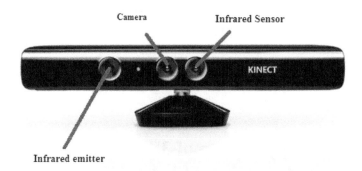

Figure 1: Architecture of Kinect.

handheld device, one can interact with the terminal [1,2] through gestures, body movements, voice, and other natural methods. This natural interactive experience has been widely accepted. Interaction technology based on the Kinect can better meet the needs of virtual sports project. The design of a 3D virtual sports project system, which takes use of this interactive technology, makes it possible for one to conduct sports training and entertainment indoors with only one Kinect somatosensory connected with a PC.

2 Skeleton tracking

2.1 Skeleton information capture

Kinect has three lenses, as shown in Figure 1. The middle of the lens is the RGB colour camera and the left is infrared emitter (Projector). The 3D depth sensor made up by CMOS camera and infrared (IR) is in the right, which has real-time sensing, motion capture, voice recognition, and skeleton tracking functions. The Kinect can infrared emission and detection reflected infrared light, calculating each pixel depth value. Main body and the shape of the object is first extracted through the depth data. Then it will match all parts of the body according to shape information and calculating the respective the position of the joint in the body and ultimately establish a 3D coordinate of each joint body [].

2.2 Movement tracking

The human body movement can be tracked by Kinect and shown in Figure 2. Taking the arm joints for an example, the key to calculate rotation angle, intensity and speed includes shoulder_r, elbow_r, wrist_r, hand_r, and finger_r joints.

We get the movement of joints as follows. First, get initial position of the joints, and then calculate x, y, z position of relative movement in three directions according to movement of each joint point. Then judge the relative movement of the joints positions through conditional threshold.

The value of two angle joints in plane XOY is calculated through X, Y coordinate is shown in Figure 3. The coordinates of shoulder shoulder_r is (X_s, Y_s,

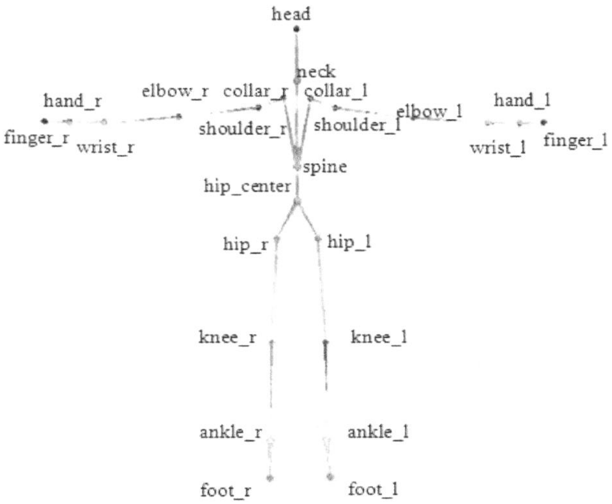

Figure 2: Distribution of the human skeleton joints.

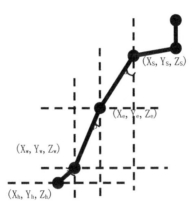

Figure 3: Arm joints angle calculation.

Z_s). The coordinates of the elbow elbow_r is (X_e, Y_e, Ze). The coordinates of the wrist wrist_r is (X_w, Y_w, Z_w). The coordinates of hand joints hand_r is (X_h, Y_h, Z_h). According to trigonometric formulas rotation angle of each joint, the transformer is as shown in Eqs. (1)–(3).

$$\alpha = \arctan(\mid X_e - X_s \mid / \mid Y_e - Y_s \mid) \tag{1}$$

$$\beta = \arctan(\mid X_w - X_e \mid / \mid Y_w - Y_e \mid) \tag{2}$$

$$\gamma = \arctan(\mid X_h - X_w \mid / \mid Y_h - Y_w \mid) \tag{3}$$

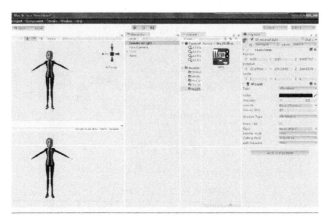

Figure 4: 3D virtual character control.

The strength of the arm is judged primarily by the movement in the Z coordinate of shoulder_r, elbow_r, wrist_r, and hand_r. Besides, the frequency of displacement on Z coordinate and threshold conditions for comparative is also taken in condition for analysis.

3 D virtual character control

Unity game engine support OpenGL graphics library interfaces. We take full advantage of its depth cues (Depth Cue), motion blur (Motion Blur), and double-buffering (Double Buffering), etc. We then combined the Kinect sensor sensing capabilities to achieve human skeletal control. First, grab data through the Microsoft Kinect SDK. Then match the joints in the character models with skeleton node in Unity3D and realize the trajectory of the character models and user actions the same reaction as shown in Figure 4.

4 Implement of 3D virtual sports project

According Kinect distribution of nodes in the human skeleton structure, we use Maya for bone structure character modeling matching, as shown in Figure 5. We take use of Maya and Unity3D to complete virtual sports scene. As it has been described in Sections 1 and 2, joints displacement, rotation angle, intensity, and speed are calculated. We successfully achieved basketball, track and field, bowling, and other sports designs. This paper mainly talks about the basketball program design and implementation as an example. Character's skeleton and human skeleton tracking are bind via Kinect in 3D virtual scene. Players can control the scene through a variety of virtual human action, such as the project menu, select (Figure 5) for various sports project action.

Basketball shooting interactive action is implemented mainly by calculating the coordinates of each joint on the arm. First, according to wrist_r or hand_r joint point Y coordinate value judgments, when drooping hands of the characters

Figure 5: Project menu change.

Figure 6: Basketball shooting demo renderings.

in the scene, there will be a basketball; when the arm lift shot, the ball will rise along with the hand. Basketball shooting angle and direction of movement of the ball is calculated according to shoulder_r, elbow_r, wrist_r, and hand_r joint point of the X and Y coordinates judgment. Determine the displacement frequency and the velocity of basketball according to wrist_r and hand_r joints change on the Z coordinate shown in Figure 6.

Judge the shot is successful or not through difference of basketball hoop coordinate. Player can cross the border for a little more difficult movement training until it reaches a specified fraction, such as farther basket, very partial fixed position or shooting under movement and so on.

5 Conclusion

In this paper, we proposed a design that uses the Kinect sensor to obtain the image depth data. Process the bone tracking data to match the various parts of the body, thereby establishing the 3D coordinate of each joint body. In accordance with the respective joints in the 3D coordinate, the displacement operation, rotation angle, intensity, and speed are determined through calculation.

Our software development environment is WIN7 + VS2012 + Kinect for Windows SDK 1.6 + unity3D4.0. We create 3D virtual scene in unity3D and complete skeletal tracking consistent character models by Maya. Then combine Kinect to complete design and implementation of 3D virtual sports project.

After completion of the project, experiments show that the 3D virtual sport project is practical and entertaining. One can stay at home to complete outdoor sports, which has a great contribution to physical education and sports training.

References

[1] Microsoft. Kinect for Windows Programming Guide [EB/OL]. [2012-05-01]. http://msdn.micro-soft.com/en-us/library/hh855348.aspx.

[2] Kang Jongwook, Seo Dongjun, and Jung Dongseok, A study on the control method of 3-dimensional space application using Kinect system. *International Journal of Computer Science and Network Security*, **11(9)**, pp. 55–59, 2011.

Risk prevention and control of rural financial institutions based on data mining technology

Yujing Zhang, Tao Wang, Ying Cao
Department of Information Management and Engineering, Hebei Finance University, Baoding, 071000 Hebei Province, China

Abstract

This article introduces the data mining technology, it mainly focus on data mining task, data mining patterns, and data mining techniques. Data mining could be used in risk prevention and control of rural financial institutions. There are many kinds of risks for financial institutions, and the risk of rural financial institutions is more complicated than business banks, so it is important to use data mining technology to do risk prevention and risk control. The paper introduces several application of data mining-related technology in rural financial institutions. Rural credit scoring model is a good way to focus on good clients so as to prevent and control the risk of financial institution, the paper uses decision tree to do data mining tasks, with all efforts, credit management system could be established based on data mining.

Keywords: data mining, rural financial institution, decision tree, risk prevention and control.

1 Introduction

Data mining is to discover and extract interesting knowledge from a huge amount of data stored in databases, data warehouses, or other information bases. Data mining is a step of knowledge discovery in database (referred as KDD), most attractive point of which is to build predictive models instead of review, therefore, data mining is an interdisciplinary, which promotes the application of data from low-level simple querying to knowledge mining from databases and decision-making support level.

Generally data mining task can be divided into two categories: description and prediction. Descriptive data mining describes data in a concise summary way and provides the common property of data. Predictive data mining analysis creates one model or a set of models and attempts to predict the behavior of the new data set.

There are many functions and pattern types of data mining [1]: concept or class description, also means characterization and distinction, a large number of detailed data usually stored in the database, through concept description, users can observe aggregated data sets in a concise way. This type of data description not only can provide an overview of a certain kind of data, or compare it to opposite kind of data, but also can be easily and flexibly describes data set through different granularities and different perspectives [3]. Correlation analysis found that associated rules, which shows the conditions of that property—values occur together frequently in a given data set [2]. Classification and prediction are two forms of data analysis which can extract description model of important data class or predict future data trends [5]. Cluster analysis, classifying the physical or abstract objects, set to make the similar objects multiple classes is called clustering. Outlier analysis might contain some data objects that are inconsistent of the general behavior or model of the data, these data objects are outliers. Many data mining algorithms attempt to minimize the impact of outliers, or exclude them [6]. Evolution analysis describes behavioral law or trend of an object over time and make modeling based on it.

On the whole, data mining techniques can be divided into statistical analysis type, knowledge discovery type and other types of data mining techniques [1]. Statistical analysis type (also known as data analysis) techniques, whose data mining model includes linear and nonlinear analysis, regression analysis, logistic regression analysis, single variable analysis, multivariate analysis, time series analysis, nearest neighbor algorithm, and clustering analysis technologies. Using these techniques can check out abnormal data, and then use a variety of statistical and mathematical models to interpret the data so as to interpret the laws of the market and business opportunities hidden behind the data [2]. Knowledge discovery type data mining technology is completely different from statistical data mining techniques. It can filter information through a lot of data from the data warehouse to find the potential operating mode of market and explore the unknown facts. It mainly includes artificial neural networks, decision trees, genetic algorithms, rough sets, rule discovery, and associated sequence. In addition to the above two types of data mining technology, there are other targeted data mining techniques, such as text data mining, web data mining, classification systems, visualization systems, spatial data mining, and distributed data mining.

The mature data mining techniques used in commercial field is sophisticated statistical analysis type, but from the perspective of business applications, knowledge discovery techniques are the common data mining technology, especially classification and prediction. Classification is a very important data mining function, which can be used to extract and describe the model of important data class or to predict future data trends.

Data classification is usually divided into three steps: The first step is to build a model to describe the predetermined set of data classes or concepts set. The second step is to assess the prediction accuracy of model (classification).There are many ways of assessing the accuracy of the model, the easiest way is the retaining method, given data is randomly divided into two separate sets: training set and test set, the training set is to export classification, the test set is to evaluate the accuracy rate. The third step is to use the model to predict new data.

2 Rural financial institutions risk

2.1 The meaning of risk

Risk is the uncertainty of no expected return on assets or the occurrence of loss. In the new, rural financial institutions developing process, the credit risk has become an important issue of its development. Because rural finance and rural economic has symbiotic relationship, the rural financial development plays an important role in promoting rural economy, while the credit risk has the largest and most immediate threat for the development of new rural institutions.

For most financial institutions, there is a huge customer information database, but without enough effective use of these data, these data cannot turn into useful information for the enterprise, so the financial institutions also have to face for high risk for its newly developed credit business. In the past, only human judgment and general database technology can be relied on to reject those high risk of potential credit applicants and conducting risk, profitability, debt forecast, the effect is not very satisfactory. Credit risk characteristics of the business for rural financial institutions and fierce competition in the market determine its urgent requirements in information technology, electronic field than other field. How to extract valuable information from enormous data for the management of rural financial institutions is an important application field of data mining.

2.2 The situation of credit management for rural financial institutions

Credit management is a key business of rural financial institutions work, and in a very important position in the daily operation of the system of the financial institutions. In the present situation, the quality of the overall economic benefits of financial institutions, the level of quality of financial assets depends largely on the level of its credit management. Management of rural financial institutions has the following characteristics:

(1) The credit management of rural financial institutions becomes increasingly standardized, but compared with commercial banks, it is relatively weak, non-performing loan ratio remains high.
(2) The number of rural credit loan customers is big, unsecured loans remains at much higher proportion and it is difficult to manage.
(3) The credit risk of rural financial institutions is high, including information is not complete, market positioning is not accurate; credit environment is poor, moral default risk is serious; credit risk is usually caused by natural disasters; risk management consciousness is low, loan administration is

not strict, loan review system is not functioning, etc. These factors will form a risk.

(4) The variety of credit products for rural financial institutions is not rich, sense of customer service is not strong, marketing means is not enough, customer management is not effective, well-preformed customers loses.

(5) Post-disbursement of the loan for rural financial institutions is not strict, the inspection after the loan, violation penalties and summing are not functioning.

2.3 Risk assessment methods

Credit risk assessment methods include credit expert systems, credit scoring system, and credit rating system. While credit rating system applies to medium-sized enterprises credit assessment and portfolio risk assessment, not to individual credit assessments.

2.3.1 Expert system

Expert system is similar to personal credit expert system for company. In expert systems, credit decision is made by experts' subjective judgments to judge the debtor's credit, with adjusting weight for several key factors. Frequently, expert system uses 5C to judge the debtor's credit status, however, the characteristics of the expert system makes expert system to face two problems while measuring credit risk: First, consistency issues, namely consistency of judge factors, different judgment factors should be varied with different debtors, there is no consistent objective factor analysis; second, subjective issues, namely how to decide the factor weight.

2.3.2 Credit scoring system

The basic principles of credit scoring is to determine the factors that affect the probability of default and give weight to calculate the score, then divide the debtor as accepting, rejecting, and gray according to scores of the debtor. In the process of establishing credit scoring models, banks need to get a lot of basic relevant data of loans, and analyze the factors which have a key influence of affecting the reimbursable loans.

3 Risk prevention and control of rural financial institutions based on data mining technology

3.1 Several application analysis of data mining-related technology in rural financial institutions

Data mining can be used in customer classification and recognition: Customer segments, for financial institutions, data mining can find qualified customers according to the criteria set in advance from the bank loan customers information stored in the database, it can also classify customers through cluster analysis,

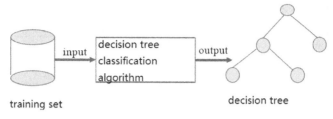

Figure 1: The basic idea of decision tree.

through analysis of customer service revenue, risk, cost, and other related factors, forecasting and optimization to find new profitable target customers. Optimize customer service: Through data mining, understanding the inherent characteristics of the customer can provide valuable discovery for financial institution. Meanwhile, the bank may take measures such as the value-added services, special treatment and loyalty incentives, and other measures to retain customers before the loss of customers with similar characteristics. Data mining can identify factors associated with customer transferring, through similar patterns to identify current customers who may transfer isolated point analysis can find the customer's abnormal behavior, so as to avoid unnecessary churn for financial institution [3]. Develop excellent customers: data mining method can create model from complex customer information database, dynamically track and monitor the customer record information in order to explore the customers, focus on valuable customers, analyze potential customer groups, make market development strategy for the different market demands and customer groups, determine the service product configuration based on customer value, thereby establish long-term relationships with excellent customers. Data mining can be used in credit assessment and credit risk management.

3.2 Rural credit scoring models based on decision tree

The biggest character of rural financial institutions is the large number of lenders, the characteristics of customers is relatively stable, with decision tree approach to classify rural customers, so that rural financial institutions could quickly make a distinction and authentication between a large number of clients, and build customer value evaluation model so that rural financial institutions could filter out the most valuable customers from a large customer base. Figure 1 shows the basic idea of decision tree.

In this paper, the credit system of rural financial institutions randomly selected 240 samples' data from farmer small loans data base, we make 160 samples as the training samples and 80 samples as test samples to test mining accuracy of the model.

Firstly, the paper calculates attributes gain and information gain ratio of the sample training set. Then it uses the decision tree algorithm to construct decision tree model. Select attributes as the test attributes whose information gain ratio is the biggest and whose information gain is not less than the average of information gain of all the attributes.

Table 1: Properties and Explanations of Credit Assessment Analysis.

Item	Property	Value	Item	Property	Value
Population	1	Bad	Labor force	1	Bad
	2–3	Middle		2–3	Middle
	>3	Good		>3	Good
Marital status	Unmarried	Bad	Net income	<10000	Bad
	Divorced	Middle		10000–30000	Middle
	Married	Good		>30000	Good
Total family property	<100000	Bad	Credit capital stock	No	Bad
	100000-150000	Middle		1000–10000	Middle
	>150000	Good		>10000	Good
Evaluation	Bad	Bad	Net Assets	<50000	Bad
	Normal	Middle		50000–100000	Middle
	Good	Good		>100000	Good
Compliance	Overdue loans	Bad			
	Repay on time	Good			

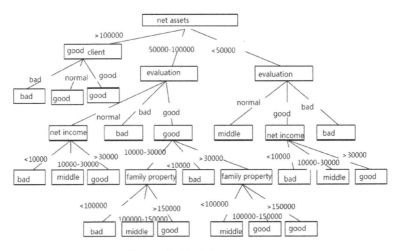

Figure 2: Decision tree.

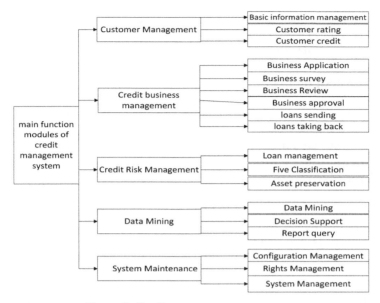

Figure 3: Credit management system.

3.3 Credit management system based on data mining

According to the data mining techniques, rural financial institutions could establish risk prevention and control system, and the main task of risk prevention and risk control is of credit risk prevention and risk control, which means good credit management work is very important, especially establishing credit management system. The main function of credit management system is credit customer management, daily management of loans, loan risk management and decision support for rural financial institutions to make credit management scientific, standardized and automated, so as to effectively prevent or defuse credit risk. The system primarily includes the following functional modules: customer management, credit operations, risk management, data mining, and system maintenance.

4 Conclusions

The rural financial institutions face many kinds of risks, which are more complicated than that of banks, and data mining could be applied in many ways in rural financial institutions, it has different kinds of assessment methods. Application of data mining technology in domestic banks is indeed a great impetus to the development of information technology for the banks, and completely changed the mode of competition among banks. However, data mining for financial institutions is still an emerging technology, it need to face many difficulties to be applied effectively in credit management for rural financial institutions, so rural financial institutions must do well in the following aspects: (1) to strengthen awareness of data mining and data warehouse construction; (2) to strengthen the construction of credit risk data for rural credit cooperatives; and (3) to emphasize on bringing up data mining talents.

Acknowledgments

The work was supported by Data Mining Technology in Hebei Province Rural Credit Risk Prediction System and Construction, Hebei Province Department of Education key project findings (project number: ZD20131083) .

References

[1] Hsin-Ginn Hwang, and Cheng-Yuan Ku, Critical factors influencing the adoption of data warehouse technology: a study of the banking industry in Taiwan. *Decision Support*, **16(5)**, pp. 56–69, 2004.

[2] S.H. Chun and S.H. Kim, Data mining for financial and prediction and trading: application to single and multiple markets. *Expert Systems with Applications*, **6(3)**, pp. 63–64, 2004.

[3] Julian Kulkarni and Richard King, Business intelligence system and data mining. *ASAS Institute White Paper*, **3(5)**, pp. 29–31, 2009.

[4] T. Fukuda, Y. Morimoto, S. Morishita et al., 'Data mining using two-dimensional optimized association rules: scheme, algorithms, and visualization. *Proceedings of the ACMSIGMOD Conference on Management of Data*, **6(13)**, pp. 56–62, 1996.

[5] R. Agrawal and R. Srikant, Fast algorithms for mining association rules. *Proceedings of the 20th International Conference on Very Large Databases (VLDB'94)*, Santiago, **8(7)**, pp. 93–95, 1994.

[6] R. Srikant and R. Agrawal, Mining sequential patterns: generalizations and performance improvements. *Proceedings of the 5th Extending Database Technology*, **9(11)**, pp. 43–45, 1996.

[7] R. Agrawal and J.C. Shafer, Parallel mining of association rules: design, implementation, and experience. *IEEE Transactions of Knowledge and Data Engineering*, **12(3)**, pp. 83–86, 1996.

Dynamic trust model of P2P networks based on task ranking

Linsheng Zhao, Xuedong Li
Shandong Jianzhu University, Shandong, China

Abstract

In recent years, P2P obtains more and more attention. People can acquire abundant network resources through using P2P technology. In the meantime, the P2P networks security disadvantages bring many inconveniences. This article builds dynamic trust model based on task classification. At first, this article evaluates P2P networks in details, focus on network classification and security problems. In the second place, it designs dynamic trust model process through task analysis principle. At last, this paper analyzes the questions when adding new nodes in the model and provides the specific codes. This article has the positive function to network security worker and software engineers.
Keywords: task classification, P2P, trust model.

1 Introduction

With network technology development, network has been a necessary part of our daily life. The abundant network resources provide great convenient to the living and working [1]. P2P (Peer-to-Peer Networks) takes full advantage of the user resources and distribute the resources away from the concentration. Following P2P network application, the disadvantages become visible [2]. In P2P networks, the nodes have less monitoring, they can enter and exit the network as will. Vicious code and virus might be propagated through P2P network and trap the entire network's performance [3].

2 P2P network

P2P is the abbreviation of Peer-to-Peer, which means partner to partner. Although the P2P network has lots of definition in IT industry, the essence is same in the

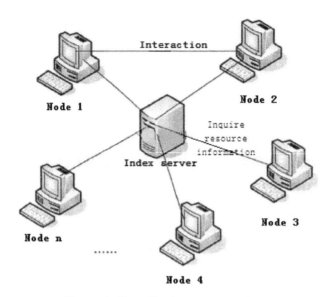

Figure 1: Centralization structure chart.

conclusion. In the P2P network, every node is peer to peer [4]. It is the distributed network, and one node is one server as well as the client. There has no special center server. The development of node number of P2P network increases the P2P network scale. Therefore, P2P network has strong expansibility.

2.1 Classification of P2P network structure

Based on the node logic and physical relationship, the topological structure of P2P network can be divided into four types [5].

(1) Centralized topology

Centralized topology is one early type of P2P network structure. It is similar to the centralized model. The difference is the center has one or multiple index servers to distribute node resources. The advantage has a high rate to find resources. The disadvantage is one server problem breaking the entire network. The structure is shown in Figure 1.

(2) Pure P2P topology

Ignore the server and every node is in the equal status in this structure. The extensive resource query makes each node to hardly influence the entire network. The disadvantage is the large network cost without security protection. The structure is shown in Figure 2 [6].

(3) Impure P2P structure

This structure can effectively combine the advantages of both centralized topology and pure topology. The valid resource query in the network can ensure node exit in order that the network will not break. The detailed information is shown in Figure 3 [7].

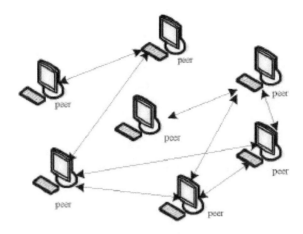

Figure 2: Pure P2P structure.

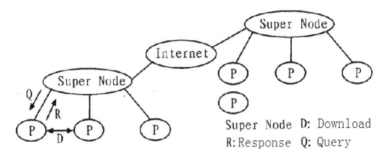

Figure 3: Impure P2P structure.

2.2 Safety problem of P2P network

The present P2P technology has been widely used in file exchange, search engine, cooperative work, peer-to-peer computing, and the instant communication. It obtains more and more focus. However, P2P network characteristics decide the disadvantages. Node and data security increase the pressure which is influenced by the following parts.

(1) Virus

P2P network has lots of nodes and they have a low security system that each node has a different precaution function. If one node is infected by a virus, it will send to other nodes through resource sharing and lead virus spread.

(2) Content identification

It can only simply read the file content through the file title. You can read the details only after downloading it.

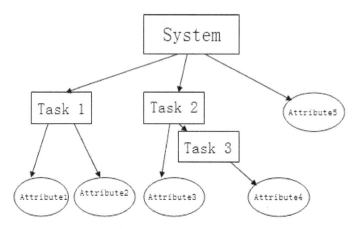

Figure 4: Measurement model of reliability.

(3) Resource location

The query algorithm of resource spread among the nodes through broadcast. It provides a chance to the malicious nodes. They can pose as the normal node to send false information or virus to other nodes.

3 Overall design of dynamic trust model

In the entire P2P network, it is impossible to build a trust model. It is reliable to divide the P2P network into several parts and build a dynamic trust model in each local area network. In P2P, each node has the unique identification. Consider about model security, we can think over between node trust value collection, node trust relationship, and the relationship of the internal node.

3.1 Task grading

Divide one system into several targets and each target has the related attribute to form every task. Then it will create the measurement model of reliability. From P2P network, the distance is different between nodes. In Figure 4, tasks 2 and 3 can interact with each other. But tasks 2 and 1 need the superior cooperation. If task 3 wants to interact with task 1, it has to get through task 2. Task 2 is reliable, and we can build the trust correlative mechanism through this task.

Task classification can increase the utilization rate of the reliable node. At the same time, it can effectively avoid vicious node and increase system efficiency.

3.2 Model design

In the dynamic trust model, node starts to operate we have to evaluate all the reliable database in local area network, and directly obtain the trust value of this node. At the same time, send broadcast to the neighbor nodes to receive the recommended information. Inquire local reliable database and read the related recommend trust, calculate the value. Then, calculate the comprehensive trust value and get the trust threshold. After that, judge the obtained trust. If it is reliable, trade with this node, update the corresponding trust value and data. Otherwise, refuse to trade with this node.

It is impossible to be unchanged for dynamic trust model. It will exit or join some new nodes. The new node has no relationship with other nodes means this node has no reliability in the entire P2P network. The trust value sets as 0. After the resource sharing and some operations with other nodes, it will increase the reliability and safe the system effectively. The high reliability node has more chance to interact with other nodes.

4   Realization of dynamic trust model

For the whole model, node quit has no big influence to the network. When adding a new node, how to make it integrate into the network is the emphasis of dynamic trust model. This article gives core code:

```
<algorithm>if (isAdd)
       {
           DataRow row = ds.Tables[0].NewRow();
           row["name"] = txtName.Text;
           row["IP"] = txtIP.Text;
           if (lvImg.SelectedItems.Count > 0)
               row["imgIndex"] = lvImg.SelectedItems[0].Index;
           else
               row["imgIndex"] = 0;

           ds.Tables[0].Rows.Add(row);
       }
       else
       {
           DataRow[] rows = ds.Tables[0].Select("Name = '" + this.name + "'
   And IP = '" + this.ip + "'");
           if (rows.Length > 0)
           {
               rows[0]["name"] = txtName.Text;
               rows[0]["IP"] = txtIP.Text;
               if (lvImg.SelectedItems.Count > 0)
                   rows[0]["imgIndex"] = lvImg.SelectedItems[0].Index;
               else
                   rows[0]["imgIndex"] = 0;
           }
       }
```

5   Summary

This article aims at the P2P networks and builds network dynamic model through task grading. For the article length limitation, this paper has not provided the description of the P2P server structure. The readers can read the related references. There provide the dynamic trust model flow of task grading and introduce the model in details. It is good for building trust model of readers.

References

[1] Tian Huirong, *Research of P2P Networks Trust Model and Incentive Mechanism.*, Beijing University of Posts and Telecommunications, 2006.

[2] Zhang Liqiang, Zhang Huanguo, and Zhang Fan, Trusted measurement mechanism of dependable computing. *Journal of Beijing University of Technology*, **5**, pp. 586–591, 2010.

[3] Yuan Wei, Li Jinsheng, and Hong Peilin, One kind of P2P networks distributed trust model and simulation. *Journal of System Simulation*, **18(4)**, pp. 938–942, 2006.

[4] Chen Shuyi, Wen Yingyou, and Zhao Hong, Trust model evaluation of dependable computing based on fuzzy set. *Computer Science*, **11**, 2008.

[5] Wu Fuzhao and Dong Wenyong, Research on P2P Web search technology. *Journal of Wut*, **29(6)**, pp. 45–49, 2006.

[6] Li Junqing, Li Xinyou, Xie Shengxian, Luo Hongbin, and Liu Guangliang, Research on dynamic fine grained access control in P2P networks. *Application Research of Computers*, **26(4)**, pp. 1467–1470, 2009.

[7] Li Zhiyuan and Wang Ruchuan, A dynamic secure trust model for mobile P2P networks. *Acta Electronica Sinica*, **40(1)**, pp. 1–7, 2012.

Constructing adaptive correlation filters based on dictionary learning

Xiaoguang Cui, Yuan Tian, Yiping Yang

Institute of Automation, Chinese Academy of Sciences, Beijing, China

Abstract

In this paper, we present a novel model for constructing adaptive correlation filters based on dictionary learning. Rather than produce a single general filter for the entire testing set, we use recently developed dictionary learning techniques to generate a filter bank, by which we can construct an accurate adaptive correlation filter for each testing image via sparse coding. With the powerful representation of the learned filter bank, the greater accuracy with regard to varied appearance changes can be achieved. In addition, to meet the real-time requirement, a nonlinear regress method that directly maps input images into corresponding filters is proposed as a substitute for the time-consuming sparse coding. Experiments were performed in optical satellite images to detect airplanes, and our model shows significant reduction in error rate compared to the classical Average of Synthetic Exact Filters (ASEF) and Minimum Output Sum of Squared Error (MOSSE) filters.

Keywords: correlation filters, dictionary learning, sparse coding, nonlinear regress, synthetic exact filters.

1 Introduction

Correlating images with a simple template [1] is a common way to detect targets. Though simple templates are successfully used in many real-world applications when there is little difference between the template and the target object, it often failed in cases when the object undergoes a significant appearance change.

To improve the predictability of varied appearance changes, a family of correlation filters has been developed for shift-invariant targets detection with tolerance to pattern distortions. They commonly optimize target localization performance by minimizing the error between the desired ideal correlation output and the correlation output

 WIT Transactions on Information and Communication Technologies, Vol. 61, © 2014 WIT Press
www.witpress.com, ISSN 1743-3517 (on-line)
doi:10.2495/MIIT130831

between the template and the training images. Recent advancement in the techniques of using correlation filters [2–4] have shown promising results in target recognition and facial feature localization. One of the useful correlation filters class is designated as Average of Synthetic Exact Filters (ASEF) [5], which produces a general filter by computing the average of multiple synthetic exact filters (SEF) and shows less susceptible to over-fitting the training data than other methods. Another one is Minimum Output Sum of Squared Error (MOSSE) filters [6], which has been proved that can produce filters that are more robust to appearance changes by minimum output sum of squared error of the synthetic exact filters.

While these approaches greatly extend the performance range of correlation filters, there is still further room for improvement. Correlation filters methods commonly produce a single general filter for the entire testing set, though the general filter has stronger ability to predict varied appearances compared to the simple template match, it tends to fail in complicate matters where objects of same class have too much different appearances. These appearance changes include scale, rotation, pose, illumination, non-ridged deformation, and so on. The single general filter becomes invalid in this case due to its poor representation power, thus a more effective method is needed to handle this difficult issue.

In this study, rather than producing a single general filter, we learn a filter bank from synthetic exact filters of the training set using dictionary learning technique, then an accurate adaptive correlation filter, which can be represented as a linear combination of the filter bank, is constructed for each testing image via sparse coding. With the benefit of the filter bank, the proposed model shows more robust to appearance changes compared conventional approaches. In addition, we propose a nonlinear regress method to directly maps input images into corresponding filters with high speed, so as to avoid the time-consuming sparse coding. The block diagram of the proposed model is shown in Figure 1. This paper is structured as follows: We present the approach of learning the filter bank in Section 2. Code prediction methods are described in Section 3. Experiment and discussion is shown in Section 4, and Section 5 is devoted to conclusion and future work.

2 Learning the filter bank

In this section, we first briefly describe the definition of the SEF, then give the details of how to learn the filter bank from SEF.

$$g_i = \sum_j e^{-\frac{(x-x_j)^2+(y-y_j)^2}{\sigma^2}} \tag{1}$$

where j indexes targets in the ith training image and the variance σ^2 specifies the radius of the peak. The filter learning task then can be easily solved in the Fourier domain using an element-wise division, as:

$$H_i = G_i \big/ F_i \tag{2}$$

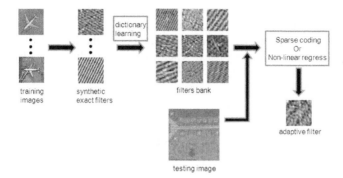

training images · synthetic exact filters · dictionary learning · filters bank · Sparse coding Or Non-linear regress · adaptive filter · testing image

Figure 1: The block diagram of the proposed model.

where capital letters indicate images in the Fourier domain. The H_i is defined as SEF due to it exactly transforms f_i to g_i. ASEF and MOSSE generate a single general filter from SEF using different approaches. Different from them, we produce a filter bank from SEF via dictionary learning to gain more powerful representations for varied appearances.

In this study, we assume that each element of SEF can be represented as linear combinations of a relatively small number of dictionary elements, which can be learned in an unsupervised way from the entire set of SEF. Actually, this linear structure assumption has been widely used in images processing such as image denoising [7], object recognition [8], and attractive results have been demonstrated its effectiveness of feature representation.

Under this assumption, a filter $H_i \in \mathbb{C}^m$, $i \in [1,N]$ can be represented using a linear combination of basis functions that are columns of the dictionary matrix (i.e., filter bank) $D = \{d^j\} \in \mathbb{C}^{m \times n}$, $j \in [1,...,n]$, using coefficients $t_i \in \mathbb{R}^n$. Since the linear system is under-determined, a sparsity constraint is added that prefers most of the coefficients to zero. The filter bank learning task leads to the following formulation:

$$L_1 = \arg \min_{D, t_i} \sum_i (\| H_i - Dt_i \|_2^2 + \lambda \| t_i \|_1)$$ (3)

where λ is a regularization parameter that establishes the relative importance of the two terms. This particular formulation has been extensively studied in dictionary learning and sparse coding algorithms [9]. A standard way to solve Eq. (3) is to alternatively optimize over the d^j filters for a given t_i coefficient (*Dictionary Update Stage*) and then over t_i for a given d^j (*Sparse Coding Stage*). The former stage can be achieved directly by Stochastic Gradient Descent, while the latter stage is obtained by first taking Stochastic Gradient Descent on the ℓ_2 penalized term and then applying the soft-thresholding operation on the t_i.

One weakness of Eq. (3) is that it cannot guarantee that two filters are independently converging to an identical solution. More specifically, a strong correlation may exist between different filters among the learned filter bank. In order to encourage filters become independent, we modify Eq. (3) by adding a penalty term that accounts for the correlation between the filters measured by the squared dot product, as follows:

$$L_2 = \arg\min_{D,t_i} \sum_i \left(\| H_i - Dt_i \|_2^2 + \lambda_1 \| t_i \| + \lambda_2 \sum_j \sum_{k \neq j} (\langle d^j, d^k \rangle)^2 \right) \tag{4}$$

where the third term penalizes filters that are strongly related with each other and whose dot product is therefore large. The modified objective formulation allows us to design a lower dimensionality dictionary without loss of useful information. This leads to many benefits including requiring less memory to store, requiring less computation to learn dictionary and requiring less computation to *code prediction* (i.e., seek *t* for a given image). Solving Eq. (4), which has the squared dot product of the filters as an additional term compared to Eq. (3), requires minimal extra effort. This is solved by Stochastic Gradient Descent, alternatively optimizing the d^j and t_i. However, different from most dictionary learning or sparse coding algorithms, both Eqs. (3) and (4) are real valued function of complex variables and care needs to be taken to the step of derivation. It is obvious that d^j is not differentiable in the ℓ_2 penalized term over the entire definition domain, thus directly seek the derivative of d^j is not infeasible. Fortunately, the linear structure presented in our model forces both the real and imaginary components to be linearly combined using the same real valued coefficients, this allows us to learn the real and imaginary components of d^j separately, leading to the following convex formulation:

$$L_3 = \arg\min_{D,t_i} \sum_i \left(\| H_i^{(re)} - D^{(re)}t_i \|_2^2 + \| H_i^{(im)} - D^{(im)}t_i \|_2^2 + \lambda_1 \| t_i \| + \lambda_2 \sum_j \sum_{k \neq j} (\langle d^j, d^k \rangle)^2 \right) \tag{5}$$

where $H_i^{(re)}, H_i^{(im)}$ and $D^{(re)}, D^{(im)}$ denote the real components and imaginary component of H_i and D, respectively. The ℓ_2 penalized term in L_2 is translated into two ℓ_2-norm terms in L_3, in which $d^{j(re)}, d^{j(im)}$ are differentiable over the entire definition domain. Although L_3 is a suboptimal strategy, it performs reliably in practice.

3 Code prediction

Given the filter bank, an accurate adaptive correlation filter can be computed (i.e., *code prediction*) for a given testing image, then the convolution operation is applied on the image with the adaptive filter to detect the position of targets.

3.1 Sparse coding

A stand way for code predication is sparse coding that performs inference by minimizing an energy function with respect to coefficients. For a given image F, we want each pixel TO produce the maximal output by convoluting with a reference filter $\tilde{H} \in \square^m$. This can be presented as the following formulation:

$$\tilde{H} = \tilde{G}\Big/_F \tag{6}$$

where $\tilde{G} \in \square^m$ is the Fourier of the desired output $\tilde{g} \in \square^m$, all elements in $\tilde{g}$ are set to 1 to achieve the maximal outputs.

With the defined reference filter $\tilde{H}$ and the learned filter bank D, we design an energy function as:

$$L_4 = \arg\min_t \left(\begin{array}{l} \square \tilde{H}^{(re)} - D^{(re)}t \square_2^2 + \square \tilde{H}^{(im)} - D^{(im)}t \square_2^2 \\ +\lambda \square t \square \end{array} \right) \tag{7}$$

A sparse coding process is then performed to solve this optimization problem as described in Section 2.

3.2 Nonlinear regress

While the sparse coding method designed above has the ability to produce accurate solutions, it will be impractically slow for real-time applications due to its time-consuming iterations. Therefore, we propose a nonlinear regress method to directly map input images F into sparse representation t. We only need to present F to the regression function to directly produce t, thus the iterative optimization is no longer required. We consider the following regression function:

$$fun(x|g, W, b) = g \tanh(Wx + b) \tag{8}$$

where tanh is the hyperbolic tangent nonlinearity function, $W \in R^{m \times n}$ is a filter matrix, $b \in R^m$ is a vector of biases, and $g \in R^{m \times m}$ is a diagonal matrix of scaling factors. This function has been shown to produce good features for object recognition [12]. In order to adapt the nonlinear regress to predict for complex variables, we create two independent regression functions to predict the real component and the imaginary component respectively:

$$\begin{cases} fun_{re}(F^{(re)}|g^{(re)}, W^{(re)}, b^{(re)}) = g^{(re)} \tanh(W^{(re)}F^{(re)} + b^{(re)}) \\ fun_{im}(F^{(im)}|g^{(im)}, W^{(im)}, b^{(im)}) = g^{(im)} \tanh(W^{(im)}F^{(im)} + b^{(im)}) \end{cases} \tag{9}$$

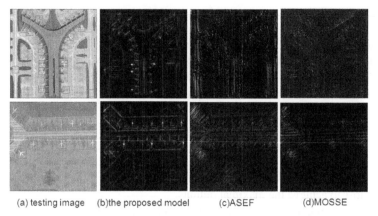

(a) testing image   (b)the proposed model   (c)ASEF   (d)MOSSE

Figure 2: Detection results using the three methods. The adaptive correlation filters are generated using the nonlinear regress.

where fun_{re} and fun_{im} is the regressor of the real component $F^{(re)}$ and the imaginary component of $F^{(im)}$, respectively. During training, the goal is to make the prediction of the two functions as close as possible to t: $fun_{re}(F^{(re)}) \rightarrow t; fun_{im}(F^{(im)}) \rightarrow t$. This optimization can be solved by stochastic gradient descent.

When D is available, given a testing image F, an accurate adaptive correlation filter $\hat{H}$ can be generated using sparse coding:

$$\hat{H} = Dt \tag{10}$$

After obtaining $\hat{H}$, we convolute F with $\hat{H}$ to get the filter response $\hat{G}$: $\hat{G} = F \square \hat{H}$, where $\square$ denotes the element-wise multiplication.

4 Experiments and discussion

To verify the effectiveness of our model, the experiment for detecting airplanes was performed on the real optical satellite images. The test dataset includes 20 gray-scale images with size of 750×750, all from Google Earth. A total of 367 targets are involved in the test set. The training set includes 100 images with size of 100×100, where contains 234 targets.

We reshape the training image to 750×750 in frequency domain, and set $\lambda_1 = 0.01$, $\lambda_2 = 0.2$, $n = 20$ empirically. In order to evaluate the detection performance, a comparison is preformed between the proposed model and two classical correlation filters technologies (i.e., ASEF and MOSSE).

It can be seen that the learned filters look very different from each other, and this leads to more powerful representations compared to other correlation filters techniques. As to ASEF and MOSSE, they only produce a single general filter,

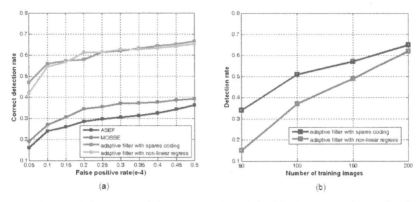

(a)   (b)

Figure 3: (a) ROC curves of the proposed model with the two code predication
methods (using 234 training images), ASEF and MOSSSE. (b) The
relationship between the detection rate and number of training images.

thus they cannot handle huge difference appearances. Figure 2 shows some
detection results using the three methods. It is obvious that our model
significantly outperforms both ASEF and MOSSE, targets which were missed in
the other two methods, were mostly detected by our model.

For the sake of completeness, we give the ROC curves computed by the
detection probability versus false alarm as shown in Figure 3(a), and we also
compared the two code predication methods using different numbers of training
images, as shown in Figure 3(b). From Figure 3, we can obtain the following
analysis: (1) along with the increase of training images, the accuracy of the
nonlinear regressor becomes more close to the spares coding. (2) Both the two
code predication methods significantly outperform both ASEF and MOSSE.

5   Conclusion and future work

In this paper, a novel model for constructing adaptive correlation filters is
proposed based on dictionary learning. We have shown the proposed model is
robust to appearance changes compared with conventional approaches. Moreover,
experimental results have indicated the designed nonlinear regress method is
efficient for real-time applications. It should be noted that more powerful
representations can be obtained by constructing a correlation filter for each pixel
of a testing image, and this is a direction of future research worth exploring.

References

[1]   R. Duda and P. Hart, *Pattern Classification and Scene Analysis*. pp. 276–
      284, 1973.
[2]   C.F. Hester and D. Casasent, Multivariant technique for multiclass pattern
      recognition. *Applied Opticals*, **19(11)**, pp. 1758–1761, 1980.

[3]   A. Mahalanobis, B.V.K. Vijaya Kumar, and D. Casasent, Minimum average correlation energy filters. *Applied Opticals*, **26(17)**, pp. 3633–3640, 1987.

[4]   B.V.K. Vijaya Kumar, Minimum-variance synthetic discriminant functions. *Journal of Optical Society of America A*, **3(10)**, pp. 1579–1584, 1986.

[5]   D.S. Bolme, A. Draper, and J.R. Beveridge, Average of synthetic exact filters. *Proceedings of the IEEE Conference on Computer Vision and Pattern Recognition*, 2009.

[6]   D.S. Bolme, J.R. Beveridge, B.A. Draper, and Y.M. Lui, Visual object tracking using adaptive correlation filters. *Proceedings of the IEEE Conference on Computer Vision and Pattern Recognition*, 2010.

[7]   M. Elad and M. Aharon, Image denoising via sparse and redundant representations over learned dictionaries. *IEEE Transactions on Image Processing*, **15(12)**, pp. 3736–3745, 2006.

[8]   Q. Zhang and B.X. Li, Discriminative K-SVD for dictionary learning in face recognition. *Proceedings of the IEEE Conference on Computer Vision and Pattern Recognition*, 2010.

[9]   M. Aharon, M. Elad, and A. Bruckstein, K-SVD: An algorithm for designing overcomplete dictionaries for sparse representation. *IEEE Transactions on Signal Processing*, **54(11)**, pp. 4311–4322, 2006.

Exploring the elevator remote monitoring system based on Internet of Things

Jiang Lian[1], Sun Yanming[1], Ding Jianjie[2]
[1]*School of Business Administration, South China University of Technology, Guangzhou, 510641, China*
[2]*Department of Computer Science, GuangDong Pharmaceutical University, Guangzhou, 510006, China*

Abstract

It is important to secure the safety and reliability of an elevator in view of the fact that elevator accident often leads to great casualties. In this paper, the authors design an elevator remote monitoring system based on Internet of Things (ERMS-BIoT), which aims to obtain real-time running information of the elevator, including running state information, location information, malfunction information, and the real-time video information. The three core technologies of Internet of Things, namely Internet & Communication Technologies, Intelligent Sensing & Embedded Technologies, and Semantic Technologies were discussed in this paper. On this basis, the authors presented the overall system architecture and software structure of Elevator Remote Monitoring System based on Internet of Things. Finally, the authors verified the functions and performance of ERMS-BIoT with the support of HT Elevator Company. The result shows that ERMS-BIoT has excellent performance, and meets the needs of elevator remote monitoring in complex environment.

Keywords: Elevator Remote Monitoring System, Internet of Things, Semantic Technologies, Internet & Communication Technologies, Intelligent Sensing & Embedded Technologies.

1 Introduction

In modern society, cities are filled with a large number of high-rise buildings, which are highly dependent on elevators. However, when the elevators experience a sudden failure, the damages to people may be fatal. According to the

 WIT Transactions on Information and Communication Technologies, Vol. 61, © 2014 WIT Press
www.witpress.com, ISSN 1743-3517 (on-line)
doi:10.2495/MIIT130841

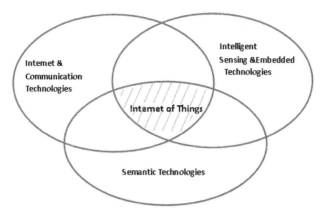

Figure 1: The paradigm of "Internet of Things".

statistics of National Municipal Supervision Bureau, there were thousands of elevator failures in recent years with a direct result of hundreds of casualties. Therefore, the elevator safety issues have attracted the attention of public and manufacturers.

With the rise of the Internet of Things technologies, it is possible for elevator manufacturers to improve elevator service quality through remote real-time monitoring about elevator running status without significant increasing in maintenance personnel. Therefore, the purpose of this paper is to design and implement elevator remote monitoring system based on Internet of Things. We believe that the results of this study may help the elevator companies to grasp the real-time operational status information, and quickly respond to the elevator failures, so as to avoid unnecessary casualties and property losses.

2 Brief reviews of Internet of Things and Elevator Monitoring System

2.1 Internet of Things(IoT)

As the name implies, Internet of Things (IoT) means "a world-wide network of interconnected objects uniquely addressable, based on standard communication protocols" [1]. According to the research results completed by Luigi [2], the Internet of Things could be considered as the integration and fusion of Internet & Communication Technologies, Intelligent Sensing & Embedded Technologies and semantic technologies, as illustrated in Figure 1.

First of all, intelligent sensing and embedded technology dedicated to solving common object recognition and information collection issues, among which Radio-Frequency IDentification (RFID) is the most mature technology and widely used. In addition, Near Field Communications (NFC), Wireless Sensor and Actuator Networks (WSAN) together with RFID are also recognized as "the atomic components that will link the real world with the digital world".

Furthermore, Sensor networks will also play a crucial role in the Internet of Things, which can cooperate with RFID systems to better track the status of things, i.e., their location, temperature, movements. As such, they can augment the awareness of a certain environment and, thus, act as a further bridge between physical and digital world [3].

Secondly, the Internet and communication technology committed to addressing remote access and control of various objects, and the communication problems among objects. Among these, IP Stack and 3G network are the key. According to the opinion of the IPSO (IP for Smart Objects) Alliance [4], the IP stack is a light protocol that already connects a huge amount of communicating devices and runs on tiny and battery operated embedded devices. This guarantees that IP has all the qualities to make Internet of Things a reality. The technology base of 3G is CDMA (Code Division Multiple Access, CDMA). Currently, there are four standard for 3G, they are: TD-SCDMA, CDMA2000, WCDMA and WiMAX [5].

Finally, the role of semantic technology is to solve issues related to how to represent, store, interconnect, search, and organize information generated by the Internet of Things. That is because, semantic technology can exploit appropriate modeling solutions for things description, reasoning over data generated by Internet of Things, semantic execution environments and architectures that accommodate Internet of Things requirements and scalable storing and communication infrastructure [6].

2.2 Elevator Monitoring System

Since most countries around the world have enacted stringent safety regulations about elevators, so far the world's major elevator manufacturers have also established their own basic elevator monitoring systems, which contains running status monitoring, some control functions, operation management, pre-fault diagnosis, and fault history data statistical analysis. According to the different way of elevator data collection, the existing elevator monitoring systems can be divided into two main categories.

The first type of elevator monitoring systems was independently developed by the major elevator manufacturers. An important feature of this type of system is that the elevator running state information is captured by the data communication interface within the elevator's own control system, in this way, the data needed to monitor can be collected accurately and timely. For example, Mitsubishi Elevator, Hitachi elevators, Otis elevators, and other large foreign manufacturers are all using this approach. However, these elevator remote monitoring systems only included remote data monitoring functions which were based on conventional sensing technologies, while the remote video monitoring capabilities were excluded because of its high cost and its high bandwidth requirements on the Internet [7].

The second type of elevator monitoring systems was developed by non-elevator manufacturers. In this mode, the collection of elevator running status information is completed by installing sensors independently from the elevator's own control system. This method has the benefit of minimizing the impact on

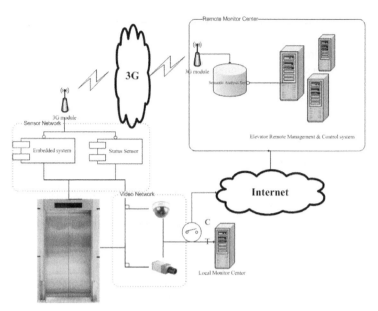

Figure 2: The overall system architecture of Elevator Remote Monitoring System Based on IoT.

elevator running because state sensors are completely out of the elevator itself, but in the meanwhile it has some disadvantages, such as complicated installation, difficult construction, and high error rate. For example, currently most of the small elevator manufacturers have adopted this approach. In this manner, some local elevator monitoring systems which used cable for data transmission contain video monitoring, but for the remote elevator monitoring systems, video monitoring is also excluded for the same reason.

3 Design an Elevator Remote Monitoring System Based on Internet of Things (ERMS-BIoT)

According to the core concept of the Internet of Things, the Elevator Remote Monitoring System Based on Internet of Things (ERMS-BIoT) presented in this paper consists of the following five parts, namely: Sensor Network, Video Network, Communication System, Local Monitor Centre, and Remote Monitor Centre. Figure 2 is the overall system architecture of Elevator Remote Monitoring System Based on Internet of Things(ERMS-BIoT).

3.1 Sensor Network

Sensor Network undertakes most of the information collection tasks referring to monitoring an elevator (except for video information). Sensor networks consist of a certain number of sensing nodes (embedded sensors and attached sensors)

communicating in a wireless multi-hop fashion. Usually nodes report the results of their sensing to a small number (in most cases, only one) of special nodes called sinks. Design objectives of the proposed solutions are energy efficiency, scalability, reliability, and robustness [8]. The data collection system is designed based on embedded system with Linux, Multi-Thread technique, socket programming and device driver are main techniques used in the system. Front Terminal takes charge of sampling the signals of elevator status, fault, and equipment. If any fault appears, through the elevator data collectors and terminal units, the distributed operating status and fault information of the elevators are transmitted timely to monitoring centre via 3G network. Elevator faults diagnosis completely, correctly, and rapidly, giving alarm in sound, light through self-sending short message [9]. In order to obtain comprehensive information on the operational status of the elevators, 15 sensors were installed on each elevator, achieving a complete coverage of the elevator's eight subsystems (namely, traction system, guidance system, car, door system, weight and balance system, power drag actuation system, electrical control system and safety system). The sensor network solutions adopted by this paper are based on the IEEE 802.15.4 standard.

3.2 Video Network

Monitoring Video includes not only the video information inside the elevator car, but also the environmental video information outside the elevator (especially the video information from the host way). Since the main characteristics of live video stream need to meet real time, continuous, timing, and large data volume , so the requirement for the transmission link of the video data are very high, even the slightest error or delays can lead to video data Masai Ka, pause and other phenomena. Considering the high error rate, bandwidth fluctuations and network latency issues prevalent in the 3G wireless network, so video information collected from the video network will be transferred to the local monitoring center by cables, in the meanwhile, according to the needs of elevator manufacturer, the video information will also be synchronized to a remote monitoring centre via Internet. In order to reduce the cost of the video information transmission, the video information does not actively transmitted to the remote monitoring center under normal circumstances. However, once the sensor network capturing abnormal signals, video network will be triggered to synchronize real video to remote monitoring center automatically.

3.3 Communication system

Communication systems, including 3G wireless networks and the Internet, are recommended to select large telecommunications providers' service in order to ensure the stability of the transmitted signal. According to our design, remote video signals are transmitted over the internet, while the remote sensing signals are sent by 3G wireless network. It should be noted that the 3G Communication Module servicing for 3G wireless network adopts ETEK TD-8311USB MODEM, which is based on Wideband Code Division Multiple Access technology and

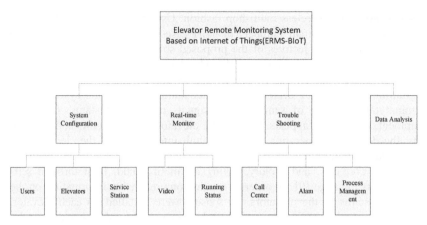

Figure 3: The software structure of ERMS-BIoT.

specially designed for professional industrial control data transmission. Because of its full support for WCDMA and GSM/GPRS/EDGE and its adequate capacity for high-speed network, coupled with its rigorous industrial design, therefore, it is particularly suitable for harsh operating environment monitoring and other outdoor data collection.

3.4 Local Monitor Center and Remote Monitor Center

The Elevator Remote Monitoring System Based on Internet of Things (ERMS-BIoT) will also be deployed in Remote Monitor Center and Local Monitor Center. Since the system is Web based, the biggest difference lies in the contents and permissions. For example, the server for running status monitoring and semantic analyzing will be unified deployed in remote monitoring center, while monitoring client and the local video server will be deployed in local monitor centers. In addition, the local monitor center only can monitor the local elevators, but the remote monitor center can monitor all the elevators that were included in the monitoring range.

The Elevator Remote Monitoring System Based on Internet of Things (ERMS-BIoT) is developed by JBuilder 9.0, following B/S three-tier structure. In the aspect of application, the system has a friendly user interface which can present elevator operation monitoring and fault diagnosis information visually. The main functions of ERMS-BIoT include: system configurations referring to user, elevators and service stations; real-time monitoring of running status and video information; trouble shooting, and data analysis. In addition, when an elevator fault occurs, staffs of remote monitoring center can hold a conversation with passengers in elevator, and notify the maintaining staffs nearby rapidly.

The software structure of ERMS-BIoT is shown in Figure 3.

In the remote monitoring center, remote sensing signals received must be sent to the semantic analysis server for pretreatment, after that, the original sensing signals were converted into information which can be understood by application

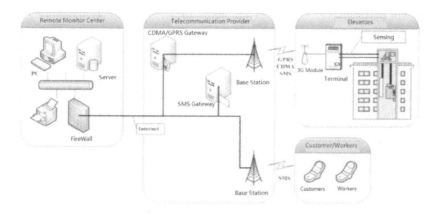

Figure 4: HT Elevator's new monitoring platform based on ERMS-BIoT.

system and users. According to this model, not only increases the scalability of the system, but also significantly improves the response performance of the system.

4 The application of Elevator Remote Monitoring System based on Internet of Things (ERMS-BIoT)

With the strong support of a famous elevator manufacturing enterprise-HT Elevator Company, it took the authors only 5 months to update the conventional HT elevator monitoring system to the elevator remote monitoring system based on Internet of Things. On this basis, HT Elevator organized a 10 person project team. After their three months of hard work, finally the project team achieved the migrating of 30000 elevators running in the Southern China area supported by HT Elevator to the new platform (ERMS-BIoT) in the end of 2012, the operation mode of the new platform is shown in Figure 4. After nearly eight months' operation, it shows that the system completely meets the remote monitoring requirements of HT Elevator, in the meanwhile, has excellent system performance and higher user satisfaction.

5 Conclusion

In this paper, the three core technologies of Internet of Things, namely Internet & Communication Technologies, Intelligent Sensing & Embedded Technologies, and Semantic Technologies were discussed in this paper firstly. On this basis, the authors presented the overall system architecture, hardware and software structure of Elevator Remote Monitoring System based on Internet of Things. Finally, the authors verified the functions and performance of the Elevator Remote Monitoring System Based on Internet of Things (ERMS-BIoT) with the support of HT Elevator Company. The result shows that ERMS-BIoT has excellent performance, and meets the needs of elevator remote monitoring in complex environment.

References

[1] L. Yuxi and Z. Guohui, Key technologies and applications of internet of things. *Proceedings 2012 5th International Conference on Intelligent Computation Technology and Automation*, IEEE Computer Society, 445 Hoes Lane, Zhangjiajie, Hunan, China, pp. 197–200, 2012.

[2] A. Luigi, I. Antonio, and M. Giacomo, The Internet of Things: A survey. *Computer Networks*, **54**, pp. 2787–2805, 2010.

[3] A. Kröner, J. Haupert, and D. Schreiber, Digital object memories for the internet of things (DOMe-IoT). *UbiComp'12 – Proceedings of the 2012 ACM Conference on Ubiquitous Computing*, Association for Computing Machinery, Pittsburgh, PA, pp. 1189–1192, 2012.

[4] M. Sveda and R. Vrba, Integrated smart sensor networking framework for sensor-based appliances. *IEEE Sensors Journal*, **3(5)**, pp. 579–586, October 2003.

[5] A. Jamalipour, T. Wada, and T. Yamazato, A tutorial on multiple access technologies for beyond 3G mobile networks. *IEEE Communications Magazine*, **43(2)**, pp. 110–117, February 2005.

[6] Estrada-Martinez, E. Paul, Semantic interactions in the Internet of Things. *International Journal of Ad Hoc and Ubiquitous Computing*, **13(3–4)**, pp. 167–175, 2013.

[7] J. Xiaomei, H. Zhengxiao, and R. Yannian, Research on intelligent elevator control system. *Advanced Materials Research*, **605–607**, pp. 1802–1805, 2013.

[8] I.F. Akyildiz, W. Su, and E. Cayirci, Wireless sensor networks: a survey. *Computer Networks*, **38(4)**, pp. 393–422, 2002.

[9] Zhang Guangming, Study on city elevator remote monitoring system based on multi-agent. *Elevator World*, **54(7)**, pp. 104–111, 2006.

The integrated safety mode study of wireless network database

Chunmin Qiu, Fei Lao
Binzhou Polytechnic, Binzhou, Shandong, 256603, China

Abstract

Wireless network communication grows continuously in recent years; however, utilization rate is still low which is one of the main reasons for the problem of information security. As the threat of unauthorized access is becoming more and more serious, in this study we focus on the security control of database access in the wireless environment. In addition, because of short circle, small bandwidth, low coverage, and easy broken line features of wireless network communication, if we simply use cable environment access control mode into the wireless environment in, then this inevitably leads to low efficiency. In this research we extend altruism lock (AL) mechanism, join the idea of enlarged donation) idea, and explain the work flow through examples. In addition, combining with multistage safety database and Priority concept, we put forward a set of integration architecture Priority/AL/MLS which is suitable for wireless network communication. The framework can not only do parallel control, but also can improve performance in a long period trading (Long-Life Transactions, LLT) and make use of MLS to improve security and avoid the threat of unauthorized access. This concept is applicable to the characteristics of the wireless environment which not only can make a priority of the user to quickly get the response of the database but also can ensure data security.

Keywords: wireless network communication, network security, database, priority, architecture.

1 Introduction

Wireless network communication grows continuously in recent years; however, utilization rate is still low which is one of the main reasons for the problem of information security. Once the wireless local area network (WLAN) arrives,

WIT Transactions on Information and Communication Technologies, Vol. 61, © 2014 WIT Press
www.witpress.com, ISSN 1743-3517 (on-line)
doi:10.2495/MIIT130851

information security and computer crime issues will only grow. Wireless Network communication is to transfer data by electromagnetic wave in the air, because of lacking for the characteristics of physical line, so it's probable to be attacked, eavesdropped, and covered. In addition, due to short circle, small bandwidth, low coverage, and easy broken line features of wireless network communication, then how to make a priority of the user to quickly get the response of the database is worth paying attention to.

Priority is one of the important concepts of quality of service (QoS). Most of the early network traffic is given priority to data, but not the concept of priority. When the network loads are too much, all of the processing network will be affected [1]. Weikum thinks that whether users will use a set of information system or not depends on the quality of service, and in [2], [3], and [4] they have mentioned that service of quality were used in the database query. Literatures also once put forward the idea of database in time, and all sorts of signs show that in the database query service quality is a very important issue [5]. In recent years, the multimedia data transmission has been increasing, so we must depend on the characteristics of the data transmission to distribute different bandwidth [6]. Because the bandwidth of wireless communication is small, how to more effectively use the existing bandwidth is particularly important [7].

Transaction is the logic unit of database processing, and trade owns four important characteristic which are respectively atomicity, consistency, isolation, and durability [8]. In order to keep the consistency of the database, we have the lock (Locking) function design, but often there will be a fast knot and poor performance problems [9]. In order to solve these problems, Salem and scholars in 1994 put forward "Altruistic lock" idea. Until 2001, Kim and other scholars have proposed a two-way donation lock architecture [9]. This study references this mechanism, and enlarges the idea of donation. According to the principle of donation lock, while locking a party of resources, we must be in the right time to release the lock resources and give them to others to avoid long occupancy. As for what can be a gift, we should consider parallel control principle, and combine with the safety level to maintain the consistency of the database multilevel security [10–12]. Wireless technology is the main characteristics of the application of information technology in the next phase and its characteristics are small bandwidth, short cycle, easy to break, and low coverage [13]. In order to solve the limitation of short link, long lock must be avoided. Locking mechanisms are often thought as poor performance, but extension altruism lock has been introduced to avoid long occupancy resources, and it looks like a better solution in short period wireless database access.

There are a lot of information security issues from insiders' intentional attacks or unintentional negligence, so database access control management is quite important. In this study, we proposed Multilevel Security Database architecture, a Subject is authorized (Clearance) a Security level C (S), an Object is classified (Classification) a Security level C (O). Safety level is in accordance with the Lattice theory combination, including, in simple safety situation the security level of Subject must be higher than that of Object, i.e., C (O)<= C (S), then we can read the data, that is not up to Read (No Read—up). When the Subject read

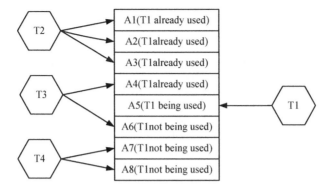

Figure 1: Two-way phase locking process.

Object O and write the data P, its level of security must be below P, i.e., C (O) <=C (P), to Write the data, that is not written down (No Write—down). There are many related research about the use of MLS in network security analysis, the framework proposed by each scholar may be different, but there is a widely used structure which can be divided into four levels, Top Secret, Secret, Confidential, and Unclassified.

2   Database lock

2.1 Two-phase lock

Long-Life Transactions, like mobile communications companies print millions of customers' bills, may be long occupied in the database of the resources which will make the database delaying and inefficient. Two-Way Phase Locking can't early release the lock data and the consequences can be explained by the following example. Assume that there are four deals T1, T2, T3, and T4, T1 represents long periodic trading, and T2, T3, and T4 represent short-life transaction (SLT). T1 uses A1, A2, A3, A4, A5, A6, A7, and A8 the eight object in sequence, A1, A2, A3, and A4 have been used, A5 is currently being used and A6, A7, and A8 has not been used.

In addition, T2 uses A1, A2, and A3, T3 uses A4 and A6, and T4 uses A7 and A8. In the 2PL framework, T2 and T3 will wait until the completion of the T1 to access the object they want. Because the T1 once locked A1, A2, and A3, but without the idea of donate which leads to that T1 has been holding a number of resources until the end of trading transaction. So the order of transaction is:

$$T4 \rightarrow T1 \rightarrow T2 \rightarrow T3$$

T1 is a LLT which will lead to bad performance of T2 and T3 waiting too long. The process of Two-Way Phase Locking is shown in Figure 1.

2.2 Read-only transaction under altruism lock

In order to solve the poor efficiency problem of last section altruistic locking mechanism is produced. In this section, the AL has two hypotheses: (1) Do not consider reading and writing. (2) Hypothesizes that trading is always successful which makes the situation simply.

The essence of AL and 2PL are exactly the same, only for the donate concept. If we take the above example, because theT1 does not useA1, A2, A3, and A4, according to 2 PL mechanism we can donate these objects for other transactions. In other words, T2 can complete the transaction, but T3 could not complete the transaction, because T3 must access A4, A5, and A6 three objects. Only object A4 was presented, but the one which accepts the gift trade must be completely in the list of wake up (Wake List). Due to the objects A5 and A6 are not in the list of wake up, so T3 must wait until the objects A5 and A6 are taken into the list of wake up to complete the transaction. So the transaction completed order:

$$T2 \rightarrow T4 \rightarrow T3 \rightarrow T1$$

Therefore, we can find T2, T3, and T4 the three can be completed as soon as possible, not low efficiency of the weak LLT caused. From the above narrative shape and we sort out two rules: (1) Two trades can't lock the same object at the same time, unless one of the gift is traded to the object. (2) The trade which accepts gifts must be completely in the same transaction awakening list. According to the second rule, we can ensure transaction serializable.

2.3 Considering the parallel control of reading and writing

Due to the data in the database is sharing, and at the same time let more than one user readable and writeable. In this case, in order to maintain the integrity of the data, we use the parallel control to maintain data integrity and consistency, and if there is no proper parallel control, it may induce the following four questions: (1) Lost Update; (2) Dirty Read; (3) Incorrect Summary; (4) Unrepeatable Read. In order to simplify the complexity of the transaction, we will read the object as concurrent, and write back to the object shall be regarded as the sequence. When considering the Lock, we use share lock to deal with Read Lock; and Exclusive Lock to deal with the Write Lock.

3 Integrated parallel control

Before explaining the algorithm, we need to explain the meaning of some parameters. First, as each object h within one database is concerned, the algorithm must maintain three parameters: rq (h), object a is trading reading locked and not released. wq (h), object a is trading Writing locked and not released. d (h) : object a is trading donated and not released. For every transaction T, the algorithm must maintain two parameters: $\eta(T)$: the transactions completely in the waking list of trade T. $\beta(T)$ the transactions which may be in the waking

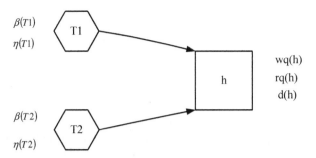

Figure 2: The parallel control integration mode 1 considering reading and writing.

Table 1: The Algorithm Process of the Parallel Control Integration Mode 1.

Number	Objective	Process	Locking
1	RL(h,T1)	i:{}, w:{}, i≦w, rq(h)={T1}, $\beta(T1)$ = {}, $\eta(T1)$ = {}, return(accept)	yes
	RL(h,T2)	i:{}, w:{}, i≦w, rq(h)={T1,T2}, $\beta(T1)$ = {}, $\eta(T1)$ = {}, return(accept)	
2	RL(h,T1)	i:{}, w:{}, i≦w, rq(h)={T1}, $\beta(T1)$ = {}, $\eta(T1)$ = {}, return(accept)	no
	WL(h,T2)	i:{}, w:{}, i≦w, return(reject)	
3	WL(h,T1)	i:{}, w:{}, i≦w, wq(h)={T1}, $\beta(T1)$ = {}, $\eta(T1)$ = {}, return(accept)	no
	RL(h,T2)	i:{T1}, w:{}, i≦w, return(reject)	
4	WL(h,T1)	i:{}, w:{}, i≦w, wq(h)={T1}, $\beta(T1)$ = {}, $\eta(T1)$ = {}, return(accept)	no
	WL(h,T2)	i:{T1}, w:{}, i≦w, return(reject)	

list of trade T in the future. And the initializations of q(h), $\eta(T)$ and d(h) are all zero, and the value of $\beta(T)$ will change as dynamic transactions.

As shown in Figure 2, T1 and T2 represent transactions, and respectively maintain $\beta(T1)$, $\eta(T1)$ and $\beta(T2)$, $\eta(T2)$. Objective a is responsible for wq(h), rq(h), and d(h), which respectively carry out RL(h,T1) and RL(h,T2), RL(h,T1) and WL(h,T2), WL(h,T1) and RL(h,T2), WL(h,T1) and WL(h,T2). The implementation process of the algorithm is listed in Table 1, and the final results found that only RL (h, T1) and RL (h, T2) can be successful executed. In other words, as long as there is writing lock, we must be sequentially processing trade.

If T1, T2, and T3 are trades, and h and u are data objects, its trading order:

RL(h,T1)->Donate(h,T1)->WL(h,T2)->Commit(T2)->RL(h,T3)->WL(u,T3) ->Commit(T3)->RL(u,T1)->Commit(T1).

The algorithm process is shown in Table 2 and Figure 3.

 WIT Transactions on Information and Communication Technologies, Vol. 61, © 2014 WIT Press
www.witpress.com, ISSN 1743-3517 (on-line)

Table 2: The Algorithm Process of the Parallel Control Integration Mode 2.

Number	Objective	Process
1	RL(h,T1)	i:{}, w:{}, i$\leq$w, rq(h)={T1}, $\beta(T1)$ = {}, $\eta(T1)$ = {}, return(accept)
	Donate(h,T1)	d(h):{T1}, return(accept)
	WL(h,T2)	i:{}, w:{}, i$\leq$w, rq(h)={T1,T2}, $\beta(T1)$ = {}, $\eta(T1)$ = {}, return(accept)
2	Commit(T2) = ULock(h,T2)	rq(h):{T1}, wq(h):{T1}, d(h):{T1}, $\beta(T1)$ = {}, $\eta(T1)$ = {}, $\beta(T2)$ = {T1}, $\eta(T2)$ = {T1}, return(accept)
3	RL(h,T3)	i:{}, w:{T1}, i$\leq$w, rq(h)={T1,T3}, $\beta(T3)$ = {}, $\eta(T3)$ = {T1}, return(accept)
	WL(u,T3)	i:{T1,T3}, w:{T1,T3}, i$\leq$w, wq(h)={T3}, $\beta(T3)$ = {T1,T3}, $\eta(T3)$ = {T1,T3}, return(accept)
4	Commit(T3)	ULock (h,T3): rq(h):{T1}, wq(h):{T1}, d(h):{T1}, $\beta(T1)$ = {}, $\eta(T1)$ = {}, $\beta(T2)$ = {T1}, $\eta(T2)$ = {T1}, $\beta(T3)$ = {T1}, $\eta(T3)$ = {T1}, return(accept)
		ULock (u,T3): rq(u):{T1}, wq(u):{T1}, d(u):{T1}, $\beta(T1)$ = {}, $\eta(T1)$ = {}, $\beta(T2)$ = {T1}, $\eta(T2)$ = {T1}, $\beta(T3)$ = {T1}, $\eta(T3)$ = {T1}, return(accept)
5	RL(u,T1)	i:{T1}, w:{T1}, i$\leq$w, rq(h)={T1}, $\beta(T1)$ = {T1}, $\eta(T1)$ = {T1}, return(accept)
6	Commit(T1)	ULock (h,T1): rq(h):{}, wq(h):{}, d(h):{}, $\beta(T1)$ = {}, $\eta(T1)$ = {}, $\beta(T2)$ = {}, $\eta(T2)$ = {}, $\beta(T3)$ = {}, $\eta(T3)$ = {}, return(accept)
		ULock (u,T1): rq(u):{}, wq(u):{}, d(u):{}, $\beta(T1)$ = {}, $\eta(T1)$ = {}, $\beta(T2)$ = {}, $\eta(T2)$ = {}, $\beta(T3)$ = {}, $\eta(T3)$ = {}, return(accept)

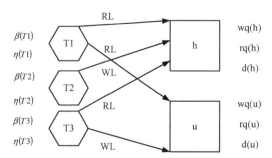

Figure 3: The parallel control integration mode 2 considering reading and writing.

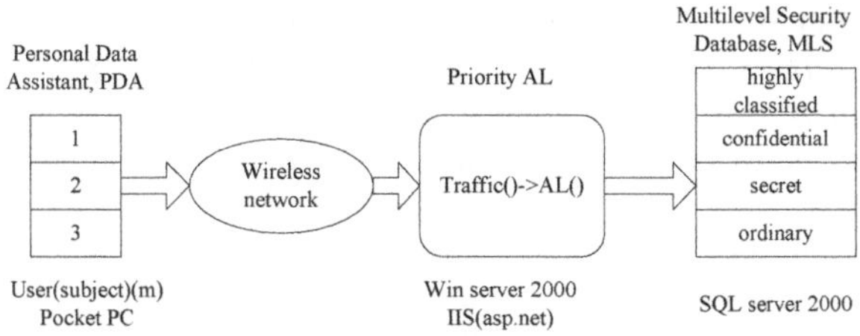

Figure 4: Integrated parallel control mode considering priority.

Generally speaking, many deadlocks occur result from two trading rights, so that the deadlocked situation. The concept of customer priority is imported, which is comfortable enough to reduce this kind of phenomenon, and schedule. Therefore, this research provides a suitable multilevel security database access structure which is adaptive for wireless communication as shown in Figure 4.

4 Conclusion

Wireless network communication is increasingly universalness, and the Client (Client) types are also increasingly numerous. May be that mobile phones, Personal digital Assistant or notebook computer, even the desktop computer, including individual utility and purpose are not uniform, which will be properly adjusted due to the needs of the customers in the future and the agreement which is applicable for accessing data also should make appropriate adjustments. This research is based on PDA as the client and puts forward a set of integrated wireless network security architecture which is fit for back end database and with priority MLS. This study uses two-way gift lock and priority to improve efficiency. In addition to using multiple security database to improve security, we are in hopes of the help of wireless network communication security.

References

[1]   Pingyuan Xi and Yandong Song, Application research on BP neural network PID control of the belt conveyor. *Journal of Digital Information Management*, **9(6),** pp. 266–270, 2011.
[2]   Guoping Zhang and Mande Xie, The design and implementation of the digital down converter based on the improved DDS and DSPBuilder techniques. *Journal of Digital Information Management*, **9(6)**, pp. 281–286 2011.
[3]   Hung-Yu Chien, Yi-Hwa Chen, Jinn-Ke Jan, and Yuh-Min Tseng, Cryptanalysis on dynamic authentication protocol for personal communication system. *Electronics Letters*, **37(14)**, pp. 895–896, 2011.
[4]   J. Dankers, T. Garefalakis, R. Schaffelhofer, and T. Wright, Public key infrastructure in mobile systems. *Electronics & Communication Engineering Journal*, **14(5)**, pp. 180–190, 2009.

[5]   Chai Wah Wu, On the design of content-based multimedia authentication systems. *IEEE Transactions on Multimedia*, **4(3)**, pp. 385–393, 2011.

[6]   William A. Arbaugh, Narendar Shankar, Y.C. Justin Wan, Your 802.11 wireless network has no clothes. *IEEE Wireless Communications*, **9(6)**, pp. 44–51, 2011.

[7]   J. Ala-Laurila, J. Mikkonen, and J. Rinnemaa, Wireless LAN access network architecture for mobile operators. *IEEE Communications Magazine*, **39(11)**, pp. 82–89, 2007.

[8]   H. Yang, H.Y. Luo, F. Ye, S.W. Lu, and L. Zhang, Security in mobile ad hoc networks: challenges and solutions. *IEEE Wireless Communications*, **30(2)**, pp. 38–47, 2004.

[9]   K. Salem, H. Garcia-Molina, and J. Shands, Altruistic Locking. *ACM Transactions on Database Systems*, **1**, pp. 117–169, 1994.

[10]   Yuxin Mao, SERCID: a secure mechanism for data collection in wireless sensor networks. *Journal of Digital Information Management*, **10(2)**, pp. 79–85, 2012.

[11]   Wei Wang, Mechanism analysis of protocols based on the FPCPN model. *Journal of Digital Information Management*, **10(2)**, pp. 86–93, 2012.

[12]   Xi Li, Zheng Ren, and Yanling Shi, An equivalent circuit model for on-chip inductors with gradual changed structure. *Journal of Digital Information Management*, **10(2)**, pp. 99–103, 2012.

[13]   Chang Su, Lili Zheng, Xiaohai Si, and Fengjun Shang, Low overhead geometric on-demand routing protocol for mobile ad hoc networks. *Journal of Digital Information Management*, **10(2)**, pp. 114–120, 2012.

An applicable design of fast transforming classroom into intelligent one based on internet of things

Jen-Chi Chang, Yongjian Li, Xiukun Zhao, Sang-Bing Tsai
Business School of Nankai University, Tianjin, 300071, China

Abstract

It's our dream to build up a future classroom for our students which can get the demanded information and resources easily. This paper presents a system design which can easily transform a traditional classroom into an intelligent one based on IOT technology. With the aid of IOT technology, it can help schools in energy saving, teaching efficiency, learning interactivity, and devices management. Furthermore, the related IOT layers are indicated as well. Finally, the future extension has been mentioned for further discussion.

Keywords: Internet of Things (IOT), Set-Top-Box (STB), RFID, smart device, intelligent school, smart school.

1 Introduction

After US President, Mr. Obama, had responded aggressively to the concept of "Intelligent Earth" proposed by IBM in 2009, IOT has been promoted as the national strategy in the United States of America [1]. Moreover, also being promoted as "Strategic Emerging Industry" by 125-Program of China in 2011, IOT has become the fastest growing domain in China. Furthermore, with the continued advocating by the developed countries, IOT has made a big stride in the technology development and lots of applicable systems have been fulfilled in each field.

From the IOT structure point of view, it can be divided into four different layers: (1) Perceptive Layer, (2) Network Layer, (3) Processing Layer, and (4) Application Layer. However, with regard to the school applications domain, we found that there exists a relationship between IOT layers and classroom. We call it "Classroom–IOT Relationship" (CIOTR).

WIT Transactions on Information and Communication Technologies, Vol. 61, © 2014 WIT Press
www.witpress.com, ISSN 1743-3517 (on-line)
doi:10.2495/MIIT130861

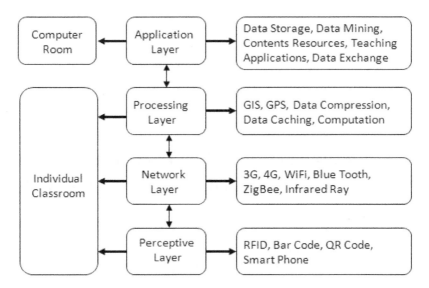

Figure 1: Classroom–IOT Relationship (CIOTR).

As shown in Figure 1 in the Perceptive Layer, teachers and students use RFID, Bar Code, QR Code as the identifier, and use the corresponding sensor or reader to identify them. And, to the Network Layer, they use Wi-Fi, 3G, Blue Tooth or ZigBee to transmit the data which are collected by Perceptive Layer. To the Processing Layer, they do some required processing like data compression, data caching, and computation on the data which are transmitted from Network Layer. Lastly, if the data requires further manipulation like contents searching, downloading or advanced mathematical calculation, Application Layer provides the related services to those of being sent by Processing Layer.

Through CIOTR, we can easily understand in what layer the classroom is positioning right now. Based on this structure, this paper presents an applicable model based on IOT to let the classroom become intelligent. More specifically, it includes four main parts to achieve. The four parts are described as below:

(1) Transform A Traditional Classroom into IOT-Based One
(2) Login STB by QR Code
(3) Collect and Analyze Students' Learning Behaviors through RFID
(4) Manage Devices Smartly

2 Transform a traditional classroom into IOT-based one

In a traditional classroom, teachers can project their course contents onto the white board by means of connecting their computer or notebook to the projector. However, in order to operate them, teachers have to go back and fore very often between computer and the white board. For some advanced classrooms, they are equipped with Electrical White Board and can eliminate those inconveniences.

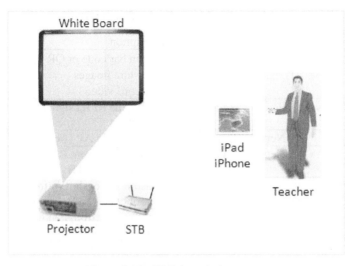

Figure 2: An IOT-based classroom.

Because it's enough for teachers to operate it on the Electrical White Board only. They don't have to operate the computer. However, to have an Electrical White Board for each classroom is a big burden for schools.

Recently, due to the trend of using Pad/Smartphone and clouding system, teachers can prepare their course contents at home, store them in the cloud, and present it in the classroom. It does bring lots of conveniences for teachers to prepare a presentation to students. Besides, teachers also can give a presentation to the students in any corner of the classroom rather than to stand at the platform steadily.

As shown in Figure 2, it's an IOT-based classroom. We can easily transform a traditional classroom into IOT-based one simply by installing a Set-Top-Box (STB) into it. With STB installation, teachers can easily present their course contents to the students simply by connecting their Pad through Wi-Fi and login STB. After then, teachers can display all the operations on Pad or Smartphone through DLNA or Air Play protocol.

The functions provided by STB are listed as shown in Table 1. Their related IOT layers are also indicated accordingly.

3   Login STB by QR Code

In order to protect STB from un-authorized access, the administrative privilege should be established in advance. There exists a back end system in the Application Layer to manage the access privilege for each teacher. Therefore, with a proper privilege setting in the back end system, school can easily protect their resources and properties from illegal use. After that, teachers can login into STB in the right classroom and right time.

Table 1: STB Funtions and Their Related IOT Layers.

Functions	IOT Layer	Description
Webcam	Perceptive Layer	• Scan bar code or QR code • Capture images • Record video
RFID Receiver	Perceptive Layer	Receive the RFID signal sent from transmitter.
Wi-Fi	Network Layer	Provide Wi-Fi AP (Access Point).
DLNA	Network Layer	Transmit data from Pad or Smartphone to STB
Wi-Fi Display	Network Layer	Transmit screenshot from Pad or Smartphone to STB.
Air Play	Network Layer	Transmit data from Pad or Smartphone to STB.
APPs	Processing Layer	Process the acquired data from network layer.

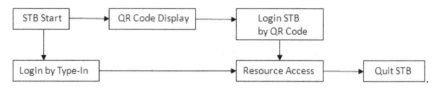

Figure 3: The process to login STB.

With regard to the login process, we can use either type-in or QR Code to login the STB. Currently, most of the existed Pad and Smartphone are equipped with the webcam. It will be more convenient for teachers to login STB by QR Code rather than type-in model. As shown in Figure 3, when the STB starts, it will display the QR Code on the screen by default. Then, teachers can launch the related APP in their Pad or Smartphone to scan it. After scanned, their identity will be identified. If they have the privilege, they can access the related resources after then. If teachers are not used to QR Code, they also can switch into the traditional way by type-in. System has remained in two modes for them.

When teachers end up their presentation in one classroom, they can quit the STB by using the quit function provided by the APP. And, when they enter another classroom, they can also follow the same process as above to login STB. What required for teachers is to bring their Pad or Smartphone with them. Under such kind of environment, it will bring three main conveniences for teachers:

- Easily connect and control the devices in each classroom.
- Easily access the campus recourses from each classroom.
- Easily bring the presentation from one classroom to another.

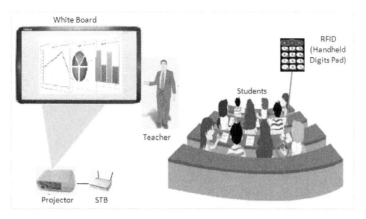

Figure 4: Classroom with RFID applications.

4 Collect and analyze students' learning status through RFID

Nowadays, RFID has been wildly used in many fields. It's become a key component in the IOT industry. From supermarket to mine, with its unique identification, we can trace things in any time and any place. In terms of school's applications, we know that some use RFID as an identification for students to trace their position. It is a good application in the consideration of security. Because parents can get understood about when and where their kids go for. Furthermore, system also can send a warm or alarm to the parents if their kids exceed the safety area.

With regard to RFID, there're two modes available for those applications. One is with passive mode, and another is with active mode. With the passive mode, RFID's existence is identified by the sensor directly and it is unable to send out any signal by RFID. However, to the active mode, RFID itself is able to send signal to the sensor.

As shown in Figure 4, it's an application of RFID with active mode in a classroom. Every student has a digit-pad embedded with RFID tag, and students can enter the digit on it for the answer and send it to STB. Inside STB, there're two layers existed to process those signals sent by students:

- Network Layer: Receive signals sent by digit-pad.
- Processing Layer: Identify students' identity and do the required statistic and analysis job.

After that, teachers can easily get the statistic or analysis of the learning status from their students. Therefore, teachers also can make a corresponding action or give related supports to their students. For example, after students have 100 mathematical questions test, teacher can realize in what part the students can't understand most. And then, teacher can put more effort on that part and give students helps accordingly. This kind of learning is full of fun, interactivity and prompt help for students.

WIT Transactions on Information and Communication Technologies, Vol. 61, © 2014 WIT Press
www.witpress.com, ISSN 1743-3517 (on-line)

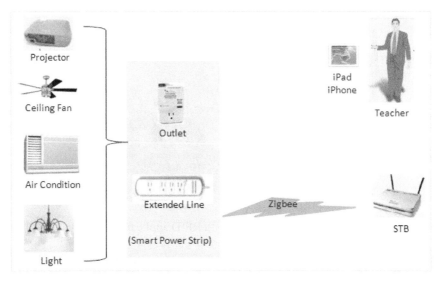

Figure 5: Electronic devices management.

5 Manage devices smartly

Now, with the appearance of smart power strip, we can turn on or off the attached electric devices simply by sending a signal remotely. As shown in Figure 4, in a classroom, we use smart outlets or extended lines which are equipped with Zigbee inside and connect them to the electric devices like projector, ceiling fan, air condition, and light. All of these attached electric devices can immediately be controlled by teachers through Pad or Smartphone's operation inside a classroom. Besides, in the Application Layer, we also can have some energy-saving's applications to manage all the electric devices of the school automatically without any human interference.

Figure 5 presents an easy and cost-saving design to transform a traditional classroom into a manageable one. There's no need for the school to re-construct their classroom. Instead, just add an STB and replace the outlets and extended lines with the smart power switch. Then, a classroom becomes intelligent and the devices become controllable. The related IOT layers for each hardware device are described as listed in Table 2.

6 Future extension

In this paper, we have presented a basic system design of transforming a classroom into an intelligent one. Based on it, there're some extendable topics or applications can be discussed further in future.

- Cross-School Authentication: As every school has their own unique or special resources, if schools can share their resources, teachers or students

Table 2: IOT Layer for Each Hardware Device.

Devices	IOT Layer	Description
Smart Power Switch	Perceptive Layer	Identify the status of the attached electronic device.
STB	Network Layer	• Transfer the data into signal • Receive and transmit the signal from and to the smart power switch
STB	Processing Layer	• Receive the data from iPad/iPhone • Transform the command into signal
iPad/iPhone	Application Layer	Operate the application software

can get more resources from other different schools. Thanks to IOT structure, we can easily get resources from other schools. According to this demand, the authentication becomes very important. In order to prevent unauthorized user, intruder or hacker from illegal use, the authentication for cross school is very important.

• IOT resources classification: In order to facilitate the usage of the resources in IOT network, every object in IOT had better to be classified. According to this classification, teachers and students can easily get the needed resources from IOT network.

7 Summary

This paper has presented a system design which can easily transform a traditional classroom into an IOT-based one. With this kind of intelligent classroom, it not only can benefit teachers but also bring lots of funs and interactivities to the students in learning. From teachers' side, they can control all the electric devices in the classroom only through their portable devices like iPad or iPhone. Furthermore, they can immediately understand the learning status of individual student or group. To the students' side, they can get more educational resources and helps promptly with this kind of IOT-based classroom.

Reference

[1] Lu Tao, You Anjun, The development strategies of internet of things in US, EU, Japan and Korea and the references to China. *Journal of Science & Technology Progress and Policy*, **29(04)**, pp. 27–29, 2012.

Study on standard system framework of the internet of ships

Wei Sun, Lun Xiao, Yaohua Dong, Lihua Dong, Chao Chen
Shanghai Maritime University, Shanghai 201306, China

Abstract

The construction of ship networking project is an important means to enhance the level of the services of information industry and implement the construction of ship networking project. It is not only the key to the construction of the ship networking project, but also the solutions for the top-level design issues. This article has pointed out the standard system framework of ship networking, including goods, marine, waterway, ports, crew, emergency, and other scenarios which are from the perspectives of the three-dimensional model and hierarchy diagram are based on the analysis on status quo of the domestic and international standardization system and the elaboration of the principles of the standard system. Furthermore, this article will focus on the refinement of technical dimension as well as providing the preparation of the table of contents for the standard system. In addition, the reference and protection will be stressed for the construction of the ship networking standard system in the research process.

Keywords: internet of ships, standard system, three-dimensional, model, two-dimensional, decomposition, hierarchy.

1 Introduction

"Ship networking" project aims to build intelligent transportation Internet of things in inland waterway, which is for the purpose of refinement in shipping management, generalization of service industry, comprehensive traveling experience [1]. Meanwhile, ship networking is based on enterprises, fishing vessels, fishermen and trading goods, and the waterway, navigation locks, bridges, ports, and terminals will be covered. By using the integrated Internet of things technology, a new intelligent navigation information service network that

 WIT Transactions on Information and Communication Technologies, Vol. 61, © 2014 WIT Press
www.witpress.com, ISSN 1743-3517 (on-line)
doi:10.2495/MIIT130871

features with people-ship-cargo information connectivity can be built. Ship networking engineering construction is an important means to enhance the level of information service industry. Ship networking standards are the technical keys to complete networking construction, and it is also the needs to carry out requirements of the central committee and the Ministry of Transport Strategy of inland water transportation. In the process of building the project, ways of how to integrate the existing information and technology to develop ship networking information industry and ways of how to implement the infrastructure construction smoothly and seamlessly with information network, to ensure that each system can connect with each other, are the roots in the process of engineering construction.

2 Ship networking standards system research status at home and abroad

2.1 The overseas present situation analysis

2.1.1 European inland waterway transport integrated information service (RIS)

RIS (River Information Services) is a trans-regional, cross-sectional, cross-inland water transport concept, a business synergies and resource integration system. It features eight functions: traffic information service, channel information service, traffic regulation, disaster management and emergency services, transportation, logistics information management, supervision and law enforcement, statistical information, and service fees. The European Union (EU), the Central Committee of the Rhine River shipping (CCNR) and other agencies are also involved, in 1998 the EU launched INDRIS project, for the first time from the RIS system was defined in the definition and function level. In 2004, the EU launched IRIS project, which means the full implementation of the pan-European RIS in strategy research and planning. In promoting the process of implementation of RIS, the EU made the four core technology standards: inland river waterway drawing standards, inland river ships electronic reporting standards, positioning of the captain to inform, and inland river ships in inland water tracking standards.

2.1.2 Japan's transport information services

In 1993, Japan set up the ISO/TC 204 national committee, ITS standardization committee is to complete information technology standards in Japan, at the same time, Japan's transport information management platform is built and governed by the Ministry, the National Police Agency, the Traffic Information Center and the Traffic Control Center. "Isolated information island" phenomenon is not allowed to happen. Meanwhile, Japan makes good use of "production," "learning" and "officer," their division and cooperation, to promote the traffic information service construction [2].

2.2 The domestic status quo analysis

On the one hand, our country has set basic standards in basic and general information, information collection, communication technology, service, and other safety requirements that are relevant to ship networking. Those basic standards have covered related applications of goods, ship, channel, the crew, and other scenarios. "Beidou satellite navigation system of ship monitoring terminal technology requirements" (JT/T 766-2009), "Traffic Information Based Data part 8: Water Transportation Information Basic Data Elements" (JT/T 697.8 2008), are two of the program files. However, the ship networking standards system construction hasn't begun yet. On the other hand, some other domestic industries, such as intelligent transportation, Internet of things, the tobacco industry, transportation, information industry, agriculture, and construction have started or have established the industry standardization system. Intelligent transportation standard system framework in general is divided into two levels, and each level of different attributes will be subdivided again; while the traffic information is designed in the perspective of the three-dimensional structure, which is widely covered and strongly applicative [3,4].

2.3 Gap analysis

Admittedly there are some developments in RIS system in the integration of existing resources accorded to China's national conditions. But there are still a great number of holes in RIS standards. Also, there is a gap between the shipping information construction in China and that in developed countries, particularly as the following two points:

(1) Standard system integrity. After American's development in the shipping information standard system, the program has formed a relatively complete system, and the relevant standard construction has also been actively developed. While China has not yet formed a widely recognized standard system, and the existing standard system can not achieve full coverage. Also, standards project and development lacks of unified guidance and coordination: Duplicate standard content, weak standard matches, and untimely update are common. In terms of the content, the standards are too fragmented or of relatively low quality, and versatility, the common and basic standards have not developed yet.

(2) Government's support and coordination. During the process of river information services collaboration and standardization in Europe, the European country not only carried out a series of integrated information services and shipping related research work, but also attached great importance to the formulation of legislation and standards with the support of EU. While, in China, we have not yet established a unified strategic alliance or set up specialized government agencies to support the promotion of China's shipping information. The legal system is imperfect. Also the standard-setting development lags behind the information technology.

3 Construction of the ship networking standards system framework

3.1 Construction principles

Referring to the standard system construction principle of GBT13016-2009 (Principles and requirements for preparing diagrams of standard system), and combined with the development features in field of ship network engineering, cognitive patterns as well as classification system in biology, principles for the standard system construction of ship network engineering can be summarized as follows.

(1) Making overall arrangements and comprehensive planning. We should devise standard system of ship network from the long run to conduct further study of magnificent tactic and reconcile the relationship among governments and industries, integrating the characteristics of ship network engineering standardization and referring to the mature experience in standard system from advanced countries basing on our own status.

(2) Rationality and distinctive nuance. Depending on the scenarios of shipping business and its operating regularity, applying fundamental principles of standard and the methods, ideological tools in systems engineering, to study and tackle relationships with the standard, making it a harmony entirety, in the meantime, standard system framework is supposed to be distinctive nuance and rationally classified.

3.2 Construction targets

This project aims at establishing a standard system framework, which is compatible with national circumstances in China and industrial development; besides, it should be in line with international standards, distinctive nuance, rationally classified, and reasonably structured. In this way, the framework can enhance both the quality and quantity of standards that wait for enactment and amendment in future. From another perspective, it is necessary to reinforce the relevancy between the standard itself and market, impel the process of marketization, which begins from the phrase of demanding, defining and enacting to the stage of popularization, application, improvement, and development, for the standard from, elevating the information level in ship network engineering from overall level thus shortening the distance with western countries.

3.3 Establishment of three-dimensional model

Most of the standard systems which have been formulated are two-dimensional. Two-dimensional structure can clearly show the relationship between the two elements. However, the shortcoming of two-dimensional structure begins to appear when the complexity of standard systems increases. It cannot accurately express the positioning of each standard in the standard system framework, also may cause the overlapping of standard setting and strong mutual interference between each standard. On the contrary, the three-dimensional structure has advantages in building the internet of ships, a complex system. Standard contains three key elements, including object, content, and level. The presence of three elements in the three-dimensional framework reflects its advance and scientificalness. The standard system uses three-dimensional structure established by India Wellman, combining with the idea of three-dimensional space and the concept of standardized three-dimensional space, using the ship's business networking applications (objects), the ship networking application technology (content), and the standard level (level) as the three-dimensional elements. It also subdivides each dimension and expanse the storage capacity of a standard, providing a broad space for the future development of the standard system, reflecting its advance and scientificalness in the structure [5].

3.3.1 Thinking of dimension subdivision and its division

After establishing the standard system frame model of the internet of ships, the standard system framework will be subdivided. Before the subdivision, the three-point relationship between each dimension of standards should be grasped.

(1) The relationship between the levels. The upper-level standards should be reflected in the lower-level ones and the lower-level standards are specific presentation of the upper-level ones. It's important to find general standard in lower-level of standards. The upper-level standards should guide and restrict the lower-level ones and the lower-level standards are the best complement to the upper ones. The upper-level standards will be applied to specific business field, which make them more applicable. The common standards will be added to standard system framework, forming a complete system.

(2) The relationship between the connotation and extension. A standard system refers to an organized whole which consist of a certain range of standard according to their internal relationships. Range refers to the scope of coverage of the standard, the scope of the standard system of the internet of ships; internal relations, the standard system framework represent the hierarchical relation, mutual coordination, convergence of the matching. The extension of the standard system need to mining the actual factors of the internet of ships based on the existing standard system framework. According to the characteristics of different application scenarios, the standard system should be subdivided in a deeper level, making standard system more complete, rich and strict and a wider coverage.

When the relationship of each axis of standard has been clearly resolved, the standard framework will be further divided, as shown in Figure 1 as an example.

Business scenario dimension (x) shows the applied fields of the internet of ships, which can be divided into cargo, ships, laneway, port, sailor, emergency, and others, total seven categories by the RIS division rules. Each specific category can be detailed as needed.

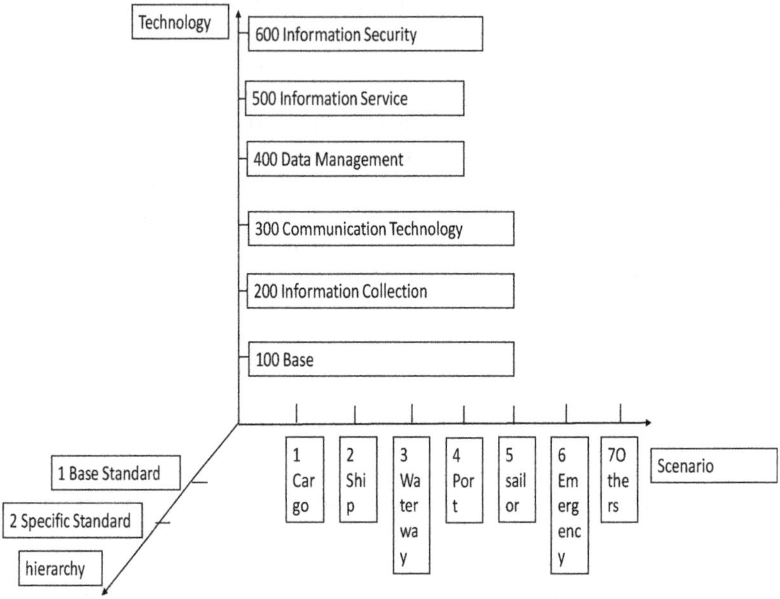

Figure 1: Standard framework of internet of ships.

Technology dimension (y) shows the techniques used during the build of internet of ships, which can be divided into general standard, information collection standard, network communication standard, data management standard, information service standard, and information security, total six categories by the streamline of information flow and the technique framework in internet of goods. Each specific category can be detailed as needed.

Hierarchical dimension (z) can be divided into base standard and proprietary standard by the scope of the standards, which ease the complexity of engineering of the internet of ships. Base standard, including terminology, code, general methods, and so on rules the general specifications during the build of the internet of ships. One the other hand, proprietary standard rules specific standard of specific territory, such as way to operate the object, detecting methods, testing methods. Hierarchical dimension rules the levels of standards. With the rise of the level, the object in the standard framework becomes more precise.

Of the three dimensions, technology is the dominant dimension, the other two will be divided as the main one to minimize redundancy and maximize the scope. The three dimensions are relatively independent, but they still have close connection between them. The grip of x, y, z shows a dot which present a child system of standard system. As regard to the size of the system, it depends on the complexity and how deep the framework is divided (the precision of the x, y, z). In brief, more division, more precise.

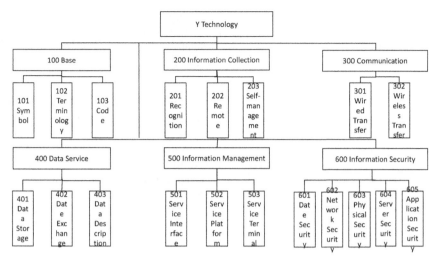

Figure 2: Technology dimension decomposition chart.

3.3.2 Two-dimensional decomposition of a three-dimensional structure

Divide the technology dimension according to the internet of goods standard framework, as shown in Figure 2 as an example.

When hierarchical dimension is divided, new standard emerges, for example, when recognition technology come across ships, a series of new standard come out. As shown in Figure 2, maximum of 16 standards can be produced. The precision of standard is depended on the complexity and the division of framework. When x axis is ship, y axis is RFID, z axis is base standard, it comes out as a base standard of RFID between ships, this can be air interface standard or other. Other standards can also come out in the same way.

3.3.3 Table of standard system

(1) Numbering method for standard system: Numbering method for this standard system comprises standard serial number, as well as Categories ID for X layer (Apply business field), Y layer (technical field), and Z layer (level field). The Categories ID adopt label form of Arabic numerals which are separated respectively by dot mark. The standard serial number also utilizes Arabic numerals increasing by degrees. As for the meaning of the number format $x.y.z.n$, the first digit x,y,z indicates the Categories ID for X layer, Y layer, Z layer, respectively, and n is standard serial number, for example 2.202.1 shows the basic standard of sensor technique applied on ships.

(2) Components in table of standard system: The table of standard system is constructed with sequence number, numbering of standard system, standard number, standard name, appropriate level setting, implementation date, adopting relationship, alternate standard and condition (Table 1). Appropriate level setting includes national standards, industrial standards

Table 1: Format of Standard System Table.

Sequence number	Numbering of standard system	Standard number	Standard name	Appropriate level setting	Implementation date	Alternate standard	Condition

and local standards. And condition is only described as "enacted" or "enacting" or "to enact". The "enacted" means the status of the standard has been issued, and "enacting" indicates that the standard is under the process which contains drafting, consulting, editing, and approving; while the "to enact" suggest arranging the order of standards according to the need of ship network engineering construction as well as urgent levels of enacting standards. So existing standards can be classified scientifically via this system, besides, the standard, especially in urgent condition, can be available in practical for the ship network engineering construction.

4 Conclusion

The study results conform to the standard system for present internet of things (IoT) and for the overall background of traffic information construction, putting forward basic principles and construction target for the ship network engineering in China. Moreover, standard system framework in three-dimensional structure has been proposed, which is in charging of the operations through the process of ship network engineering construction, covering the goods, ships, ports, channels, seamen, emergency tackling. Technical fields relating to ship network engineering have been subdivided according to the techniques of IoT, reflecting its scientifically of the standard system framework. Meanwhile, detailed construction methods have been presented for the table of standard system, and offer valuable references to the standardization of ship network engineering. So the standard system construction of ship network engineering, which has established the construction blueprints of standard system for areas of ship network engineering, provides scientific basis for scientific management of founded standards and initiating or deploying a related project.

References

[1] Dong Yaohua, Sun Wei, Dong Lihua, The investigation on the framework of internet of ship. *Port & Waterway Engineering*, **8**, pp. 145–149, 2012.
[2] Zhou Junhua, Luo Bencheng, Jie Yuling, The promotion of European RSI and learning experience for our country. *Shipping Management*, **5**, pp. 22–26, 2009.
[3] Yang Qi, Wang Xiaojing, Qi Tongyan, The investigation on intelligent vehicle-highway system. *Journal of Highway and Transportation Research and Development*, **7**, pp. 91–94, 2004.

[4] L. Atzori, A. Iera, G. Morabito, The internet of things: a survey. *Computer Networking*, **54(15)**, pp. 2787–2805, 2010.
[5] Liu Dan, Liu Xian, Constructional study on agricultural mechanized standard system in China. *Journal of Agricultural Mechanization Research*, **6**, pp. 24–26, 2005.

The exploratory analysis based implementation of system of systems engineering in the marine environment comprehensive monitoring system

Xichen Zhou, Nan Li, Xiao Tang, Peng Zhou
College of Economics and Management, Nanjing University of Aeronautics & Astronautics, Nanjing 210016, China

Abstract

Along with the social development, more practical events have to be modeled and described by the System of Systems Engineering (SoSE). In this paper, the three-dimensional architecture of SoSE is established on the basis that an exploratory analysis based "1+4+1" model for System of Systems (SoS) implementation is discussed. Finally, the applications of the architecture and the model in the Marine Environment Comprehensive Monitoring System (MECMS) are demonstrated.

Keywords: system of systems engineering, exploratory analysis, marine environment comprehensive monitoring.

1 Introduction

Traditional system engineering is oriented to the complexity of Family of Systems (FoS). Along with the social development, the events encountered by people are becoming more and more complicated. Many actual systems are difficult to be modeled and described by FoS. Therefore, the term "System of Systems" (SoS) has come into use to well describe such systems; and the engineering technologies and methodologies for SoS science are called SoS Engineering (SoSE). Though there is no universally accepted definition for SoS, it has been commonly agreed that the SoS relates to multiple Interdependent Systems (ISs) but not a "Family of Systems" (FoS) which is simply a grouping of them. With its own goals, an SoS is an integration of multiple ISs and has its new emergent behavior [1].

Up to now, people have attempted to apply the SoS concept to many fields, such as ballistic missile defense systems, cost accounting systems, intelligent power grids, and global food security issues as well, and have achieved significant results. Currently the research of SoS is focused on its concept and frame architecture. Garrett et al. considers that a successful SoS relies on not only the subsystems involved, but also the coupled relationships of them. For the characterization of a whole complex system, three dimensions as subsystem, engineering and SoS are consolidated to form an architecture of SoSE [2].

Compared with the common systems, an SoS is much more complicated structurally involving many uncertainties, for instance, technical risks and unfixed demands, which are quite critical and require reasonable treatments for a successful realization of the whole system. An exploratory analysis (EA) is capable of examining different results of various projects with the existence of a large number of uncertainties. In this paper, a "1+4+1" model for implementing SoSE is proposed on the basis of the three-dimensional architecture of SoS with the combination of EA and SoS theories; and the relationships among different dimensions of SoS are discussed. Finally, the applications of the SoS architecture and the "1+4+1" model in the practical development of Marine Environment Comprehensive Monitoring Systems (MECMS) are demonstrated. The MECMS is a large complex electronic information system for detecting marine environments and sea targets, identifying their characteristics and utilizing them. Being widely applied in meteorological observation, marine engineering and national defense, it plays an important role in both national economy and military development. Comprising sensors and processors, the system functions to acquire information like oceanographic parameters, target data and characteristics, and to identify and classify environments and targets. For special dynamic applications, the performances of the system can be improved through the responses given by the dynamic combinations of resources such as sensors. The MECMS can be viewed as an SoS for its long process of development, extensive technological applications, complicated technologies involved, high uncertainty of demands, difficult organization of resources, and strong coupling effects among subsystems. A successful MECMS relates greatly to the decision of strategies, action policies and detailed tasks. The purpose of SoS research about MECMS is to provide a new approach to the development and engineering implementation of MECMS [3,4].

2 Three-dimensional architecture of SoS

An SoS is composed of several subsystems (Si) which involve different phases of development; and likewise, such SoS involves different phases of engineering. Besides, subsystems (Si) can be combined to form different SoSs according to different missions and applications. Therefore, the three dimensions of system, engineering and SoS can be used to describe the architecture of SoSE, which is shown in Figure 1.

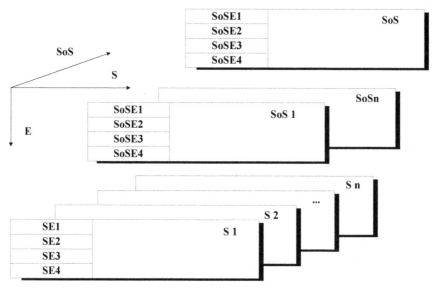

Figure 1: The three-dimensional architecture of SoS.

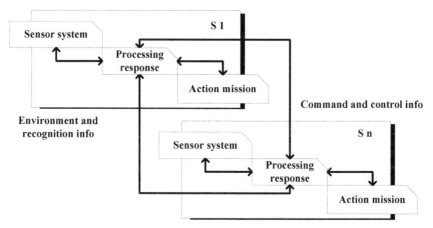

Figure 2: The information interactions among subsystems (Si) involved in SoS.

2.1 Dimension of subsystem (Si)

The dimension of subsystem in the architecture of SoSE refers to major applied technologies and functions, and a group corresponds to one Si. Each Si has its own domains of definition, function, and technology, and shows different states and characteristics in different SoSi. Instead of being isolated, subsystems Si have interactions like information exchange and behavior control, which may result in emergent behavior and ensure the fulfilment of the general goals of SoS. Figure 2 illustrates the connections among the subsystems (Si) of the entire SoS.

2.2 Dimension of subsystem (Si)

Both SoS and its component subsystems Si involve such phrases as SE1, SE2, SE3, and SE4, among which SE1 primarily functions to study and analyze the environments, and form conceptual models and customer usage models; SE2 functions to decide basic principles and technical specifications, verify key technologies and parts and develop and demonstrate prototypes; SE3 functions to develop subsystems and demonstrative systems and assess development risks and capabilities; and SE4 functions to form architectures, realize information interactions, control technical states, optimize system development, and normalize standards and forms. Apparently, the technical elements, like engineering technologies, are mostly included in SE1 and SE2; whereas nontechnical ones, like situations of resources, are in SE3; and issues related to system architectures are in SE4.

2.3 Dimension of SoS (SoSi)

As shown in Figure 1, multiple complex subsystems Si may form one or several SoSi with new functions.

The three-dimensional architecture of SoSE well consolidates the involved environments, demands, technologies, tasks, and plans of development, as well as system integration, making the research of SoSE cover both technical and nontechnical fields rather than being restricted to only the technical. The analysis of SoS in an S-SE-SoS architecture can integrate the three dimensions (subsystem, engineering, SoS) originally belonging to the different domains as an entirety and realize the research of their relationships, which is quite critical for the fulfiling of the goals of SoS.

3 An EA-based "1+4+1" model for SoSE implementation

Methodologically being a spirally raising cognition process from qualitative analysis to quantitative one, and then from quantitative to qualitative, the EA includes two processes: one is a top-down analytical process, in which macrocognition is achieved prior to more details, and the connection between the variables of the top specifications and that of the bottom ones is established; the other is a bottom-up comprehensive process, in which the variables of bottom specifications are computed by the model with high resolution, and the multiple results of bottom computations are statistically processed and comprehensively assessed according to the specifications. Here with the SoS theory-based architecture, we establish an EA-based "1+4+1" model for SoSE implementation according to the four processes involved in both Si and SoSi. The detailed procedures are as follows.

Step 1: Recognize General Goals and Demands of SoS
Design and analyze the scenario space by using the top-level design of SoS. Based on the defined SoSE1–SoSE4, determine the basic goals of SE1–SE4

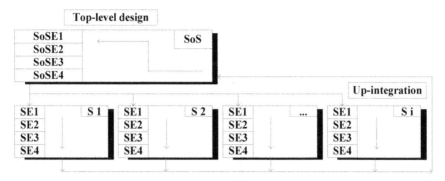

Figure 3: The EA-based "1+4+1" model for SoSE implementation.

which are not constant but are continuously improved and perfected as the state and development process of Si change.

Step 2: Realize Si

(1) Analyze and design the scenario space of Si within the Si-SE1-SoS architecture, define major technologies, specifications, and functions. Due to the demand uncertainties, the space for essential factors is unfixed. The influence of the space uncertainties on demands is analyzed through prospects analysis, and a space of essential factors satisfying the demands is defined.

(2) Within the Si-SE2-SoS architecture and on the basis of item (1), transfer the demands to technical implementation to realize the integration of technical resources. This step is for project demonstration and technical research of systems and the interoperable relationships among Si are recognized to form a model of technical integration.

(3) Within the Si-SE3-SoS architecture, start the development of Si, include it in the plans and quality management of research and manufacture, and finish the development and test verification of Si. This step is for equipment or system implementation, which is not only the verification of item (2), but also the result of integration and management of nontechnical resources.

(4) Within the Si-SE4-SoS architecture, realize the integration of Si, and do test and effectiveness assessment of the interoperability of Si. This step is for implementations of Si capabilities and integrative network, in which the verified technical states and criteria of Si are decided, and the proposals for functional optimization and improvement of Si are raised.

Step 3: Integrate Si to Form SoS

On the basis of step 2 and according to the technical state of Si and the primary integration and test results of SoS, evaluate the processes of SoSE1–SoSE4 of SoS to judge their performances of satisfying environments and demands, adjust the specifications of uncertainties of space for essential factors, and make evaluation of system effectiveness. In addition, define the coordination model of action missions and system applications and propose a path for technical evolution and upgrade of SoS.

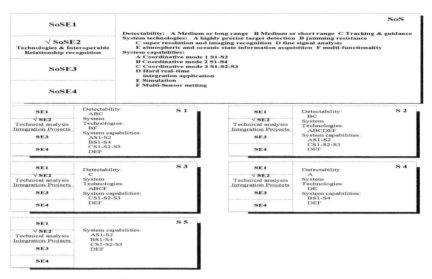

Figure 4: The architecture of SoSE2 and SE2 of MECMS.

As shown in Figure 3, the establishment of an EA-based "1+4+1" model for SoSE implementation is a process of extensive exploration, in which general comprehension of an event is achieved prior to the research of details, exploration and solution are carried out for the space of uncertainties of Si and SoSi, and then analysis is made for the results of solutions to get satisfying strategies.

4   Application of SoSE Theory in MECMS

In the interest of a more powerful MECMS in system capabilities, it is analyzed with reference to the three dimensional architecture of SoS depicted in the previous chapters, and its EA-based "1+4+1" model for engineering implementation is presented.

4.1 Analysis of Three Dimensional Architecture of MECMS

The MECMS is required to integrate four capabilities, which are situation awareness, air/sea target recognition, complicated environment endurance and disaster forecast and information support for emergency. These four capabilities can be integrated in one SoS. Due to its missions of covering coastal, littoral and open sea areas, as well as specific targeted areas and making uninterrupted, comprehensive observations on low altitude, sea surface and even underneath, the MECMS is designed with the aid of current advanced technologies to contain the subsystems such as medium or long range observation subsystem S1, short or medium range observation subsystem S2, photoelectrical subsystem S3,
passive observation subsystem S4 and integrated observation platform subsystem S5, which are not only independently working, but also cooperative and dependent to ensure the whole MECMS with function diversity, interoperability

and quick response. For the dimension of engineering, the four processes SoSE1(SE1) ~ SoSE1(SE4) of the SoS remain unchanged; and prominence is given to the demonstrations of technologies and interoperable relationship recognition.

4.2 "1+4+1" Model for MECMS Implementation

The phase of engineering management and its basic relationship of both SoSE1~SoSE4 and SE1~SE4 are initially formed on the basis of the "1+4+1" model through the top-level design. For the Si, the engineering processes SE1~SE4 are formed. The SE4 leads the MECMS engineering to the phase of up-integration, wherein the verifications and test run of the four capabilities of SoSE1~SoSE4 are done to accumulate test data in actual environment and evaluate whether the overall performances and capabilities of the MECMS can meet the requirements or not.

Taking SoSE2 and SE2 as examples, Figure 4 shows the basic thoughts and results of technologies establishment. Analysis is made on the major employed technologies in marine environment monitoring. Technologies and specifications are formed and technologies are sorted and mapped on Si. With the technical verification and simulation, the interoperable relationships among Si are recognized. For instance, such relationship between S1 and S2 ensures the SoS with precise multi-target tracking ability, remarkably improved anti-jamming ability, and real-time, multi-scale, extensive, and comprehensive observations.

5 Conclusions

Along with the social development, many practical events are required to be modelled and described by SoS. In this paper, the three dimensional architecture of SoSE is discussed on the basis of the existing references. The EA based "1+4+1" model for implementation is analyzed. The combination of the SoS theory and the EA can not only enable a general comprehension of complex technical or nontechnical systems, but also successfully deal with the uncertainties encountered in the realization of SoSE. Besides, the SoS theory is applied in the MECMS to analyze and integrate the system. The proposed three dimensional architecture of SoS and the EA-based "1+4+1" model for implementation are verified to be rational, which provides a new approach to the development and engineering implementation of other SoSs.

Acknowledgements

This paper is supported by the National Natural Science Foundation (71101071, 70903031); Philosophy and Social Science Foundation of Jiangsu Province (08SHB017); Education Department of Philosophy and Social Science Foundation of Jiangsu Province (08SJD6300063); School Philosophy and Social Science Foundation (V0853-091, S0758-091).

References

[1] Sage, A.P. & Cuppan, C.D., On the Systems Engineering and Management of Systems of Systems and Federations of Systems. Information. Knowledge . *Systems Management*, 2, pp. 325–345, 2001.
[2] Garrett, R.K., Anderson, S., Baron, N., et al, Managing the Interstitials, a System of Systems Framework Suited for the Ballistic Missile Defense System. *Systems Engineering*, 14(1), pp. 87–109, 2011.
[3] Lanel, J.A. & Valerdi, R., Synthesizing SoS Concepts for Use in Cost Modeling. *Systems Engineering*, 10(4), pp. 297–308, 2007.
[4] Luo, Y., Wang, Y.Y. & Wang, A.S., A Conceptual Layered Cooperative System of Systems Model for Smart Grid. *Electric System Automation*, 33(17), pp. 6–9, 104, 2009.

Research of software engineering based on complex networks

Dali Li
College of Computer Science & Technology, Jilin University, Changchun, China

Abstract

With the continuous development of software technology, the requirement of software's function and structure has become more and more stringent. Software engineering will effectively solve the problem encountered in the developing process. This article is based on the complex network to do research about software engineering. First, it analyzed the complex network theory, introducing the development, characteristics, and parameters of complex networks; then described the software metrics theory and software metrics indicators in detail; finally aiming at the software companies, analyzing software companies by software engineering, described the BA model algorithm, deducing it to make it closer to reality. This paper has a positive effect for both software engineers and testers.

Keywords: complex networks, software metric, nodes agglomeration.

1 Introduction

Since computer being born, the software design patterns constantly evolved, from the structured design in early times to object-oriented design, till the component-oriented design now [1]. The software system function has become more and more powerful, the scale has become more and more huge, and its control has become more and more complex [2]. To the software systems, the needs analysis, design, development, testing, maintenance, operating environment, business strategy, and cooperation has all become a part of the entire software system. Therefore, software engineering research is no longer confined to some key components, but analyzes the system structure from the macro. Complex network theory proposed us a new idea of researching software engineering [3].

WIT Transactions on Information and Communication Technologies, Vol. 61, © 2014 WIT Press
www.witpress.com, ISSN 1743-3517 (on-line)
doi:10.2495/MIIT130891

2 Complex network theory

Currently, complexity science is attended more and more by domestic and foreign and has become an emerging interdiscipline [4]. It makes revolutionary breakthrough to the linear, balanced, and simple problems shown in the traditional model and increased the research to nonlinear, nonbalanced, and complex issues. It greatly improves research and development of the deep science to further strengthen people's awareness of the objective things and provide great impetus for the further development of science [5].

2.1 Development of complex network

The objective world is composed by a large number of complex systems, and these systems can be described by a variety of networks. As known to all, the network is combined with numerous nodes and connecting lines. In each specific network, the node represents the actual individual in the system, and the connecting line represents the relationship between the individuals. In real life, no matter Internet, interpersonal communication networks, or the body's neural network can be described through a complex network.

In the seventeenth century, the mathematician thought that system characteristics were determined by the system's network topology. The idea of different topologies forming different systems made the concept of graph theory. The earliest graph theory was used to solve problems in the game. With the accumulation of a large number of theories and results, the applying scope of graph theory was expanded. The continuous development of society made graph theory applied in the grid and organic chemistry, and later combined with computer starting to solve transportation, communications, manufacturing, and military issues in real life.

In the middle of last century, the graph theory had made tremendous breakthroughs and proposed the concept of random graph theory. It used this concept analyzing the communication network and the life sciences network to effectively connect nodes in the network to simulate these two networks, which made the research more concise and provided a new opportunity for the development of graph theory. To the problem whether the nodes in the network connected, the random graph theory used the form of probabilistic to calculate and determine whether the two nodes are connected.

Random network provides a great help to people for solving the problem of computer network. However, with further research, it was discovered that the system topology structure in the real world is not completely random nor completely fixed. We call this network model combined with dynamics and network topology as complex networks.

2.2 Characteristics of complex networks

(1) Scale free
   Complex network analyzes practical systems and can effectively simulate the practical system. University of Notre Dame analyzes the World Wide

Figure 1: Regular network evolutes to random network.

Web. According to the characteristics of people visiting the website (many of them randomly open a web page), they consider the World Wide Web will build a random network. But the experimental results are completely different from theoretical analysis. The World Wide Web is connected by a small number of high-visits pages, and nearly 80% of pages are connected to less than five connections, while in the whole network the proportion of high-visits nodes (connected over 1000) is less than one ten-thousandth. The study found that the number of page visits follows the power law that means the probability a node connects with other k nodes is proportional to $1/kn$. The differences from random network are mainly reflected in: the existence collecting and distributing point in a network, it is impossible to occur in random network; a peak will appear in random network, and the complex networks are described by continuous decreasing function; deviation node is almost impossible to appear in random network; complex network has better robustness.

(2) Small-world effect

Small-world network model randomly modifies every line (edge) in a regular network with probability p, which is to connect a connected edge to a new node with probability p, and avoid to coincide with a connected edge, thus forming a new network. This network is between the regular network and random network, namely forming a small-world network. The value of p determines the network structure, when $p = 0$, then the regular network will not change; when $p = 1$, it gets a random network; when p is from 0 to 1, the course of the regular network changing to the random network shown in Figure 1.

2.3 Parameters of complex network

(1) Degree and degree distribution

Degree is the basic parameters to describe the local characteristics of complex networks. The degree of node in complex network refers to the number of edges formed of node connecting to other nodes. Degree distribution means the variation that the probability of the node varies with the value of the degree.

(2) Average distance of network

Length of the one or several paths that passes least nodes to connect two nodes can be expressed by the formula:

$$L = \frac{1}{\frac{1}{2}n(n+1)} \sum_{i \geq j} d(i, j) \qquad (1)$$

wherein $d(i, j)$ represents the shortest between distance node i, j. If there is no connection between them, it is expressed by infinity.

(3) Dimensionality clustering coefficient

The network distributes according to the group. The nodes in a group connect to each other more and the association between groups is less. It's called dimensionality clustering coefficient to describe the network with topology relationship.

(4) Correlation

The correlation between degree and dimensionality clustering coefficient is the description of differences between network structures.

3   Software metrics

3.1 Software quality metrics

To software system, its quality can be analyzed and defined in two aspects. In the narrow sense, it represents the software failure free; broadly speaking, in the software development process, the formed middleware and intermediate processes are failure free, and to guarantee the final software product failure free.

Early on, in the software design process, there is no clear definition about if the software is faulted and the software quality entirely depends on the personal experience of the programmer. The software metric can effectively improve the development structure, reduce costs, and reduce development cycles to improve work efficiency.

A sign is that a discipline in maturity is if there is a clear metrics of its studying object. Software quality metrics can make the software development process visible, as high as possible to improve software quality. Therefore, software quality metrics has the characteristics of simplicity, computability, objectivity, language independent, effective feedback, and consistency.

3.2 Index of software metrics

For software development, it mainly adopts structure-oriented design or object-oriented design. Their metrics is not the same.

(1) Metrics index of structure-oriented design

People have a wealth of experience on structure-oriented design to develop software system, so studying more about this aspect of software metrics, forming a relatively complete theoretical system.

Annular Complexity Theory: It is a software metrics to provide quantitative measurement for the program logic complexity. Using the metrics to calculate the number of basic independent paths in the program, it will ensure that all statements at least execute once the upper bounds of measure numbers. There are mainly three methods for annular complexity calculation. First, annular complexity $V(G)$ = number of areas; Second, $V(G) = E - N + 2$, where E is the number of edges in the graph, N is the number of nodes; Third, $V(G) = P + 1$, where P is the number of determines nodes in the graph.

Axiomatic Metrics: This metric aims at analyzing the three main structures, sequence, selection, and loop in a structured program. Analyzed by a given function, if the function satisfies the following rules, the metrics is appropriate.

Sequential structure: $m(begin\ s_1;\ s_2;...s_n\ end) \geq \sum m(s_i)$

Selective structure: $2(m(s_1 + s_2)) \geq m(if\ p\ then\ s_1\ else\ s_2) > m(s_1 + s_2)$

Loop structure: $2m(s) \geq m(while\ p\ do\ s) > m(s)$

Giving the corresponding theorem, $m_1,\ m_2,...,\ m_n$ representing an appropriate metrics of software complexity, weighted linear combining these metrics it would be the standard metrics of the entire software system.

(2) Metrics index of object-oriented design

Since the object-oriented design used in software, significant changes happen to the software functionality and structure, and it effectively improves the work efficiency. The accompanying is to analyze the quality of the software. The new software quality metrics theory has been proposed, in that the C&K metric method is famous, which is based on inheritance tree.

Object-oriented design is mainly composed of classes, and inheritance tree is formed by the root nodes and the leaf nodes. Therefore, the indicators of C&K metric are: the weighted method number of each class, the depth of inheritance tree, the number of sub-class, the response collection of class, a collection of object classes and cohesion lacking a degree of methods.

4   Applications of complex network in software engineering

Software companies mainly manage information processing and analysis. In the progressing course of software technology, it requires the software design and development to combine with the expertise theory of other areas, finally forming practical, cross information processing technology.

Software development needs more and more complex talents. In order to well-accomplish software project development for specific companies, it needs more technical talents of different disciplines to participate. The specific companies want the software development cycle as short as possible, and the development cost as little as possible. But in fact, in the developing process, the software companies are getting more and more difficult to control developing cycle and cost. At present, the software industry carries out internal cooperation and outsourcing is better means and method.

Cooperation between software companies can effectively analyze risks and costs, forming complementary in knowledge and technologies. But it also has its shortcomings. The increasing personnel increases pressure on the team management. The unbalanced ability between the two sides will make developing difficulty greater. Therefore, when choosing a partner, merit-based selection is very important.

To explain the generation mechanism of power law, it proposed the scale-free network model (BA model). BA model has two features. The one is growth property, the so-called growth property indicating that the scale of the network is constantly enlarging, and in the researched network, nodes are also constantly increasing; the other is the priority connection mechanism, this feature indicating that the new nodes prefer to connect with the node of larger connectivity.

BA model algorithm as follows:

(1) Set n nodes.
(2) Add new nodes and edges in each time period.
(3) According to the priority connecting mechanism to connect the nodes, in accordance with the preferred probability $P(k_i) = k_i/\sum(k_i)$ to select the nodes to be connected, wherein k_i is the degree of node i.

According to the characteristics of software companies in reality, the BA model has been unable to meet the practical developing needs of current software companies. This requires the improving of the BA model in order to adapt to the current social development. Improving through the following aspects:

(1) Assign the value of the nodes to differ their competitiveness vary.
(2) Preferentially connect the nodes with higher priority.
(3) According to the survival of the fittest principle, delete inferior node.
(4) Continuously adjust the relationship among nodes.

The improved algorithm is described as follows:

(1) Set n_0 nodes.
(2) Based on the original network, calculating the competitiveness coefficient of the nodes, the coefficient value mainly depends on the line coupled to the node. When the obtained competitiveness coefficient is greater than the average coefficient, that indicates a higher priority, and while it is far below the average coefficient values, directly delete it.
(3) Calculate every node in the network, and adjust the connecting lines.
(4) In a time period, calculating the nodes to obtain the node with the highest priority, give it priority connection.
(5) Repeat the operation in step 2.

5 Summary

This paper studied the complex network in software engineering and focused on describing the software quality metrics. Due to space limitations, about the application of software engineering, it only gave the BA model algorithm and its improvement, and did not give the test results. In addition, to the metrics value of software quality, although this paper provided a detailed description and analysis, the value was inevitably inadequate due to the complex software engineering system, and the complicated link among the internal units in software. Hope readers would do further research on this basis.

References

[1] Han Mingchang, Networked characteristics in software and its contribution to software quality. *Computer Engineering and Applications*, **3**, pp. 22–25, 2006.
[2] Yang Yang, A synthetic evaluation method for software quality. *Mini-micro Systems*, **3(2)**, pp. 19–22, 2000.
[3] Cheng Duping, Qian Hongbing, Software quality and metric. *Computer Engineering and Applications*, **4(10)**, pp. 21–22, 2002.
[4] Wang Xiaofan, Li Xiang, Chen Guanrong, *Complex Networks Theory and Application*. Tsinghua University Press, Beijing, 2006.
[5] Li Bing, Wang Hao, Software complexity metrics based on complex networks. *Acta Electronica Sinica*, **4(2)**, pp. 13–15, 2006.

Strategies for teaching Java programming language to economics and management majors

Xiuguo Wu

School of Management Science and Engineering, Shandong University of Finance and Economics, Jinan, 250014, China

Abstract

A course well experienced will leave students with good programming habits, the ability to learn on their own, and a favorable impression of programming. At present, many institutions, even economic and management universities, have set up Java programming language as a compulsory course aiming to improve programming capacity and enhance their logical thinking skills. However, there are many differences in Java program language teaching methods and contents between economics and management (EM) major's students and computer science and information major's students for the sake of their knowledge background. This paper discusses some of the peculiarities of the Java programming language that make it difficult to learn and some suggestions to overcome them for EM students. Aiming to problems such as not clearly teaching objects, too professional teaching contents, focusing on theory but ignoring practice, and too single form of assessment, we proposed such strategies: understanding the importance of curriculum; arranging content reasonably; adding case teaching and improving the teaching experiments, in order to enhance the quality of teaching effect in Shandong University of Financial and Economics (SDUFE) based on many years of teaching experience. Specifically, as well as some of the teaching paradigms and programming tools we have employed. From the student's feedbacks and scores in the end of seminar, we know the effectiveness and validity of teaching reforms. In addition, learning interest and high score rate have greatly improved in the past five years.

Keywords: Java programming language, teaching methods, economic and management majors.

 WIT Transactions on Information and Communication Technologies, Vol. 61, © 2014 WIT Press
www.witpress.com, ISSN 1743-3517 (on-line)
doi:10.2495/MIIT130901

1 Introduction

Java is a general-purpose, concurrent, class-based, object-oriented computer programming language, which is specifically designed to have as few implementation dependencies as possible. The course aims to introduce object-oriented computer programming and to develop students' skills so that they become competent programmers able to work independently on completion of the unit [1]. As one of the most part in modern information technology, more and more universities choose Java and related techniques (such as J2EE technology) to build their application teaching plan. Such course learning leaves students with good programming habits, the ability to learn on their own, and a favorable impression of programming as a profession. However, it is a challenge for the students except those in computer science and information majors, though Java programming language can develop skills and accumulate experiences in project development efficiently. For the reason that common student misunderstand about the concept of object-oriented clearly, even though interfaces and exceptions [2, 3].

The same problems we have encountered in teaching Java to economics and management majors, which involve economics majors and management majors (EM). It is very useful for economics and management majors' students to master a computer programming language, for the reason that it provides a powerful tool to solve the problems in management domains. On the other hand, computer programming language can enhance their logical thinking skills, further enhancing their management capabilities [4, 5].

According to curriculum of Shandong University of Finance and Economics, Java programming language is a senior subject based on computer basic application. However, a lot of problems have emerged from the beginning, including student learning interest and the teaching method. In this paper, we will examine the essence of the problems in teaching Java programming language on the way to program, and the success of Java programming language teaching reform we have achieved in the past five years.

The remainder of the paper is organized as follows: Section 2 analyzes the difficulties in teaching Java programming language for economics and management students (EMs). Section 3 gives the corresponding strategies in teaching Java programming language for EMs. Section 4 presents the results and the evaluation. Finally, Section 5 addresses our conclusions.

2 Discussed problems

It is conceivable that teaching Java programming language to economics and management (EM) students in College of Business have many differences with teaching computer science (CS), for the reason of their background and prerequisite course. We chose to teach Java programming language because of its dominance in web applications, it is less complex and easier to debug than C++, and it has a syntax based on C/C++, making it easier for students to transition to those languages once they graduate.

Unlike CS students, EM students do not have rich knowledge in statistics and mathematics. More often than not, these courses are usually put off from their teaching plan, which leads to a poor mathematical background [6]. In addition, EM students only take one course whose primary purpose is to teach programming fundamentals. In this way, many problems emerged includes: (1) unclear teaching objects; (2) put emphasis on theory, not on practice; and (3) simple form of assessment.

Although CS and EM students may have different educational backgrounds, their learning and problem-solving styles are fundamentally similar. So, it is important for us to find a teaching mode suitable for EM students [7, 8].

3 Strategies in teaching Java programming language for EMs

In this section, we will present strategies for teaching Java programming language in practice.

3.1 Recognizing the importance of learning Java programming language

A course well experienced will help students with good programming habits, even the capability of problem solving. In addition, we can recognize the importance from the following aspects:

(1) Learning Java programming language has close ties with future occupations. Most of the EM students will engage in trades or managements in the future, which involve Gold Card, Golden Customs, Golden Finance, and so on. In this way, the subjects-related information systems engineering can supply rich basic knowledge, which will qualify them for the future job. For example, the students in auditing major are required to master the simple programming skills in order to work for different industries, for the reason that there is no unified system for auditing until now.

(2) Need for training senior personnel. As an EM student, he or she not only should have good professional knowledge, but also has a good ability of communication with information technology persons. Java programming language can effectively enhance the comprehension of computer principle, structure, and method.

(3) It is necessary for modern student to master the basic of computer programming language, for becoming complex talent in the near future.

3.2 Simplifying Java compile tools

Java platform is the name for a bundle of related programs from Sun that allow for developing and running programs written in Java programming language. The platform is not specific to any one processor or operating system, but rather an execution engine (called a virtual machine) and a compiler with a set of libraries that are implemented for various hardware and operating systems so that Java

```
    ...
    while (AuctionTimes<=3)
      { highest_price=gethighest_price();
       if (cur_price<Highest_price)
         {Cur_price= Highest_price;
          AuctionTimes=0;}
       else
          AuctionTimes= AuctionTimes+1;
       }
    ...
```

Figure 1: Auction program design.

programs can run identically on all of them. However, most EM students are interested in the results of Java program, and tired of cumbersome debugging procedure, such as using command line and input command javac and java. So, it is urgent for teachers choose a better tool which can simplify program debugging procedure. These tools usually contain graphical interface, such as Ultraedit, NetBeans, Eclipse, and so on. Similarly, some concepts, such as java virtual machine, class libraries, are difficult to understand for EM students, especially at the start beginning.

3.3 Case-based teaching

Generally speaking, the case-based teaching can effectively improve students' interest in learning Java programming language, for the reason that cases supply a real environment in our society.

However, most of examples on current textbooks mainly focus on the application of grammar test, ignoring the inspiration of students learning interest. If we teach students Java programming method, corporation with a series of cases related with their professions, then significant effects will get. For example, in the way to learn flow control statements, we can use a real case-auction case with a short code, but the program execution process can be clearly described and is shown in Figure 1.

We have designed nearly 17 cases in the whole teaching, which is shown in Table 1.

3.4 Teaching content be concise

Java programming language teaches students how to develop Java applications. And topics covered include the Java programming language syntax, OO programming using Java, exception handling, file input/output, threads, collection classes, and networking. Students will develop and test Java applications (typically) using Eclipse.

Traditional Java programming language teaching contents weaken the learning enthusiasm to some extent, for its comprehensive content which has little relation with their research fields. Learning Java is not only to learn a more popular programming language, but also the study of object-oriented development technology. In this way, it is particularly important to design the suitable teaching content for EM students. Table 1 describes the content, which includes seven core modules and one optional module.

3.5 Attach importance to experimental teaching

Experimental teaching is one of the most important parts in learning Java program language. And we must hold a belief that the programming ability is from practice, not from repeat of memory. We not only put emphasis on curricular experiments, but also after-class experiments. Also an experimental point for basic knowledge is necessary in checking their homework. Experiment content should be in accord with the knowledge that involves their research domains, and should pay more attention to the difficulty degree between questions gradually. Similarly, these experiments can be from source of certifications exams, computer grade examination, such as NCRE (National Computer Ranked Examination) and CST (Computer Software Test).

3.6 Assessment methods

Traditional assessment mode, such as close paper test is rigid, inflexible, not really reflect real knowledge level, but weaken the enthusiasm of learning Java program language. So, it is important to change traditional book exams, some evaluations that can effectively reflect their programming capabilities, and debugging capabilities, should be proposed for EMs students. For example, to add several statements to a simple program for completing a sample program in set up period.

In this way, as an example, we have designed experiment assessment system including six parts.

(1) Prepare for experiments.
    Full marks: understand the aims, demands and basic principle;
    In other circumstance, we can act accordingly.
(2) Practical programming.
    Full marks: the program and result are correct;
    Half marks: the program or result is correct;
    Or else, the marks of program is zero.
(3) Record of experiments.
    Full marks: keep record on every experiment;
    Half marks: only keep key record on every experiment.
(4) Report of experiments.
    Full marks: format and content are correct;
    Half marks: format or content is correct.
(5) Experiment report.
    In addition, we will check report of experiment through ftp server.
    Full marks: correct and complete report of experiment;
    Half marks: only keep a part of record on report;
    Or else: zero.

Table 1: Java Programming Language for EMs Contents.

No	Title and Contents	Type	Cases
1	Introductions to Java Programming Language: What is Java; its history; versions; two types of simple Java programs.	Core	Case 1: A simple Java program; Case 2: A simple Java applet
2	Fundamentals of Java Programming Language: Primitive data types; comments; structure of Java program, key words.	Core	Case 3: Josephus Ring Case 4: Random generated data
3	Flow control statements: The for statement, the if statement, the while and do while statements, operators.	Core	Case 5: Process design of auction (1) Case 6: Determine whether a string is a palindrome
4	Object-oriented Program: Defining new data types; constructors; the String class; the Date class; the import statement.	Core	Case 7: Class design of a student Case 8: Class design of stocks
5	Methods: Method Signatures; arguments and parameters; passing objects to methods; method overloading; static methods; the Math class.	Core	Case 9: Method implementation for Class student Case 10: Method implementation for Class stocks
6	Arrays: Processing arrays; copying arrays; passing Arrays to methods; arrays of Object.	Core	Case 11: Stock class design and implementation Case 12: Bidding program design
7	GUI Design and Implementation: JApplet; Event handling; Java GUI class.	Core	Case 13: Game theory program design Case 14: Process design of auction (2)
8	Database programming: Database connection; insert, delete, update record in tables.	Core	Case 15: Social security audit program Case 16: Cycle Guaranty in banks program
9	Java Advanced Programming: Threads; Networking; Exceptions	Optional	Case 17: Chatting room on Internet program design

(6) Comprehensive assessment.

Score=(score of Practical programming+ score of record experiments +score of record experiments+ score of report experiments)/4.

(7) Final score.

$$\text{Final score} = \sum_{i=1}^{n} (Score_i \times k).$$

Table 2: Experiment Evaluation.

Score	Grade
90–100	Excellent
80–89	Good
70–79	Moderate
60–69	Pass
Below 60	Fail

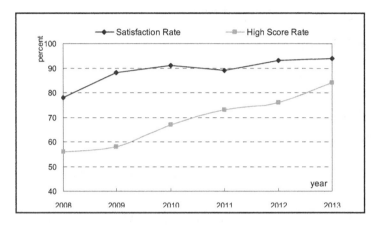

Figure 2: High score and satisfaction rate.

k is the coefficient, which can be determined by a teacher. And the final experiments score can be calculate from Table 2.

4 Evaluations of our strategies

Shandong University of Finance and Economics (SDUFE) is founded on 4, June 2011 from the union of Shandong University of Economics and Shandong University of Finance, which is managed by the Ministry of Education, the Ministry of Finance and the provincial government of Shandong. In the past years, a lot of reform strategies have been put in practice in Java programming language. In the new edited teaching plan, Java programming language is regarded as a subject in many majors, such as major in business administration, tourism management professional, human resources management, real estate management, and marketing.

In order to improve the teaching quality, and promote the development of students' theoretical level and the practice ability, we have reformed in teaching contents, teaching methods, teaching mode of exploration. At the end of each semester, all of the students will evaluate Java programming language from the teaching method; teaching content; teaching effectiveness questionnaire in the past five years (the first three years in Shandong University of Economics)

(2009–2013). And results show measurable improvement in both score and satisfaction and the result is shown in Figure 2.

5 Conclusions

It is necessary that practical computer courses must keep up with the pace of social development. And teachers should master enterprise knowledge and use modern teaching methods for student in EMs Java program language learning. In the future, we will further increase the curriculum reform to match teaching and social needs, especially for EM students.

Acknowledgments

The research work was supported by Shandong Province Top Quality Courses Project-IT supported curriculum group for Economics and Management Majors (No. 2012BK154).

References

[1] W. Xiuguo, C. Jie, Reform and practice of Java programming language for economics and management specialties. *Computer Times*, **3**, pp. 49–51, 2013.

[2] C.S. Horstmann, *Java Core Technology Research I: Basics*. Mechanical Industry Press, Beijing, 2005.

[3] Mei Bruce, Eckel Zhu, *Java Programming Ideas*. Mechanical Industry Press, Beijing, 2005.

[4] C.D. Manning, Programming for linguists: Java TM technology for language researchers. *Language*, **81(3)**, pp. 740–742, 2005.

[5] M. Kölling, J. Rosenberg, Guidelines for teaching object orientation with Java. *ACM SIGCSE Bulletin*, **33(3)**, pp. 33–36, 2001.

[6] C. Noll, M. Wilkins, Critical skills of IS professionals: A model for curriculum development. *Journal of Information Technology Education: Research*, **1(1)**, pp. 143–154, 2002.

[7] J. Lewis, Myths about object-orientation and its pedagogy. *ACM SIGCSE Bulletin*, **32(1)**, pp. 245–249, 2000.

[8] S. Cooper, W. Dann, R. Pausch, Teaching objects-first in introductory computer science. *ACM SIGCSE Bulletin*, **35(1)**, pp. 191–195, 2003.

Study on the quality of government statistics based on the background of big data era

Yingying Yu

Management School of Information, Beijing Information Science and Technology University, Beijing, 100192, China

Abstract

This article systematically elaborated the meaning of statistical data quality, contrasted the domestic and international quality standards and security framework. And on this basis, from the angle of connotation of the statistical data quality, this article analyzed the existing problems of data quality and the challenges of big data era in China. In the end, the research was placed in the background of big data era to discuss how to improve data quality.

Keywords: big data, government statistics, data quality.

1 Introduction

With the enhancement of degree and level of informatization, the big data era characterized by large-scale production, sharing and applying data has come. The quality of government statistical data affects the correctness and scientificity of macro decision-making and influences the reputation of government statistical agency. Study has been carried out in the fields of statistics and the new trends arise. On the one hand, the concept of data quality develops from the narrow sense to the broad sense and the concept of multidimensional and comprehensive data quality is put forward. On the other hand, establishing a comprehensive and systematic statistical data quality evaluation and management system has become an important part for the government and international organizations to improve statistical data quality.

The Chinese government has carried out much fruitful work on statistical data quality. But at present there are still some data quality problems caused by many factors, which become the social focuses. As the bottleneck of statistical development, only if the principal contradiction of data quality is solved, the statistical data quality would be improved, and the government credibility would be enhanced. So government statistics should be in line with international standards and meet the different statistical data needs of users.

2 Connotation of statistical data quality

The quality of statistical data in the traditional sense refers only to the accuracy, usually measured by the error in statistical estimation. Nowadays the concept of quality has been broadened. The concept of "statistical data quality" has also been broadened correspondingly and the multidimensional and comprehensive data quality arises. The International Organization for Standardization (ISO) defines the quality as the totality of characteristics that the product or service satisfying implicit or explicit demands. For government statistics, quality includes not only statistics itself but also the production, collation, and analysis of statistical data. The data quality must meet the demands of macro decision-making and the demands of the social public.

At the end of last century, foreign experts and scholars in related fields had systematic research on the statistical data quality. Dalenius [1] put forward that the measurement vector of statistical data quality included accuracy, economy, confidentiality, correlation, timeliness, the degree of detail. Gordon and Brackstone [2, 3] proposed six dimensions of statistical data quality including correlation, accuracy, timeliness, accessibility, interpretability, and consistency. This literature further described the management methods of the statistical agency for each dimension and also put forward five subsystems required by the effective data quality management. The five subsystems are as follows, contact system, cooperation system, standardization system, release system, and process monitoring system. Lee Dongmyeong and ShonAelee [4], John Cornish [5] put forward the statistical data quality evaluation index system and specific methods to improve government statistical data quality according to the statistical experiences of their own country.

At present, the government statistical agencies and relevant international organizations still have divergence on understanding the meaning of statistical data quality. And there is no unified standard on the range of statistical data quality. Different country establishes different data quality standard based on its own actual situation and its own understanding of the meaning of data quality. Statistical data quality connotation has gradually extended to the accuracy, timeliness, consistency, comparability, applicability, confidentiality, economy, objectivity, accessibility, scientificity of method, statistical independence, index matching, and index interpretation. The accuracy of statistical data refers to the degree that the statistical data reflecting the objective reality. Timeliness refers to the interval between benchmark survey period and statistical data release. Consistency refers to the relational and logical relations between different survey, different organizations, and different period. Comparability refers to the degree that statistics can be compared in different time and different spatial extent. Applicability means the degree that the statistical data meets requirements of users in different content, caliber, and scope. Confidentiality means the data is confidential and the identification information will not be divulged. Economy means the comparison between cost of statistical data survey and social economic benefits. Objectivity (integrity) means that the statistical agencies must comply with objectivity principles when collecting, processing, and publishing the data. Accessibility refers to complexity that users get the statistical data and relevant information. Scientificity of method means using the international standard, concept, methods, scope, and classification. Statistical independence refers to maintaining the statistical system of justice, openness, independence, and transparency. Index matching refers to whether the matching degree of related index accords with the logical relationship. Index interpretation means when the statistical data are published, the supplementary information should also be published at the same time. Here the supplementary information refers to the explanation of statistical data.

3 Statistical data quality standards and security framework

With the acceleration of global economic integration process, the exchange and cooperation between the countries are more and more frequent. The international society established some international standards and data quality assurance frameworks in various areas to reduce friction and contradiction and provide a standardized procedures and practices for data quality assessment and control. For example, the International Monetary Fund (IMF) promulgated the "Special Data Dissemination Standards" (SDDS), "General Data Dissemination System" (GDDS), "Data Quality Assessment Framework" (DQAF), and other international standards to improve the statistical data quality of member country and provide guidance for the data production, information release, and quality evaluation for member country.

In 2013, National Bureau of Statistics of China has established the national statistical quality assurance framework, which uses the UN Statistical Commission "national quality assurance framework (NQAF) template" as the reference basis. "Framework" expands the relevant requirements in "Statistic Law" and put forward seven evaluation criteria including the accuracy, timeliness, consistency, comparability, applicability, availability, and economy. It not only includes the statistical data quality of production, also contains the statistical data quality of service, and the evaluation standard is more comprehensive. At the same time, "Framework" defines the quality control requirements and standards of every link, highlighting the concept of whole process quality control. Otherwise, in order to improve the statistical data quality, "Framework" puts forward safeguard measures in five aspects including statistic laws and regulations, statistic system and mechanism, statistic institutional methods, statistic resources, and statistic culture. Putting the statistical quality management and the statistical work into the standardization and legalization, which would help to reduce the statistical data quality questions and further improve the credibility of the government statistics. In addition, "Framework" could help China's statistical quality management to be in line with international standards, and help China involved in international cooperation.

4 The arrival of big data era

Although the study of the government statistical data quality problems has been more systematic and perfect, with the big data era coming, the government statistical data quality in big data era faces up with new opportunities and challenges. Big data is a kind of phenomenon and also a kind of trend. The one owning the data occupies the commanding heights and regains the initiative. Based on the government perspective, big data would become the information foundation of macroeconomic control and social management; based on the enterprise perspective, the one can make effectively use of big data, who could win the market opportunity. Now many developed countries have improved the application of big data to national strategic level. China should adapt to this trend, regard big data as national strategic resources, actively embrace big data era, and actively seize the opportunity and meet the challenge. If the government ignores the impact of big data on government statistics, government statistics will gradually lose the purpose and value of existence.

Compared with traditional data, big data includes not only the structured data, but also large amounts of unstructured data. Big data has the characteristics of large amount of data, high application value, high production speed, large index range, and large data fluctuation. The big data can provide the government statistics with general, unstructured, rich raw data, which can greatly reduce the data acquisition time, reduce the statistical investigation burden, and improve the statistical data quality. Enterprise is the forerunner of big data utilization. The government actively promotes the establishment of big data statistic system and standard, and promotes development and utilization of big data to be scientific, unified, normative, which will create a good environment for the enterprises using big data. At the same time, the application of big data in the government statistics will further promote the government statistical agencies to improve statistical power, statistical data quality, and government credibility of statistical data. Finally, the big data would play an important role in the national economic construction and social development, and realize the complementary advantages and win-win between government and enterprise.

5 Chances and challenges of data quality in the big data era

To improve statistical data quality, Chinese government agencies have unremittingly carried out active exploration. But there are still many problems can not be ignored about the data quality criteria for evaluation, which means a long way to enhance the government statistical data quality. In this paper, from the connotation of statistical data quality, the existing problems on statistical data quality and challenges confronting with big data are as follows.

Firstly, on the way of accuracy and data interpretation, it is lack of interpretation about average wage of staff and workers, consumer price index, the rate of year-on-year price increases for new urban residential builds, and some other index data in China. And there is a certain gap between the published data and the public feelings, which places the government statistics in the teeth of the storm of public criticism. The network information in big data era can be processed immediately. If the data are effectively utilized, it can promote the statistical data quality; otherwise, the government will fall into the quagmire of struggling to explain. So perfecting data release and strengthening data interpretation can better meet the diverse public demands of statistical data.

Secondly, about timeliness and accessibility, part of the annual index data released late in our country, and it is difficult for the public to obtain the detailed aggregate data packet. There is a long way for our country to publish the government statistics in public freely. For the age of big data, network information is relatively more convenient. The timeliness and accessibility of network information tend to precede the government statistical data, which will lead public opinion or seize the statistics of blind spot area.

Thirdly, about consistency, the contradiction phenomena of same index data from different agencies still objectively exist. So the communication of index interpretation between the different statistical agencies needs to be strengthened and the statistical indicator standardization needs to be deepened. While in the era of big data, the index data are in advance of government statistics. By widely collecting all kinds of big data already existed and increasing, and comparing the difference between big data index and government traditional data index in quantity, scope, connotation, and definition, could do advantage to help government statistics to design, adjust, improve, and apply big data index system.

Fourthly, about the independence, the existing statistical management system partly continues the pattern of planned economy period. There is too many management levels and administrative interference, which obstructs the statistical independence and influences the data authenticity. The big data come from the society and have little human disturbance, which are helpful to spur the government at all levels to enhance the data quality.

Fifthly, about comparability and consistency, the longitudinal connection and cross matching of comprehensive data in China is poor. The arrival of big data era puts forward high requirement on comparability and consistency. The big data statistic standard including the definition of the index, caliber, scope, classification, calculation method, and index code must be established immediately.

Sixthly, about the scientificity, there are some problems with lack of scientific standard such as the ambiguity of our existing system design, imperfection of comprehensive data quality assessment control mechanism, and unbalance of data processing means. Lack of corresponding workflow control ultimately affects the statistical authority. According to the characteristics of the big data, government must unify standardized application of big data investigation, collecting, processing, analysis, evaluation, and control, especially pay special attention to collection of unstructured data and the way of standardized processing.

Seventhly, about confidentiality and objectivity, the guarantee of public opinion, technology, human resource, law, and culture are all required. The basic statistic work and the primary statistician quality are weak at present stage in our country, which is the hidden danger of confidentiality and objectivity. While the big data era puts forward higher requirements to network technology, personnel quality, and legal system construction.

Eighthly, about applicability, now many government statistical data have little practical value, while the valuable information demanded has not been set appropriate statistical indicators. Along with the explosion of information, the big data era puts new challenge for the government statistical power on how to mine the useful information in the ocean of data.

Finally, about economy, in developed countries, statistical projects must be supervised and approved by budget. So there is higher demand about whether achieving the expected target. While in our country, on the one hand, there is lack of sufficient fund support of statistic innovative work; on the other hand, there exists inefficient working process lack of supervision. These problems above must be avoided in the era of big data.

6 Conclusions

Big data has played an important role in daily life, but the application of big data is still based on germination stage. The statistical agencies of government in China should seize and make best use of opportunities to improve the application of big data, which could bring cooperation and sharing to a new height. Based on the connotation of statistical data quality, this article analyzes the existing problems in government data quality and the challenges in big data era, which has laid a solid basis for further research.

Acknowledgments

This work is supported by Project of Beijing municipal philosophy and social science planning under grant Nos. 13JGC093 and Social Research Common Program of Beijing Municipal Education Commission under grant Nos. SM201210772003.

References

[1]   T. Dalenius, Errors and other limitations of survey. *Statistical Methods and the Improvement of Data Quality*. Academic Press Inc., London, pp. 2–5, 1973.
[2]   Gordon Brackstone, Managing data quality in a statistical agency. *Survey Methodology*, **25(2)**, pp. 2–21, 1999.
[3]   Gordon Brackstone, Managing data quality at statistics Canada. www.nso.go.kr.2000-08-07.
[4]   Lee Dongmyeong, Shon Aelee, Korea's experiences in statistical quality assessment. www.nso.go.kr,2000-08-07.
[5]   John Cornish, Management of quality in statistics in New Zealand. www.nso.go.kr.2000-08-07.

[6] Youyuan Yu, Liangneng Feng, Management study on the government statistical data quality in China. *Economic Research Guide*, **34**, pp. 207–209, 2009 (In Chinese).

[7] Gao Chen, Causes and countermeasures of our government statistical data quality. *Contemporary Economics,* **1**, pp. 84–85, 2012 (In Chinese).

[8] Si Shen, Analysis of influencing factors on government statistical data quality. **2**, pp. 54–55, 2013 (In Chinese).

Lossless information hiding scheme for two-dimensional CAD engineering graphics based on coordinate modification

Zhengqiao Lei
Department of Computer of Chongqing Industry Polytechnic College, Chongqing, 401120, China

Abstract

Lossless information hiding can ensure that the distortions induced by data embedding be removed after the hidden bit is extracted. Although two-dimensional CAD engineering graphics are widely used, how to realize their lossless embedding has seldom been investigated. In this paper, a lossless hiding scheme for CAD graphics is proposed by modifying the special digit bit of the coordinate based on AutoCAD DXF files. This scheme extracts the coordinate of the primitives in the engineering graphic and presets the edge detection threshold to obtain a flag set, which indicates whether a watermark can be embedded into the current coordinate or not. During the data embedding process, four sets, that is, the coordinate set, the flag set, the hidden data set and the embedded data set, are involved. At the same time, some related techniques are also smartly utilized, including RLE (run length encoding) compression and precise calculation by transformation between the floating-point number and character string. This scheme is strictly lossless. The original cover engineering graphic can be exactly recovered after extracting the hidden bits. The experiments are performed on graphics with different amount of primitives. The results show the capacity is approximately proportional to the number of embedded primitives, and it is approximately inversely proportional to the edge detection threshold. The potential applications of the proposed scheme include graphic data authentication and right protection.

Keywords: lossless information hiding, two-dimensional CAD engineering graphics, coordinate modification.

 WIT Transactions on Information and Communication Technologies, Vol. 61, © 2014 WIT Press
www.witpress.com, ISSN 1743-3517 (on-line)
doi:10.2495/MIIT130921

1 Introduction

Hiding information into digital data is very useful for data protection. However, ordinary information hiding usually results in permanent distortion in data itself. On the contrary, the lossless information hiding can ensure that the distortions induced by data embedding be removed after extracting the hidden bits. Lots of lossless hiding algorithms have been proposed in recent years [1–4]. However, the targets of the majority are digital images that are stored as integers from 0 to 255. Only a few algorithms focus on 2D vector maps of GIS [5,6]. Voigt et al. [5] first proposed the method to reversibly hide data in vector maps. They hide the data by modifying the integer discrete cosine transform coefficients of the map coordinates. Since the scheme is realized in the transform domain, the distortion controlling mechanism in their scheme seems to be complicated. Based on the idea of difference expansion, Wang et al. [6] adopted the coordinates of vertices and the Manhattan distances between neighbor vertices as the cover data to propose two reversible data-hiding schemes for 2D vector maps. But this scheme cannot be applied to maps or computer-aided design (CAD) curves where data are represented by parametric curves or other different forms.

In this paper, a lossless hiding scheme for CAD graphics is explored by modifying the special digit bit of the coordinate based on AutoCAD DXF files. This scheme extracts the coordinate of the primitives in the vector graphic and presets the edge detection threshold to obtain a flag set, which shows whether a watermark can be embedded into the current coordinate or not. During the data embedding process, four sets, that is, the coordinate set, the flag set, the hidden data set, and the embedded data set, are involved. The original cover engineering graphic can be exactly recovered after extracting the hidden bits.

2 Preliminaries

2.1 DXF file

DXF (Drawing exchange File) is a drawing file format developed firstly by Autodesk for AutoCAD drawing data exchanging. It becomes the actual standard which is supported by most CAD systems. DXF file has seven sections, such as HEADER, CLASSES, TABLES, BLOCKS, ENTITIES, and so on. Here, ENTITIES describes all the entities in the file, which is our focus for data embedding. VERTEX is the most popular geometric primitive of ENTITIES.

2.2 Basic idea of floating coordinate modification

For a floating-point number f_1, under the limitation of precision, it can be transformed to a floating-point number f' by adding another floating-point number f_2, namely

$$f' = f_1 + f_2 \qquad (1)$$

Through inverse transformation, f_1 can be recovered as follows:

$$f_1 = f' - f_2 \qquad (2)$$

If f_2 is so small that the affection of f_2 to f_1 can be neglected, then the difference between f' and f_1 is not obvious. Starting from this point, we can transform the watermark b into f_2, then hide it in f_1. The idea has the following features: the embedded data should be integer. A graphic is composed of geometric primitives, and the geometric primitive has coordinate data. It is all the geometric primitives that share the distortion induced by watermarking.

2.3 Floating-point precise representation based on character string transformation

In our proposed scheme, floating-point arithmetic will be inevitably involved. Since the floating point digits supported by different computing platforms are different, the same floating-point arithmetic may result in different results. Enlightened by big number arithmetic implementation, we transform every floating-point number to a character string. In this way, if we want to get the sum of two floating-point numbers, we take out each character from two strings, respectively, and carry out operations one by one. In each step, we only need to store one result character and one carry character.

3 Lossless information hiding scheme based on coordinate modification

3.1 Four sets

In DXF file, each VERTEX in ENTITIES is composed of parameter coordinates X, Y, and Z. All the coordinates of VERTEX can be represented as the sets $M_x=\{x_1,x_2,x_3,\dots\}$, $M_y=\{y_1,y_2,y_3,\dots\}$, $M_z=\{z_1,z_2,z_3,\dots\}$, each with N items in the set. In the following embedding scheme, we only take X direction as a sample. During the data embedding and extracting process, four sets, that is, the coordinate set in X direction M_X, the flag set F, the hidden data set W, and the embedded data set W', are involved.

An edge detection threshold τ is preset by the user. The corresponding flag set F can be obtained by judging whether the precision of each item x_i in the set M_X satisfy the threshold as follows:

$$f_i = \begin{cases} 1, & \text{precision}(x_i) \prec \tau \\ 0, & \text{precision}(x_i) \geq \tau \end{cases} \qquad (3)$$

where $i=1,2,3,\dots$, and precision() is a function to extract the maximum number of digits after decimal of x_i. If $f_i=1$, the corresponding coordinate is suitable for data hiding.

The hidden data W is composed as follows:

$$W = \text{comp}F + P \tag{4}$$

Comp( ) represents a lossless compression algorithm. In order to embed W into the cover data, W should be pre-transformed into the embedded data suitable for embedding, the transformation is as follows:

$$W' = f(W) \tag{5}$$

where, f ( ) is an invertible function:

$$f(x) = x * 10^{-p\max} \tag{6}$$

where $p$max equals to the maximum precision of x plus one. Through the inverse function, the hidden data W can be recovered easily.

$$W = f^{-1}(W') \tag{7}$$

Obviously, set W and W' both have N items. They can be represented as $W=\{w_1, w_2, w_3, \ldots\}$ and $W' = \{w'_1, w'_2, w'_3, \cdots\}$, respectively.

3.2 Data embedding

Through the above steps, four sets, that is, the coordinate set in X direction M_X, the flag set F, the hidden data set W, and the embedded data set W', are obtained. Let $M'_x = \{x'_1, x'_2, x'_3, \cdots\}$ represent the watermarked cover data set. The embedded data set W' is embedded into the cover data M_X as follows:

$$\begin{cases} x'_i = x_i, & f_i = 0 \\ x'_i = x_i + w'_i, & f_i = 1 \end{cases} \tag{8}$$

where $i=1,2,3,\ldots$. If $f_i=0$, the corresponding coordinate is not suitable for data hiding. Therefore, the original cover should not be modified. If $f_i=1$, it means that the corresponding coordinate is suitable for data hiding. So, x_i with the embedded data w'_i are written into the DXF file.

3.3 Data extracting and the original graphic recovering

Similar to the embedding process, the watermarked cover data set $M'_x = \{x'_1, x'_2, x'_3, \cdots\}$ can be obtained firstly. Then $t'=t+1$ is used as the edge detection threshold to extract W' as follows:

$$w_i' = \begin{cases} \text{embedpos}(x_i'), & \text{precision}(x_i') < \tau' \\ No \quad \text{extracting}, & \text{precision}(x_i') \geq \tau' \end{cases} \qquad (9)$$

where $i=1,2,3,\ldots$, and embedpos() is a function to extract the bit where the data are embedded. For each item x_i' in the set M_x', if its precision satisfies the edge detection threshold, the embedded bit should be extracted; otherwise, no extracting happens. Repeat the above process until the end of M_x', the embedded data set W' can be extracted. According to the inverse function in Eq. (7), the hidden data set W can be obtained. And then, according to the ending message "*END*" in (4), *compF* and *P* can be separated, and the payload *P* can be obtained.

In the following, the original cover graphic can be recovered. Firstly, *compF* is decompressed to obtain the flag set *F*. Then according to the flag set *F*, the original graphic can be recovered as follows:

$$\begin{cases} x_i = x_i', & f_i = 0 \\ x_i = x_i' - w_i', & f_i = 1 \end{cases} \qquad (10)$$

where $i=1,2,3,\ldots$. If $f_i=0$, no bit is embedded in this data. So it can be kept in the file. If $f_i=1$, there is bit hidden in this data. So the embedded bit should be removed and then the data can be written into the file. In this way, the original cover graphic can be recovered exactly after extracting.

4   Performance analysis and experiment result

4.1 Invisibility and losslessness

Three kinds of graphics with different quantities of geometric primitives are used as the original graphics to test the performance of the scheme. The experimental results on three graphics after data hiding are shown in Figures 1–3.

Figures 1(a), 2(a), and 3(a) are three original graphics and the others are the watermarked graphics. The comparison between the original and the watermarked graphics indicates that the distortions induced by data hiding can be well controlled in all the tests. The invisibility of the scheme, that is, the distortions induced by data hiding, depends on the choosing of τ. We set τ to be 10^{-11}, 10^{-7}, and 10^{-2}, respectively, and carry out the corresponding tests. The test results indicate that the smaller τ is, the better the invisibility is. And the bigger τ is, the worse the invisibility is. Since the graphics in DXF file are parameterized, the minor modification on floating-point coordinate will not affect the shape of the graphics.

After the hidden data have been successfully extracted, we also checked the reversibility of the scheme by comparing the hash values of the original graphic and the recovered graphic. The experimental result indicates that two hashes are exactly matched. Both proposed schemes can recover the original graphic exactly.

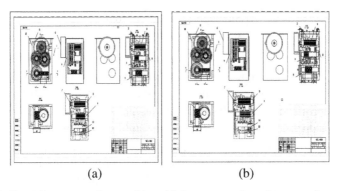

(a)   (b)

Figure 1: Experiments on the graphic with large quantity of geometric primitives: (a) original graphic (b) watermarked graphic.

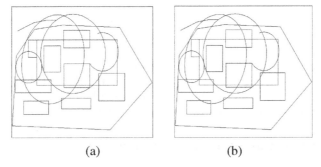

(a)   (b)

Figure 2: Experiments on the graphic with medium quantity of geometric primitives: (a) original graphic (b) watermarked graphic.

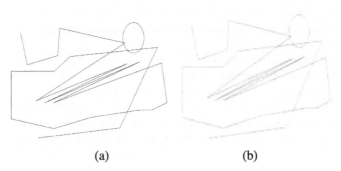

(a)   (b)

Figure 3: Experiments on the graphic with small quantity of geometric primitives: (a) original graphic (b) watermarked graphic.

Table 1: The Scheme Capacity Affection of the Quantity of the Geometric Primitives.

Graphic Type	Total Units	N_E	compF	P	Bit/vertex	τ
With large quantity of geometric primitives	35263	14098	9089	5008	1.136148	10^{-10}
With medium quantity of geometric primitives	177	48	44	4	0.135593	10^{-10}
With small quantity of geometric primitives	24	24	6	18	5.666667	10^{-10}

Table 2: The Scheme Capacity Affection of the Value of T.

Graphic Type	Total Units	N_E	compF	P	Bit/vertex	τ
With large quantity of geometric primitives	35263	14098	9089	5008	1.136148	10^{-10}
With large quantity of geometric primitives	35263	14107	9074	5232	1.141563	10^{-8}
With large quantity of geometric primitives	35263	35263	8816	26446	5.999716	10^{-3}
With large quantity of geometric primitives	35263	35263	8816	26446	5.999716	10^{-1}

4.2 Capacity

By analyzing the structures of the hidden data W in the proposed scheme, it could be found that the scheme capacity is composed of two parts, $compF$ and L. Suppose the number of the expandable units in a scheme is N_E, the payload space provided by those units should be

$$N_E - len(compF) \qquad (11)$$

Actually, the expandable units N_E is equal to the number of "1" in the F set. According to Eq. (11), the higher the redundancy of F set is, the smaller the length of $compF$ is, and thus the bigger the scheme capacity is. Generally speaking, more expandable units and higher redundancy of F set will result in higher capacity.

Tables 1 and 2 show the scheme capacity results by adjusting the quantity of the geometric primitives and the value of τ, respectively.

It seems that to increase scheme capacity by adjusting the quantity of the geometric primitives is not reliable. The reason is that the scheme capacity is restricted by τ, no matter how many geometric primitives exist. The better way to increase scheme capacity is adjusting the value of τ. That is to say, increase the number of the expandable units by increasing the edge detection threshold.

However, from the last two rows in Table 2, we find that the scheme capacity can no longer increase after τ reaches some special value. The reason is as follows: the coordinate parameters in the DXF file are represented in floating-point number. When the value of τ is equal to the maximum tolerance number of digits after decimal in the file, the scheme capacity approaches the biggest number. Even τ gets bigger, it is of no use for capacity increase.

4.3 Robustness

The robustness of the proposed scheme is also investigated. The scheme can not resist the attack of low-amplitude additive noise. However, changing the digit of the coordinate for data hiding is a practical measure to enhance the robustness of the scheme. By selecting a smaller edge detection threshold, some lower digits will be excluded for hiding data; besides, some random numbers can be placed on the lowest digit to mislead the attacker. Some experiments are carried out to verify the practicality of this kind of enhancement.

5   Conclusions

In this paper, a lossless information hiding scheme for CAD graphics is proposed by minor modifying the special digit bit of the coordinate based on DXF file. The original cover engineering graphic can be exactly recovered after extracting the hidden bits. It is simple, efficient and practicable. It is a good candidate for graphic data authentication and right protection.

References

[1]   J. Tian, Reversible data embedding using a difference expansion. *IEEE Transactions on Circuits System Video Technology*, **13(8)**, pp. 890–896, 2003.
[2]   H.J. Kim, V. Sachnev, Y.Q. Shi, J. Nam, A novel difference expansion transform for reversible data embedding. *IEEE Transactions on Information Forensic Security*, **3(3)**, pp. 456–465, 2008.
[3]   Z. Ni, Y.Q. Shi, N. Ansari, S. Wei, Reversible data hiding. *IEEE Transactions on Circuits System Video Technology*, **16(3)**, pp. 354–362, 2006.
[4]   L. Luo, Z. Chen, M. Chen, X. Zeng, Reversible image watermarking using interpolation technique. *IEEE Transactions on Information Forensic Security*, **5(1)**, pp. 187–193, 2010.
[5]   M. Voigt, B. Yang, C. Busch, Reversible watermarking of 2D-vector data, in Proc. ACM Int. Workshop on Multimedia and Security, Magdeburg, Germany, pp. 160–165, 2004.
[6]   X. Wang, C. Shao, X. Xu, Reversible data hiding scheme for 2-D vector maps based on difference expansion. *IEEE Transactions on Information Forensic Security*, **2(3)**, pp. 311–320, 2007.

Study and realization of equipment management information system adaptable in wind power generation enterprise

Jia He, Xiao Li, Weilin Zhu, Yujie Liu
School of Power and Mechanical Engineering, Wuhan University, Wuhan, 430072, China

Abstract

At present, the information technology's level of equipment management in wind power generation enterprise is generally low, and there is lack of informational equipment management methods in conformity with the characteristics of wind power generation enterprises. In order to solve the problems efficiently, this paper designs an equipment management information system based on .NET, through studies on wind power generation enterprises' features of hierarchical relationship complexity between equipment, personnel insufficiency, flat organizational structure, and workflow mutability. By trialling in wind power generation enterprises, this system is proved well applicability.

Keywords: wind power, equipment management, information system, workflow flexibility, KANBAN.

1 Introduction

Wind power generation enterprise is a capital intensive enterprise, whose equipment management is very complicated. With the scale growth of wind power generation enterprises and the improvement of equipment automation degree, the information volume becomes larger and larger in equipment management. Traditional equipment management method which uses paper or electronic document as medium becomes unable to satisfy the demands of wind power generation enterprise. It may even become the short slab in the development of wind power generation enterprise [1].

With the rapid development of information technology, enterprises are constantly reforming their management mode and attaches greater and greater importance on information technology in asset management [2]. To increase the efficiency of equipment management and reduce management costs, this paper designs and realizes an equipment management information system (EMIS) which is adaptable for the workflow and usage habit in wind power generation enterprises.

2 Study on the demands of EMIS in wind power generation enterprise

As an important part of enterprise management information system, EMIS covers the whole process of the equipment's life cycle. Typical EMIS includes equipment asset management, configuration management, equipment maintenance management, spare parts management, and the functions and structure are different in accordance with current situation of enterprise, management system of enterprise and equipment management organization structure [1]. The functions of EMIS in wind power generation enterprises should be suitable for its current conditions and meet its actual demands.

By analyzing the equipment management mode in general enterprises and researching on the management status in wind power generation enterprises, this paper summarizes the functional demands of EMIS in wind power generation enterprises. Its differential demands mainly include:

(1) The equipment amount is huge with wide distribution in wind power generation enterprise. The hierarchical relationship among equipment is complex. This paper shall establish equipment hierarchical system in aspects of device object, geographical position, and functional location with no restriction on layers and complexity. At the same time, because of the limitation of professional level of operating and maintaining personnel in wind power generation enterprise, the hierarchical structure of the equipment should achieve visualization, which can directly show the incidence relation among equipment, so as to make the system easy to use.

(2) Wind power generation enterprises are characterized by more equipment with fewer personnel. In order to ensure the maintenance management of numerous equipment is clear without missing, the system must bring in KANBAN of maintenance plan which provides the function of presenting the maintenance plan of equipment.

(3) The majority of domestic wind power generation equipment are placed in service for a short time and are still in warranty period, adding that the professional ability of maintaining people is not strong enough to cope with the maintenance after warranty period, so the system must has the abilities of processing, tracking, and storage of maintenance information and provide a platform for maintenance experience and knowledge accumulation.

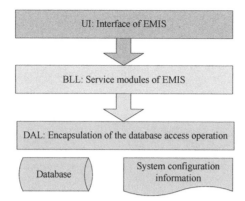

Figure 1: Structure of the wind power generation enterprise EMIS.

(4) Wind power generation enterprises in China are generally set up late with insufficient management experience in wind power generation field. In terms of management system, most enterprises use other power generation enterprises for reference. The current workflow is immature and changing. So the system must support the workflow of elimination, rating, and transaction. In addition, the workflow should have certain flexibility, which can be customized or changed by users, so as to suit the changeable situation of workflow.

(5) There are not many staffs in wind power generation enterprises and there is delayering in organization structure with complicated interaction among people, which requires high execution ability of staffs. The system must establish a tracking system of staff interaction, thus helping managers master the execution status in time and carrying out relevant assessment and evaluation.

(6) The system must present the operation status of assembling unit equipment and electric equipment visually.

3 Design of EMIS in wind power generation enterprise

3.1 Development of environment and structure of the system

The system introduced in this paper uses the classic C/S structure and create program which is of superior interactive performance with .NET. As the integrated development environment with superior performance, .NET supports varieties of object-oriented languages [3]. The C/S structure is proposed on basis of resource nonidentity and to realize sharing. At present, the widely applied C/S structure is composed of three layers which can be divided into UI, BLL, and DAL [4]. This paper adopts such structure which is shown in Figure 1.

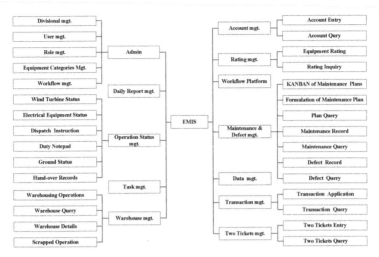

Figure 2: Functional structure of the wind power generation enterprise EMIS.

3.2 Design of functions of the system

According to the needs of EMIS and idea of modular programming in wind power generation enterprises, this paper designs the functional structure of EMIS as shown in Figure 2.

The management backstage module is used to realize senior management function of the system; account management module conducts overall management to all equipment to present the status of each equipment; rating management module is used to achieve the workflow of equipment rating to manage the information flow produced in the rating process; maintenance and defect management module realizes functions of regular maintenance plan KANBAN management, plan formulation, maintenance and defect record and query; transaction management module is used for workflow of equipment alteration and change management; technical data management module provides functions of filing, managing, querying, and using of equipment technology documents; two tickets management module incorporates the functions of information recording, querying, and counting of work ticket and operation ticket in wind facility; warehouse management module realizes the connection of spare parts and equipment to achieve clear management to spare parts inventory; daily report management module realizes documental management of daily production report; operation status management module realizes the query and management of operation status of assembling unit and electric apparatus; task management module tracks the interactive task, instruction and commission among staffs; workflow platform module tracks the process object after the instantiation of workflow model.

3.3 Design of logical relation between data in this system

This paper uses SQL Server 2008 as the system database platform. SQL Server is a safe, stable, high efficient, and intelligent database management system [5],

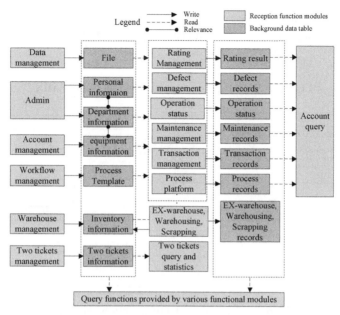

Figure 3: The overall logical relation between system data of the wind power generation enterprise EMIS.

which can satisfy the needs of EMIS of fast, safety and high efficiency in data processing. The overall logical relation between system data is shown in Figure 3.

4 Realization of EMIS in wind power generation enterprise

This paper realizes the EMIS in wind power generation enterprises under the conditions of .NET platform. And apart from realizing general EMIS functions, this paper focuses on the practical functions of workflow management and regular maintenance KANBAN management in accordance with the characteristics of wind power generation enterprises.

4.1 Workflow management

Introducing workflow management into EMIS is to incorporate the workflow process and operation rules into the system in forms of workflow model-workflow engine-workflow instance. Developers only define the node rules in workflow engine and the users build the model through workflow, formulate nodes, and operation conditions. Then the system will explain and operate the process. Users can choose the agreed node type and formulate various types of customized workflow model to realize workflow flexibility.

Based on the reference model provided by Workflow Management Coalition (WFMC) [6], this paper presents a system workflow management model after simplification, see Figure 4.

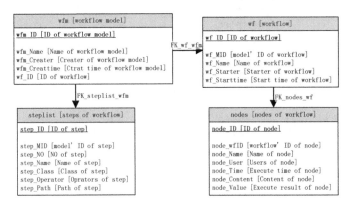

Figure 4: Workflow management model of the EMIS.

Figure 5: Physical model of workflow database.

Figure 6: The transaction flow chart.

In Figure 4, the workflow model is defined by users. When the user is establishing a new process object, namely generate a workflow instance in accordance with this model, the workflow engine generates the tracking records of each object in compliance with the node table in workflow model.

This paper realizes this model in database environment, and according to the model shown in Figure 4, establish relevant data sheet in SQL database. Physical model of database is shown in Figure 5.

The following part takes the transaction process of equipment as an example to elaborate the algorithm realization of workflow management. Figure 6 is the typical transaction flow chart.

Table 1: The Model of Transaction Workflow.

No.	Node Name	Type	Executor	Path rules
0	Inititate	General	Initiator	1
1	Reporting	General	Initiator	finish: 2; cancel:9
2	Distribution	Distribution (3,4,5)	–	3,4,5
3	Checkup	General	User 1	6
4	Checkup	General	User 2	6
5	Checkup	General	User 3	6
6	Joint checkup	Merger (3,4,5)	–	3: 7; 2: 1; 1: 1; 0: 1;
7	Examination	General	Verifier	true: 8; false: 1;
8	Approval	General	Approver	true: 9; false: 1;
9	Abnormal close	General	–	–

Figure 7: The flow of the build process of KANBAN.

In this process, the joint checkup node is executed parallelly by three people. After summarizing the reviewing opinions, one needs to determine the next node orientation. This paper establishes the model of this workflow, setting "distribution" nodes before the checkup and "merger" nodes after the checkup. The executor of each node is in blank, meaning that this step is completed by the system. Other nodes like joint checkup, examination, and approval are all classified into "General" category, see Table 1.

This model stipulates the operation mode of transaction workflow completely. The system can "draw" the process as shown in Figure 6 by calling node types and path rules. According to the nodes in the model, the system distributes the nodes to executors and completes the tracking of a transaction workflow instance.

4.2 KANBAN of maintenance plans

KANBAN management originates from TOYOTA production system, whose core is to express all kinds of detailed information in the production process the manager concerned by means of centralized visual display [7]. In the equipment maintenance, most wind power generation enterprises adopt the method of combining correction maintenance and planned maintenance. When managing the maintenance plan of numerous equipment with less human resource, the enterprise aims to get an overall and visual understanding of the regular maintenance plan of all equipment as well as the completeness of each plan. This paper realizes the KANBAN management of regular maintenance plan, and the flow of the build process of KANBAN is shown in Figure 7.

5 Conclusions

This paper designs and realizes an EMIS system on basis of .NET technique according to wind power generation enterprise's characteristics of hierarchical relationship complexity between equipment, personnel insufficiency, flat organizational structure, and workflow mutability. Trail of this system in wind enterprises has demonstrated that the EMIS realized in this paper can satisfy the actual demands of general wind enterprises, and effectively solve the problems of lacking suitable informational equipment management methods. It also provides certain reference for the design and development of similar systems.

References

[1] Shijing Wu, *Equipment Management Engineering*. China Electric Power Press, Beijing, pp. 321–324, 2005 (in Chinese).

[2] D. Naranjo-Gil, Management information systems and strategic performances: The role of top team composition. *International Journal of Information Management*, **29(2)**, pp. 104–110, 2009.

[3] D. Esposito, Which ASP. NET is better? *Information Week*, **(1307)**, pp. 50–52, 2011.

[4] P. Sharma, Advanced applications of data warehousing using 3-tier architecture. *DESIDOC Journal of Library & Information Technology*, **29(2)**, pp. 61–66, 2009.

[5] M. Stonebraker, SQL databases v. NoSQL databases. *Communications of the ACM*, **53(4)**, pp. 10–11, 2010.

[6] P. Grefen, R.R. de Vries, A reference architecture for workflow management systems. *Data & Knowledge Engineering*, **27(1)**, pp. 31–57, 1998.

[7] M. Lage Junior, M. Godinho Filho, Variations of the KANBAN system: Literature review and classification. *International Journal of Production Economics*, **125(1)**, pp. 13–21, 2010.

The research of enterprise informationization evaluation index system

Shan Lu, Yi-Ping Yang

Abstract

This article explains the purpose of enterprise informationization evaluation. It analyzes the system components that include enterprise information object, evaluation standards, the enterprise Informationization evaluation model of enterprises informationization, enterprise informatization evaluation index system and evaluation of enterprise informatization data. The establishment of index system of enterprise information must adhere to the following principles: reasonable structure index layer and index number, principle of dynamic continuity, principle of quantitative and qualitative combined, principle of objective, principle of overall, principle of science, principle of operability, principle of comparability, principle of independence. To improve the objectivity and reliability of enterprise informationization evaluation results, enterprise information index calculation should be used in fuzzy comprehensive evaluation method.

Keywords: information system, informatization, informatization evaluation, informatization evaluation index system.

1   Purpose of enterprise informationization evaluation

Enterprise information is the foundation of informationization of the national economy, is the inevitable choice for meeting the challenge of global economic integration, and is the important way to improve the enterprise management level. To establish a scientific evaluation index system of enterprise informationization and informative, can provide the objective basis for the enterprise itself. It can promote enterprises' virtuous circle of fabric, focused, purposeful, and measures to enhance their core competitiveness [1].

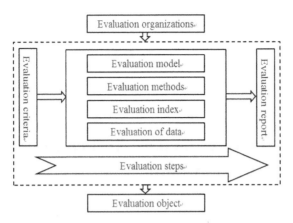

Figure 1: Basic composition of enterprise informationzation evaluation system.

2 Basic composition of enterprise informationization evaluation system

Evaluation of enterprise informationization evaluation system is separated into enterprise information object, evaluation standards, the enterprise informationization evaluation model of enterprises informationization, Enterprise informatization evaluation index system and evaluation of enterprise informatization evaluation data and enterprise information, and several other aspects of the report (Figure 1).

3 Construction of the evaluation index system of enterprise informationization

3.1 Significance of establishment of index system of enterprise informationization

The twenty-first century is an era of rapid development, has in today's world from the industrial age toward the era of the information age and knowledge economy. Information industry has become an important part of the national economy.

Enterprise informationization is the basis of the national economy and an important symbol of enterprise modernization. At present, the overall situation is not so satisfactory enterprise information in China, as most enterprise information is weak and low level, compared with the developed countries having a larger gap. Under the wave of global information technology, enterprises are faced with a more wide space, more anxious time, competition on the strength of better living environment, we only have the opportunity for development, advantages, actively and steadily promote the informationization of enterprises. Therefore, as soon as possible to establish a scientific and objective reflect the status quo of enterprise informationization in China and the guiding roles of enterprise informatization of enterprise informatization evaluation index system of important theoretical and practical significance.

In theory, enterprise informatization evaluation index system of enterprise information is insufficient in research to further strengthen the enterprise informationization evaluation content. Governments around the world are all on enterprise informationization construction of great concern and have commissioned a special study, developed a number of sets of evaluation index system, but there are some shortcomings. Formulated a comprehensive, scientific and practical enterprise informationization evaluation index system on the promotion of rapid economic growth is of great strategic and practical significance.

In practice, enterprise informationization construction, if there is no set of evaluation index system of scientific in reasonable, situation of informationization construction of enterprises would not be able to judge their own condition, unable to determine further information construction of center of gravity, may cause abnormal development of enterprise informatization construction. An evaluation index system, to a certain extent, is a frame of reference in the construction of enterprise informationization. A certain reference provides information for enterprise application assessment tools, so as to further raise the level of informatization of enterprises to improve their own capacity and market competitiveness, further optimization of enterprise information systems, will help to advance the process of enterprise information. At the same time, establishment of evaluation index system of enterprise informationization to objective evaluation of enterprise informatization development, compare the differences and characteristics of enterprise informationization level between the government to develop economic development strategies, improvement of information industry development policy, optimizing information construction environment, and proper guidance is of important significance to the development of enterprise information.

3.2 Principles of index system of enterprise informationization

Study on evaluation index system of enterprise information not only is a relevant piece of work but also is a challenging task. Index system of enterprise informationization in scope contains information. Its primary focus is on content to set up a scientific, systematic, standardized set of indicators system to make a full and objective picture of the enterprise informationization construction. According to the characteristics and evaluation of index system for evaluating enterprise informationization and its own characteristics, the establishment of index system of enterprise information must adhere to the following principles:

(1) Reasonable structure index layer and index number.
   To any object, you need to build a number of quantitative targets and indicators, and evaluation to achieve the desired effect. However, the number of indicators and targets are not the more, the better, because it according to the actual situation. If the number of index levels and

indicators are too more, it will result in the evaluation process too complex, reduced the evaluation accuracy. If the indicator levels and indicators are too less, it will not be able to evaluate the scientific and effective manner. Therefore, the number of structure indicator levels and indicators must be reasonable.

(2) Principle of dynamic continuity.

Enterprise informationization is a dynamic process of development and constantly. Therefore, it must reflect the status quo of enterprise informationization indicator system, while reflecting the trends and potential and reveal its inherent law. Principle of dynamic continuity is embodied in two aspects, the use of independent assessment and evaluation of the various modules to reflect the effect of enterprise informationization; B is the index that took into account the static and dynamic indicators of integration, using static indexes reflect the status and development trend of enterprise information, using dynamic indicators that reflect the enterprise informationization development prospects with predictive function.

(3) Principle of quantitative and qualitative combined.

Enterprise informationization evaluation is a very complex engineering system in identification and comprehensive evaluation of enterprise informationization should integrate quantitative and qualitative indicators of the effects of enterprise information. Enterprise informationization evaluation system should be based on quantitative indicators, and moderate use of qualitative indicators, quantitative analysis is the key to an accurate evaluation of enterprise informatization. Because some cannot directly statistically evaluate the enterprise informatization of qualitative indicators, such as intangible economic benefits of enterprise information, business information, social benefits, the enterprise information environment indicators only as qualitative judgments.

(4) Principle of objective.

The establishment of enterprise informatonization index system, aiming to make enterprises realize their informationization level, conducts effective information system construction. By measuring the status of the informationization, the enterprises will find out the shortcoming and solve it, sum up the experience of it and improve it.

(5) Principle of overall.

Evaluation index system of enterprise informationization level must be accurately and fully reflected the status of enterprise informationization. As informationization technology of enterprise not only involved in material things but also involved in the quality of personnel, business culture, spiritual factors. The aim is to improve the economic efficiency of enterprises, including raising social benefits.

(6) Principle of science.

Establishment of index system of enterprise informationization, must be based on the theory of economic theory and statistical information, combined with its own characteristics, drawing on published national information on indicators and international comparison of general theories and methods of informatization, as Paula methods and methods of information index, raised the enterprise informationization evaluation indicator system and evaluation methods.

(7) Principle of operability.

The meanings are clear, in formations are concentration, data are easy to get in the process of constructing evaluation index. In addition, selected indicators to be simplified, straightforward calculation method, enables the selected indicators to objectively reflect the problems, reduce or remove some minor indicator of effects on the evaluation results. If there is no maneuverability will lose its significance, establishment of indicator system always around the target application can actually receive.

(8) Principle of comparability.

Comparability principle is referring to the comparison between different periods and different objects; this requires designing evaluation index system, not only to continue in time, but also to expand on the content. It is easy for the enterprise compare with others and also with different time of itself.

(9) Principle of independence.

At the time of designing evaluation index, contains relationships should be avoided as far as possible. It is evident that among the indicators, the implicit correlation handle as far as possible be weakened, elimination, seeks to target independent, minimizing the overlap of indicators, to make evaluation more credible and efficient.

3.3 Design of evaluation index system of enterprise informationization

Currently, scholars have made some evaluation programme on enterprise information evaluation, but due to enterprise information meaning of awareness exists differences, effect enterprise information level of factors comparison complex, and information construction of effectiveness in many area mutual cross reflected, causes, makes these programme more will be focus placed in information technology in enterprise in the application area, or too stressed soft, and hardware of technology conditions, does not attention information technology and enterprise management business of combined; or index system of qualitative, subjective too strong, operability and quantify the degree is not enough.

Evaluation of enterprise information, from both the enterprise informationization and enterprise informatization efficiency evaluation is primarily designed for enterprise informationization level evaluation index system on enterprise informationization evaluation of the situation, helping organizations understand their information level. The evaluation index system is mainly from the information environment, information support system construction, information technology application, and information talent are the four aspects of evaluation.

Enterprise informatization construction should pay attention to benefits based on the information, success of the construction of information can benefit from

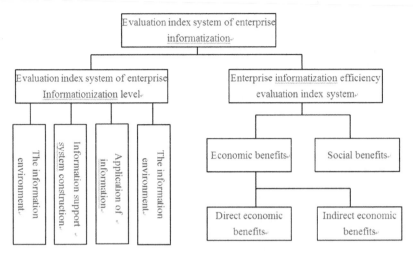

Figure 2: Composition of evaluation index system of enterprise informatization.

information construction reflected, one thing can be determined not revenue-generating information construction is definitely fails. Enterprise informationization efficiency evaluation index system is used for testing the success of enterprise information. Evaluation index system is evaluated from economic benefits and social benefits. Economic benefits is divided into direct and indirect.

4 Conclusions

Enterprise informatization is continuously advance in depth and breadth. With the establishment of a set of scientific, operational enterprise informatization evaluation index system, the inevitable choice for enterprises is to deal with the global economic integration challenges. To improve the objectivity and reliability of enterprise informationization evaluation results, enterprise information index calculation should be used fuzzy comprehensive evaluation method. Establishment of evaluation system of enterprise informationization, will enable the evaluation of the enterprise more reasonable, scientific, objective, and fair.

Acknowledgments

The paper would express sincere appreciation to the support from Beijing "Youth Talent Plan"; improve scientific research funding of Capital University of economics and business(No. 0791254430107); the National Natural Science Foundation (No. 71240002,71371128); Ministry of Education humanities social sciences research project (No. 13YJC630012); Beijing Philosophical Social Science Project (No. 13SHB015,11JGB077); Beijing Natural Science Foundation Project (No. 9122003, 9123025); Beijing education science Project (No. AAA13003, KM2012100038001).

References

[1] W.-Y. Qian, A.-J. Li, Adaptive differential evolution algorithm for multiobjective optimization problems. *Applied Mathematics and Computation*, **201**, pp. 431–440, 2008.

Research on the architecture model building for food safety information digitization based on cloud computing

Meng Zhang, Guoliang Liu, Yawei Wang, Nan Wang
School of Management, Jilin University, Changchun, 130022, China

Abstract

Current researches on digitization of food safety information rarely involve the application of cloud computing technology. By first analyzing the possibilities and the necessities of introducing cloud computing to the digitization of food safety information, the present paper constructed an architecture model for the construction of the food safety digital information system which composed of a layer for user service request, a layer for infrastructure construction and service application and a layer for the build, implementation and detection of the multi-tenant management services system based on three types of cloud services: Infrastructure as a Service, Platform as a Service, and Software as a Service. This paper opens up a new idea for the study of the food safety information digitization, which is meaningful to the information share and the guarantees of the food security.

Keywords: food safety, information digitization, cloud computing, architecture model.

1 Introduction

Food safety information asymmetry caused by the lack of enough relevant information is the main reason for the constant food safety incidents [1,2]. Therefore, the management to food safety information is particularly important.

As early as 2004, China government issued *the Decision of the State Council on Further Strengthening Food Safety Work*, requiring all local authorities to speed up the food safety information construction. In November 2010, Ministry of Health of the People's Republic of China in conjunction with Ministry of

 WIT Transactions on Information and Communication Technologies, Vol. 61, © 2014 WIT Press
www.witpress.com, ISSN 1743-3517 (on-line)
doi:10.2495/MIIT130951

Agriculture of the People's Republic of China, State Administration for Industry and Commerce of the People's Republic of China, General Administration of Quality Supervision, Inspection and Quarantine, Commerce Department of the People's Republic of China, Ministry of Commerce of the People's Republic of China and China Food and Drug Administration developed *Regulation for Food Safety Information Publish and Management*, accelerating the utilization of food safety information. In April 2013, the State Council issued the 2013 food safety focus of work, clearly promoting the food safety information digitization. Apparently, Chinese government attaches great importance to the construction for food safety digital information. Digital food safety information resources can make it more convenient and efficient for the store, process, and share food safety information. The present paper introduced the idea of cloud computing which has obvious advantages on massive information storage and dynamic information allocation to the digital construction of the food safety information and constructed an architecture model base on this, which make it possible for the automatic management and dynamic use of hardware and software resources.

2 Food safety information and cloud computing

2.1 Food safety information in food supply chain

Food safety information come from many links and fields and involve many stakeholders. From the perspective of the supply chain, food safety information run through the entire links of the food supply chain which include the primary agricultural production, food processing, food logistics, food sales, food storage [3]; from distribution areas, the food safety information cuts across all departments, industry, and different regions; from stakeholders, the sources of information at all levels involved in food and raw material suppliers, processing and sales enterprises, consumers and government. In summary, the food supply chain food safety information include the following [4]:

Information of food businesses: There are enterprises and organizations information, product and sales information, and information about rewards and punishment, etc.

Food identity information: Agricultural planting and breeding information, brand name information, food production units, food supply units, food production date, batch number, purchase date and shelf life.

Food geographic information: Food location information.

Government regulation information: Government regulatory system, regulatory approach, laws and regulations about food safety, special rectification information, warning information about food safety risk, news release information about food safety, government sampling reports.

The characteristics of food safety information make it more difficulty to be managed. So it necessarily requires powerful information processing technology to support the efficient management and utilization of food safety information.

2.2 Core technology and features of cloud computing

The cloud computing era officially arrived since Amazon launched Elastic Compute Cloud (EC2) services to small and medium enterprises to purchase computing capacity from the Amazon data center according to their needs in 2006 [5]. Its appearance quickly changed the existing computing model.

Cloud computing is developed from distributed computing, parallel computing, utility computing, and grid computing, at the same time, it also mix the evolution of virtualization technology, load balance, infrastructure as a Service, Platform as a Service and Software as a Service [6,7]. Simply put, in the future, the software is installed in the cloud; the cloud data is also stored in the cloud; users process data by remote computing through the browser; the results are displayed in the client [8]. Such computing model is the cloud.

The core technology of cloud computing system is parallel computing, called parallel computing. Parallel computing refers to a process to solve the calculation by using multiple computing resources simultaneously. It first completes processing the data through the parallel computing cluster, then returns the processed result to the user. It is an effective means of improving computing speed and processing capability. In general, the main technology of cloud computing has massive data storage technology, massive data management technology, virtualization technology, cloud computing platform management technology, information security management technology. Cloud computing can achieve the dynamic allocation, the pooling and the transparency of resources, and can satisfy the user's demand for self-help services. What's more, the components and the overall architecture of cloud computing are connected by networks, so as long as the user buys cloud services, you can visit the resources anywhere and anytime through the network equipment required without acquiring specialized IT knowledge [9].

2.3 Possibilities for applying cloud computing to food safety information management

The wide range of food safety information sources can be digitized and put in the internet through Internet of Things [10], then be virtualized some cell modules which can be allocated automatic and dynamic, achieving the assign, expansion, recovery and reuse of the hardware and software resources [5]. The users of the food safety information can select the appropriate server, database, and network resources through appropriate levels of data isolation layer according to their needs to facilitate the conduct of its own data. At the same time, the cloud services providers determine the user's ability to access resources based on user authentication and authorization services, then automatically assign virtual database resources, information storage resources according to user needs through middleware service system.

3 Advantages analysis of applying cloud computing in food safety information management

The food safety regulatory system implemented in China now is "Sectional supervision based, Variety regulation supplemented" and "Hierarchical management of local government instead of Vertical management below the provincial level in industry and commerce and qualitative inspect department" [11]. In this context, there are many problems coming to the food safety information management, such as information release from different main body, poor universality of information, duplication of information release, fragmentation of information resources, etc. in view of the current status quo of China's food safety information management, applying cloud computing center to the construction of food safety information platform will be feasible and necessary.

Firstly, the massive data storage and management technology cloud computing center have the ability to bring various information from food supply chain and decentralized regulatory information from government departments together and can make all information resources uniformly managed and scheduled, which can greatly improve the effectiveness, the extent of sharing and transparency degree of information.

Secondly, information dynamically allocated on-demand technology can meet the need from the regulatory authorities, businesses, and consumers at different levels. Regulatory authorities can achieve the transfer of information throughout the regulation through the cloud computing data center; enterprises can have a full range of food quality and safety control by obtaining food information about production, storage, sales, and other information for the cloud; consumers can gets food safety information concerning themselves from the cloud through SMS, telephone, internet, food safety information inquiry terminals, etc.

Thirdly, cloud computing centers can integrate existing distributed information resources and information platforms, breaking the existing monopoly of resources [12], reducing duplication investment of constructing food security information system, saving public resources, and providing technical support for establishing a food security information management platform at national level which can achieve unified management and backup, unified control, unified deployment, uniform distribution of national food security information.

4 Architecture model for food safety information digitization based on cloud computing

There are three types of cloud services: Infrastructure as a Service (IaaS), Platform as a Service (PaaS), and Software as a Service (SaaS) [13]. IaaS refers to services provided in the form of servers, storage and networking hardware, using grid computing to establish a virtualized environment [14]; PaaS refers to providing platform for application development and deployment to the developer in the form of services, generally containing a database, middleware and development tools, all provided in the form of services through the internet [15]; SaaS refers to providing Java Applications to the users though the browser in the form of services [16]. Combining the characteristics of food safety information digital construction, we constructed the model based on these three services of cloud computing [13] (Figure 1).

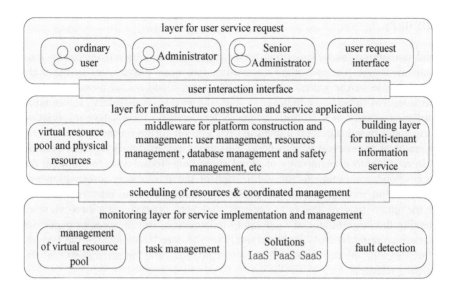

Figure 1: Architecture model for food safety information digitization based on cloud computing.

The first level: layer for user service request. This layer sets three permissions according to the users, which are ordinary, user, administrator, and senior administrator, respectively. This three user permissions are in ascending order. Users obtain their resources according to their permissions they have. In addition, user request interface is also set, user's requests for food safety information achieved through this interface.

The second level: layer for infrastructure construction and service application. This layer is the core of the architecture model. This layer set up virtual resource pools, physical resources, and information resource management middleware [10] for food safety platform construction. And multi-tenant information services also constructed in this layer. The virtual resource pool collect the same type of food safety information resources together and the related technology enable pooling and dynamic allocation of food safety information. Management middleware mainly achieves user management, resource management, database management, and security management to provide a reliable and safe service to the upper layer.

The construction of multi-tenant information service layer is mainly to achieve the individual needs of many users for food safety information through appropriate technology.

The third level: layer for the build, implementation and detection of the multi-tenant management services system. This layer includes virtual resource pool management, task management, solutions, and fault detection to achieve synergy scheduling and deployment of food safety information resources. Solutions are general three service types: Iaas, Paas, and SaaS.

Summary

Cloud computing, as an emerging technology, has obvious advantages in data management. At present, cloud computing has been playing an increasingly important role in the game, education, meetings, cloud social aspects, but the application of cloud computing in the domestic food safety information digitization is only in a preliminary stage. Research on food safety information management based on cloud computing has not yet formed a theoretical system and practical experience is also poor. This study put aside a lot of the existing literature to explore technology of cloud computing, focused on introducing the idea of cloud computing to the digitization of the food safety information and constructed an architecture model, which is meaningful to the information share and the guarantees of the food security and also opened up a new view of managing the large mount of food safety information. But the present paper did not study comprehensively and thoroughly on the core technology of the system, so architecture model needs further verification and improvement in the following research.

References

[1] C. Ritson, L.W. Mai, The economics of food safety. *Nutrition & Food Science*, **98(5)**, pp. 253–259, 1998.

[2] J. Caswell, How labelling of safety and process attributes affects markets for food. *Agricultural and Resource Economics Review*, **27(2)**, pp. 151–158, 1998.

[3] Zhang Yun-Hua, Kong Xiang-Zhi, Yang Xiao-Yan, Luo Dan, Game analysis on quality and safety of food supply chain, *China Soft Science magazine*, **11**, pp. 23–26, 2004 (in Chinese).

[4] Liu Yun-Feng, On the construction of food safety informatization platform. *Information Science*, **30(6)**, pp. 899–902, 2012 (in Chinese).

[5] R. Buyya, C.S. Yeo, S. Venugopal, et al., Cloud computing and emerging IT platforms: Vision, hype, and reality for delivering computing as the 5th utility. *Future Generation Computer Systems*, **25(6)**, pp. 599–616, 2009.

[6] M.A. Vouk, Cloud computing–issues, research and implementations. *Journal of Computing and Information Technology*, **16(4)**, pp. 235–246. 2004.

[7] M. Armbrust, A. Fox, R. Griffith, et al., A view of cloud computing. *Communications of the ACM*, **53(4)**, pp. 50–58, 2010.

[8] Li Chun-Lan, Deng Zhong-Hua, On the value of cloud computing. *Library and Information*, **4**, pp. 42–46, 2009 (in Chinese).

[9] Chen Quan, Deng Qian-Ni, Cloud computing and its key techniques. *Journal of Computer Applications*, **29(9)**, pp. 2562–2567, 2009 (in Chinese).

[10] Zhang Chang-Li, Shen Wei-Zheng, Application of internet of things in agriculture. *Journal of Northeast Agricultural University*, **42(5)**, pp. 1–5, 2011 (in Chinese).

[11] Wang Yao-Zhong, A study on horizontal and vertical configuration of food safety administration. *China Industrial Economy,* **12**, pp. 64–72, 2005 (in Chinese).

[12] S. Subashini, V.A. Kavitha, Survey on security issues in service delivery models of cloud computing. *Journal of Network and Computer Applications*, **34(1)**, pp. 1–11, 2011.

[13] Zhang Xing-Wang, Li Chen-Hui, Qin Xiao-Zhu, Research on model construction of digital information resources based on cloud computing. *Information Theory and Practice*, **34(8)**, pp. 100–105, 2011 (in Chinese).

[14] S. Bhardwaj, L. Jain, S. Jain, Cloud computing: A study of infrastructure as a service (IAAS). *International Journal of Engineering and Information Technology*, **2(1),** pp. 60–63, 2010.

[15] L.M. Vaquero, L. Rodero-Merino, J. Caceres, et al., A break in the clouds: Towards a cloud definition. *ACM SIGCOMM Computer Communication Review*, **39(1)**, pp. 50–55, 2008.

[16] P. Buxmann, T. Hess, S. Lehmann, Software as a Service. *Wirtschaftsinformatik*, **50(6)**, pp. 500–503, 2008.

The effect of Cloud Computing and the internet of things on traditional IT outsourcing

Yawei Wang, Xinhua Bi, Meng Zhang
School of Management, Jilin University, Changchun, 130022, China

Abstract

At present, the Cloud Computing is a kind of network service and is a trend for future computing, while the Internet of Things refers to a variety of information sensing devices and the Internet combine to form a huge network, will enable all of the items and network connections to facilitate the identification and management. Both would change our lives. At the same time, they would definitely change the traditional IT outsourcing. In this perspective, it's so important to analyze the effect of Cloud Computing and the Internet of Things on traditional IT outsourcing, so we can provide some suggestion for enterprises. For this purpose, we present some comparison between traditional IT outsourcing and the new IT outsourcing based on Cloud Computing and the Internet of Things. With the help of these, enterprises which are seeking IT outsourcing can make better decision and get efficiency.
Keywords: IT outsourcing, Internet of Things, information technology.

1 Introduction

Since Kodak outsourced its main IT operations in 1989, IT outsourcing obtained the swift and violent development. Now the business environment changes rapidly, technology changes with each passing day. Do what you do best and outsource the rest has become an irreversible trend. The role of information technology in the enterprise is increasingly important. Therefore, in order to reduce operating costs, improve management flexibility, grip the cutting-edge IT technology more quickly and accurately, more and more enterprises adopt IT outsourcing to build their IT capability. The global IT outsourcing services market reached $100 billion in 2007 according to IDC's report.

WIT Transactions on Information and Communication Technologies, Vol. 61, © 2014 WIT Press
www.witpress.com, ISSN 1743-3517 (on-line)
doi:10.2495/MIIT130961

The quality of IT outsourcing relies on the quality of information technology. Along with the development of information technology, some new forms of information technology have arisen, such as Cloud Computing, the Internet of Things, big data and so on. These new forms of technology are bound to affect the traditional IT outsourcing model.

Cloud Computing is an Internet-based super-computing model, which is the integration of distributed computing, parallel computing, and grid computing. Cloud Computing is a current trend that reveals the next-generation application architecture. Gartner Market Research estimates that this infrastructure, as a service market, will grow from $3.7 billion in 2011 to $10.5 billion in 2014 [1], while cloud services such as web-mail, Flickr, and YouTube have been widely used by individuals for some time. It is not until relatively recently that organizations have began to use cloud services as a tool for meeting their IT needs [2]. Christof Weinhardt described a technical classification of Grid and Cloud Computing for a profound discussion on the business opportunities of the Cloud Computing paradigm [3]. Anyway, Cloud Computing is the trend of a new generation of information revolution, the rapid development is overwhelming.

Internet of Things as an emerging global, Internet-based information service architecture facilitating the exchange of goods in global supply chain networks is developing on the technical basis of the present Domain Name System; drivers are private actors [4]. The emergence and development of the new forms of technology such as Cloud Computing, and networking not only promote the role of IT outsourcing, but also affect and change the traditional IT outsourcing and new forms of IT outsourcing may arise.

2 The effect of Internet of Things on traditional IT outsourcing

IT has been developed over 20 years since the IT outsourcing concept came up. In the traditional sense, IT outsourcing refers to outsourcing all or parts of IT functions to an external party to completed professional companies. IT outsourcing is the most cost-effective way for companies to hire qualified individuals for specific IT jobs without having to commit to the significant costs of maintaining a year-round in-house team. This works well for both parties.

According to the literal meaning of explanation of things, also known as the sensor network, refers to a variety of information sensing devices and the Internet combine to form a huge network, will enable all of the items and network connections to facilitate the identification and management. From the concept, we can see that the development of the Internet of Things also relies on the information technology, which means the Internet of Things will affect the traditional IT outsourcing thinking ways and concepts to some extent.

2.1 The effect of Internet of Things on traditional IT outsourcing concepts

In 2005, the International Telecommunication Union (ITU) extended the concept of Internet of Things in "The Internet of Things" report, also brought forth the

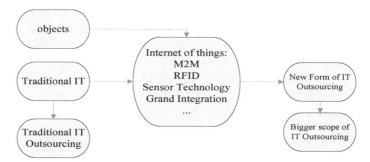

Figure 1: Effect of Internet of Things on IT outsourcing scope.

new development prospect which is interconnected between the objects at any time, any place, and the ubiquitous network and computing. Sensor technology, nanotechnology, intelligent terminals, and other technology will be more widely used apart from RFID technology. Now the Internet of Things combine the "objects" with "IT technology." In other words, the Internet of Things integrates the reinforced concrete, the cable, the chip, and the broadband into a unified infrastructure, which expends the scope and area of IT outsourcing (Figure 1).

When objects can both sense the environment and communicate, they become tools for understanding complexity and responding to it swiftly. What's revolutionary in all this is that these physical information systems are now beginning to be deployed, and some of them even work largely without human intervention.

2.2 The effect of Internet of Things on traditional IT outsourcing market

Unquestionably, the main strength of the Internet of Things idea is the high impact it will have on several aspects of everyday-life and behavior of potential users [5]. The development of sensing information industry brought by Internet of Things will change the traditional outsourcing pattern. First the information system integration business will increase, which means the increasing outsourcing market of the system integration. The three major telecom operators including China telecom, China Mobile, China Unicom will make a wide range of cooperation on the Internet of Things, which means they will undertake a lot of task, such as system design, system integration, and platform design. So it is bound to seek more cooperation with external IT vendors, resulting in a lot of IT outsourcing business, and expanding the IT outsourcing market (Figure 2).

Internet of Things covers different modes of communication: things-to-person communication and thing-to-thing communications, including mMachine-to-machine (M2M) communication. These connections can be established in restricted areas (intranet of things) or made publicly accessible (Internet of Things). All of these are based on the IT technology, which means it will need more and more cooperation among different enterprises on IT things, resulting in bigger IT outsourcing market.

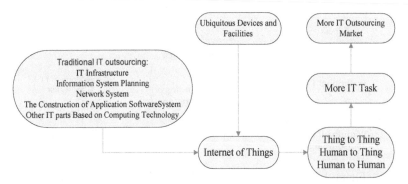

Figure 2: Bigger market of IT outsourcing brought by Internet of Things.

3 The effect of Cloud Computing on traditional IT outsourcing

Cloud Computing is a concept of using the Internet to allow people to access technology-enabled services. It allows users to consume services without knowledge of control over the technology infrastructure that supports them. But until now, there is no established definition yet. Lawton briefly describes the type of applications that is run in Clouds: Web-based applications that are accessed via browsers but with the look-and-feel of desktop programs. Kenji [6] pointed out Cloud Computing should be conceived as a dynamically configured utility: A service that combines the scalable, always available, pay for use, and economically critical—attributes of traditional utility models with the configurable, technologically differentiated, and non-geographically bound aspects required by a highly competitive services market [7]. Users simply procure from providers the "amount of computing" they want without needing to invest in computing infrastructure. Most scholars only put forward the concept of Cloud Computing from the technology angle.

Anyway, the Cloud Computing is also a kind of information technology in essence, but with more contemporary style, more newness, more scalability, and strong compatibility. So we take Cloud Computing as a special kind of information technology to study, which is different from traditional concept.

3.1 Comparison of Cloud Computing and traditional IT technology

Traditional IT is known as collectively computing technology used in management and information processing. It is mainly applied to designing, developing, installation, and implementation of information systems and application software. It is also defined as Information and Communications Technology, While Cloud Computing is advanced as a new high-level kind of information technology (Table 1).

From above, we can find that Cloud Computing is an upgraded version of the traditional information technology.

Table 1: Comparison of Cloud Computing and Traditional IT Technology.

Property	Traditional IT Technology	Cloud Computing
General definition	A set of interrelated information technologies that work together to process, store, collect, and distribute information.	Integrated all IT resources

Subject contents	1. Computer hardware
	2. Computer software:
	  Application programs
	  Word processing
	  Presentation
	  Spreadsheets
	3. Data and information management
	4. Computer networking
	5. Applications of networking: Internet, Intranet
		1. Network Computing: Network is computer (client—server) Separation of functionalities
		2. Cluster Computing: Tightly coupled computing resources: CPU, storage, data, etc. Managed as a single resource Commodity, Open source
		3. Grid Computing
		4. Utility Computing

Characteristic	The main foundation is computer technology, mainly including the construction of computer hardware, and the designing, development, and installation of software, which is used to support enterprise management and operation.	1. Ultra-large-scale data storage and network computing capabilities. 2. The services provided is virtual, allowing users getting application service at any location and with any kind of terminal device. 3. Less requirements for terminals and easy to use. 4. High and dynamical scalability, meeting the need of applications, and the growth of user scale. 5. Economic savings. Users do not need a one-time investment, only pay for service depending on the type, quality, and quantity.
Commonality	All of these areinformation technology in essence.	
Dissimilarity	Focusing on the using of computer hardware and software.	Focusing on providing IT service.

3.2 A new type of IT outsourcing: Cloud Outsourcing

Nowadays, Cloud Computing rapidly becoming a hot topic in IT field. At the same time, many the domestic enterprises also grasp the opportunity and launch their own cloud plan. Along with the development, some new IT terms appear, such as "Cloud hosting," "Cloud Storage," "Cloud Platform," "Cloud Outsourcing."

Among them, Cloud Outsourcing is a new type of IT outsourcing based on Cloud Computing. In order to clearly analyze the Cloud Outsourcing, we need to find out the service model based on Cloud Computing. According to the authoritative definition from NIST, there are three kinds of Cloud Computing service models, including SaaS, PaaS, and IaaS.

1. Software as a Service (SaaS)
    Under this model, the provider host and dispose the applied software unified over the network, supplying software pattern through browser. The user can subscribe applied software service from the manufacturer through Internet without purchasing hardware and software and pay for the service according to the actual demand.
2. Platform as a Service (PaaS)
    PaaS provides a computing platform and a solution stack as a service, and facilitates the deployment of applications. The providers supply service to the users, such as server platform, develop environment, web service integration, hardware equipment, and so on. And the users can develop and design their own application, without the cost and complexity of buying and managing the underlying hardware and software and provisioning hosting capabilities.
3. Infrastructure as a Service (IaaS)
    The providers often offer additional resources such as IP addresses, virtualization service, software bundles, storage resources, and so on to the users. The users install operating system and application software on the cloud infrastructure. In this model, the providers typically charge the users for IaaS according to the amount of resources allocated and consumed.

Under the three Cloud Computing models, we can define the Cloud outsourcing as a new type of IT outsourcing based on Cloud Computing consisted of SaaS, PaaS, and IaaS (Figure 3).

In a word, the advantage of cloud outsourcing is that the provider maintains and manages all IT resources, the users can get access to the cloud to get the IT capability everywhere when they own the terminal which can log in Internet. Under this model, the users just need to pay for some rents rather than constructing traditional IT structure which made users to spend much funds on them. This is the most benefit IT outsourcing pattern based on network application.

3.3 Comparison of cloud outsourcing and traditional IT outsourcing

A principle is that the developed productivity would definitely lead to the new relations of production, so the Cloud Computing leads to the cloud outsourcing which has broadened the IT outsourcing market (Figure 4).

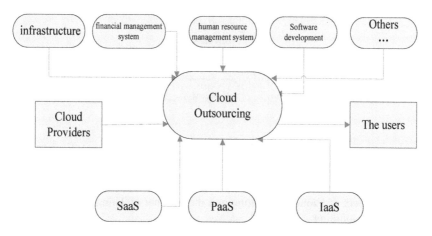

Figure 3: Cloud outsourcing structure.

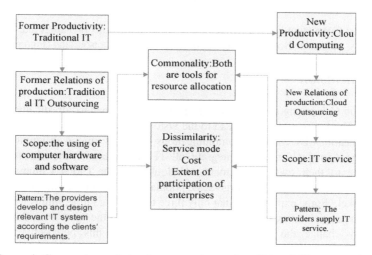

Figure 4: Comparison of cloud outsourcing and traditional IT outsourcing.

From above, we can find three differences between them, as following:

1. Service mode: The traditional IT outsourcing includes the construction and maintenance of information technology equipment backup and disaster. The cloud outsourcing services provide a relatively uniform standards.
2. Cost: Under cloud outsourcing, the users just need to pay for some rents resulting in bigger cost advantage.
3. Extent of participation of enterprises: In order to use cloud service efficiently, the enterprises not only need to manage the implementation of cloud computing, but also need to do some in-company training.

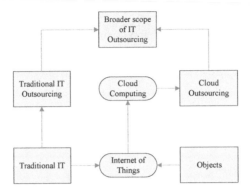

Figure 5: Effect of Cloud Computing and the Internet of Things on traditional IT outsourcing.

4   The effect of Cloud Computing and the Internet of Things on traditional IT outsourcing

The Cloud Computing like the human brain, while the Internet of Things like our eyes, nose, ears, and limbs. Both of them have much effect on IT outsourcing (Figure 5).

5   Conclusion

The Cloud Computing and the Internet of Things have changed drastically the way we live. The Internet of Things lead to the vision of "anytime, anywhere, anything" communications by enabling communications with and among different objects, while the Cloud Computing integrate all IT resources for the clients to use according to their own requirements. Undoubtedly, the Cloud Computing and Internet of Things would be a large-scale popularity to become a trillion-scale high-tech market. Some experts said that only three to five years time, things will be full access to people's lives, change people's way of life. At the same time, they would definitely change the traditional IT outsourcing. In this perspective, it's so important to analyze the effect of Cloud Computing and the Internet of Things on traditional IT outsourcing, so we can provide some suggestion for enterprises.

   In this paper, we have analyzed the new information technology and their influence, the effect on traditional IT market and pattern. We believe that, given the conclusion will be a powerful driving factor for deeper research in both industrial and academic laboratories. And most importantly, this paper provides valuable advice for enterprises which are thinking about using IT outsourcing to construct their IT capability.

References

[1]   M. Lilienthal, A decision support model for cloud bursting. *Business & Information Systems Engineering*, **2**, pp. 71–81, 2013.

[2] A. Lina, Nan-Chou Chenb, Cloud computing as an innovation: Percepetion, attitude, and adoption. *International Journal of Information Management,* **32**, pp. 533–540, 2012.

[3] C. Weinhardt, B. Blau, J. Stößer, Cloud Computing—A classification, business models, and research directions. *Business & Information Systems Engineering,* 2009.

[4] R.H. Weber, Internet of things—Need for a new legal environment? *Computer Law & Security Review,* **25**, pp. 522–527, 2009.

[5] L. Atzori, A. Iera, G. Morabito, The Internet of Things: A survey. *Computer Networks,* **54**, pp. 2787–2805, 2010.

[6] G. Lawton, Moving the OS to the web. *Computer,* **41(3)**, pp. 16–19, 2008.

[7] K.E. Kushida, J. Murray, J. Zysman, Diffusing the Cloud: Cloud Computing and implications for public policy. *Journal of Industrial Competitive Trade,* **11**, pp. 209–237, 2011.

Interacting multiple model filter-based vehicle motion state tracking using networked sensors

Jie Ma[1], Qing Wu[2], Zichao Huang[1,2], Weiliang Tian[1,2]

[1]*Intelligent Transport Systems Research Center, Wuhan University of Technology, 430063, China*
[2]*School of Logistics Engineering, Wuhan University of Technology, 430063, China*

Abstract

Vehicle-infrastructure cooperation provides a new way for automotive vehicle active safety applications. Smart roadside sensing technology is the fundamental basis of the vehicle-infrastructure collaborative applications. However, problems like the incompleteness of perception information of local sensors, target being blocked and sensors being affected by noise of the environment still exist, and how to extract accurately and track the motion states, such as position and velocity, is the key issue need to be resolved for vehicle-infrastructure cooperation safety initiative applications. This paper presents a fusion approach for the estimation of vehicle motion state using roadside networked sensors. On the basis of the establishment of multi-model of vehicle movement, this method achieves an integration of the roadside sensed information using interactive multiple model (IMM). Simulation results show that, in the case of considering multi-model of vehicle motion, the vehicle state tracking performance based on multiple roadside sensors covering different surveillance directions are improved significantly since the complementary advantages of the disturbed information.

Keywords: vehicle-infrastructure cooperation, vehicle motion state tracking, IMM, networked sensors.

1 Introduction

Vehicle-infrastructure cooperation has become a hot research and cutting-edge technology in ITS. Using a variety of roadside deployed sensors to perceive the state of road traffic and road conditions, and achieving the full temporal and spatial data exchange between the vehicle and infrastructure can compensate for the lack of perception of the vehicle itself. This also provides basic knowledge for vehicle active safety applications and coordinated traffic controls based on vehicle-infrastructure cooperation [1].

In addition to the vehicle's own perception system, roadside sensing system is also an important factor for the vehicle-infrastructure cooperation. Roadside sensing system collect traffic state information, road vehicles and pedestrians' movement and broadcast the information through wireless channels. It realizes the inter-data exchanging between the vehicle and infrastructure and ultimately implement the vehicle-infrastructure cooperation on traffic safety and efficiency applications. Visual sensors like visible light cameras as well as infrared cameras can be used for vehicle trajectory extraction, and besides, some driving behaviors, such as lane changing and turning [2], can be inferred through video image processing. Some researchers also detect and track the state of road vehicles and pedestrians by deploying Lidar or laser-scanner on the roadside. These roadside sensing technologies provide a good solution for the application of vehicle-infrastructure cooperation.

However, problems like the incompleteness of perception information of local sensors, target being blocked, and sensors being affected by noise of the environment still exist, and how to extract accurately and track the manoeuvring state information (such as position and velocity) is the key issue need to be resolved for vehicle-infrastructure cooperation safety initiative applications. Therefore, this paper attempts to combine the data of roadside networked sensors to complement the advantages of multiple sensor information, thereby improve the performance of vehicle state tracking.

2 Problem statements

We consider a surveillance scenario where multiple laser-scanners are set on roadsides profiling a certain area at a horizontal plane, so that the data of vehicle body are measured, and motion state parameters of each vehicle are tracked when it passes through the area. In general, vehicle position, velocity, acceleration, and direction are the most important parameters which need to be nicely estimated, since these factors are the significant factors for both traffic efficiency and safety applications. Besides, most of current commercial vehicles equipped with low cost location systems, such as GPS (Global Positioning System), cannot offer such data with enough accuracy to meet the requirements of these applications. Therefore, the challenge we address is to find an optimal way to integrate all the roadside laser-scanners and make a fusion of the multi-sensor data to improve the tracking performance.

The diversity and dynamic characteristic of the motion model must be taken into consideration when estimating and tracking the vehicle state. The major problem is that it is very difficult to choose an optimal model for all driving conditions. Usual manoeuvring states of road vehicles can be represented by the appropriate kinematics at each instant, what can be defined by different kinematic models. The models that are suitable for straight roads are CV (constant velocity), where for curved roads, CT (constant turning) may be one suitable model. To adapt to changing vehicle dynamic characteristics under various road conditions, we propose an interacting multi model (IMM) filter based vehicle state tracking system using fusion of multiple roadside laser scanners.

3 Motion models and measurements

3.1 Vehicle motion model sets

In order to represent the various vehicle maneuvers, we used two simple models to describe the vehicle motion:

(1) CV model:

$$
\mathbf{x}_k = \begin{pmatrix} 1 & 0 & T & 0 \\ 0 & 1 & 0 & T \\ 0 & 0 & 1 & 0 \\ 0 & 0 & 0 & 1 \end{pmatrix} \begin{bmatrix} x_{k-1} \\ y_{k-1} \\ \dot{x}_{k-1} \\ \dot{y}_{k-1} \end{bmatrix} + \mathbf{q}_{k-1}
\tag{1}
$$

where the state vector is $\mathbf{x}_k = \{x_k \quad y_k \quad \dot{x}_k \quad \dot{y}_k\}$, T denotes the time step, x_k and y_k are the positions in two-dimensional Cartesian coordinates, $\dot{x}_k$ and $\dot{y}_k$ are the velocities toward the two coordinates axes, and $\mathbf{q}_{k-1}$ is Gaussian process noise with zero mean and power spectral density q.

(2) CT model:

$$
\mathbf{x}_k = \begin{pmatrix} 1 & 0 & \sin(\dot{\psi}_{k-1}T)/\dot{\psi}_{k-1} & (\cos(\dot{\psi}_{k-1}T)-1)/\dot{\psi}_{k-1} & 0 \\ 0 & 1 & (1-\cos(\dot{\psi}_{k-1}T))/\dot{\psi}_{k-1} & \sin(\dot{\psi}_{k-1}T)/\dot{\psi}_{k-1} & 0 \\ 0 & 0 & \cos(\dot{\psi}_{k-1}T) & -\sin(\dot{\psi}_{k-1}T) & 0 \\ 0 & 0 & \sin(\dot{\psi}_{k-1}T) & \cos(\dot{\psi}_{k-1}T) & 0 \\ 0 & 0 & 0 & 0 & 1 \end{pmatrix} \begin{bmatrix} x_{k-1} \\ y_{k-1} \\ \dot{x}_{k-1} \\ \dot{y}_{k-1} \\ \dot{\psi}_{k-1} \end{bmatrix} + \begin{pmatrix} 0 \\ 0 \\ 0 \\ 0 \\ v_{k-1} \end{pmatrix}
\tag{2}
$$

where the state vector is $\mathbf{x}_k = \{x_k \quad y_k \quad \dot{x}_k \quad \dot{y}_k \quad \dot{\psi}_k\}$, $v_k \sim N(0, \sigma_\psi^2)$ is univariate white Gaussian process noise. Thus, the state vector is extended with a turning rate (yaw rate) parameter $\dot{\psi}_k$, which is to be estimated along with the other state parameters including the position and the velocity for this study. In the following, we shall refer the CV model as model 1 and the CT model as model 2.

3.2 Measurment model

Laser scanners (Lidar) have a wide range of applications including distance measurement and environmental mapping for robotic applications. Typically, Lidar sensors use near infra red light with a fixed wave length in the range from 800 to 2500 nm to image objects. Two basic sensor outputs are useful for motion tracking: one is *range* which is the distance from the sensor's axis system to the target; the other is *azimuth* which is the bearing angle in the sensor coordinate system (i.e., relative to the sensor bore sight) at which the target is detected. Thus, the measurement model for laser sensor i is defined as:

$$z_k^i = \begin{pmatrix} \rho_k^i \\ \theta_k^i \end{pmatrix} = \begin{pmatrix} \sqrt{(x_k - s_x^i)^2 + (y_k - s_y^i)^2} \\ \arctan((y_k - s_y^i)/(x_k - s_x^i)) \end{pmatrix} + \mathbf{r}_k^i \tag{3}$$

where (x_k, y_k) is the target position to be tracked and (s_x^i, s_y^i) is the location coordinate of laser sensor i, $\mathbf{r}_k^i$ is zero mean white Gaussian measurement noise.

4 IMM-UKF-based vehicle state tracking

IMM filter is a computationally efficient and in many cases well-performing suboptimal estimation algorithm for Markovian switching systems. Based on the established vehicle motion mode sets: CV and CT model, the overall process of the IMM filter for the proposed state tracking system consists of four major steps:

(1) Interaction: In the initialization for each time step, the state estimates generated by all filters from the previous time step are combined with a mixing weight that can be written as:

$$\mu_{k-1|k-1}^{j|i} = \frac{1}{\hat{\mu}_{k|k-1}^i} \pi_{ji} \mu_{k-1}^j \quad (i, j = 1, 2) \tag{4}$$

where μ_{k-1}^j is the model probability of model j in the previous step, and π_{ji} is the Markov transition probability indicating the probability that the vehicle model transition occurs from state j to state i. The mixing probabilities $\hat{\mu}_{k|k-1}^i$ are represented as:

$$\hat{\mu}_{k|k-1}^i = \sum_{j=1}^{2} \pi_{ji} \mu_{k-1}^j \quad (i = 1, 2) \tag{5}$$

The initial mixing state and their corresponding covariances of model i can be computed as follows:

$$\tilde{\mathbf{x}}_{k-1|k-1}^{i} = \sum_{j=1}^{2} \hat{\mathbf{x}}_{k-1|k-1}^{j} \mu_{k-1|k-1}^{j|i} \quad (i=1,2) \tag{6}$$

then

$$\tilde{\mathbf{P}}_{k-1|k-1}^{i} = \sum_{j=1}^{2} \mu_{k-1|k-1}^{j|i} \times$$
$$[\hat{\mathbf{P}}_{k-1|k-1}^{i} + [(\hat{\mathbf{x}}_{k-1|k-1}^{i} - \tilde{\mathbf{x}}_{k-1|k-1}^{i}) \times (\hat{\mathbf{x}}_{k-1|k-1}^{i} - \tilde{\mathbf{x}}_{k-1|k-1}^{i})^{T}] \tag{7}$$
$$(i=1,2)$$

(2) Specific filtering: Now, for each vehicle model, the filter predicts its state and covariance using the initial mixing state and the covariance of the interacting step. To address the nonlinearity caused by the manoeuvring vehicle and its motion behaviors, unscented Kalman filter (UKF) is chose as the basic filter for our IMM estimator, and its prediction and update steps are marked with UKF_p and UKF_u, correspondingly.

$$[\overline{\mathbf{x}}_{k|k-1}^{i}, \overline{\mathbf{P}}_{k|k-1}^{i}] = UKF_p(\tilde{\mathbf{x}}_{k-1|k-1}^{i}, \tilde{\mathbf{P}}_{k-1|k-1}^{i}, \mathbf{f}_{k-1}^{i}, \mathbf{Q}_{k-1}^{i}) \quad (i=1,2) \tag{8}$$

$$[\hat{\mathbf{x}}_{k|k}^{i}, \hat{\mathbf{P}}_{k|k}^{i}] = UKF_u(\overline{\mathbf{x}}_{k|k-1}^{i}, \overline{\mathbf{P}}_{k|k-1}^{i}, \mathbf{z}_k, \mathbf{h}_k^{i}, \mathbf{R}_k^{i}) \quad (i=1,2) \tag{9}$$

(3) Mode probability update: Each predicted mode probability is updated with respect to the model innovation. The likelihood of the measurement for each model filter, under the Gaussian assumption, is given by:

$$\Lambda_k^i = \frac{\exp[-0.5(\mathbf{v}_k^i)^T (\mathbf{S}_k^i)^{-1}(\mathbf{v}_k^i)]}{\sqrt{|2\pi\mathbf{S}_k^i|}} \quad (i=1,2) \tag{10}$$

where $\mathbf{v}_k^i$ is the measurement residual and $\mathbf{S}_k^i$ is the covariance for model i in the UKF update step. The probabilities of each model i at time step k are calculated as:

$$\mu_{k|k}^i = \frac{\mu_{k|k-1}^i \Lambda_k^i}{\sum_{j=1}^{2} \mu_{k|k-1}^j \Lambda_k^j} \quad (i=1,2) \tag{11}$$

(4) Estimate fusion: In the final stage of the algorithm, the combined state and its covariance are computed as:

$$\hat{\mathbf{x}}_{k|k} = \sum_{i=1}^{2} \mu_{k|k}^i \hat{\mathbf{x}}_{k|k}^i \tag{12}$$

$$\hat{\mathbf{P}}_{k|k} = \sum_{i=1}^{2} \mu_{k|k}^i [\hat{\mathbf{P}}_{k|k}^i + (\hat{\mathbf{x}}_{k|k}^i - \hat{\mathbf{x}}_{k|k})(\hat{\mathbf{x}}_{k|k}^i - \hat{\mathbf{x}}_{k|k})^T] \tag{13}$$

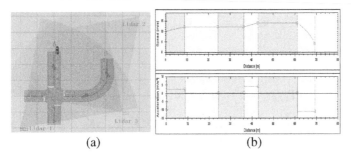

(a)	(b)

Figure 1: Simulation scenario: (a) pre-specified path; (b) vehicle speeds and accelerations.

5 Simulation results

The proposed tracking approach was analyzed through intensive simulation which was performed using PreScan. A surveillance scenario is constructed, as shown in Figure 2, three laser scanners are set on roadsides, profiling the intersection from different directions. All scanners are assumed to be connected through a network to a data center where the data integration and tracking process are performed. The laser scanner used to conduct the simulation tests is a so-called TIS sensor that forms the basis for PreScan's detailed sensors. The measuring output for each scanning includes *range* and *azimuth* angle as discussed in Section 3.2. The scanning angle and the scanning resolution are set to 70° and 0.2°, respectively, and the range distance might be up to 70 m. The sensor has a scan rate of approximately 20 Hz, and the noises are considered only on the detection reflection which are zero mean Gaussian distributed values with standard deviations 0.05 m and 0.05 rad for *range* and *azimuth,* respectively.

A car (*Audi A8*) from the vehicle pool is selected as our study object that the tracking process is verified on estimating the car's motion states. The simulation is carried out under variable speed conditions and a driving path is pre-specified with which the car is supposed to follow, as shown in Figure 1(a), the curve from the beginning point A to the ending point B. Figure 1(b) represents the vehicle speeds and accelerations changing over the different simulation phases.

The Markov transition probability matrix is set as:

$$\pi_{ji} = \begin{pmatrix} 0.9 & 0.1 \\ 0.1 & 0.9 \end{pmatrix} \tag{14}$$

where the index number $i, j = 1$ represents the CV motion model, and the index number $i, j = 2$ refers to the CT motion model. The variances of process for the two models are assumed to be a priori known parameters and can be calculated using the power spectral density of the noise $q=0.01$m/s for model 1, and the variance of the noise $\sigma_{\psi} = 0.5$ rad/s for model 2.

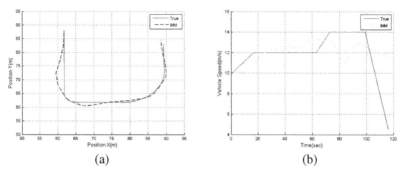

Figure 2: Vehicle position and speed tracking results using 3 sensors: (a) position estimates output; (b) speed estimates output.

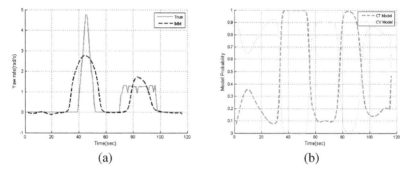

Figure 3: Vehicle yaw rate tracking results and model probability using 3 sensors: (a) Yaw rate estimates output; (b) model probability.

To begin with, all the three TIS sensors are used for the testing. The tracking results are shown in Figure 2, where (a) presents the trajectory results, the solid red line is the actual trajectory of the vehicle going through, and the blue dotted line is the estimated value, (b) is about the speed tracking result, the solid red line is the true speed curves and the green dotted line is the estimated value. Figure 3 shows the yaw rate tracking results and the model probability carvers.

In order to analyze the influence of the number of sensors on tracking performance, we shield the signals of the sensor labelled with 3 in the experimental scene, conduct the experiments again and the acquired results are shown in Figures 4 and 5.

To elaborately analysis and compare the two sets of experiments. Root mean square errors (RSME) are calculated for each estimation. For the scene using all the 3 sensors, we have RMSE-Position (3 sensors)=1.53m, RMSE-Speed (3 sensors)=3.18m/s, RMSE-Yaw (3 sensors)=0.67rad/s. For the scene using the 2 sensors, we have RMSE-Position (2 sensors)=8.26m, RMSE-Speed (3 sensors)=4.91m/s, RMSE-Yaw (3 sensors)=1.09rad/s.

WIT Transactions on Information and Communication Technologies, Vol. 61, © 2014 WIT Press
www.witpress.com, ISSN 1743-3517 (on-line)

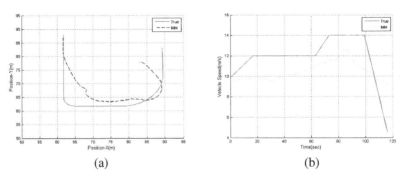

(a)   (b)

Figure 4: Vehicle position and speed tracking results using 2 sensors: (a) position estimates output; (b) speed estimates output.

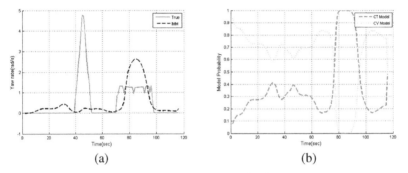

(a)   (b)

Figure 5: Vehicle yaw rate tracking results and model probability using 2 sensors: (a) Yaw rate estimates output; (b) model probability.

Then, we can infer that the arrangement of the sensors influence greatly on the tracking results. Deploying multiple sensors with different viewing directions can improve the state estimation accuracy remarkably.

6 Conclusions

Considering the problem of vehicle state estimation and tracking involved with the vehicle-infrastructure cooperation applications for vehicle active safety, we propose a fusion approach for roadside networked sensors. This method is based on the establishment of multi-model of vehicle movement, and a combining of IMM and UKF is implemented for the estimation. Experiments under simulation environment verify the performance of the proposed method. The further studies should take more vehicle motion models under different working situation into consideration, and verify as well as optimize the method.

Acknowledgments

The research work is supported by National Natural Science Foundation of China under Grant No. 61203236 and No. 61174173, and by National High-tech R&D Program of China (863 Program) (No. 2011AA110402).

References

[1] J. Piao, M. McDonald, N. Hounsell, Cooperative vehicle-infrastructure systems for improving driver information services: An analysis of COOPERS test results. *IET Intelligent Transport Systems,* **6(1)**, pp. 9–17, 2012.

[2] R. Rad, M. Jamzad, Real time classification and tracking of multiple vehicles in highways. *Pattern Recognition Letters*, **26(10)**, pp. 1597–1607, 2005.

A Stackelberg game model for knowledge coordination mechanism of supply chain system

Lijun Yang

Department of Logistics Engineering, Wuhan University of Technology, Wuhan, 430000, China

Abstract

Knowledge resources allocation and knowledge innovation can be realized by means of flow, sharing, and cooperation of knowledge resources in the supply chain members, so as to enhance the competitive advantage of the whole supply chain system. In order to solve the problem of supply chain knowledge coordination realization, the author presents a theory consists of interest-risk mechanism and relationship mechanism under decentralized decision structures. In this paper, author investigates a coordination mechanism of Stackelberg game for a supply chain system. The model is consists of a supplier and a manufacturer. In the model, supplier and manufacturer take the profit maximization as the objective function. The two sides focus on the optimal procurement quantity, the purchase price, and the intelligence capital investment and other parameters to start the game. The theory research and numerical experiments show that cooperative game profit between supplier and manufacturer is far greater than the noncooperative game. The intellectual capital investment is the key to realize the cooperative game.

Keywords: supply chain, coordination, coordination mechanism.

1 Introduction

In this study, we consider a mechanism of supply chain knowledge coordination in the decentralized decision-making structure faced with deterministic demand. The Stackelberg model is applied to the design of supply chain knowledge coordination mechanism based on theory of supply chain and game theory. The model is composed of one supplier and one manufacturer which start the game around the interest risk factors and relationship factors. In the model,

WIT Transactions on Information and Communication Technologies, Vol. 61, © 2014 WIT Press
www.witpress.com, ISSN 1743-3517 (on-line)
doi:10.2495/MIIT130981

manufacturer and supplier cooperate with each other by developing a new product to meet market demand urgently. To achieve this objective, two sides make intellectual capital investment and asset specificity investment from the knowledge flowing and sharing each other. Manufacturer and supplier start the game around the parameters, such as purchase quantity, intelligence capital investment, and asset specific investment, to realize the sharing of benefits, risk sharing, and profits maximum.

Supply chain coordination means that two or more enterprises cooperate with each other to achieve greater and more lasting individual performance while company pursuit the whole supply chain competitive advantage. Allocation of resources across organizational boundaries and cooperation is the core problem of supply chain management based on the relationship of competition and coordination.

So far there is no a unified and widely accepted definition on supply chain coordination. Anne thinks the coordination of supply chain which can be described as information sharing, knowledge sharing, benefit sharing, and risk sharing is a kind of way that all enterprises in the supply chain cooperate effectively for a common goal [1]. Bauknight believes that cooperation is a process values creation [2].

Some researchers believe that supply chain coordination that is closely related to the competitive advantage of supply chain and exert strategic significance. They propose supply chain coordination from the height of strategy [3]. The integration of management view emphasizes that supply chain coordination is a business and management activity in which supply chain member integrate internal and external resources. Xue believes that the so-called coordination refers to the integration of the internal and the various parts of cross-organization through joint action to achieve the multiple benefits [4]. Larsen proposed that coordination refers to some coordination business activities, such as joint planning, joint product development, exchange of information, integration of information system, long-term cooperation, and share the profits and risks [5].

Although there is no uniform definition, but the supply chain coordination at least has several prominent characteristics:

1) It involves two or more than two enterprises' complex management activities.
2) It pursues the overall performance of the supply chain. This concept (Philosophy) has brought a fundamental change in business management.
3) It is a dynamic adaptation to competitive environment. In Anne's opinion, the enterprise will not be alone but to seek the coordination of partners if the competition, responsiveness, and customer satisfaction are the key factors for successful management [1].

In one word, the supply chain coordination is defined in this paper that enterprises in the supply chain achieve a target of supply chain integration operation through sharing benefits and risk, coordinating mutually, and operating synchronously in one or more links of supply chain to create more customer value and competitive advantage greater than the independent operation.

Numerous studies have shown that coordination has a positive impact on the performance of supply chain and is the essence and the key success factor of supply chain. It is directly related to the performance of whole supply means greater value creation. Sainsbury points out that the value-added process of globalization is also carried out by the multi-national corporation supply chain member [6]. Meanwhile, the lack of cooperation brings negative impact on supply chain. Fisher who quoted the United States food industry data estimated that American loses $30000000000 a year because of the lack of coordination of supply chain [7].

On the other hand, knowledge is the most potential intangible resources and the foundation of competitive advantages. Coordination is the essential feature of the supply chain. Knowledge coordination of supply chain can realize knowledge resources allocation and knowledge innovation by means of flow, sharing, and cooperation of knowledge resources in the supply chain members, so as to enhance the competitive advantage of the whole supply chain.

2 Model description

2.1 Theory framework

The role of mechanism is to coordinate the interests of all parties and achieving the goal of compatibility. Coordination mechanism is the inherent driving factors of coordination behavior. It can spontaneously adjust the participant enterprises in the behavior, and stimulate or inhibit, promote or eliminate desired behavior. Coordination mechanism is bidirectional roles which are both with incentive mechanism and penalty (constraint) mechanism. This mechanism can unify the partnership goals of supply chain; coordinate their decision-making and operation activities in order to make the system and the overall performance optimization.

2.1.1 Interest-risk mechanism

No doubt, interest is expected to be the strongest driving force in a decentralized decision-making structure to promote sustainable coordination behavior of member enterprises, but the risk was breaking force of coordination. This kind of mechanism is attributed to interest-risk mechanism with dual role of incentive and restraint. Interest-risk mechanism can be divided into direct and indirect mechanisms. Direct mechanisms include benefit sharing, the interests of the game and relates to the distribution of benefits, risk sharing contract mechanism. Indirect mechanism including information sharing, joint operation planning, joint decision-making is to ensure benefits better realization. Ideally, the benefits of supply chain coordination associated with each participant enterprises, chain enterprises, so cooperative mechanism should be reasonable distribution of benefits according to risk factors such as cost, the size of investment on their own resources to promote coordination production. Since most of the supply chains are constructed around a core enterprise, the whole supply chain coordination yield relatively concentrated reflected in the performance index of the core enterprise, and transfer along the supply chain through the distribution mechanism of interests. Overall, coordinated with the overall performance of the supply chain, supply chain coordination is to achieve lower costs, improve product quality and market pertinence, quick customer response, and reduce the system uncertainty (bullwhip effect) target.

2.1.2 Relationship mechanism

In decentralized decision-making structure, interest-risk mechanism is not always effective, due to the incomplete contract, asymmetric information, and externality problem. A strong degree of information asymmetry between the independent legal person enterprises is not only closely related to coordination efforts of member enterprises, but also brings opportunism behavior and "adverse selection" to reduce the interests of its member enterprises expected. The existence of externalities "hitchhike" possibility also reduce the coordination efforts. In other words, benefit induction is not always effective, especially when the risk cannot be effectively controlled. Therefore, there need a link, which is the relationship of mutual trust between the members of supply chain enterprises, the paper called the relationship mechanism to make up for the defects of interest-risk mechanism.

Mutual trust relationship between the members enterprises in the supply chain must be accompanied by long-term trading, established in the basis of mutual understanding. However, stable coordination relationships must be created by specific asset investment. Supply chain is the "relationship chain" and the relationship is constructed by mutual trust, commitment and a specific asset investment. The specific asset investment such as a production line, personnel recruitment, technology and knowledge transformation, the relocation site, product structure and function adjustment and so on, aims to build mutual trust, increase the cost of opportunism behavior. No matter what form, specific asset investment is a kind of durable investment to support a cooperative behavior. It will be locked in a specific form once invested in special area, and the second choice will greatly be devalued, thus it has the dual role of incentive and restraint. The specific asset investment may be tangible investment, also an intangible investment, such as the Toyota production system which is a typical intellectual capital investment in the supplier.

2.2 Notation

We first define the notation as follows:

Q_m—sales quantity of manufacturer; Q_s—sales quantity of supplier;
P_m—price of manufacturer's product; P_s—price of supplier's product;
C_m—unit cost of manufacturer; C_s—unit cost of supplier;
R_m—research cost of manufacturer; R_s—research cost of supplier;
I_m—quantity of intelligence capital investment from manufacturer to supplier;
I_s—quantity of intelligence capital investment from supplier to manufacturer;
F_m—cost of intelligence capital investment for manufacturer;

F_s—cost of intelligence capital investment for supplier;
L_m—risk factor of knowledge coordination for manufacturer;
L_s—risk factor of knowledge coordination for supplier;

Further description of the parameters:

(1) Cost reduce of R&D because of knowledge coordination:

$$R_m = R_{m0} - K_m Q_m I_s$$

R_{m0}—cost of R&D without knowledge coordination;
K_m—factor of knowledge absorption and transformation;
$K_m Q_m I_s$—R&D cost savings of manufacturer because of knowledge coordination;
Likewise:

$$R_s = R_{s0} - K_s Q_s I_s$$

(2) Quantity of sales and purchase:

$$Q_m = Q_s = Q$$

And $Q=a-bPs$ $a>0, b>0$ a, b are constant.
(3) The risk of knowledge coordination:

$$F_m = L_m I_m$$

F_m means cost of intellectual capital investment and risks are positive related.
Likewise:

$$F_s = L_s I_s$$

(4) Objective functions of manufacturer and supplier:

$$\Pi_m = P_m Q - C_m Q - P_s Q - R_{m0} + K_m Q I_s - L_m I_m \tag{1}$$

Π_m—the profit of manufacturer;

$$\Pi_s = P_s Q - C_s Q - R_{s0} + K_s Q I_m - L_s I_s \tag{2}$$

Π_s—the profit of supplier

2.3 The game process

2.3.1 First stage

Supplier seeks the optimal price, the optimal intellectual capital investment. According to the backward induction of dynamic game, first to analyze the supplier.

$$
\begin{aligned}
\Pi_s &= P_s Q - C_s Q - R_{s0} + K_s Q I_m - L_s I_s \\
&= Q(P_s - C_s + K_s I_m) - R_{s0} - L_s I_s \\
&= (a - b P_s)(P_s - C_s + K_s I_m) - R_{s0} - L_s I_s
\end{aligned}
\tag{3}
$$

If

$$
\frac{\partial \Pi_s}{\partial P_s} = 0
$$

Then:

$$
P_s^* = \frac{a + b C_s - b K_s I_m}{2b} \quad \text{(Optimal price)}
\tag{4}
$$

Substitute Eq. (4) in Eq. (3), then:

$$
\Pi_s = \left(a - b \frac{a + b C_s - b K_s I_m}{2b} \right) \left(\frac{a + b C_s - b K_s I_m}{2b} - C_s + K_s I_m \right) - R_{s0} - L_s I_s
$$

$$
Max \Pi_s = \frac{(a - b C_s + b K_s I_m)^2}{4b} - R_{s0} - L_s I_s
\tag{5}
$$

Obtain from Eq. (5) when $I_s=0$, supplier achieve maximum profits.

2.3.2 Second stage

Manufacturer seeks the optimal quantity of purchase, the optimal intellectual capital investment according to the supplier's price and intellectual capital investment.

$$
\Pi_m = P_m Q - C_m Q - P_s Q - R_{M0} + K_m Q I_s - L_m I_m
$$

$P_m = A - BQ$ $A>0$ $B>0$ A and B are constant.
Substitute P_s^* 和 I_s, then:

$$\Pi_m = Q(P_m - C_m - P_s^* + K_m I_s) - R_{m0} - L_m I_m \tag{6}$$

s.t $P_s < P_m$ $R_{m0} > 0$; $K_m > 0$; $L_m > 0$
  If:

$$\frac{\partial \Pi_m}{\partial Q} = 0$$

then:

$$Q^* = \frac{A - C_m - P_s^*}{2B} \quad \text{(Optimal quantity of purchase)} \tag{7}$$

When $I_s = 0$:

$$\Pi_m = QP_m - QC_m - QP_S^* - R_{m0} - L_m I_m \tag{8}$$

Substitute $P_s^* = \dfrac{a + bC_s - bK_s I_m}{2b}$ in Eq. (8), then:

$$\Pi_m = QP_m - QC_m - \frac{Q(a + bC_s)}{2b} - R_{m0} + I_m \left(\frac{K_s Q}{2} - L_m \right)$$

When $\dfrac{K_s Q}{2} > L_m$, then Π_m increase with the increase of I_m.
Substitute $P_m = A - BQ$ in Eq. (8), then:

$$\begin{aligned}
\Pi_m &= Q(A - BQ) - QC_m - QP_s^* - R_{m0} - L_m I_m \\
&= Q(A - BQ - C_m - P_s^*) - R_{m0} - L_m I_m
\end{aligned} \tag{9}$$

Substitute $Q^* = \dfrac{A - C_m - P_s^*}{2B}$ in Eq. (9), then:

$$\begin{aligned}
Max \prod_m &= \frac{A - C_m - P_s^*}{2B} \left(\frac{A + P_s^* + C_m - 2P_s^* - 2C_m}{2} \right) - R_{m0} - L_m I_m \\
&= \frac{(A - C_m - P_s^*)^2}{4B} - R_{m0} - L_m I_m
\end{aligned} \tag{10}$$

Table 1: The Results of Game.

Index	Noncooperative Game	Cooperative Game
Quantity of sales	415	580
$\prod_m$	131,625	
$\prod_s$	85,800	
$\prod_m + \prod_s$	217,425	275,500

Because $I_s=0$, we can see that the game is a noncooperative game when the two sides get maximize profits but not achieve the system optimization. In case of repeated game, supplier and manufacturer have seen the synergistic effect and reached cooperation game.

2.3.3 Third stage: cooperative game

If supplier and manufacturer make mutual cooperation and active collaboration, then:

$$\prod = \prod_m + \prod_s$$
$$= P_m Q - C_m Q - P_s Q - R_{m0} + K_m Q I_s - L_m I_m + P_s Q - C_s Q - R_{s0} + K_s Q I_m - L_s I_s$$

Further assume that the supplier and manufacturer have cooperative intention to the same degree, the risk assessment is the same, there are:

$$K_m = K_s = K \quad L_m = L_s = L$$
$$\prod = Q[P_m - C_m - C_s + K(I_s + I_m)] - R_{m0} - R_{s0} - L(I_m + I_s) \tag{11}$$
$$I = I_m + I_s$$

If $\dfrac{\partial \prod}{\partial Q} = 0$ then:

$$Q^* = \frac{A - C_m - C_s + KI}{2B} \quad \text{(Optimal quantity of purchase)}$$

$$Max\prod = \frac{(A - C_m - C_s + K_m)^2}{4B} - R_{m0} - R_{s0} - LI \tag{12}$$

$$P_m^* = \frac{A + C_m + C_s - KI}{2} \quad \text{(Optimal sale price)} \tag{13}$$

2.4 Numerical experiments

$A=1000$, $B=1$; $a=600$, $b=2$; $C_m=100$, $C_s=40$; $K_m=0.5$, $K_s=0.5$; $L_m=L_s=1.5$; $I_s=200$, $I_m=400$; $R_{m0}=40000$, $R_{s0}=20000$.

3 Conclusions

In the paper, this model can realize the benefit sharing and risk sharing through interests risk and the relationship mechanisms. The model also found the relationship of mutual trust between manufacturer and supplier is very important to the knowledge coordination. It can be drawn from the analysis of the game results that product sales rose 39.8%, profit increased by cooperative game 26.7% than noncooperative game.

Acknowledgments

The research work was supported by National Natural Science Foundation of China under Grant No. 71271077 and Humanities and Social Sciences project of education Department Henan Province No. 2013-ZD-016.

References

[1] France-Anne Gruat La Forme, Vale´rie Botta Genoulaz, Jean-Pierre Campagne, A framework to analyse coordination performance. *Computers In Industry*, **58**, pp. 687–697, 2007.
[2] Bauknight, The supply chains future in the e-economy and why many may never see it. *Supply Chain Management Review*, pp. 28–35, 2000.
[3] L. Xu, B. Beamon, Supply chain coordination and cooperation mechanisms: An attribute-based approach. *The Journal of Supply Chain Management*, **42(1)**, pp. 4–12, 2006.
[4] Xiaolong Xue, Xiaodong Li, Qiping Shen, Yaowu Wang, An agent-based framework for supply chain coordination in construction. *Automation In Construction*, **14,** pp. 413–430, 2005.
[5] S.T. Larsen, European logistics beyond 2000. *International Journal of Physical Distribution and Logistics Management*, **30(6)**, pp. 377–387, 2000.
[6] L. Sainsbury, Race to the top: A review of the Government's science and innovation policies. Independent HM-Treasury Report, HMSO, 2007, October.
[7] M.L. Fisher, A. Raman, A.S. McClelland, Rocket science retailing is almost here: Are you ready. *Harvard Business Review*, **72(3)**, pp. 83–93, 1994.

A web service based management system of degree theses: research and implementation

Wei Dong

College of Electrical and Information Engineering, Southwest University for Nationalities, 610041, Chengdu Sichuan, China

Abstract

In this paper, we propose a web service based management system of degree theses. The purpose of this system is to automate the entire cycle of degree theses, which includes instructors providing research projects, students choosing their projects, instructors advising students, and students completing and submitting their theses. In order to reach a good extensibility in this system, we adopt web service based method. Since web services are based on open standards such as HTTP and XML-based protocols including SOAP and WSDL, web services are hardware, programming language, and operating system independent. Consequently, our system has a good scalability so that new functions can be easily extended to the system. Adding a new function to the system equals defining a new type of service, which is rather convenient for web service based applications. In addition, we design the system with ER model and then turn the model into several relational tables. To demonstrate our design, we implement new client software to test functions of the system. We test all the functions of the system and the results show that the system works well. It is expected the new system will achieve more productivity than traditional methods.

Keywords: web services, SOAP, management system, degree theses.

1 Introduction

As information technology penetrating very corner of university life [1] the need for systematic and efficient management of degree theses arises.

For this purpose, we develop a web service [2] based management system of degree theses. By utilizing such system, all degree-related electronic documents of students and advisers in a university is automatically collected and stored in a server. All employers in the university have access to these files via Internet.

Currently, the methods to manage degree theses are rather outdated. Although almost all students write their theses on computer and a final version of theses will be collected after completion, the entire cycle is not automated by a system and manually managed. Let's review the process of a life cycle of a thesis, that is, from research subject selection to thesis completion. Normally, before graduation many research subjects are first proposed by instructors and then all candidates gather in a meeting room to select their own interest subjects. After subject selection, graduating students will conduct some research on their own subjects, and may write some reports about the progress of the research about degree theses. For traditional methods of degree theses management, there are several disadvantages. First, in the full cycle of a thesis, only paper submissions are involved by computer and other processes are only managed by traditional methods. Consequently, many research materials, such as midterm reports, are not stored anywhere to let others to access these files. Second, in the initial phase of a thesis, there is no involvement of computer, which is not convenient for all instructors and students.

In this paper, we propose a web service based management system of degree theses. The purpose of this system is to automate the entire cycle of degree theses, which includes instructors presenting projects, students choosing their projects, instructors advising students, and students completing their and submitting their theses. In this system, in order to reach a good extensibility we adopt web services method. Since web services are based on open standards such as HTTP and XML-based protocols including SOAP and WSDL, web services are hardware, programming language, and operating system independent. Consequently, our system has a good scalability so that new functions can be easily extended to the system.

2 A web service based management system of degree theses: research and its implementation

2.1 System architecture

The design architecture of the system is illustrated in Figure 1. As can be seen from the figure, it consists of two big parts, that is, the client and the server network.

The client network is where clients are resided. Normally, a client will issue a request to the server using a kind of software. Since web services are adopted in this system and web services are software independent, client software can be an application, or a browser. It is noted that there are three roles in this system which includes student role, instructor role, and administrator role. And, each role has its own access rights and functions to the system. For instance, a student can select his research subject for his thesis, while an instructor can provide several research subjects for candidates to choose from. On the other hand, the administrator of the system has full access rights of the system.

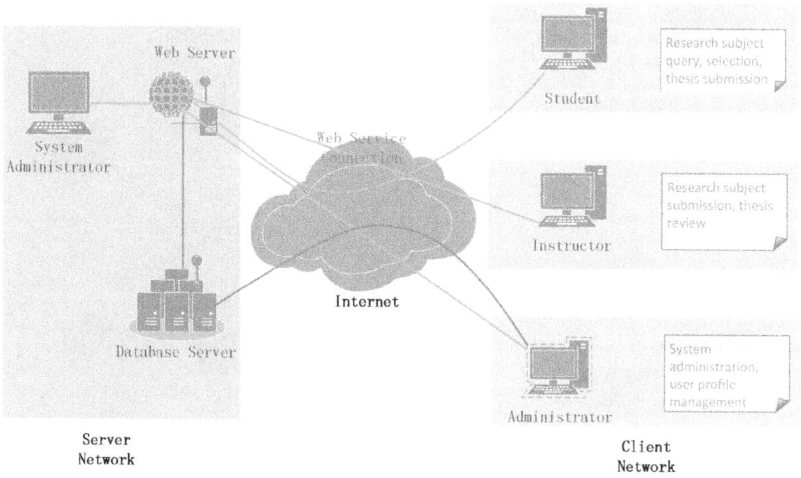

Figure 1: The system architecture of web services based management system of degree theses.

The server network is where web services are provided. It consists of two parts, web server, and database server. The former provides all web services related to the system. If we want to extend the system and add a new function, the only thing we need to do is adding a new type service. The latter is database server which stores all data of the system. When a client requests to access the system, the client software will call corresponding web service which then accesses the database server and acquires related data. After all these operations are done, results will be returned to the client.

2.2 Database design

In this section, we design the database of the system following the classic database design principle.

First, we analyze system requirements of the system. The main functionality of the system is to automate the full cycle of a degree thesis. There are three system requirements which are explained as follows. First of all, instructors can present their own research subjects for selection. Then, a student can choose an interested subject for his degree thesis. After that, a student will conduct research on his chosen subject, and some reports and a final version of thesis will be submitted during this research process. And during the research process, the instructor can also get the research processes of his advised students.

Based on the above-mentioned system requirements analysis, the system is modeled with ER method. The ER model is illustrated in Figure 2. As can be seen from the figure, it consists of four entities which include instructor, research subject, department, and student and three relationships. The entity of instructor represents an instructor which will provide research subjects to choose from. The research subject entity includes all information about a research subject. Since

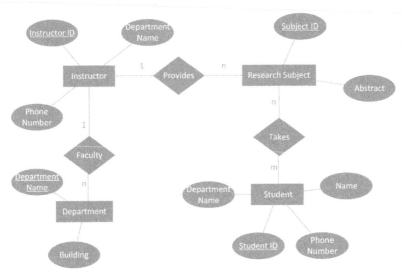

Figure 2: The ER model of the system.

there are many departments in a university, we design department as an entity. The fourth entity is the student entity, which covered related information about a student. There are three relations among all these four entities, that is, an instructor provides zero or many research subjects, a student may choose zero or one subject, and there are many instructors in one department.

After the ER model is designed, we need to turn the ER model to its corresponding relational model since we will adopt a relational database management system. The relational model of the system is shown in Figure 3. As shown in the figure, there are five relations (i.e., tables) in this model which comprises of four relations corresponding to four entities and two relations corresponding to relationships in the ER model.

3   Implementation and system test

In this section, to demonstrate our design we implement the system. From Figure 1, we know that the system can be divided into two parts, the client part and the server part. Since web services technology is adopted, our client is application independent. Consequently, we can choose B/S or C/S technology in the client part, which is irrelevant to the design. In the client side, we adopt B/S architecture and in this architecture it mainly contains HTML, EasyUI, CSS, DIV technologies. In other words, a browser can be utilized to access the system. In the server side, we adopt Apache as the web server and MySQL as the database server.

To test our system implementation, we simulate a full cycle of degree thesis. The following processes are been validated which include an instructor presenting research subjects, a student choosing a research subject, a student updating her research contents, an instructor reviewing some research reports

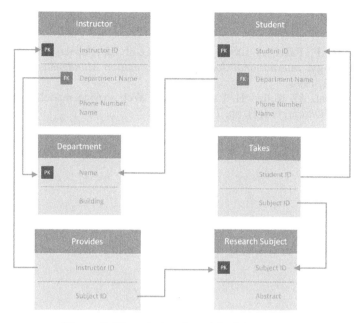

Figure 3: The relational model of the system.

from his graduation candidates, and a student submitting his reports and final thesis. All test results show that the system works well.

4 Conclusions

In this paper, we propose a web service based management system of degree theses. The purpose of this system is to automate the entire cycle of degree theses and in order to reach a good extensibility we adopt web services method. Since web services are based on open standards such as HTTP and XML-based protocols including SOAP and WSDL, web services are hardware, programming language, and operating system independent. Consequently, our system has a good scalability so that new functions can be easily extended to the system. In addition, we design the system with ER model and then turn the ER model into several relational tables. To demonstrate our system, we design a new client to test functions of the system. We test all the functions of the system and the results show that the system works well. It is expected the new system will achieve more productivity than traditional methods.

Acknowledgments

This paper was sponsored by the Fundamental Research Funds for the Central Universities (Project No. 13NZYBS03).

References

[1]   J. Ang, F. Pavri, A survey and critique of the impacts of information technology. *International Journal of Information Management*, **14(2)**, pp. 122–133, 1994.
[2]   D. Roman, U. Keller, H. Lausen, et al., Web service modeling ontology. *Applied Ontology*, **1(1)**, pp. 77–106, 2005.

A novel multi-view face detection based on modified SVM

Dianhu Cheng[1], Xiangqian Ding[1], Nan Song[2], Peijiang Liu[2]
[1]*Ocean University of China, Shandong, Qingdao, 266071, China*
[2]*Shandong Tobacco Research Institute, Shandong, Jinan, 250101, China*

Abstract

As multi-view face detection is an important problem in computer vision research field, in this paper, we propose a novel multi-view face detection based on a modified multi-class SVM, which can solve the limitations in standard SVM. Firstly, the structure of the SVM classifiers for multi-view face detection is present, of which the face detection problem is divided into three categories ("Front view", "Left view", and "Right view"). Secondly, the left projecting vector and the right projecting vector are defined, and the the constraint conditions of multi-class are illustrated as well. Furthermore, the multi-class classification problem is converted to finding the best solution from all feasible solutions. Thirdly, visual features of images are extracted to construct the image vector space, and then the testing images can be classified by the multi-class SVM to make multi-view human face detection. Finally, to make performance evaluation for the proposed algorithm, experiments are conducted using some standard human face datasets, and the conclusions can be drawn that the proposed is quite effective.
Keywords: multi-view, face detection, SVM, vector space.

1   Introduction

As is illustrated in Wikipedia, face detection refers to a specific case of object-class detection. In object-class detection, the task aims to find the locations and sizes of all objects in an image that belong to a given class. Examples include upper torsos, pedestrians, and cars. On the other hand, face detection can be regarded as a more general case of face localization. In face localization, the task can be represented to find the locations and sizes of a known number of faces [1].

As is well known that significant progress has been made in the field of face detection and recognition. However, most of the existing work concentrates on the face detection only in the front face view. Considering there are many human faces which are taken in different multi-views, it is of great importance to detect the human faces with multi-views.

2 Related works

In this section, some typical multi-view face detection is listed as follows.

Chen et al. proposed a novel statistical system for automatic multi-view face detection and pose estimation. The five-module detection system is based on significant local facial features (or subregions) rather than the entire face. The low- and high-frequency feature information of each subregion of the facial image are extracted and projected onto the eigenspace and residual independent basis space in order to create the corresponding PCA (principal component analysis) projection weight vector and ICA (independent component analysis) coefficient vector, respectively [2].

Xu present a reconfigurable architecture model for rotation invariant multi-view face detection based on a novel two-stage boosting method. A tree-structured detector hierarchy is designed to organize multiple detector nodes identifying pose ranges of faces. The authors also propose a boosting algorithm for training the detector nodes. The strong classifier in each detector node is composed of multiple novelty designed two-stage weak classifiers. With a shared output space of multicomponents vector, each detector node deals with the multidimensional binary classification problems.

Wang et al. present a statistical learning method to extract features and construct classifiers for multi-view face detection. Specifically, a recursive nonparametric discriminant analysis (RNDA) method is presented. The RNDA relaxes Gaussian assumptions of Fisher discriminant analysis (FDA), and it can handle more general class distributions. RNDA also improves the traditional nonparametric discriminant analysis (NDA) by alleviating its computational complexity [3].

Zhang et al. propose a novel method to solve multi-view face detection problem by Error Correcting Output Codes (ECOC). The motivation is that face patterns can be divided into separated classes across views, and ECOC multi-class method can improve the robustness of multi-view face detection compared with the view-based methods because of its inherent error-tolerant ability [4].

3 Multi-view face detection algorithm based on modified SVM

As the multi-view face detection problem should consider the front, right, and left view of human faces, we utilize the multi-class SVM to make face recognition, and structure of the SVM classifiers for multi-view face detection is shown in Figure 1.

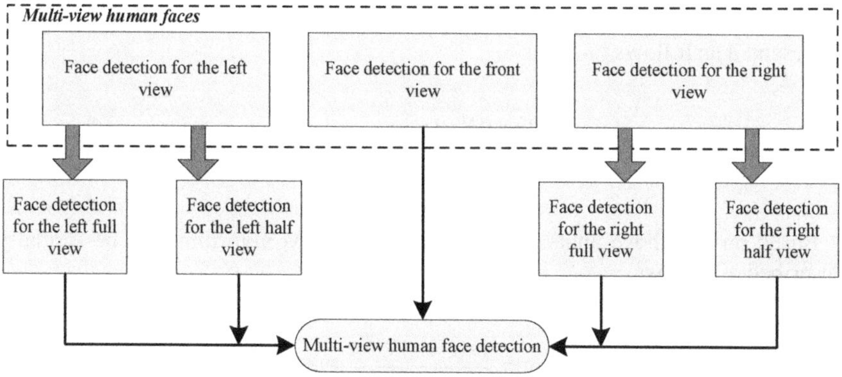

Figure 1: Structure of the SVM classifiers for multi-view face detection.

Support vector machines (SVM) have been developed to solve the classification problem. Particularly, SVM classifier uses the radial basis kernel function to make the nonlinear transformation of the input data, and then map the input data to feature spaces. The main ideas of SVM can be illustrated in Eq. (1).

$$f(\vec{x}) = sign\left(\sum_{i=1}^{N} \alpha_i \cdot \exp\left\{-\frac{\left|\vec{x}-\vec{x}^i\right|^2}{\sigma^2}\right\}\right), i \in \{1,2,\cdots,N\} \qquad (1)$$

where parameter σ refers to the width of a priori parameter, and α_i denotes to the Lagrange multiplier. However, there are some limitations in the standard version of SVM, hence, in this paper, we design a multi-class SVM classifier to calculate the hyperplanes.

Supposing u and v denote the left projecting vector and the right projecting vector, respectively, the k couples of u and v are defined in the proposed algorithm (denoted as $\{u_j\}_{j=1}^{k}$ and $\{v_j\}_{j=1}^{k}$). Furthermore, we defined that $U=[u_1,u_2,...,u_k]\in R^{m\times k}$ and $V=[v_1,v_2,...,v_k]\in R^{n\times k}$, and the constraints can be represented as follows.

$$\begin{aligned} y_i(Tr(U^T X_i V)+b) &\geq 1-\xi_i \\ \text{s.t.}\, \xi_i &\geq 0, i \in \{1,2,\cdots,l\} \end{aligned} \qquad (2)$$

Afterward, the objective functions of the proposed multi-class SVM is defined as follows.

$$\sum_{j=1}^{k} u_j^T X_i v_j = Tr(X_i VU^T) = (Vec(UV^T))^T Vec(X_i) \qquad (3)$$

Furthermore, the tensor extension of the initial objective function can be represented as follows.

$$\frac{Tr(UV^TVU^T)}{2} + C \cdot \sum_{i=1}^{l} \xi_i \qquad (4)$$

Based on the above analysis, our multi-class SVM algorithm can be formally described as follows.

$$\arg\min_{U,V,\xi,b} \frac{Tr(UV^TVU^T)}{2} + C \cdot \sum_{i=1}^{l} \xi_i$$
$$\text{s.t. } y_i(Tr(U^T X_i V) + b) \geq 1 - \xi_i \qquad (5)$$

where $\xi_i \geq 0$ and $i \in \{1,2,\dots,l\}$ should be satisfied. Afterward, visual features of images are extracted to construct the image vector space, which includes (1) colour features, (2) texture features, and (3) shape features, and then a testing image can be classified into four classes: (1) Nonhuman face, (2) Front view of human face, (3) Left view of human face, and (4) Right view of human face.

4 Experiments

We conduct the performance evaluation through the training sample set in CMU PIE dataset, which is made up of 11400 frontal face images, of which 4260 images are left profile face images, 4080 images are right profile face images, and others are belonged to non-face images. Particularly, each of standard size is normalized to 32×32. The exhaustive spatial template set within 32×32 image window is 832351. After implementing the reduction redundancy process, 180 spatial templates are evaluated to extract spatial histogram features. Our multi-view face detector is made up of these base classifiers. Furthermore, the CMU PIE dataset is conducted by collecting a database of 41368 images of 68 people. By extending the CMU 3D Room this dataset can record each person under 13 different poses, 43 different illumination conditions, and with 4 different expressions.

Firstly, we will test the face detection precision for four different multi-view face detection method, (1) our algorithm, (2) Rowly, (3) Viola, and (4) Schneiderman. Furthermore, nine angles are chosen to make performance evaluation from -90 to 90 with the interval 30 [5].

From Figure 2, we can see that our algorithm performs better than other three typical methods and the proposed algorithm perform best for the face of the front view. Afterward, we test the classification error rates of our algorithm for the multi-view face pattern classifier in Table 1.

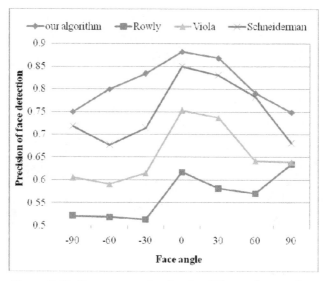

Figure 2: Performance evaluation for different face angles.

Table 1: Classification Error Rates for Our Algorithm.

Class	Number of Testing Image	Error Rate of Face Detection (%)
Nonface	6378	6.52
Front view of face	5411	1.43
Left view of face	3297	6.54
Right view of face	3317	5.98
Total	18403	5.12

As shown in Table 1, it can be seen that our proposed algorithm can effectively detect multi-view human faces particularly for the front view faces, the average precision detection of our algorithm is 5.12%. Hence, we can see that our algorithm is quite suitable for multi-view human face detection. To make the systems performance explanation more accurately, an example of multi-view face detection is given in Figure 3.

5 Conclusions

In this paper, we present a novel multi-view face detection based on a modified multi-class SVM. The structure of the SVM classifiers for multi-view face detection is present, and the face detection can be classified into three views: (1) "Front view", (2) "Left view", and (3) "Right view". Particularly, the multi-class classification problem is converted to an optimization problem. Afterward, visual features of images are extracted to construct the image vector space, and then the testing images can be classified to obtain human face detection results.

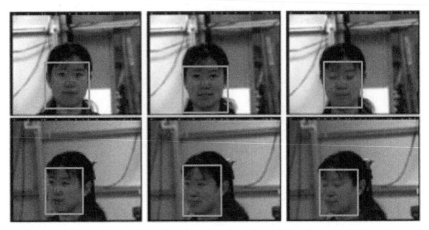

Figure 3: An example of multi-view face detection results.

Acknowledgment

This work was financially supported by grant from the National Twelfth Five-Year Science and Technology Support Program of China (2012BAF11B02).

References

[1] J. Michael, V. Paul, Fast multi-view face detection. *Mitsubishi Electric Research Lab TR-20003-96*, **3**, pp. 14–25, 2003.

[2] Chen Ju-Chin, Lien Jenn-Jier James, A view-based statistical system for multi-view face detection and pose estimation. *Image and Vision Computing*, **27(9)**, pp. 1252–1271, 2009.

[3] Wang Peng, Ji Qiang, Multi-view face and eye detection using discriminant features. *Computer Vision and Image Understanding*, **105(2)**, pp. 99–111, 2005.

[4] Zhang Hongming, Gao Wen, Chen Xilin, Robust multi-view face detection using Error Correcting Output Codes. Computer Vision – ECCV 2006, PT 4, *Proc., Lecture Notes in Computer Science*, **3954**, pp. 1–12, 2006.

[5] H. Rowly, S. Baluja, T. Kanade, Neural network-based face detection. *IEEE Transactions on Pattern Analysis and Machine Intelligence*, **20(1)**, pp. 23–38, 1998.

A novel RFID anti-collision algorithm in Internet of things

Wang Yong[1], Sun Yongdao[2], Han Yong Yin[1], Wang Xia[1]
[1]*Xuzhou College of Industrial Technology, Xuzhou 221140, China*
[2]*Xingtai Vocational and Technical College, Xingtai Steel Road No.552, 054035, China*

Abstract

At present, Radio Frequency Identification has been ranked as one of the most 10 important technologies in this century. This paper presents spread spectrum ALOHA algorithm combining LS code. This paper introduces the related concepts, and then puts forward the basic idea of algorithm, and then makes mathematical analysis on the stability of algorithm. Finally, throughput of algorithm is simulated, showing that this novel algorithm has higher throughput.

Keywords: Radio Frequency Identification, anti-collision, spread spectrum.

1 Introduction

Radio Frequency Identification (RFID) is a speedy, real time, accurate information collection and processing of high tech and information, which has been ranked as one of the most 10 important technologies in this century. It can be widely used in all kinds of field. This is because RFID has the advantage of non-contact and can bring the data more than the traditional bar code. However, as the application of an emerging technology, there are still a number of shortcomings in RFID's applications such as recognition accuracy is not high, RFID's standardization process is slow. Among them, one of the most important issues in RFID system is its inefficient recognition by tag collision and reader collision. It is a very significant issue to research on rapid, accurate, and effective anti-collision solution, which has a vital role in the development of RFID's technology [1].

In this paper, the basic principles, structure, characteristics, and the relevant theoretical knowledge of the RFID technology are introduced. Especially, we

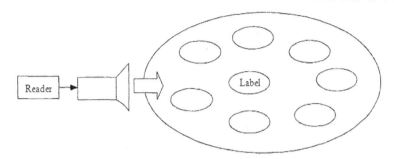

Figure 1: Wireless radio type.

have done an in-depth research on the data transmission in the issue of anti-collision. This thesis focuses on the anti-collision algorithms of the RFID system. There are several effective anti-collision algorithms that are used in all kinds of RFID systems. In order to resolve the tag collision problem, we need to use multiple access protocol. Recent years, the time division multiple (TDMA) has being generally accepted. According to TDMA, there are ALOHA protocol and binary tree protocol [2].

RFID have been used widely. Especially in low-frequency RFID technology area. On the other hand, the high-frequency RFID has not been well developed. With the development of the RFID technology, it is time to research the area of high frequency. The author has done a deep research on the issue of the label anti-collision based on the amount of domestic and international literature search, collating, analysis, and synthesis.

The paper is organized as follows. In the next section, we introduce principle of anti-collision. In Section 3, we propose a novel anti-collision algorithm based on spread spectrum ALOHA. Section 4 presents a mathematical model for anti-collision algorithm based on spread spectrum ALOHA. The simulation is made to illustrate the efficiency of the algorithm. Finally, we conclude our paper in Section 5.

2   Principle of anti-collision

The first is a wireless radio type. There are multiple transponders within the scope of a reader, data streams from the reader are received by multiple transponder at the same time. It is similar to hundreds of electronic tags receiving and sending information at the same time, and information is launched by a reader. This is shown in Figure 1.

The second is that there are more than one transponder transmitting data to the reader at the same time in the scope of reader and this kind of communication is called multiple access communication. This is shown in Figure 2.

The third one is that multiple readers transmit data to more than one transponders at the same time. Now this kind of situation is rarely met in RFID system, we often encounter multiple access communication. Each communication

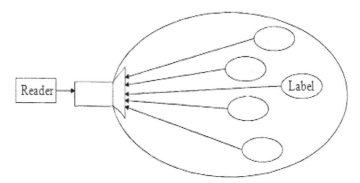

Figure 2: Multiple access communication.

path has certain channel capacity. The channel capacity is determined by the maximum data rate, the communication path, and time slot. The channel capacity assigned to each transponder must satisfy when more than one transponder transmits the data to a single reader, mutual collision cannot appear.

3 A novel anti-collision based on spread spectrum ALOHA

3.1 Spread spectrum code design

Professor of Beijing university of posts and telecommunications Li Daoben proposed a new method of spread spectrum code structure, according to this method the generated code is called LS code (Link Space Code), and its basic idea is complementarily related. Known in binary and multiple domain, complex domain and real number domain, autocorrelation function is zero in addition to the origin point and cross-correlation function is zero, which are known as the ideal-related group, but theory research tells us that this code number only has one. Further consider complementary ideal-related group, the so-called ideal complementary-related group is that each element in the group is divided into two parts, C and S (similar to the characteristics of cosine and sine, known as C code and S code). C and S are not ideal relevant group, but absolute value of the autocorrelation function (except the origin) and cross-correlation function is equal. Symbols are opposite, therefore it has nature of ideal related group, this code is called an ideal complementary-related group. The existence of ideal complementary-related group can be proved, but there are only two elements in real-number domain. However, to construct a group of codes in the actual useful, two elements is too little, especially in CDMA communication. Although we can't find ideal complementary-related group with the element more than 2, consider from the reality, it does not need ideal correlation. Multipath propagation delay in practice is limited, or actual measurement requirement, is only part of the length of the code, it is required only in an area near the origin, autocorrelation function (except the origin), and zero cross-correlation function

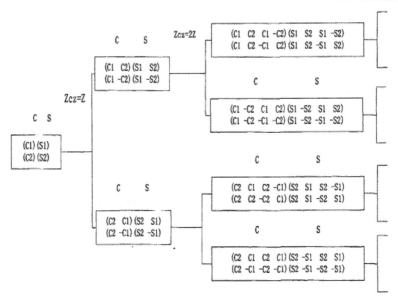

Figure 3: LS code construction.

are zero. A group of this nature is called zero window complementary-related group, based on this, we can construct required LS code. Walsh code autocorrelation function is not ideal, and there is considerable sidelobe values, which is difficult to capture, so it cannot be used as spread spectrum code independently. LS code with good autocorrelation function and the characteristic of zero correlation window can be used as spread spectrum code directly.

LS construction used in this paper is shown in Figure 3. It can be seen that LS code can be divided into two parts A and B of the same structure. LS code can be expressed as Eqs. (1) and (2):

$$LS_i^n = (A_i^n, B_i^n), \quad 1 \le k \le 2n, \quad (n = 2^k) \tag{1}$$

$$LS^n = (LS_i^n)_{i=1,2,\dots 2^{n+1}} \tag{2}$$

A_i^n is the ith sequence of the nth layer of part A and B_i^n is the ith sequence of the nth layer of part B.

3.2 Algorithm description

Spread spectrum ALOHA algorithm is to introduce spread spectrum and spread time, on the basis of original ALOHA mechanism. In this algorithm, it includes a time-division uplink channel, a downlink broadcast channel, a reader, and a certain number of labels. All the labels in the network use the same spread sequence, namely LS code. LS code can prevent multiple access interference in

CDMA communication system, each tag at any time can send signals to the reader, the reader with a matched filter (or related) can receive signals for all users. The subtraction circuit extracts the first arrival and the strongest signal according to the signal pecking order one by one, until the only one signal is rest. And then insert signal, which has been deducted from the signal in the reader, to identify signals of different users. Reader broadcasts a timing control signal via the downlink channel, in order to adjust each user signal arrival time, thus reducing the degree of the collision or overlap of each user signals.

4 Mathematical model and experiment analysis

Assuming that time interval of group arriving at the base station obeys negative exponential distribution, and each packet length is fixed length T_0, which is composed of L bit. Pseudo-code length is N, amount of system business is G, successful transmission business is S, each chip length is $T_c = T_0/(LN)$. The resolution of the matched filter is 1. Based on autocorrelation characteristic of spread spectrum code, each bit conflict interval in a packet is δ chip. Total conflict window length is $\delta T_0/N$. In time interval $2T_0$, the average arrival rate of data packet is λ and probability of K number of data groups arriving at the channel is:

$$f(K) = (2\lambda T_0)^K e^{-2\lambda T_0} / K! \tag{3}$$

Probability of successful transmission of each data group in K number of data groups is:

$$Q_E(K) = (1 - \delta/N)^{K-1} = (1 - P_{cc})^L \tag{4}$$

P_{cc} is average bit error probability caused by packet conflict, which is as follows.

$$P_{cc} = 1 - (1 - \delta/N)^{(K-1)/L} \tag{5}$$

Throughput performance of spread spectrum ALOHA can be defined as:

$$S = E(KQ_E(K)) = \sum_{K=1}^{\infty} KQ_E(K)f(K) \tag{6}$$

S is throughput, $E(\ )$ is mathematical expectation, and $f(K)$ is arrival distribution probability of data packet. Relation of throughput and load is:

$$\begin{aligned} S &= \sum_{K=1}^{\infty} KQ_E(K) \cdot (2\lambda T_0)^K e^{-2\lambda T_0} / K! \\ &= Ge^{-G} + Ge^{-G} \sum_{K=1}^{\infty} G^K / K! \, Q_E(K+1) \end{aligned} \tag{7}$$

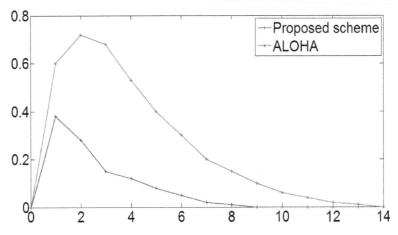

Figure 4: Throughput comparison of two algorithms.

$G = 2\lambda T_0$ is network load of the system. At last S can be expressed as:

$$S = Ge^{-G} + Ge^{-G} \sum_{K=1}^{\infty} G^K / K! (1 - \delta / N)^K$$

In order to illustrate the feasibility and effectiveness of the algorithm, here we selected time slot ALOHA method for comparison, $N=4$. Throughput comparison of our proposed spread spectrum ALOHA anti-collision algorithm and time slot ALOHA anti-collision algorithm is shown in Figure 4. It can be seen that our proposed spread spectrum ALOHA anti-collision algorithm has wider stable range than time slot ALOHA anti-collision algorithm.

5 Conclusions

This paper presents spread spectrum ALOHA algorithm combining LS code.

This paper introduces the related concepts, and then puts forward the basic idea of algorithm, and then makes mathematical analysis on the stability of algorithm. Finally, throughput of algorithm is simulated, showing that this novel algorithm has higher throughput.

References

[1] A. Oztekin, F.M. Pajouh, D. Delen, L.K. Swin, An RIFD network design methodology for asset tracking in healthcare. *Decision Support System*, **49**, pp. 100–109, 2010.
[2] L. Atzori, A. Iera, G. Morabito, The Internet of Things: A survey. *Computer Networks*, **54(15)**, pp. 2787–2805, 2010.

Research on the low-carbon tourism region evaluation system based on ANP approach

Rongrong Yang, Chang Liu
Society and History College, Harbin Normal University, Harbin, 150025, P.R.China

Abstract

As the rapid growth of modern tourism industry, its negative effects on ecological environment are taking increasing attention, which eagerly calls for the protection of ecology. With the development of global low-carbon economy, low-carbon tourism has become the direction to achieve sustainable development of tourism industry. building low-carbon tourism regions or scenic spots is in urgent demand. And it is necessary to construct a low-carbon tourism region evaluation system. This paper, adopting ANP (analytic network process) approach and based on interviews of 15 experts, summarizes the assessment indexes of low-carbon tourism regions in the aspects of low-carbon tourism region management, low-carbon buildings and infrastructure, low-carbon food and beverage, low-carbon tourist souvenirs and protection of tourism region's ecology. These indexes are compared in pairs according to experts' suggestions. By using the super decision software, the paper makes index weight value assessment and consistency test, calculates the weight of each index, and puts these indexes in order in accordance with the degree of significance. The paper constructs a complete low-carbon tourism region evaluation system, aiming at providing reference and guidance for the development, and administration of low-carbon tourism regions in the future.
Keywords: low-carbon tourism region, evaluation, ANP, super decision software.

1 Introduction

With the development of the world industrial economy, the explosive growth of population and the unrestrained ways of production and lifestyle, the increasing CO_2 emissions and frequent occurrence of global catastrophic climate change

WIT Transactions on Information and Communication Technologies, Vol. 61, © 2014 WIT Press
www.witpress.com, ISSN 1743-3517 (on-line)
doi:10.2495/MIIT131021

have seriously threatened the living environment and the health and safety of human being. It was in response to this situation that the concept of "low-carbon economy" came into being, which was introduced in 2003 by British government in UK Energy Paper named Our Energy Future—Creating a Low Carbon Economy. Low-carbon economy refers to higher resource productivity producing more with fewer natural resources and less pollution, which provides opportunities for and means of higher living standards and a better quality of life. It creates the opportunity to develop, apply, and export leading-edge technologies as well as new businesses and more jobs. Afterward, in order to control the global CO_2 emissions, 141 members of the UN jointly signed Kyoto Protocol that came into effect in 2005 [1].

Driven by the development of global low-carbon economy, the growth of low-carbon tourism attracts increasing attention and has become the inevitable choice to achieve a sustainable tourism industry. "Low-carbon tourism region" is derived from the concept of "low-carbon tourism," which requires not only adhering to the idea of low-carbon and low-carbonization operation but also an excellent social environment advocating low-carbon tourism [2]. Currently, the study of low-carbon tourism regions focuses on definitions and development countermeasures while rare study on the evaluation system for low-carbon tourism regions from the angle of quantitative point has been made. Tan Jin and Cheng Qian, taking Gongga Yanzigou tourism region of Sichuan Province as an example, to construct the low-carbon tourism region evaluation system from the five aspects: low-carbon landscape, scenic vegetation, the quality of water and air in the tourism region, and the environment around tourism region. However, their study was only of theoretical analysis and research but didn't form a specific index system by means of quantitative analysis [3]. Zhao Jinling and Gao Jun has studied the low-carbon evaluation mode based on an ANP approach, but, due to few expert interviews and on competition index selection, seldom consideration was made of these important factors that may influence the growth of low-carbon tourism regions such as low-carbon management, low-carbon food and beverage, and low-carbon tourist souvenir [4]. This paper, drawing on the achievements of these scholars and based on interviews of 15 experts, summarizes the assessment indexes of low-carbon tourism region in six aspects, that is, low-carbon tourism region management, low-carbon traffic, low-carbon architecture and infrastructure, low-carbon food and beverage, low-carbon tourist souvenirs and protection of tourism region eco-environment, and determines the weight of each index, aiming at providing reference and guidance for the development and administration of low-carbon tourism regions in the future.

2 The construction of low-carbon tourism region evaluation system based on ANP approach

2.1 The selection of assessment techniques

ANP (analytic network process) is a decision-making approach introduced by Thomas L. Saaty, a famous professor at University of Pittsburgh, USA in 1996, which is a newly developed practical decision method based on AHP (analytic hierarchy process) [5]. AHP does not take the feedback relationship between different dimensions and claims that elements in the same dimension are independent of each other, which has limited its application in complex decision making. Among the actual problems of low-carbon tourism regions, the internal elements in the scope of one dimension are usually dependent on each other, and the structure of the system is more like network. Because it is a decision-making approach appropriate for this demand, ANP is applied to the construction of low-carbon tourism region evaluation system in this paper [6].

2.2 The principles of constructing the evaluation system

A scientifically constructed low-carbon tourism region evaluation system can help assess the development state of existing tourism regions, determine the specific direction of tourism region growth so as to achieve sustainable development of tourism economy. Having considered its complexity and significance, the construction of this evaluation system in this paper follows the following principles:

The Scientific Principle: The low-carbon tourism region evaluation system should be constructed under the guidance of correct theory and by scientific study method. Besides combining theory with the real state of low-carbon tourism regions and adopting ANP approach, experts' opinions are fully considered in the construction of the system. According to the opinions of 15 experts, three rounds of index selections/screening have been made, and 30 items of indicators have been identified of which the consistency of expert opinions reaches 98%, thus ensuring the scientific and reasonable evaluation index. And super decision software is used in the calculation of index system, including weighing calculation and consistency test to ensure the calculation result is scientific and precise.

The Systematic Principle: The low-carbon tourism region evaluation system is a multidimensioned and diversified one, which is composed of 30 specific indicators in six aspects, that is, low-carbon tourism region management, low-carbon architecture and infrastructure, low-carbon food and beverage, low-carbon tourist souvenirs and protection of tourism region eco-environment. These items have been applied to the construction of the evaluation system according to their internal connection.

The Practical Principle: In the selection of the 30 indicators, such factors as comparability and measurability of indexes, feasibility of data collection and the combination of quantitative analysis and qualitative analysis are taken into consideration to ensure the practicability of the system, which will lay foundation for the application and extension of the new evaluation system.

2.3 The construction of the evaluation system

While ANP is adopted in constructing the evaluation system, calculation software is used in solving practical problems. The super decision software has successfully been applied to the computation process of ANP. Specific steps are as follows.

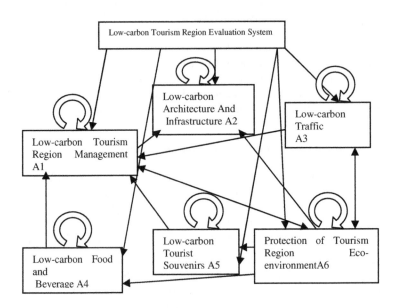

Figure 1: The network structure model of the low-carbon tourism region evaluation system.

Evaluation index selection, first of all, can list all the practical indexes used by the former scholars in the research of low-carbon tourism region on the basis of current research literature. Then rank on each index by applying Frequentness Statistical Method. Finally conduct an expert consultation according to the relations between indexes [7]. This paper adopted Frequentness Statistical Method, Theoretical Analytic Method, setting of Expert Consultation Method, and screening index. Determine the evaluating indicators and construct the network structure in accordance with the 15 experts' opinions in the fields of low-carbon energy, low-carbon economy, tourism region management, and planning, as shown in Figure 1.

Form a unified view based on an expert opinion survey. And then assess and compare the important levels according to Table 1 by using questionnaire mode and matrix mode, as shown in Figures 2 and 3 [8].

Check the inconsistency. It is qualified when the value of the inconsistency is less than or equal to 0.1, or it requires modification, as shown in Figure 4. In ANP, the judge preference of decision makers or experts should go through detection of consistency. All evaluation matrices have been up to the standards of consistency.

Construct the supermatrix and then obtain the unweighted supermatrix, weighted supermatrix, and limit supermatrix by calculation. First, integrate all the pairwise comparison matrices into the unweighted supermatrix. If the total value of all lines is not equal to 1, appropriate weight is added to make it equal to 1,

Table 1: The Fundamental Scale for Making Judgments.

1	Equal
2	Between Equal and Moderate
3	Moderate
4	Between Moderate and Strong
5	Strong
6	Between Strong and Very Strong
7	Very Strong
8	Between Very Strong and Extreme
9	Extreme
	Decimal judgments, such as 3.5, are allowed for fine tuning, and judgments greater than 9 may be entered, though it is suggested that they be avoided.

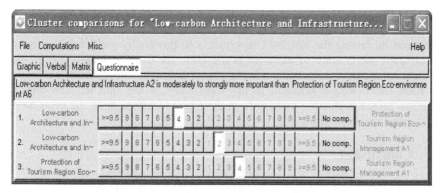

Figure 2: Assessment and comparison by questionnaire mode.

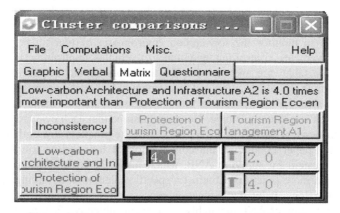

Figure 3: Assessment and comparison by matrix mode.

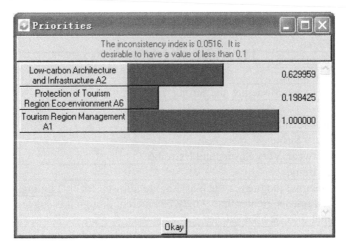

Figure 4: Inconsistency test.

which is called the weighted supermatrix. Furthermore, the limit supermatrix is obtained by raising the weighted supermatrix to powers by multiplying it times itself until the column of numbers is the same for every column. This is the weight value that represents the relative relation among all the elements.

Each index weight obtained in the supermatrix is put into the low-carbon tourism region evaluation table to form the final index weight of the evaluation system, as shown in Table 2.

3 Conclusion

Put these indexes in order according to their degrees of significance (as shown in Table 2). It is shown that the following 11 factors have more important effects on low-carbon tourism regions, that is, making specific plans for low-carbon protection, energy recycling, the proportion of using renewable energy like solar energy and wind power, publicity and introduction of low-carbon knowledge in tourism region, salvage recycling rate, measures to improve salvage recycling, mechanisms to monitor the low-carbon environment of tourism region, using low-carbon vehicles, controlling the number of vehicles, controlling the provision of disposable tableware and utensils. These factors should be taken into prior consideration in the construction and assessment of low-carbon tourism regions.

In the evaluation of low-carbon tourism region, it mainly made use of AHP before, which is relatively simple. However, assume that each evaluation index is mutual independent, which is discrepancy with the practical low-carbon tourism region. This paper conducted the construction of low-carbon tourism region evaluation system by applying ANP, which made the evaluation system more scientific and more practical. Conduct a specific calculation by taking advantage of super decisions. It let the evaluation process more convenient and accurate. But the application of ANP inevitably involves in subjective factors, so deviation

Table 2: Low-Carbon Tourism Region Evaluation System.

Dimensions	Assessment Index	Weight	Rank
Low-carbon Tourism Region Management A1	Publicity and introduction of low-carbon knowledge in tourism region B1	0.062	4
	Educating local residents in low carbon and environment protection B2	0.010	24
	Times of employee training about low-carbon knowledge per year B3	0.013	22
	Measures to compensate low-carbon tourism region B4	0.023	18
	The proportion of income used in the maintenance of low-carbon tourism region B5	0.035	12
	Mechanisms to monitor the low-carbon environment of tourism region B6	0.050	7
	Making plans to protect the low-carbon environment of tourism region B7	0.138	1
Low-carbon Architecture and Infrastructure A2	Localization and natural environment protection of building materials B8	0.026	14
	Utilizing the renewable energy like solar energy, wind power, etc. B9	0.026	15
	Recycling hot and cold energy facilities B10	0.024	17
	The service life of architecture and infrastructure B11	0.007	27
	Using energy-saving products B12	0.026	16
	Providing temporary tent accommodation B13	0.004	29
Low-carbon Traffic A3	Using low-carbon vehicles B14	0.046	8
	Controlling the number of vehicles B15	0.046	9
	Building low-carbon parking lots B16	0.010	25
	Design of low-carbon traffic routes B17	0.014	21
Low-carbon Food and Beverage A4	Providing low carbon and green food B18	0.012	23
	Controlling the provision of disposable tableware and utensils B19	0.041	10
	Providing large, middle, and small dishes and eliminating waste B20	0.007	28
Low-carbon Tourist Souvenirs A5	Selling local distinctive souvenirs B21	0.003	30
	Prohibiting overpacking and waste B22	0.009	26
	Using low-carbon packaging B23	0.023	19
Protection of Tourism	The proportion of using renewable energy like solar energy, wind power, etc. B24	0.072	3

Region Eco-environment A6	Energy recycling rate B25	0.072	2
	Protecting the original ecological landscape and bio-diversity B26	0.019	20
	Green coverage rate of tourism region B27	0.034	13
	Salvage recycling rate B28	0.061	5
	Measures to improve salvage recycling B29	0.051	6
	Measures of rubbish bio-safety disposal B30	0.036	11

is existed undoubtedly. Therefore, establish perfect evaluation experts' database will be more important. The research of this paper basically calculated on the evaluation of estimate for low-carbon tourism region, as well as conducted a further study on the grade estimation and identification of low-carbon tourism region according to evaluation of estimate.

References

[1] Huang Wensheng, On the low-carbon tourism and the creation of low carbon tourist attractions. *Ecological Economy*, **218(11)**, pp. 100–102, 2009 (in Chinese).

[2] Zeng Manqiong, On the construction of tourism regions in low carbon economy. *Journal of Harbin Vocational & Technical College*, **4**, pp. 109–110, 2010 (in Chinese).

[3] Tan Jin, Cheng Qian, On the construction of low-carbon tourism region assessment system based on the case of Gongga Yanzigou tourism region of Sichuan Province. *Economic Research Guide*, **11**, pp. 117–118, 156, 2010 (in Chinese).

[4] Zhao Jinling, Gao Jun, Assessing the low carbon mode for tourism regions based on an ANP approach. *Resources Science*, **33(5)**, pp. 897–904, 2011 (in Chinese).

[5] Thomas L. Saaty, *Decision Making with Dependence and Feedback*. RWS Publication, Pittsburgh, pp. 68–113, 1996.

[6] Thomas L. Saaty, Decision making the analytic hierarchy and network process. *Journal of Systems Science and Systems Engineering*, **3**, pp. 32–43, 2004.

[7] Jiang Qin, Evaluation index system of Low carbon scenic spots. *Resources & Industries*, **14(5)**, pp. 140–146, 2012 (in Chinese).

[8] Thomas L. Saaty, Fundamentals of the analytic network process dependence and feedback in decision making with a single network. *Journal of Systems Science and Systems Engineering*, **13(2)**, pp. 129–157, 2004.

An implementation of the humanoid violin robot with AHRS

Weijia Xu, Jianming Huang, Weizheng Ren
School of Electronic Engineering, Beijing University of Posts and Telecommunications, Beijing, China

Abstract

Researching and developing a robot in a highly humanoid appearance, and it has ability to play the violin which is presented for a robot's entertainment and ornamental. By model for keeping moving range of the mechanical structure, a method makes the robot that has the possibility of playing the violin. Based on ARM core intelligent control with AHRS is used to realize control of the robot behavior. Finally, the present study realizes the humanoid violin robot with the flexible right hand, which can play the full repertoire in artificial assisted, thus push forward the humanoid violin robot research progress. It is an important milestone the violin robot research in the course.

Keywords: humanoid robot, violin, AHRS, sensor feedback system.

1 Introduction

As a result of scientific and technological advances in development, there are many technology products in our lives almost constantly, ubiquitously, and pervasively. Intelligent robot is a high-tech product integrating mechanical technology, electronic technology, and information technology. Intelligent robotics in the range of subjects involved are: mechanics, robot topology, mechanics, electronics and micro-electronics, computer, biology, artificial intelligence, systems engineering, and so on. But developing a violin playing robot is also difficult for robot researchers, because giving those abilities to robots is nearly exceeds the present state of the art. It is also challenging. Though only a few violin playing robots have been developed [1].

Most of the robot gives the impression of cold server machine, so it is hoped that let people feel the pleasure of science and technology through research and

Figure 1: The CATIA mechanical modeling.

development of the violin robots. The experimental results indicate that research and development of the humanoid music robots are indeed to be more objective entertainment, a good man–machine interaction and have a reference value.

2   Violin robot basic

For violin, when the strings vibration be caused by bow and strings friction, through the bridge to make the panel vibration, then the sound column to take the back plane vibration, E string vibration is less, while the G string vibration is larger, so that the bass bar has greater vibration, and vibration caused by sound box. Whether to make the music into full play, it depends on the strings and tension, the bridge quality, pressure, and speed of the bow.

If the music of the various sound quality is expressed, it needs the above plus the performer's bowing, fingering and vibrato, and elastic string playing skills. The method of making a violin robot is to study the violin playing skill. For the purposes of this robot play skill, we are particularly concerned about the bow and strings friction, and friction techniques. The robot arm driven bow accurately friction to each string is one of the basic tasks to complete the humanoid robot. The two is the basic task in the violin performance process will have to switch to bow to the friction of the string, and the switching process guarantee smooth, fast, otherwise the music may not be coherent, and music performance effect will be impacted seriously [2].

The mechanical structure of the robot is very important. If you want to play beautiful music, it must have sufficient space degrees of freedom. The following description of a mechanical structure of playing violin possibility, namely in the mobile space range of all motor controlled, respectively it has in full contact and friction with four strings, and can be smoothly sliding distance space. The mechanical structure is modeled in order to meet the above requirements (Figure 1).

The circuit control board is the core of robots, robot arm control is the key to the violin robots. The arm 10 platform will be used on the core control circuit board, this realizes mainly robot automation, intelligent, and entertaining. The

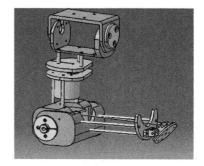

Figure 2: The body of 3D simulation figure.

Figure 3: The robot arm simulation diagram.

robot integrates with voice recognition, sensing, and automatic control technology. Violin robot arm with three degrees of freedom and can be freely control the bow. The violin robot is to control the robot arm accurately constantly switching friction all strings by the core control board, thus play a smooth music.

3 Mechanical structure and humanoid appearance

The general design requirements for mechanical structure: moving in space within the range of all motor control, respectively it has in full contact and friction with four strings, and can be smoothly moving distance space. Only meet the requirements of mechanical structure that has the possibility of full playing the violin. Good mechanical design not only can be achieved by playing the violin, but also can reduce the control and the difficulty of programming, enhance the reliability of the whole system. Then the main mechanical structure of robot is explained in detail (Figures 2 and 3).

Key Components: The key mechanical part of the violin is humanoid arm. The design of right arm has three degrees of freedom and a linkage device, three degrees of freedom by the shoulder tilt degrees of freedom, the arm tilt degrees of freedom, an elbow swivel degrees of freedom, and wrist tilt degrees of freedom. The robot hand is composed of a linkage device.

The Trunk Part Design: The robot main body plays a supporting role, and lightweight, flexible, trunk, and feet by using simplified design, which makes the robot more concise, and its main function is more prominent. Such a design with fewer degrees of freedom to achieve performance requirements, reduce the difficulty of control, but also ensure the humanoid appearance.

4 Electrical design

Design requirements for the control system are: rapid control, fast feedback. As already mentioned the importance of coherence for violin playing is not to repeat them here. That is why control core processing speed as well as the AHRS sensor

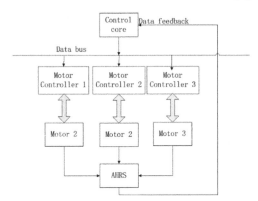

Figure 4: Control system block diagram.

to the control core of feedback speed is the focus of the design of the control system.

4.1 Design and implement of the hardware system

For the overall control system, with the ARM 10 platform of the ARM 8019, the computing speed is fast, the highest frequency can reach 520 MHz, interface types number is rich, can meet the communication requirements between different modules. ART1020, a kind of motor control card is used by the system, which can be output 1 Hz 4 MHz wide frequency range of the PWM waves, the card can be quickly and precisely control the pulse frequency (motor speed), number of pulses (motor rotation), and can meet the requirement of controlling the speed of the violin.

The motor of each joint of the humanoid robot are stepper motor control, a humanoid robot with only three motors, so three control cards are used for control. The control core using PC104 interface is connected to the motor control card. The control card using 34P gray line is connected up stepping motor drive, and through the gray line output PWM signal, after the stepper motor drive signal is amplified to drive voltage signals can be used for motor rotation. In addition, the power of each motor is independent, the whole system is a distributed power supply. This can be very stable for the power supply of each motor, reduce the interference between the motor (Figure 4).

4.2 AHRS sensor feedback part of the design and implementation

Using AHRS as a sensor, the feedback data are there on the space angle, the feedback frequency is 75 Hz, largely to ensure fast feedback the situation, which makes the system to achieve fast control.

It is mounted on the robot arm, the relative position of the mechanical arm to the violin is determined by actual measurements. Space angle information is transmitted from the RS232 serial port feedback to control the core ARM. Control core monitor serial port to the angle information and processing. Through

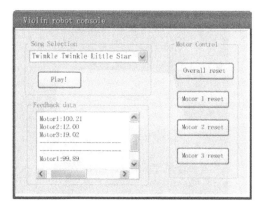

Figure 5: Man–machine interface.

continuous feedback, operation, control, ultimately the mechanical arm has achieved the desired position.

For the overall circuit feedback of playing the violin, the movement of operator speed for high demand and the larger signal delay will cause not synchronous mechanical movement, and even make the mechanical movement ended in abnormal state. Using the high speed operation ability of ARM and high speed feedback angle information of AHRS, the possibility of abnormal motion can be greatly reduced, thereby the reliability of the whole circuit will be improved.

5 Control programming

The man–machine interface can facilitate debugging of robot control (Figure 5). The interface can be real-time feedback of robots running parameters, it can give a command to control the violin robot motion. The interface includes three parts of playing violin action, the feedback data, and motor resetting. The feedback data interface can return the real-time angle parameter, bringing great convenience to site commissioning.

6 Experimental testing

6.1 AHRS practical effect

In the trial, AHRS played a very good role in spatial orientation. Although the accuracy to be improved, it can make the robot to complete a number of basic movements. The feedback speed of data can meet the bow in motion dynamic positioning (Figure 6).

6.2 The robot's appearance and playing music

The robot has a specific humanoid structure, and it can be dressed up to reach more realistic appearance, as shown in Figure 7.

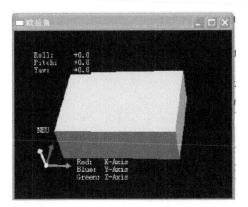

Figure 6: AHRS test figure.

Figure 7: Robots real-time test looks.	Figure 8: Robot real performance chart.

According to the design of the robot mechanical structure, it can just drive bow to make friction with four different strings, so that different tones are produced. In the right hand with artificial compressing string, the robot can play simple slow music, such as "Twinkle Twinkle Little Star." In the actual performance, the bow has basically full contact with the strings, shows a stable timbre and moderate tone loudness (Figure 8).

7 Conclusion

The humanoid robot can control more flexible right arm driven to cause respectively bow friction four strings, and it can complete the music playing in artificial pressing strings, also do some humanoid action and dialogue, therefore it has high ornamentation and entertainment. The robot does not realize the left hand function during this phase, because the project is complex, and it will proceed in several stages. This also resulted in no artificial auxiliary case, the robot not be able to play the entire music.

For the above problems, the next step will focus on the implementation of R&D of robot left function, through the sound feedback robotic violin can realize the automatic tuning. I hope that a violin robot with more performance skills will be developed in the future.

Acknowledgments

The research work was supported by Undergraduate Innovation Foundation of Beijing University of Posts and Telecommunications.

References

[1] M. Kajitani, Development of musician robots. *Journal of Robotics and Mechatronics*, **1(3)**, pp. 254–255, 1989.

[2] Koji Shibuya, Koshi Fukatsu, Sigenori Komatsu, Influences of timbre on right arm motion in bowing of violin playing. *Journal of Biomechanisms Japan*, **28(3)**, pp. 146–154, 2004 (in Japanese).

Fusion topic model transfer learning for cross-domain recommendation

Lei Wu, Wensheng Zhang, Jue Wang
Institute of Automation, Chinese Academy of Science, Beijing, 100190, China

Abstract

It remains a challenge to deal with the diversity of the cross-domain feature space when using transfer learning in the recommendation system. To solve the difficulty, we propose a fusion topic model to extract the latent topic in the cross-domain. There are two layers in the proposed model. Firstly, the model simulates the user–item relationship in every subdomain with an author–topic model separately, and extracts the subdomain level topics. In addition, the model extracts the full-domain level topics in the whole domain using subdomain level topics as words in the author–topic model. By using Gibbs sampling, the method can extract two different levels of topics. The experiment on the public dataset shows our method has good performance. The results of the experiment indicate that extracting multilevel topics can help to discover the correlation in the MovieLens dataset and the Book-Crossing dataset, and to extract the cross-domain feature space.

Keywords: transfer learning, recommendation system, author–topic model.

1 Introduction

As the development of the internet technology and the electronic commerce, the recommendation system has become significantly popular. The goal of recommendation is to discover the rule for the preference of observed users on every observed rating item, and provide users with satisfied commodities. There has been a lot of works in industry and academia on the recommendation system, such as the research on recommending webpage visitors for movies or books [1].

However, there are still some problems in the recommendation system. One main challenge is the sparseness of data. The data-sparsity issue is more severe

 WIT Transactions on Information and Communication Technologies, Vol. 61, © 2014 WIT Press
www.witpress.com, ISSN 1743-3517 (on-line)
doi:10.2495/MIIT131041

for new users and new items. In order to alleviate the difficulty, some researchers use transfer learning in multiple domains. Transfer learning assumes the E-commerce websites attract similar users and provide similar items. Transfer learning use dense source domain data to help to learn the sparse target domain. For example, we can use the dense preference information in movies to learn the rating information in the sparse data in books. If a person likes the movie Twilight, he or she may like the book Twilight. However, one of technological difficulties of transfer learning in the cross-domain is that the feature space is different in different domains. In this paper, we suppose that every subdomain feature space is only a part of the real-world feature space. And we propose a fusion topic model to bonding the subdomain feature space and achieve the cross-domain recommendation.

The recommendation system has been classified into three methods: collaborative filtering [2, 3], content-based [4, 5], and hybrid methods [6–8]. However, these methods are based on the homogeneous domain. Some researchers provide an improved LDA model for the recommendation in the cross-domain [9]. It not only utilizes the word and topic information, but also uses the user-generated text information. Some researchers translate the relationship of users and items into the collective link prediction, using the kernel function [10]. In this paper, we use the author–topic model to simulate the linkage between users and items, which is a kind of hidden variable probabilistic graphical model [11]. This model can express the structure between variables explicitly.

2 Fusion topic model transfer learning

Topic modeling ensembles [12] is a single domain ensembling method. The method classifies a domain dataset into several parts, and employs a topic model in each part. Then there will be several subdomain topics. At last, the method puts these topics totally into author–topic model. By extracting two levels of topics, the method maps the data into the better feature space and gets the improved performance. In this paper, we reference the framework of extracting topic variables repetitiously and apply it to the task in the cross-domain recommendation.

2.1 Basic topic model in the single domain

Different from the original model [12], our model uses the author–topic model [13] to simulate the user–item relationship. We consider a user as an author in the author–topic model. Every user generates a set of item ratings, which is like a paper with many words. One item is viewed as a word in this model. If an item is preferred by a user, then its frequency in the paper is high. The parameters used in this paper is described as follows. The topic proportion θ_d for a particular document d follows a Dirichlet distribution with parameter α. The author proportion x follows a Dirichlet distribution with the parameter a_d. Given θ_d and x, a particular topic z is drawn from a multinomial distribution. A word w is from a

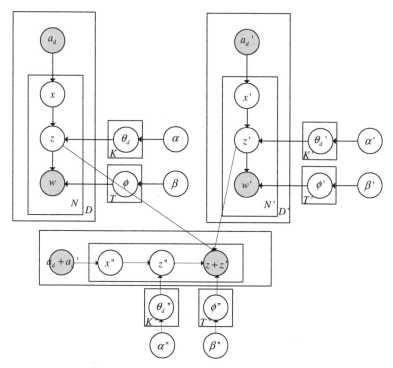

Figure 1: The plate graphical model for the fusion author–topic model.

multinomial distribution given the topic z, and ϕ follows a Dirichlet distribution with β.

2.2 Topic model fusion in the cross-domain

In the next step, we rank the topics in every domain with the frequency to translate them into the full-domain. At last, the new topics are input into a new author–topic model, and the new topics are features in the predicted full world feature space. Figure 1 shows the graphical model of the proposed fusion topic model.

3 Algorithm

The author–topic model has a set of latent variables. So there is a set of parameters to be computed. We apply the method which is employed by the single domain author–topic model. It uses an approximate computing method Gibbs sampling to obtain the posterior distribution over parameters.

For each item, which is considered as a word in the author–topic model, the topic and user assignment is sampled from the distribution as follows:

$$P(z_j = t, x_i = u \mid w_j = i, z_{-j}, x_{-j})$$

$$\propto \frac{C_{i,t}^{W,T} + \beta}{\sum_{i'} C_{i',t}^{W,T} + I\beta} \frac{C_{u,t}^{A,T} + \alpha}{\sum_{t'} C_{u,t'}^{A,T} + T\alpha}$$

where $z_j = t$ and $x_j = u$ indicate the jth word in the document belongs to the topic t and the author u, respectively. $W_j = i$ represents the jth word is i in the lexicon, and z_{-j} and x_{-j} show all topics and authors not including the ith. $C_{i,t}^{W,T}$ is the number of times that the word i belongs to the topic t, but not including the current instance, and $C_{u,t}^{A,T}$ is the number of times that the author u belongs to the topic t, but not including the current instance. I is the length of the lexicon.

4 Experiments and analysis

In this section, we show the experiments on two real-world datasets.

4.1 Datasets

We use two datasets in our experiments. We consider the movie ratings dataset as the target domain and the book ratings dataset as the source domain.

MovieLens: This dataset is widely used in the movie recommendation. It has 100,000 ratings with scale 1–5. The ratings are from 943 users on 1682 movie items.

Book-Crossing: This dataset is an SQL fomat dataset. We only use a subset of this dataset, which includes 40,000 ratings from 6333 users. The ratings here scales from 1 to 10. For the convenience of experiment, we map the ratings to 1–5 as follows:

$$map(1, 2) \rightarrow 1$$
$$map(3, 4) \rightarrow 2$$
$$map(5, 6) \rightarrow 3$$
$$map(7, 8) \rightarrow 4$$
$$map(9, 10) \rightarrow 5$$

In this paper, we use the Book-Crossing dataset as our source domain data and consider the MovieLens datasets as the target domain data.

4.2 Evaluation

In this paper, we use Mean Absolute Error (MAE) to evaluate the performance of the method. The computational formula is as follows:

$$MAE = \frac{\sum_{(u,i) \in R} \mid r_{ui} - \hat{r}_{ui} \mid}{\mid R \mid}$$

Table 1: The MAE Performance on Five Different MovieLens Train/Test Sets.

No.	Single Domain, Single Model	Multi-Domain, Fusion Model
1	0.9237	0.9089
2	0.8391	0.8211
3	0.8185	0.8194
4	0.8537	0.8216
5	0.8236	0.8312
mean	0.8517	0.8404

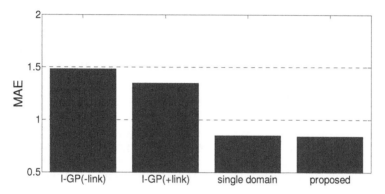

Figure 2: The performance of our method comparing with other methods.

where r_{ui} represents the true value from the user u on the item i and $\hat{r}_{ui}$ denotes the predicated value, $|R|$ is the number of test ratings. The smaller is the MAE value, the better is the performance.

Table 1 indicates the advantage of extracting multilevel topics. By importing the heterogeneous domain information and extracting the multilevel feature representation, the experiment shows that the proposed method reduces the MAE in most subsets of the data, and the average behavior of the proposed method performs well. The reason of this phenomenon is that extracting the single level topic in a single domain may induce that the feature extracted overfits the training feature space. However, the target training domain feature space cannot represent the real-world feature space. Therefore, extracting multilevel topic may enhance the generalization ability of the method.

Figure 2 indicates the advantage of the proposed method comparing with other algorithms. Independent Link Prediction using nonlinear matrix factorization via GP (I-GP) [10, 14] is a link prediction method, which is a hot technique in the recommendation system. This method treats different link prediction tasks independently. However, the author–topic model express the relationship between users and items explicitly, but not by the kernel function. And the second level of the author–topic model combines the different two domains together.

5 Conclusions

Transfer learning has been used to deal with the data-sparsity difficulty in the recommendation system. In this paper, we propose a fusion author–topic model to solve the heterogeneousness in the cross-domain. The two levels of topic in the proposed model can express the information in cross-domain in different levels. The subdomain topics can express the single domain feature space, while the full-domain topics can represent the predicted real-world feature space. The results of the experiment indicate that extracting multilevel topics can help to discover the correlation in cross-domain, and to extract the real-world feature space.

Acknowledgments

The paper was supported by National Natural Science Foundation of China under Grant No. U1135005 and the Project for the National Basic Research 12th Five Program under Grant No. 0101050302.

References

[1] G. Adomavicius, A. Tuzhilin, Toward the next generation of recommender system: A survey of the state-of-the-art and possible extensions. *IEEE Transactions on Knowledge and Data Engineering*, **17(6)**, pp. 734–749, 2005.

[2] J.A. Konstan, B.N. Miller, D. Maltz, J.L. Herlocker, L.R. Gordon, J. Riedl, GroupLens: Appling collaborative filtering to Usenet news. *Communications of the ACM*, **40(3)**, pp. 77–87, 1997.

[3] B. Sarwar, G. Karypis, J. Konstan, J. Reidl, Item-based collaborative filtering recommendation algorithms. *Proc. of the 10th Int. Conf. World Wide Web*. ACM: Hong Kong, pp. 285–295, 2001.

[4] M. Pazzani, D. Billsus, Learning and revising user profiles: The identification of interesting web sites. *Machine and Learning*, **27(3)**, pp. 313–331, 1997.

[5] R.J. Mooney, L. Roy, Content-based book recommending using learning for text categorization. *Proc. of the 5th ACM Conf. on Digital Libraries*. ACM: New York, NY, pp. 195–204, 2000.

[6] P. Melville, R.J. Mooney, R. Nagarajan, Content-boosted collaborative filtering for improved recommendations. *Eighteenth National Conf. on Artificial Intelligence*. American Association for Artificial Intelligence: Menlo Park, CA, pp. 187–192, 2002.

[7] M. Balabanovic, Y. Shoham, Fab: content-based, collaborative recommendation. *Communications of the ACM*, **40(3)**, pp. 66–72, 1997.

[8] H. Ma, I. King, M.R. Lyu, Effective missing data prediction for collaborative filtering. *Proc. of the 30th Annual Int. ACM SIGIR Conf. on Research and Development in Information Retrieval*. ACM: New York, NY, pp. 39–46, 2007.

[9] S. Tan, J. Bu, X. Qin, C. Chen, D. Cai, Cross domain recommendation based on multi-type media fusion. *Neurocomputing*, **127(2014)**, pp. 124–134, 2014.

[10] B. Cao, N.N. Liu, Q. Yang, Transfer learning for collective link prediction in multiple heterogeneous domains. *Proc. of the 27th Int. Conf. on Machine Learning*. ACM: New York, pp. 159–166, 2010.

[11] D. Kollar, M. Friedman, *Probabilistic Graphical Models Principle and Techniques*. MIT Press: USA, pp. 713–715. 2009.

[12] Z. Shen, P. Luo, S. Yang, X. Shen, Topic modeling ensembles. *2010 IEEE Int. Conf. on Data Mining*. IEEE: Sydney, Australia, pp. 1031–1036, 2010.

[13] M. Steyvers, P. Smyth, T. Griffiths, Probabilistic author–topic models for information discovery. *Proc. of the 10th SIGKDD Conf. Knowledge Discovery and Data Mining*. ACM Seattle, USA, pp. 306–315, 2004.

[14] N.D. Lawrence, R. Urtasum, Non-linear matrix factorization with Gaussian processes. *Proc. of the 26th Int. Conf. on Machine Learning*. ACM: Canada, pp. 601–608, 2009.

A star structure with HashMap

Ningning Gao
Department of Computer, Information College, Minzu University, Beijing, 100081, China

Abstract

This paper makes a study of HashMap, a sort of collection, for the data of a star-structure supporting by a data warehouse. This aim in Java language is quite successful, which the data of a star structure was displayed thoroughly. Furthermore, around the result, there was a series of discussing and programming. These activities caused some useful conclusions. The result suggests that further research in collection structure of Java should be worthwhile for the mass data processing.
Keywords: star structure, HashMap, data expression, mass data.

1 Introduction

It is a study item using a collection framework for processing multidimensional data recently. A collection represents a set of objects; while the collection framework is an object provided by Java which can be composed of other objects. The collection framework is an architecture, which can be unified and represented collections, even operated on the collections [1]. The collection framework provides interfaces, classes, and algorithms for object management. It should be very useful for the storing and processing object data.

As the information society developing for today, more and more people realize that it is very important for them to have the useful information. And this desire beyond the speed of the development of information technology promotes the development of data processing technology further more. In the past few decades, many enterprises use a relational database to store and manage business data and establish the corresponding application system to support daily operations. This is called on-line transaction processing (OLTP) application, its storing data is called operational data or business data. With the increasingly fierce competition for the market, enterprises emphasize the decision accuracy and timeliness, which make the application supporting management decision analysis as the main aim to rise rapidly, and this type of application is called on-line analytical processing (OLAP), the storing data is called information data [2]. Modern OLAP system is generally based on data warehouse, which is a subcollection of extracting detail data from the data warehouse supplies data for the front-end analysis tools through necessarily accumulating and storing.

Being to the study of storage and processing of mass data is just unfolding, the data warehouse, OLAP, data mining technologies are most prominent in this area, and they are paid close attention by more and more senior decision people and management people of the enterprises. This paper describes the research work which is mainly about the multidimensional data with the Java collection framework, and the results were researched and discussed. It is hoped that this research will cause some relevant people's attention and promotes the development of mass data storing and processing research.

2 The main method

Object oriented programming (OOP) makes the effective multidimensional data processing. In the star model shown in Figure 1, three tables can be expressed with class Product, class Seller, and class Fact, as follows:

```
<algorithm>class Product{            //Product Table
  public String proID = "";
  private String Name = "";
  private String Origin = "";
  private String Brand = "";
  ….…..
  public String getProductproID()
  {
    return proID;
  }
  public String getProductName()
  {
    return Name;
  }
  ….…..
  public void setProductproID(String proid)
  {
    proID = proid;
  }
  …..…..
  public void setProductBrand(String brand)
  {
    Brand = brand;
  }
```

```java
  public String toString()
  {
   String information = "ProductID："+proID+", Name："+Name;
   if(!Origin.equals(""))
    information += ", Source："+Origin;
   if(!Brand.equals(""))
    information += ", Brand："+Brand;
   return information;
  }
}
class Seller{                    //Seller Table
  public String seID = "";
  private String Name = "";
  private String Store = "";
  private String Area = "";
  .........
  public String getSellerseID()
  {
   return seID;
  }
  public String getSellerName()
  {
   return Name;
  }
  ........
  public void setSellerseID(String seid)
  {
   seID = seid;
  }
  public void setSellerName(String name)
  {
   Name = name;
  }
  ........
  public String toString()
  {
   String information = "Seller ID："+seID+", Name："+Name;
   if(!Store.equals(""))
    information += ",Position："+Store;
   if(!Area.equals(""))
    information += ", Area："+Area;
   return information;
  }
}
class Facts{                          //Fact Table
```

```
public String proID = "";
public String seID = "";
private float unitPrice = 0;
private int Num = 0;

public Facts(String proid, String seid, float unitprice, int num)
{
  proID = proid;
  seID = seid;
  this.unitPrice = unitprice;
  this.Num = num;
}

public String getFactsproID()
{
  return proID;
}
public String getFactsseID()
{
  return seID;
}
.........
}
```

An object is an instance of a class, object data are sealed by classes. However, for the data and its structure as shown in Figure 1, how would you think? That is star logical model and a physical model of a data warehouse. If the star model can be described using Java language, the storage and operation of the star data will be very favorable.

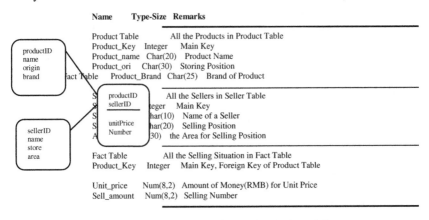

Name	Type-Size	Remarks
Product Table		All the Products in Product Table
Product_Key	Integer	Main Key
Product_name	Char(20)	Product Name
Product_ori	Char(30)	Storing Position
Product_Brand	Char(25)	Brand of Product
		All the Sellers in Seller Table
	teger	Main Key
	har(10)	Name of a Seller
	har(20)	Selling Position
	30)	the Area for Selling Position
Fact Table		All the Selling Situation in Fact Table
Product_Key	Integer	Main Key, Foreign Key of Product Table
Unit_price	Num(8,2)	Amount of Money(RMB) for Unit Price
Sell_amount	Num(8,2)	Selling Number

Figure 1: Star logic model to physical model.

The vector class implements an extendable data array. The map interface (mapping) is a collection of storing key value, which is also called key value collection [3]. The implementing class of this interface is HashMap based on a hash table. And their reasonable combination can achieve the star logical model as follows:

```
<algorithm>Vector productVec = new Vector();
Vector sellerVec = new Vector();
Vector factVec = new Vector();

HashMap map = new HashMap();
map.put ("proID", productVec);
map.put ("seID", sellerVec);
map.put ("proID", factVec);
```

Here a vector object is created first in order to call object data of a table [4]. Then map, a HashMap object is created to store a key value pair for the relations of tables. Although put method is a method of map interface, its implementing son classes can use this method to add the key value that has the relation of tables to the time and space domain of map object.

3 Results

3.1 A star structure with HashMap

In fact, a data star structure is realized with HashMap of Java language. In this way, any data structure can be obtained no matter how many dimensions the star structure has. Some programs show that data and their relations can be collected in the vector and HashMap, respectively.

3.2 Data expression

For the collection of data [5], a thorough expression can be displayed according to the type of object in a star structure with HashMap [6], like the following codes:

```
<algorithm>for(int i=0; i<productVec.size(); i++)
  {
    Product one = (Product)productVec.get(i);
    System.out.println((Product)productVec.get(i));
  }

  for(int i=0; i<sellerVec.size(); i++)
  {
    Seller one = (Seller)sellerVec.get(i);
    System.out.println((Seller)sellerVec.get(i));
```

```
C:\WINDOWS\system32\cmd.exe                                    - □ ×

E:\xx-2013\test5>java FactsEx
ProductID: 0001A, Name: Clothes, Source: XinYuan, Brand: XinXinYuan
ProductID: 0002A, Name: Clothes, Source: XinYuan, Brand: XinXinYuan
SellerID: 010001, Name: LeSi,Position: 030, Area: JiangSu
SellerID: 010005, Name: WangWu,Position: 007, Area: ShanDong
ProductID: 0001A, SellerID: 010001, Unit Price: 28.8, Number: 58
ProductID: 0001A, SellerID: 010005, Unit Price: 28.8, Number: 101

E:\xx-2013\test5>
```

Figure 2: Results for data expression.

```
}

for(int i=0; i<factVec.size(); i++)
{
  Facts one = (Facts)factVec.get(i);
  System.out.println((Facts)factVec.get(i));

}
```

The result of execution is shown in Figure 2. There are the data of Product Class, Seller Class, and Facts Class in it. Although there are only two records for each class, it is suggested that the data sealed by a star structure with HashMap can be displayed.

4   Discussion

4.1 Multidimensional data cube

With the help of HashMap, it is easy to display multidimensional data cube, as mentioned above. It means that multi-OLAP can be carried at least in form as relation OLAP. The reason is that HashMap is a son of Map, which has a put method. This method would make the key and its value added to the Map, as well as their relation. And if the key exists already, the put method only adds the value, makes the relation to the existed key.

In the past, there were ROLAP (Relational OLAP), MOLAP (Multidimensional OLAP), and HOLAP (Hybrid OLAP) for OLAP. Now, they can be united under the real OLAP for study. Moreover, in theory, it can build any complicated multidimensional data cube. For example, either vector type object or HashMap type object can be put into a star structure with HashMap. It depends on the real requirements of processing data.

4.2 No storage effect

It is a little pity that the work mentioned didn't observe any storing effect although it was used to be wished. In fact, the collection can only be accepting

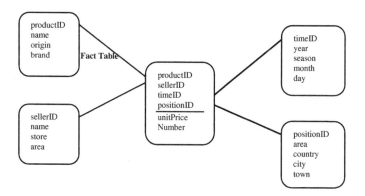

Figure 3: Adding two dimensions for OLAP.

the star structure and making more complicated query. Of course, for this reason, it will be a very convenient way to make any query for a data warehouse with a star model.

For example, if one wants to know about money, just change the codes as the following:

```
<algorithm>for (int i=0; i<factVec.size(i); i++)
{
    Fact one = (Fact) factVec.get(i);
    String proID = one.getFactporID();
    float unitPrice = one.getFactunitPrice();
    int Num = one.getFactNum();
    float Money = unitPrice * Num
    System.out.println( "ProductID: " +proID+ " \t Amount of Money: "
+String.valueOf(Money));
}
```

Although the method didn't reach the aim of storing data, it can manage or watch the data from a warehouse at least.

4.3 Supporting OLAP

It is obviously that the method can analyze a multidimensional cube through queries as mentioned above. And so does OLAP. For instance, adding time-dimension and position-dimension to the fact table see Figure 3.

These new dimensions can be used to multidimensional analysis, such as drilling, slicing. In Java, Figure 3 can be described as following:

```
<algorithm>Vector productVec = new Vector();
Vector sellerVec = new Vector();
```

```
Vector timeVec = new Vector();
Vector posVec = new Vector();
Vector factVec = new Vector();

HashMap map = new HashMap();
map.put ("proID", productVec);
map.put ("seID", sellerVec);
map.put ("timeID", timeVec);
map.put ("posID", postVec);
map.put ("proID", factVec);
```

5 Summary

Study on collection, such as Map and its implementing classes, shows that there is a hope to realize a star structure of a data warehouse. Programming in Java to this aim is not an easy work. And a successful star structure with HashMap is obtained. Its data are clearly displayed further.

However, during interpreting the program to implement a star structure with HashMap, some warnings on data type occurred, as Java is strong type and very rigid interpretive language. Nevertheless, this is a good start at the beginning in some sense. With the help of OOP, data watching, data querying, data managing shall be carried on in the star structure of a warehouse.

Acknowledgments

Thanks for my mother, Jinying Wang, for her tolerance of seeing me working back.

References

[1] Yongqing Pang, Lijuan Pang, *Learn in 21 Dats*. Publishing House Of Electronics Industry: Beijing, pp. 366–385, 2009 (in Chinese).
[2] Yoonjae Choi, Pum-Mo Ryu, Hyunki Kim, Changki Lee, Extracting events from web documents for social media monitoring using structured SVM. *IEICE*, E96-D No.6, pp. 1410–1414, 2013.
[3] Yongjie Li, Xinwei Chen, *Concise Course of Java Program Design*. Publishing House of People's Post and Telecommunications: Beijing, pp. 152–153, 2008 (in Chinese).
[4] Zhenhua Jia, Lianying Zhuang, Siqingbara, Yongsheng Shi, *Program Design of Java Language* (2nd Edition). Publishing House Of Water Conservancy and Electricity of China: Beijing, pp. 110–116, 2010 (in Chinese).
[5] Binhua Huang, *Boast Java*. Publishing House of Science: Beijing, pp. 277–279, 2009 (in Chinese).
[6] Lankeshwara Munasinghe, Ryutaro Ichise, Link prediction in social networks using information flow via active links. *IEICE*, E96-D No.7 pp. 1495–1502, 2013.

Comparison of different methods of the e-commerce system

Bijian Xu

Chongqing Three Gorges University, Wanzhou, Chongqing, China

Abstract

Through the comparison of the four levels of the global layer, the conceptual design layer, the navigation design layer, as well as the system implementation layer of five development methods of RMM, OOHDM, CMU2WEB, WSDM, and Autoweb of the e-commerce system, we can conclude the following points: the CMU2WEB method is only a conceptual model and its support for the entire development process of the e-commerce system is not perfect, so it's not of too much practical significance; OOHDM and WSDM methods adopt the idea of object-oriented modeling, this model-driven design approach, compared to those traditional data-driven approaches, can better adapt to the complex and changeable characteristics of the e-commerce system; Autoweb is the most striking and it performs well in each project of the comparative framework and the only development method that establishes the CASE environment, which will greatly reduce the intensity of the work of developers and improve the efficiency of the development of the e-commerce system.

Key words: e-commerce system; structured analysis; design methods.

1 Introduction

The e-commerce system is a multimedia and a Web-based information system; like other types of information systems, the e-commerce system needs analysis and design methods in line with its own characteristics. The correct analysis and design of the e-commerce system is one of the conditions for the correct implementation of the e-commerce system. Since the early 1990s, researchers have begun the research on analysis and design methods of the Web information system; despite the endless research results, most of them are still in the stage of theoretical research and only a very small number of them are applied; besides, the existing e-commerce system has not yet the dominant analysis and design method similar to the structured analysis and design methods at that time, which also indicates that a perfect method recognized by the industry hasn't appeared. Therefore, it's an urgent need to compare the mainstream analysis and design methods, to analyze their advantages and disadvantages, to learn from each other and complement each other and to constantly improve them.

2 Comparative framework of development methods of the e-commerce system

2.1 The basis to establish the framework

Lee [1] once made simple comparison study for major development methods of the e-commerce system and one comparative perspective is the phasing of development methods, but he only listed stages of various methods and there was no comparison. In this study, I attempted to make detailed comparison of the development process and put forward the comparative framework from the following two aspects. First, in accordance with the method of software engineering, system development is generally a structured process, especially for the large-scale system development like the e-commerce system. Second, the development of the e-commerce system has its own uniqueness. After comparison of a number of the e-commerce system's development processes, Baskerville [2] summarized the characteristics of the development process, including short development cycle, uncertainty of the demand, prototyping method, constantly upgrading versions, parallel development, fixed design structure, programming according to their own styles, negotiability of system quality, relying on excellent technicians, necessity of a new structure to integrate resources.

On the basis of the above considerations, the comparative framework for the e-commerce system's development methods can be designed for four levels: the global layer, the conceptual design layer, the navigation design layer, and the system implementation layer.

2.2 The global layer

The global layer compares and analyzes the characteristics of the design and development of various methods from an overall point of view. What's compared in this level includes the development stage, the output of each stage, and the degree of support of CASE in the entire process. In the development stage, compare whether the development method covers all stages of system development; the typical stages of development of an e-commerce system should include the requirement analysis stage, the conceptual design stage, the navigation design stage, the system implementation stage, and the system maintenance stage.

Certainly, we cannot evaluate the advantages and disadvantages of a development method only by checking how many development stages are

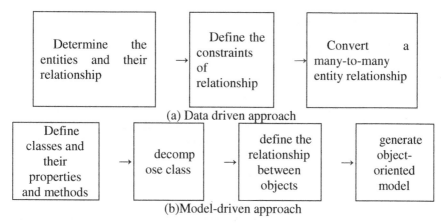

Figure 1: (a) The data-driven and (b) the model-driven approach.

covered; it also needs to look at the depth of the support of the various stages of development methods. Therefore, the purpose of comparing output results at all stages is to compare whether the various development methods can clearly output the results of system development at all stages and whether these results are of sufficient readability. The comparison of the development environment supports is whether different development methods can provide the support of CASE tools for the development of the e-commerce system in various stages.

2.3 The conceptual design layer

The conceptual design layer is the first level of the development of the e-commerce system and is the basis of the entire development process, covering all stages from the system demand analysis to the system concept modeling. What's compared in this level includes drive approaches of design and support for network resources and media.

The drive approaches of the e-commerce system design are mainly divided into two types: the data-driven approach and the model-driven approach. The data-driven approach is a drive approach of design with the structured design and the model-driven approach adopts the object-oriented design idea; their design steps are shown in Figure 1.

One of the most important differences between the e-commerce system and traditional information systems is that the e-commerce system can take full advantage of the resources of the network and perform information in a variety of media forms. The main content of support of network resources and media is the support means of development methods of the e-commerce system for network resources and the media, that is, how these development methods represent and organize images, sounds, videos, texts, and other information.

2.4 The navigation design layer

Navigation design is the characteristic of the development of the e-commerce system and is also called dynamic design. At this level, developers need to establish navigation path and links that meet the system requirements for entities, objects, relationships, and information in the conceptual design level. At this level, it mainly compares the link ways of the system and the access structure of the system. The link ways of the system mainly compare the level of support of the development method for the nodes of the system, all kinds of information as well as the relationship passing between the nodes and the information. The comparison will also bring in some situations to test whether these development methods are able to fully or in part perform system synchronization, page generation, external links, and other special circumstances. The structure of the system access is definition means and the set environment used to analyze and compare the access structure of the e-commerce system of various development methods. In the comparison, it mainly compares from the two aspects of the access unit and access methods.

2.5 The system implementation layer

The system implementation layer makes analysis and comparison from the physical implementation layer of the e-commerce system; at this level, the developers will take advantage of a variety of tools provided by development methods to convert the logical model formed in the previous level into actual physical system, thus completing the construction work of an e-commerce system. What's compared in this level includes is given in the following sections.

2.6 The physical performance form of the system

It mainly studies whether various development methods cover the process of generating a physical system from the logical model; if they cover it, how they respectively carry out the process. It makes evaluation mainly from the study on the interaction of the physical system's client side and server side, the interaction of system database and handling conditions of system events.

2.7 The automation degree of system generation

It mainly makes research on the degree of support of various development methods in the process of converting the logical model into a physical system for the automatically generated page. It makes tests on the support degree for generating dynamic page from database and the support degree for generating static pages from a template.

2.8 The support degree of system maintenance

Compare whether each development method supports system maintenance; if it does, which part of the system can be maintained and which cannot be maintained. The project mainly makes test on the degree of difficulty of system expansion and the degree of support for maintaining system links (including discovering and repairing inoperative links).

3 Comparison of the analysis and design of different development methods of the e-commerce system

RMM [3], OOHDM [4] CMU2WEB [5], WSDM [6], and Autoweb [7] are normally used methods in modern days. We will compare these five development methods of the e-commerce systems.

3.1 Comparison in the global layer

3.1.1 The development stage

Due to the special nature of the e-commerce system development, the conceptual design stage and the navigation design stage are the development stages covered by all five development methods. In addition, because the ultimate purpose of the system development is to generate the actual physical system available, there are four ways covering the system implementation stage. Finally, the Autoweb method is the most comprehensive and complex, covering all of the system's development processes and even the maintenance stage of the other four methods do not cover.

3.1.2 Output of various stages

For developers, the convergence of the various stages of the development of the e-commerce system is particularly important and it is mainly manifested in, on the one hand, which results on the previous stage are exported to the next stage; on the other hand, the next stage needs to rely on which output of the previous stage as the basis. This is the so-called consistency of the system development. Only the continuous consistency can ensure that each stage of the system development is around the same theme. In these five ways, RMM is of the highest consistency; in its development process, each stage of it takes full advantage of the result of the output of the previous stage. For example, the fragment design needs to use the ER diagram generated by the physical design, while the ER+ diagram generated by the fragment design is also precisely the necessary design information for the navigation design. In addition, the consistency of Autoweb approach is also high, especially in the process of the infrastructure design, the access path design, and the expression design; the three designs connect with each other in a chain and each is designed to provide a basis and clue for the subsequent design. The CMU2WEB method is of minimum consistency, which is caused mainly because this method focuses on the conceptual design stage of the system.

3.1.3 Support of the development environment

If the development method can provide CASE environment to assist developers to develop, it will greatly accelerate the speed of development of the system and improve the efficiency of the work of developers. CMU2WEB and WSDM have no support of the development environment; in contrast, Autoweb's development method provides developers with the CASE environment except the system maintenance stage, which means that this development method can greatly simplify and accelerate the development process of the e-commerce system.

3.2 Comparison of the conceptual design layer

3.2.1 Design the drive approach

The RMM method is inherited from the ER approach and therefore it is a data-driven approach; the OOHDM method uses the object-oriented design idea and is a model-driven approach; the main part of the CMU2WEB method is the entities and relationships, and therefore it belongs to the data-driven approach; the WSDM method begins with the user classification and modeling and is a model-driven approach; the Autoweb method's conceptual design stage uses the HDM-lite model, so it is a model-driven approach.

3.2.2 Support for network resources and media

As the most important difference between the e-commerce system and traditional information systems, support of various developing methods for the network resources and media is an important criterion to evaluate them. In addition to CMU2WEB, other four development methods all make use of an entity or object attribute to express a variety of network resources and the media; for example, in the OOHDM development method, we can define a property for the product object appearance, and then the property can be used to add the image information that can demonstrate the appearance of the product.

3.3 Comparison of the navigation design layer

3.3.1 Link ways of the system

Good and systematic links will direct users of the system to properly use system resources; therefore, the link way of system is also a basic design aspect of the e-commerce system.

The RMM method uses three different types of links: the condition index link, the condition guiding link, and the condition index guiding link. The condition index link is mainly used for database retrieval; the condition guiding link is used for the system guiding guidance; the condition index guiding link can be applied to integrate condition of both cases.

OOHDM and WSDM both use the object-oriented design idea, so they only have one link way, which uses simple directional arrows to represent the links between objects.

As the navigation performance is a fundamental indicator of the e-commerce system, the CMU-WEB method relies mainly on the link to determine the availability of the application system. In the CMU2WEB model, links have three forms: one represents the relationship between the information blocks; one represents the relationship between the information block and its description; another represents the navigation path between the information block and pages.

In the Autoweb model, the links between the various sets of information are divided into the following four types: the index link, the guide link, the index and guide link, and the complete link. Each of these links aims for different conditions of system navigation.

3.3.2 The system access structure

The system access methods are mainly divided into two types: one is the directional arrow and the other is the navigation restriction. The directional arrow adopted by these methods of OOHDM, CMU2WEB, and WSDM only can simply represent a unidirectional or bidirectional link between the access unit, but the navigation restriction adopted by these methods of RMM and Autoweb can add more dimension for the links to the system; for example, when a customer buys goods online, the system designed by the Autoweb method can take advantage of the index and guide link to provide customers with the relevant information.

3.4 Comparison of the system implementation layer

3.4.1 The physical manifestations of the system

A good development method needs to grasp the smooth transition from the design stage to the implementation stage and should provide the relevant tools to simplify the process of transition from the logical model to the physical system. In this regard, these five development methods have different levels of support:

The RMM method adopts the method generating HTML template and associates each object with the nodes and access units of the logical model in the HTML page.

The OOHDM method has specialized and abstract interface design stage and the system implementation stage. Navigation objects, user interface objects, and multimedia objects are described in the abstract interface design; in the system implementation stage, OOHDM provides the specialized OOHDM-Web environment to help developers generate the page template.

The CMU-WEB method does not cover the system implementation stage.

The WSDM method has the implementation design stage and the system implementation stage; in the implementation design stage, developers need to start from the system's availability and design the implementation program of the entire e-commerce system based on the guiding principles of the WSDM method, and then put it into practice in the system implementation stage.

Compared with other developers, the Autoweb method has better physical design stage; at this stage, the developers create the system expression model and the style form and then automatically generate Web pages in the CASE environment provided by Autoweb.

3.4.2 The degree of automation of the system generation

Methods of RMM, CMU2WEB, and WSDM do not provide any auxiliary tools to automatically generate pages of the e-commerce system; OOHDM and

Autoweb provide tools that can automatically generate pages to a certain extent. OOHDM provides the OOHDM2Web environment; in the environment, the software automatically generates pages that combine the HTML code and the OOHDM2Web library calls, so its generated page must be operated in the OOHDM2Web environment.

Otherwise, Autoweb provides an automated system generator called "Schema & DataEntryGenerator"; when developers input the designed conceptual model of HDM2lite, the system will automatically output a relational database as well as the corresponding system page; therefore, it has wider applications.

3.4.3 The support level of system maintenance

In addition to Autoweb, the other four development methods do not support adaptive type and perfect type of system maintenance, thereby greatly reducing the scalability of the e-commerce system developed by them, which is now a point where the e-commerce system's development methods need an urgent improvement. However, because most development methods (except for CMU-WEB) have a very thorough analysis stage, most of them support the error correction type of system maintenance, that is, the process of the system design can be repeated. On the other hand, Autoweb provides far more maintenance support for the system than other development methods and provide a lot of help for updating, expanding, and improving of the e-commerce system.

4 Conclusions

Through the comparison of five development methods of RMM, OOHDM, CMU2WEB, WSDM, and Autoweb of the e-commerce system, we can conclude the following points:

(1) Although the CMU2WEB method makes a breakthrough in using quantitative criteria to evaluate the availability of the e-commerce system's design program, it is only a conceptual model and its support for the entire development process of the e-commerce system is not perfect, so it's not of too much practical significance.

(2) OOHDM and WSDM methods adopt the idea of object-oriented modeling; this model-driven design approach, compared to those traditional data-driven approaches, can better adapt to the complex and changeable characteristics of the e-commerce system.

(3) Autoweb is the most striking and it performs well in each project of the comparative framework; besides, among these five methods, Autoweb is the only development method that establishes the CASE environment, and the CASE environment will greatly reduce the intensity of the work of developers and improve the efficiency of the development of the e-commerce system.

References

[1] H. Lee, C. Lee, C. Yoo, A scenario based object oriented hypermedia methodology. Information and Management, **36**, pp.121–138, 1999.

[2] R. Baskerville, Racing the e-bomb : How the Internet is redefining information systems development methodology. In: *Realigning Research and Practice in Is Development: The Social and Organizational Perspective*, Kluwer, New York, pp. 49–68, 2001.

[3] T. Isakowitz, E.A. Stohr, P. Balasubramanian, RMM: a methodology for structured hypermedia design. Communications of the ACM, **38(8)**, pp. 34–44, 1995.

[4] D. Schwabe, G. Rossi, The object 2 oriented hypermedia design model. Communication of ACM, **38(8)**, pp. 45–46, 1995.

[5] A. Bajaj, R. Krishnan, CMU2WEB: a conceptual model for usablemweb applications. Journal of Database Management, **10(4)**, pp. 33–43, 1999.

[6] O. De Troyer, K. Leune, WSDM: a user centered design method for web sites. In: *Proceedings of the Seventh International WWW Conference*, Elsevier, Brisbane, Australia, pp. 85–94, 1998.

[7] P. Fraternali, P. Paolini, A conceptual model and a tool environment for developing more scalable and dynamic web applications. In: *Proceedings of International Conference on Extending Database Technology*, Springer, Valencia, Spain, pp. 421–435, 1998.

A hybrid simulated annealing algorithm for infinite multi-person co-opetition game

Jie Su[1], Chuanliang Jia[1], Junfeng Li[2]
[1]*School of Management Science and Engineering, Central University of Finance and Economics, Beijing, P.R. China*
[2]*China Huayou (Group) Corporation, Beijing, P.R. China*

Abstract

Co-opetition game is one important type game other than the traditional cooperative game and competitive game; however, there are both cooperative and competitive relationships in the same co-opetition game. And it is much more complex for the two cross types of relationship act simultaneously. The decision-making of a type of infinite multi-person co-opetition game (IMCG) is discussed, in which the competitive players would achieve themselves profits severally by coming to terms finitely. And the generalized equilibrium of IMCG is defined, then the lexicographical goals of mathematical model for which is proposed. Thereafter a homogeneous mutative scaled simulated annealing (SA) algorithm for the generalized equilibrium is put forward and the numerical simulation of example demonstrates the effectiveness and feasibility of the approach.

Keywords: co-opetition game, infinite multi-person, generalized equilibrium, homogeneous mutative scaled simulated annealing.

1 Introduction

There are two contrary kinds of traditional relationships among players in a game—cooperation and competition [1]. But in the recent 20 years, the relationships among enterprises or persons have become much more complex, and "we win, you win" has come to replace "we win, you lose" in many times. The reason is that enterprises or persons can be benefitted from both cooperation and competition simultaneously.

Wilkinson and Young [2] show that both cooperation and competition are needed in vertical relationships. Luo [3] introduces the co-opetition as a new

WIT Transactions on Information and Communication Technologies, Vol. 61, © 2014 WIT Press
www.witpress.com, ISSN 1743-3517 (on-line)
doi:10.2495/MIIT131071

business strategy that combines the advantages of both competition and cooperation system. If both the elements of cooperation and competition are visible in one game, the relationship between the players is named as co-opetition [4]. Bengtsson and Kock [5] study the co-opetition among industries in business networks. Loebbeche et al. [6] discuss co-opetition in the knowledge transfer. Hausken [7] study the co-opetition between group competitions. Liu et al. [8] discuss the equilibrium for a special co-opetition game.

The complexity of co-opetition relationships lies on that there are two different logics of interaction. And the relationship between cooperation and competition can have different shapes depending on the degrees and the action fashions of cooperation and competition.

In this paper, we discuss the decision-making of a type of infinite multi-person co-opetition game (IMCG); in the game, competitive players would achieve themselves profits severally by coming to terms finitely. In the section "The decision-making of IMCG," the lexicographical goals mathematical model for the co-opetition continuous multi-person game is proposed, and the definition of generalized equilibrium for IMCG is brought forward. A homogeneous mutative scaled simulated annealing (SA) algorithm for the optimal decision-making is put forward in the section "The mutative scaled SA algorithm for IMCG." And computational results show the feasibility and efficiency of the SA algorithm in the section "Computational results and discussion."

2 The decision-making of IMCG

In this section, we focus on the cooperative relationships among the competitive players and then establish an optimization model of IMCG.

2.1 The basic structure of IMCG

Similar as cooperative game and competitive game, a co-opetition infinite multi-person game is consisting of the three parts:

(1) The set of finite players $N = \{1,2,\ldots,n\}$
   There are n independent players in the game, where $n \geq 3$. And it is equality between the players.
(2) The state-space of game X
   The strategy set of player i is denoted as

$$X_i = \{x_i\} \subseteq \mathfrak{R}^{M_i} \tag{1}$$

for $i \in N$. And for any $x_i \in X_i$, x_i is a strategy of player i. Then

$$X = X_1 \times X_2 \times \cdots \times X_n \subseteq \mathfrak{R}^M \tag{2}$$

is the state-space of game, where $M = M_1 + M_2 + \cdots M_n$ and "×" is Descartes multiply operation. Let

$$X_{\bar{i}} = X_1 \times \cdots \times X_{i-1} \times X_{i+1} \times \cdots \times X_n \tag{3}$$

then $X = X_i \times X_{\bar{i}}$ for $i = 1,2,\ldots n$. Similarly, $x = (x_1, x_2, \ldots, x_n) \in X$ can be noted as $x = (x_i, x_{\bar{i}}), i \in N$.

In fact, because of the interaction among the behavior of all players and the existence of some restriction in practice, the state-space X is not always effective, i.e., there always are some situations in X which cannot be achieved.

Since the effective strategy of each player will be affected from the others, set X_i will be influenced by $X_{\bar{i}}$, $i \in N$. Furthermore, if strategy set X_i of player i could be described with function constraints.

(3) The partially order set on the state-space " $\succeq$ "

Let " $\succeq_i$ "denotes the partially order of player i on the state-space X, $i \in N$, and the partially order set in the game is

$$\succeq = \{\succeq_1, \succeq_2, \cdots, \succeq_n\} \tag{4}$$

And the main differences is the three types of games rest with the type of the partially order. In competitive game, the partially order $\succeq_i$ $(i \in N)$ is self-governed by player i completely without caring the others partially orders. Contrarily, in cooperative game, all players have the same partially order, i.e., $\succeq_1 = \succeq_2 = \cdots = \succeq_n$, for that all players just devote themselves attention to the team behalf.

However, other than the two types above, the partially order in co-opetition game involves both of the individual's profit and the team behalf—although each player has own partially order, but they also can come to some terms based on their partially orders. So there are two sides in the partially order of player i, one is his or her own self-governed partially order, noted as $\succeq_i^1$, the other is the partially order of team behalf, noted as $\succeq_i^2$. Hereby in IMCG, the partially order is the interaction of $\succeq^1$ and $\succeq^2$. Moreover, in the infinite game, we can use utility functions to express the material form of partially orders.

Summing up the above, an IMCG can be expressed as $\langle N, X, \succeq^1, \succeq^2 \rangle$.

2.2 The generalized equilibrium of IMCG

First, we introduce the optimization model of IMCG in the form of mathematical programming.

Suppose that the strategy set of player

$$X_i = \{x_i : g_i(x_i, x_{\bar{i}}) \geq 0, h_i(x_i, x_{\bar{i}}) = 0\} \tag{5}$$

where $g_i : \Re^M \to R^{k_i}$ and $h_i : \Re^M \to R^{m_i}$ are constraint functions, $i \in N$. The utility function of player i's own self-governed partially order $\succeq_i^1$ is noted as

$$u_i(x_i, x_{\bar{i}}) : \Re^M \to R, \quad i = 1, 2, \dots, n \tag{6}$$

The partially order of team behalf $\succeq^2$ is defined as to maximizing the degree of everyone's satisfaction on condition of doing justice to everyone, and large of small degrees of player i's satisfaction rest with many or few profits of his or her.

And for equilibrium programming (EP), problem has been made use of to illuminate Nash equilibria [10,11]. Therefore, the model of IMCG just with partially order $\succeq^1$ can be described as an EP problem

$$
\begin{aligned}
\max_{x_i} \quad & u_i(x_i, x_{\bar{i}}) \\
s.t. \quad & g_i(x_i, x_{\bar{i}}) \geq 0, \quad i = 1, 2, \dots, n \\
& h_i(x_i, x_{\bar{i}}) = 0;
\end{aligned} \tag{7}
$$

Now we focus that how the partially order of team behalf $\succeq^2$ will affect the decisions of players in IMCG.

If there are some terms among all players in game, then apparently, the most satisfactory result of player $i(i \in N)$ should be that he or she acts the only leader and the others obey him or her, so his or her decision model should be

$$
\begin{aligned}
\max_{x_i} \quad & u_i(x_i, x_{\bar{i}}) \\
s.t. \quad & g_i(x_i, x_{\bar{i}}) \geq 0, \quad i = 1, 2, \dots, n \\
& h_i(x_i, x_{\bar{i}}) = 0, \quad i = 1, 2, \dots, n
\end{aligned} \tag{8}
$$

and denote the optimal solution and optimal value of problem (8) by $(x_i^0, x_{\bar{i}}^0)$ and $u_i^0, i \in N$.

By contrary, it must be quite discontented for player i to only submit to the others decisions as a follower but not to make his own decision. So the minimum value of u_j^0 for all $j \neq i$ is the worst choose for player i.

Both competitive and cooperative relationships are involved in IMCG and nobody can act as the leader, so for all players the above two extreme cases will not occur generally. However, u_i^0 and $\min_{j \neq i} u_j^0$ could offer the upper and lower bounds for player i's satisfaction, noted as u_i^U and u_i^L, $i = 1, 2, \dots, n$.

Thus the degree of player i's satisfaction for every situation $(x_i, x_{\bar{i}}) \in X$ can be defined as the following:

Definition 2.1: For any situation $(x_i, x_{\bar{i}}) \in X$, we call

$$\lambda_i(u_i(x_i, x_{\bar{i}})) = \begin{cases} 1, & \text{if } u_i(x_i, x_{\bar{i}}) \ge u_i^{U} \\ \dfrac{u_i(x_i, x_{\bar{i}}) - u_i^{L}}{u_i^{U} - u_i^{L}}, & \text{if } u_i^{L} < u_i(x_i, x_{\bar{i}}) < u_i^{U} \\ 0, & \text{if } u_i(x_i, x_{\bar{i}}) \ge u_i^{U} \end{cases} \quad (9)$$

the degree of player i's satisfaction for situation $(x_i, x_{\bar{i}}) \in X$, where $f^i(x, c^i, a^i, b^i)$ is the optimal objective value of problem (7).

And the generalized equilibrium situation of IMCG could be defined as the following:

Definition 2.2: The generalized equilibrium situation of IMCG is the situation $(x_1^*, x_2^*, \ldots x_n^*) \in X$, which maximizes the minimum value of the degrees of all players' satisfaction λ_i ($i = 1, 2, \ldots, n$) and minimizes the gap among them simultaneously.

And then the generalized equilibrium situation of IMCG can be found by solving the lexicographical goals mathematical program with two level objectives as follows:

$$\begin{aligned} &\max_{x, \lambda} \quad \lambda \\ &\max_{x, \lambda} \quad \{\max_i \{\lambda_i(u_i(x_i, x_{\bar{i}}))\} - \max_i \{\lambda_i(u_i(x_i, x_{\bar{i}}))\}\} \\ &\text{s.t.} \quad \lambda_i(u_i(x_i, x_{\bar{i}})) \ge \lambda, \quad i = 1, 2, \ldots, n \\ &\qquad\quad g_i(x_i, x_{\bar{i}}) \ge 0, \quad i = 1, 2, \ldots, n \\ &\qquad\quad h_i(x_i, x_{\bar{i}}) = 0, \quad i = 1, 2, \ldots, n \end{aligned} \quad (10)$$

where the two level goals submit to lexicographic order, i.e., we try to find the second level objective within the set of optimal solutions to the first level.

3   The mutative scaled SA algorithm for IMCG

In this section, we propose a mutative scaled SA algorithm for IMCG via suitably designing search parameters and iterative operators.

3.1 The transmutation model for IMCG

Note that there are multi-constraints in model for model (10), and it is quite complex to estimate all of them at the same time. So we introduce the penalty function method to the model to solve the trouble. And it is very effectively to deal with constraints with penalty function method in SA algorithm [12].

The penalty function is chosen as

$$p(x,\lambda) = P\sum_{i=1}^{M} \{\min\{\lambda_i(u_i(x_i,x_{\bar{i}})) - \lambda, 0\} + \min\{g_i(x_i,x_{\bar{i}}), 0 - |h_i(x_i,x_{\bar{i}})|\}\} \quad (11)$$

where $P > 0$ is the penalty parameter, and usually it is large enough for P to range from 10 to 104 [13].

For the two level objectives in problem (10) submit to lexicographic order, so it cannot be incorporated into one objective, but it is enough to just employ the penalty function method in the first level objective.

Then the model (10) can be transformed into the nonconstrained problem with two level objectives via penalty parameter P as follows:

$$\max_{x,\lambda} \quad F(x,\lambda) = \lambda + p(x,\lambda) \quad (12)$$

$$\max_{x,\lambda} \quad D(x,\lambda) = \{\max_i\{\lambda_i(u_i(x_i,x_{\bar{i}}))\} - \min_i\{\lambda_i(u_i(x_i,x_{\bar{i}}))\} \quad (13)$$

3.2 The search operators and procedure of SA algorithm

We propose a homogeneous mutative scaled SA algorithm to obtain the optimal solution for problem (10). First, the search parameters and iterative operators are designed as follows:

(1) The initial temperature is chosen as

$$t_0 = \frac{F_{\min} - F_{\max}}{\ln p_0} \quad (14)$$

where $p_0 \in (0,1)$ is the initial acceptance probability, $F_{\max}$ and $F_{\min}$ are the maximum one and the minimum one of the first level objective values of initial solutions, respectively.

(2) The temperature descending policy is

$$t_{r+1} = \alpha t_r \quad (15)$$

where $\alpha(0 \leq \alpha \leq 1)$ is the temperature descending coefficient. And the nearer to 1 α is, the slower the iterativeness is; usually α is chosen between 0.8 and 0.95.

(3) A new solution $z' = (x', \lambda')$ is obtained from the current solution $z = (x, \lambda)$ based on the neighborhood function which is created by Cauchy distribution disturbance, i.e.,

$$z' = z + \eta \cdot \xi \tag{16}$$

where η is the step length, the probability density function of random variable $\xi \in (-\infty, +\infty)$ is

$$f(\xi) = \frac{1}{\pi} \frac{\alpha_r}{\alpha_r^2 + \xi^2} \tag{17}$$

and $\alpha_r = 2 \times (0.99)^r$ is the mutative scale parameter which is the function of temperature generation r.

(4) The circular number in the same temperature is a fixed positive integer s which is decided by the size of problem.

(5) There are two stopping criteria in the SA algorithm. One is zero method— i.e., the algorithm stops if temperature $t_r \le \varepsilon$, where ε is a given small positive number. The other is immovable rule—the algorithm stops if the current best solution cannot be improved within Q consecutive generations.

Summarize the above design; the procedure of the homogeneous mutative scaled SA algorithm is described as follows:

Step 1 Set up the degree of all players' satisfaction functions.
Step 2 Initialize the search parameters. Produce the initial solutions randomly and choose the optimal one to be the current solution z. Initialize the best solution $z^* := z$. Let $k := 0$ and $r := 0$.
Step 3 Produce new solution z' from the current solution z, and let $k := k + 1$.
Step 4 If $k = s$, go to Step 6; else, go to Step 5.
Step 5 If $\exp[(F_{z'} - F_z)/t_r] > \text{random}(0,1)$ or $F_{z'} \ge F_z$, let $z := z'$; and farther if $F_{z'} = F_z$ and $D_{z'} > D_{z*}$ or $F_{z'} > F_{z*}$, let $z^* := z'$. Else, return to Step 3.
Step 6 If z^* does not change in Q consecutive generations, the algorithm stops; else, let $t_{r+1} := \alpha t_r$ and $r := r + 1$, go to Step 7.
Step 7 If $t_r \le \varepsilon$, the algorithm stops; else, return to Step 3.

4 Computational results and discussion

An example of IMCG with three players is given as follows:

$$\begin{array}{ll} \max\limits_{x_1} & u_1(x_1, x_2, x_3) = 2x_1 + x_2 - x_3 \\ \text{s.t.} & x_1^2 + x_2^2 + x_3^3 \le 20 \\ & x_1 \ge 0 \end{array} \qquad \begin{array}{ll} \max\limits_{x_2} & u_2(x_1, x_2, x_3) = (x_1 - 2)^2 + (x_2 - 1)^2 + x_3^2 \\ \text{s.t.} & x_1 x_2 x_3 \ge 16 \\ & x_2 \ge 0 \end{array}$$

Table 1 The Results of Simulations of the SA Algorithm.

Simulation Order	Fuzzy Best Solution			Membership of Fuzzy Best Solution μ
	x_1	x_2	x_3	
No. 1	2.739295	3.422193	0.779938	0.812537
No. 2	2.970856	3.475086	1.466626	0.824372
No. 3	0.859941	3.575023	1.44401	0.933182
No. 4	1.298875	1.632071	5.038921	0.957633

$$\max_{x_3} \quad u_3(x_1, x_2, x_3) = (x_1 - 3)(4 - x_2)(x_3 + 1)$$
$$\text{s.t.} \quad x_1 - 2x_2 + x_3 \leq 4$$
$$x_3 \geq 0$$

The search operators are chosen as $t_0 = 100$, $\varepsilon = 2$, $\alpha = 0.9$, $s = 10$, $Q = 100$, $P = 150$, $L = 50$, and $p_0 = 0.1$, then a series of numerical simulations, using the SA algorithm in this paper, are given in Table 1.

From the simulation results, we can get the advantages of the SA algorithm:

(1) *Optimality*. All the values of fuzzy membership grade μ in the results in Table 1 exceed 0.8, which shows that the algorithm can obtain the optimal solutions for all factors in equilibrium system with high satisfactoriness.

(2) *Multi-solutions*. The different simulation results show that the algorithm can provide the factors with a group of approximate fuzzy optimal solutions on similarly fuzzy optimal grade. So it is easier and more reasonable to achieve the equilibrium decision for the factors.

(3) *Robustness*. Although the initial solutions and search operators are stochastic (as shown in Figure 1), the best solutions are consistent on a similarly fuzzy optimal grade. It illuminates that the SA algorithm has preferable robustness on the initial value.

(4) *Speediness*. It runs in less than 0.6 scond by Visual Basic program on Pentium III of the SA algorithm, for example. Furthermore, in Figure 1, the best results are achieved within 80 times of temperature descending averagely, so the average rate of convergence is speedy.

So, the SA algorithm in this paper is feasible and effective to find the generalized equilibrium for the IMCG.

5 Conclusion and future research

In this paper, the decision-making of a type of IMCG is discussed, in which the competitive players would achieve themselves profits severally by coming to terms finitely. Then the mathematical model for IMCG is proposed and the generalized equilibrium of which is defined. Then a homogeneous mutative scaled SA algorithm for IMCG is put forward and the numerical simulation of example demonstrates the effectiveness and feasibility of the algorithm.

For future research, we can study the property of other relationship in the co-opetition games and design hybrid optimal algorithms, such as GA algorithm incorporated with SA and neural network with hybrid SA algorithm.

References

[1]   R.B. Myerso, *Game Theory, Analysis of Conflict*, Harvard Business Press, Cambridge, MA, 1991.
[2]   I.F. Wilkinson, L.C. Young, Business dancing—the nature and role of interfirm relations in business strategy. *Asia–Australia Marketing Journal*, (**2**), pp. 67–79, 1995.
[3]   Y.D. Luo, *Co-opetition in International Business*, Copenhagen, 2004.
[4]   M. Bengtsson, S. Kock, Co-operation and competition among horizontal actors in business networks, *Interorganizational Research*, (**8**), pp. 23–25, 1996.
[5]   M. Bengtsson, S. Kock, "Co-opetition" in business networks-to co-operate and compete simultaneously. *Industrial Marketing Management*, (**29**), pp. 411–426, 2000.
[6]   C. Loebbeche, P.C. Fenema, P. Powell, Knowledge transfer under co-opetition. *American Management System*, (**2**), pp. 215–229, 1997.
[7]   K. Hausken, Cooperation and between-group competition. *Journal of Economic Behavior and Organization*, (**42**), pp. 417–425, 2000.
[8]   H.H. Liu, J.Y. Yu, M.D. Qi, Z.C. Mi, Co-opetition game and approach to seek its equilibrium. *Forecasting*, (**24**), pp. 73–75, 2005.
[9]   W.I. Zangwill, C.B. Garcia, Equilibrium programming: the following approach and dynamics. *Math Programming*, (**21**), pp. 262–289, 1981.
[10] A.S. Antipin, Methods for bilinear equilibrium and game problems. *International Conference on Optimization and Optimal Control*, pp. 77–84, 2002.
[11] Z. Wang, T. Zhang, H. Wang, Simulated annealing algorithm based on chaotic variable, *Control and Decision*, (**14**), pp. 381–384, 1999.
[12] S.Y. Hu, B.Z. Chen et al., Simulated annealing method on global optimization of nonconvex NLP problems. *Journal of Tsinghua University*, (**6**), pp. 5–9, 1997.

Automated remote sensing image registration algorithm based on adjacent spectrum

Ming Zhu[1,2], Dong Liang[1,2], Yan Pu[2,1]
[1]*Key Lab Intelligent Computing and Signal Ministry of Education, Anhui University, Hefei, China*
[2]*School of Electronics and Information Engineering, Anhui University, Hefei, China*

Abstract

This paper presents an automated remote sensing image registration algorithm by using adjacent spectrum. Firstly, the feature points are extracted by Harris detection algorithm; secondly, the adjacent spectral method is used for feature points matching; thirdly, the incorrect matches are removed by a simple method using the first K similar neighbors correspondence; fourthly, the transform model is estimated by using affine transformation; finally, the resampling is done by bilinear interpolation. Experimental results indicate the effectiveness and feasibility of the proposed method.

Keywords: remote sensing; image registration; adjacent spectrum; affine transformation.

1 Introduction

Remote sensing image registration is a process to align remote sensing images taken under different conditions (e.g., time, perspective, sensor technology, resolution, and spectral band), which is fundamental in remote sensing image processing and is also an open problem in remote sensing. Traditionally, the remote sensing image registration is performed by human experts by manually selecting the ground control point pairs between the images, followed by estimating the mapping function that aligns the images together. The manual process of selecting ground control point pairs is very time consuming, and the registration accuracy is usually not high. Therefore, the automated remote sensing image registration algorithms are demanded to reduce processing time and improve registration accuracy.

Over the years, literatures reported many registration methods [1–5], that mainly consisted of the following steps [6]: feature detection, feature matching, transform model estimation, image resampling, and transformation.

Overall, the registration methods can be broadly classified into two categories: area-based methods and feature-based methods. Area-based methods put emphasis on the feature matching step rather than on their detection. Fourier transformation [4], cross-correlation [7], and mutual information [3,8] belong to this category. However, area-based methods are not well adapted to the problem of multisensor image registration, since the gray-level characteristics of images to be matched are quite different, and the fundamental assumption that the joint intensity probability is the maximum when two images are spatially aligned is not always true for any two different modality images [9]. On the other hand, feature-based methods do not use the gray values to describe matching entities; they use salient image features extracted by a feature detection algorithm. Features used for image registration may be points, edges, lines, or areas. Invariant moment method [5], structure matching method [9], and wavelet-based feature extraction method [10] are typical feature-based methodologies.

Over the past few years, spectral graph theory was introduced to the area of image processing, such as point pattern matching, shape representation and matching, and clustering. Although spectral graph representations are susceptible to the effect of structural error, spectral methods still offer an attractive route to correspondence matching, since they provide a representation that can be used to characterize graph structure at the global level, and the spectral representation can be used for rapid matching by comparing patterns of eigenvalues or eigenvectors.

In this paper, we aim to use adjacent spectrum for remote sensing image registration.

2 Automatic remote sensing image registration algorithm

2.1 Feature detection

In order to select some salient and distinctive feature points, Harris corner detector is employed. The computation of Harris corners [16] is efficient; it does not require setting of a threshold. The same number of the feature points is chosen to be matched in the following step.

2.2 Feature matching

In this section, adjacent spectral method for feature points matching is introduced.

Let I and J be two related Harris feature point sets which both contain s points respectively. Denote the points in I by p_i ($i = 1,2,...,s$), and the points in J by q_i (($i = 1,2,...,s$)).

For the point set I, the weighted adjacent matrix A_I is defined as follows:

$$A_I(i, j) = \begin{cases} \exp\left(\dfrac{-r_{ij}^2}{2\sigma^2}\right), & i \neq j \\[2mm] 0, & i = j \end{cases} \tag{1}$$

where the weight r_{ij} is the Euclidean distance between p_i and p_j of I and σ is the smoothing coefficient. The matrix A_J could be defined in the same way.

Perform spectral decomposition on A_I and A_J:

$$A_I = U\Delta_I U^{\mathrm{T}}, \ A_J = V\Delta_J V^{\mathrm{T}} \tag{2}$$

Where $\Delta_I = \mathrm{diag}\{\lambda_1,\ldots,\lambda_s\}$ ($\lambda_1 \geq \cdots \geq \lambda_{s-1} \geq \lambda_s$) is a diagonal matrix whose diagonal elements are eigenvalues of A_I, and $U = \{u_1 \cdots u_s\}$ is an orthogonal matrix whose column $u_i(i = 1,\ldots,s)$ is the eigenvector of A_I corresponding to λ_i. $\Delta_J = \mathrm{diag}\{\theta_1,\ldots,\theta_s\}(\theta_1 \geq \cdots \geq \theta_{s-1} \geq \theta_s)$, $V = \{v_1 \ldots v_s\}$.

The eigenvectors of A_I or A_J are unique up to the sign. Sign correction is needed to correct the column vectors of U and V due to the fact that the signs of eigenvectors can be assigned arbitrarily. To be brief, if U is given, we only need to correct the signs of the columns of V. In fact, the process of revising the signs is just to find an optimal sign matrix S that minimizes the set $\{\ \|U - PVS\| : P$ is a permutation matrix$\}$, where a sign matrix S is a diagonal matrix with 1 or -1 along its diagonal. Denote the revised V by $\hat{V}$.

The ith row vector $u(i)$ of U (and the jth row vector $\hat{v}^{(j)}$ of $\hat{V}$) is treated as the characteristic of the ith feature point p_i of I (and the jth feature point q_j of J). And the distance M_{ij} between $u^{(i)}$ and $\hat{v}^{(j)}$ is computed to measure the difference between feature point p_i and q_j for each $i = 1,\ldots,s$ and $j = 1,\ldots,s$.

$$M_{ij} = \| u^{(i)} - \hat{v}^{(j)} \| \tag{3}$$

The value M_{ij} reflects the level of difference between p_i and q_j. Considering the matching matrix M consisting of entries M_{ij}, if M_{ij} is the smallest element both in the corresponding row and column, then we conclude that the ith feature point p_i of I matches the jth feature point q_j of J.

2.3 Incorrect matches removing

The incorrect matches will lead to a breakdown registration. Since the way of making the initial matching might not be very accurate, some matching pairs are likely to be incorrect. In order to obtain the accurate matches, the incorrect matches must be removed once the initial matching results are given.

For incorrect matches removing, there have been several well-known methods, such as the random sample consensus algorithm (RANSAC) [17], Softassign

[18], and GTM [1]. RANSAC approach is based on a geometric transformation model, and Softassign and GTM are both based on graphs. In Ref. [1], the authors showed that GTM outperforms the other two methods in most cases. The GTM removes the outliers through constructing a median K-nearest-neighbor (K-NN) graph for each point sets and comparing the structures of the two median K-NN graphs. The Euclidian distance between any two points of each point set is calculated, and the median of all distances between pairs of vertices is employed as a threshold to control the edges' existence. A nondirected edge (p_i,p_j) exists when p_j is one of the K closest neighbors of p_i and also $\| p_i - p_j \| \le \eta$, here η is the median of all distances between vertex pairs.

In a graph, *the commute time* $CT(p,q)$ is the expected time for the random walk to travel from point p to reach point q and then return. $CT(p,q)$ can be expressed as follows [13]:

$$CT(p,q) = \mathrm{vol} \sum_{i=1}^{|V|-1} \frac{1}{\lambda_i} \left(\frac{u_i(p)}{\sqrt{d_p}} - \frac{u_i(q)}{\sqrt{d_q}} \right)^2 \tag{4}$$

Qiu and Hancock [13] point out that since commute time is a metric on the original graph and it captures global information rather than the local information, it is likely to be relatively stable to structural modifications. GTM [1] removes incorrect matches with the iteration framework.

In this paper, we use the following simple method to remove incorrect matches. It does not need to employ the time-consuming iteration framework.

With the initial matching results, we search for the first K similar neighbors, relying on U and $\hat{V}$, for each point of I and J, respectively. The similarity between p_i and p_j is defined as

$$S(p_i, p_j) = \exp(-CT(p_i, p_j)), i \ne j \tag{5}$$

The similarity can be defined for the feature points of J in the same way. From the above definition, we find that two feature points p_i and p_j are more similar if $S(p_i, p_j)$ is larger. For a given positive integer number K, we sort other feature points of I in descending order according to their similarity to p_i and select the first K points as the first K similar neighbors of p_i. If p_i matches some point q_j of J, then the first K similar neighbors of p_i must match those of q_j in order, otherwise we consider p_i and q_j as an incorrect match.

2.4 Transform parameters estimation and resampling

After the feature points matching and outliers removing have been completed, the mapping function should be estimated.

The most frequently used transformation model in registration applications is the affine transformation. This model is sufficiently general, as it is able to handle rotations, translations, scaling, and shearing [3]. Consider that the sensors always capture images at far distance and varying electromagnetic wave bands with different resolutions from different perspectives; the reference image and the sensed image mainly differ at the global level. In this paper, affine transform model is employed. The affine transform model can be represented as

$$x_{\text{ref}} = a_{11}x_{\text{in}} + a_{12}y_{\text{in}} + b_1, \quad y_{\text{ref}} = a_{21}x_{\text{in}} + a_{22}y_{\text{in}} + b_2 \tag{6}$$

where x_{ref} and y_{ref} are abscissa and ordinate of feature point in the reference image, respectively. x_{in} and y_{in} are abscissa and ordinate of feature point in the sensed image, respectively.

Once the transformation is completed, the sensed image is resampled to the reference image by bilinear interpolation.

3 Experiments

3.1 Synthetic data experiment

The synthetic data is a fish shape consisted of 98 feature points which are represented by "+," as shown in Figure 1. An affine transformation $X' = AX$ is played on this data, that is

$$\begin{bmatrix} x' \\ y' \\ 1 \end{bmatrix} = \begin{bmatrix} -0.5660 & 0.4950 & 0 \\ 0.5660 & 0.4950 & 70.7110 \\ 0 & 0 & 1 \end{bmatrix} * \begin{bmatrix} x \\ y \\ 1 \end{bmatrix}$$

where A is a nonsingular matrix. Figure 2 shows the result of the affine transformation. The data in Figure 1 is treated as the reference image, and that in Figure 2 is treated as the sensed one. The matching result given by adjacent spectral method is shown in Figure 3, in which there are 95 pairs of points get matched. Figure 4 shows the result of incorrect matches removing; four pairs linked by cyan lines are detected as incorrect matches, although three correct matches are treated as incorrect matches, the remaining 91 pairs are correct matches. With the remaining matching pairs, the parameters (a_{11}, a_{12}, a_{21}, a_{22}, b_1, b_2 $a_{11}, a_{12}, a_{21}, a_{22}, b_1, b_2$) of the affine transform model are estimated by using least square method and expressed as follows:

$$x_{\text{ref}} = -0.8834x_{\text{in}} + 0.8834y_{\text{in}} - 62.4655, \quad y_{\text{ref}} = 1.0101x_{\text{in}} + 1.0101y_{\text{in}} - 71.4253$$

Figure 5 shows the registration result.

3.2 Remote sensing images experiment

In this section, we will confirm our algorithm through real-world data experiments, in which the experimental images are remote sensing images.

Figure 1: The synthetic data.   Figure 2: Affine transformation.

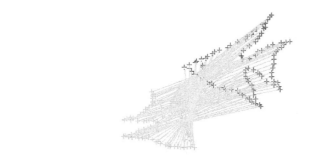

Figure 3: Matching results.

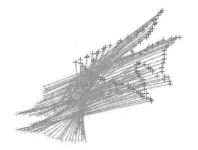

Figure 4: Result of incorrect matches removing.   Figure 5: Registration result.

We have used two images, as shown in Figure 6, in which the left image is treated as the reference image, and the right image is treated as the sensed one. Those images were transformed into gray monochannel images, so that each of them is 256×256 pixel large. Fifty feature points are selected for each image. The adjacent spectral method is used to match the feature points, and the matching result is shown in Figure 7, from which we may find that some pairs are matched incorrectly. Figure 8 reports process of incorrect matches removing; the 40 pairs linked by the pink lines are treated as the correct matching pairs, while the pairs linked by the cyan lines are treated as incorrect matches. The registration result is shown in Figure 9, which reports the accuracy result of our algorithm.

Figure 6: The initial remote sensing images for registration; the left image is treated as reference image and the right one is the sensed image.

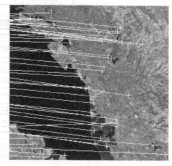

Figure 7: Matching results given by adjacent spectral method.

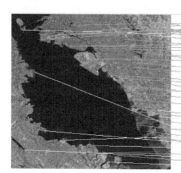

Figure 8: Matching results checking with $K=2$.

4 Conclusion

This paper presented an automatic and point-feature-based registration technique for remote sensing images. The proposed algorithm utilizes various techniques including the Harris corner detector, the adjacent spectral method, and affine transform model. Experimental results support the effectiveness and the

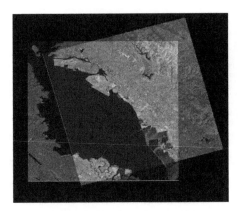

Figure 9: Registration result.

efficiency of the proposed fully automatic registration process. Our future work will apply our approach to multimodal analysis in remote sensing.

Acknowledgment

The authors gratefully acknowledge the financial support of National Science Foundation of China (Grant No. 61172127, 11071002), Anhui University Startup Project of Doctor Scientific Research (Grant No. 02303319-33190182); Anhui University Young Backbone Teachers Training Project (Grant No. 02303301-12333010284), and Innovative research team of 211 project.

References

[1] W. Aguilar, Y. Frauel, F. Escolano, M.E. Martinez-Perez, A. Espinosa-Romero, M.A. Lozano, A robust graph transformation matching for non-rigid registration. *Image and Vision Computing*, **27(7)**, pp. 897–910, 2009.

[2] A. Wong, D.A. Clausi, AISIR: automated inter-sensor/inter-band satellite image registration using robust complex wavelet feature representations. *Pattern Recognition Letters*, **31(10)**, pp. 1160–1167, 2010.

[3] I. De Falco, A.D. Cioppa, D. Maisto, E. Tarantino, Differential evolution as a viable tool for satellite image registration. *Applied Soft Computing*, **8(4)**, pp. 1453–1462, 2008.

[4] Cideciyan, A.V. Jacobson, S.G. Kemp, C.M. Knighton, R.W. Nagel, Registration of high resolution images of the retina. *The International Society for Optical Engineering, Medical Imaging VI: Image Processing*, **1652**, pp. 310–322, 1992.

[5] X.L. Dai, S. Khorram, A feature-based image registration algorithm using improved chain code representation combined with moment invariants. *IEEE Transactions on Geoscience and Remote Sensing*, **37(5)**, pp. 2351–2362, 1999.

[6] B. Zitova, J. Flusser, Image registration methods: a survey. *Image and Vision Computing*, **21**, pp. 977–1000, 2003.

[7] A. Roche, X. Pennec, G. Malandain, N. Ayache, Gigid registration of 3-D ultrasound with MR images: a new approach combining intensity and gradient information. *IEEE Transactions on Medical Imaging*, **20(10)**, pp. 1038–1049, 2002.

[8] P. Viala, W.M. Wells, Alignment by maximization of mutual information. *International Journal of Computer Vision*, **24(2)**, pp. 137–154, 1997.

[9] A.D. Ventura, A. Rampini, R. Schettini, Image registration by recognition of corresponding structures. *IEEE Transactions on Geoscience and Remote Sensing*, **28(3)**, pp. 305–314, 1990.

[10] I. Zavorin, J. Le Moigne, Use of multi-resolution wavelet feature pyramids for automatic registration of multisensor imagery. *IEEE Transactions on Image Processing*, **14(6)**, pp. 770–782, 2005.

.

An algorithm for mining maximal frequent patterns based on FP-tree

Ligang Cui, Yong Kang, Wei Huang, Hui Wang, Yongqing Zhang
Dalian Airforce Communication NCO Academy, Dalian, China

Abstract

The FP-growth algorithm compact all frequent patterns in a tree based on divide-and-conquer approach so that the mining algorithm in main memory cannot realize in larger database. This paper brings an improved FP-tree construction algorithm, which diminishes breadth of FP-tree to reduce occupation space by using dynamic node insert technique to construct the FP-tree and improves the efficiency of mining algorithm by increasing the length of shared prefix. Because mining completely frequent patterns set in intensive data is very difficult, so a new algorithm for mining maximal frequent patterns based on the improved FP-tree-IFPmax is proposed, which uses the rank of nodes to prejudge, labels already exist nodes according to the nature of maximal frequent patterns, and effectively avoids redundant traversal and improves the time efficiency of the maximal frequent pattern mining algorithms. The results of experiments based on different standard data sets show the effectiveness of the algorithm.
Keywords: data mining, association rules, maximal frequent patterns, FP-tree.

1 Introduction

The mining of association rules is one of the most active research methods for data mining. It was firstly proposed by Agrawal and Imielinski [1], which can be used for defining the relationship between transaction items of transactional databases. The mining problems of association rules can be divided into two subproblems and can be used for finding out the frequent item subset and producing association rules. The finding of frequent item subset is the critical technique and step for data mining applications as the mining of association rules, the sequencing model, and the like. As a result, most studies focus on the mining of frequent patterns. The Apriori algorithm [2] is the classic algorithm of association rule mining. However, with the intensive study, the disadvantages of the Apriori algorithm are exposed. It needs to scan the database for several times, a high I/O load is required, and a huge candidate sets can be produced.

Han et al. [3] have proposed the FP-growth algorithm which conducts the frequent pattern mining based on the frequent pattern tree (FP-tree). This algorithm makes uses of the main information stored in the database by the FP-tree. The search space is greatly reduced. But the amount of frequent pattern may be increased in the form of index for dense database or small support degree. To reduce the redundancy in the frequent pattern, various methods have been adopted. The main methods include the mining frequent closed item (FCI) set [4] and the maximal frequent item (MFI) set [5].

The MFI has the minimum scale. It can derive the FCI set and the frequent item set through the MFI set. As a result, the finding of frequent item set can be switched to the finding of MFI set. In addition, it only needs to find the MFI set in the data mining application. It is unnecessary to find the frequent item set, thus the finding of MFI set has significant meaning for data mining.

2 Problem description

At present, the available mining algorithms of MFI set include the Max-Miner [6], the DMFI [7], the DMFIA [8], and other algorithms. This paper proposes a new maximal frequent mining algorithm on the basis of improved FP-tree. This algorithm can be used for conducting a prejudgment before detecting the subset with the sequence of node and marking the existing nodes according to the property of the maximal frequent pattern, thus effectively avoiding the redundancy travel of nodes. It not only can increase the time efficiency of mining algorithm of maximal frequent pattern but also save a quantity of memory space and realizes the rapid mining of MFI set.

Provided the transactional database D is a set composed of transactions T; each transaction T is the set of items; and $I = \{i_1, i_2, \ldots, i_m\}$ is the set of all items in D. One item in this paper is corresponding to one URL and $T \subset I$. Each transaction is provided with an identifier, which is called as the TID. Provided A is one item set, the transaction T can include A only when $A \subset T$.

One association rule is the implication in the form of $A \Rightarrow B$, wherein $A \subset I$, $B \subset T$, $A \cap B = \varphi$.

Definition 1

The support of association rule $A \Rightarrow B$ in the database D is the ratio between the number of transactions A and B in the database D and the number of all items, as shown in formula (1).

$$\sup(A \Rightarrow B) = |T : A \cup B \subset T, T \in D| / |D| \tag{1}$$

Definition 2

The confidence of association rule $A \Rightarrow B$ in the database D is the ratio between the number of transactions A and B in the database D and the number of transactions A in database D, as shown in formula (2).

$$\mathrm{conf}(A \Rightarrow B) = |T : A \cup B \subset T, T \in D| / |T : A \subset T, T \in D| \qquad (2)$$

Definition 3

For the frequent pattern p, if it is not found, then q include p and p is the maximal frequent pattern MFP.

3 Basic ideal of algorithm

It is known by analyzing the FP-tree structure and FP-tree structure algorithm that the size of space is mainly depended on two factors, the depth and breadth of tree (direct proportion). The two factors are in direct proportion. The depth of tree is the max item quantity of single transaction, while the breadth of tree is the average item quantity included in each layer. As a result, the space of compressed tree shall be mainly worked out from the breadth of the frequent pattern.

This paper adopts the dynamic node insert technique to construct the FP-tree, namely the improved FP-tree (IFP-tree). With this algorithm, any node sequence of transaction T, to be inserted in the IFP-tree, shall be variable in certain conditions. The limitation is that the node to be replaced shall have the same support. Analyzed from the aspect of probability, the nodes having the same support will have the same occurrence probability in the next branch. This can avoid the unnecessary expense caused by frequent replacement when the nodes to be replaced have relatively high support. The IFP-tree can avoid the new branch by dynamically changing the node sequence of transactions to reduce the width of tree and finally reduce the memory space occupied by the tree. Meanwhile, it can effectively increase the sharing performance of prefix branch to reduce the traveling time of mining algorithm based on this structure and increase the efficiency of algorithm.

4 Algorithm description

Definition 4

IFP-tree is the oriented tree data structure complying with the following conditions:

(1) It comprises one root node marked as null, one children node (prefix subtree of item), and one frequent item table.
(2) Each node of the prefix subtree comprises three domains, the item-name, the count, and the node-link. The item-name represents the name of item carried by the node; the count records the number of node appearing on the subpatch of this node; and the node-link is used for connecting the

node having the same name. If the node having the same name is unavailable, the value of the node-link is null.

(3) The head table of frequent item includes the item-name, the item-count, and the head of node-link.

Definition 5

IFP-tree is one oriented tree. The branches of the tree can be deemed as the sequence composed of nodes. The maxim public prefix of the two branches is called as the shared prefix. The nodes contained in the shared prefix are called as the length of the shared prefix. The minimum supporting degree of nodes in the shared prefix is called as the sharing degree.

The IFP-tree construction algorithm inherits the advantages of FP-tree that no candidate item sets are produced. The database is scanned to times in two steps:

Step 1: The transactional database D is scanned once to produce the frequent 1 item set and obtain the supporting degree counting. The frequent item sets are condescendingly ranked according to the counting of supporting degree and represented by L.

Step 2: Create one IFP-tree root node and mark with "null." For each transaction in D, the following operations shall be executed: select the frequent items in transactions and sort the frequent items according to the sequence in L. Suppose the frequent item table after the ranking is $[p|P]$, p is the first element and P is the table of the residual elements. Call the insert_tree $([p|P],T)$. The execution of this procedure is as follows:

(1) If T has children N and N.item-name=p.item-name, then the counting of N shall be added by 1.

(2) Otherwise, find the node s after p and judge whether N.item-name is equal to the s.item-name.

(3) If they are equal and s.count is not greater than p.count, N.count++, switch p and s.

(4) Otherwise, a new node N shall be created and provided with the counting setting of 1. The node N shall be linked to its parent node T and linked to the node having the same item-name through the node-link structure. If p is not null, the insert_tree $([p|P],N)$ process shall be called recursively.

The dynamic insertion of node can be realized by comparing the node supporting degree with the improved algorithm. By doing so, the production of new node can be avoided at the largest degree and the breadth of the pattern tree can be compacted. Meanwhile, the limitation condition can be set and the system expense caused by frequent replace is effective avoided.

5 Mining of maximal frequent patterns

The maximal frequent patterns have the properties below:

Property 1: Any superset of the maximal frequent pattern is not frequent.
Property 2: Any subset of the maximal frequent pattern is frequent.

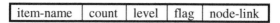

Figure 1: Node domain of improved IFP-tree nodes.

Seen from properties 1 and 2, the maximal frequent pattern is the bounder line of frequent pattern and the nonfrequent pattern. The sets below the maximal frequent pattern have the frequent pattern, while those above the maximal frequent pattern have the non-frequent pattern. As a result, once all maximal frequent patterns are found out, all frequent patterns can be obtained.

The FPmax mining algorithm of maximal frequent pattern was proposed by Grahne and Zhu [9], which is the important algorithm in the mining field of maximal frequent patterns. But this algorithm still requires a mass of time when traveling all FP-tree nodes. As a result, the main ideal of improving the algorithm is to increase the efficiency mining system by reducing the node traveling quantity. Because the supporting degree of children nodes in IFP-tree is certainly not greater than that of the parent node, when the children nodes on one branch of the IFP-tree are totally traveled and stored in the maximal frequent pattern tree after the subset detection, the parent node is certainly included in the maximal frequent pattern set. It is unnecessary to travel this parent node again. Based on this consideration, the IFP-tree-based improved FPmax mining algorithm (IFPmax) of maximal frequent pattern is proposed in this paper. The IFPmax algorithm optimizes the FPmax algorithm, reduces the number of nodes to be traveled during the subset detection, reduces the time consumption of subset inspection, and increases the efficiency of mining algorithm of maximal frequent pattern.

The definition to the IFP-tree structure is given before providing the new IFPmax algorithm: the each node in IFP-tree has five domains, the definitions of the item-name, count, and node-link are identical to those of the FP-tree. Two domains level and flag are added; the level represents the sequence of node; the flag domain means that whether this node has been traveled. If flag=1, it means that this node has been traveled. If flag=0, it means that this node hasn't been traveled yet. It is as shown in Figure 1.

If one route $\beta = i_1, i_2,...,i_k$ in IFP-tree has the maximal frequent pattern, any subset of the route does not have the maximal frequent pattern according to the properties 1 and 2. Namely, any combination of the nodes in this route does not have the maximal frequent pattern. Thus, it is unnecessary to travel the nodes $i1$, $i2,...,i_{k-1}$ in this route to produce the maximal frequent pattern. At this moment, the flag marks of $i_1, i_2,...,i_{k-1}$ can be changed that the other nodes in this route cannot be traveled again. The node traveling time can be reduced by $k-1$ times.

The execution process of IFPmax is as follows:

Input: IFP-tree T α, min_sup
Output: MFS

MFS refers to the maximal frequent pattern set with the initial value of null. The flag of all nodes is 0.

if (T α is the tree with only one branch)
//b_i is the last node of the branch, is the IFP-tree in the condition of b_i
{Call MINE-MAX(β, b_i, MFS) for T α
Else   //T α has several branches
   {For each node a_i(i=n,n-1,......,1)of item header table
         Do
         {If (flag(a_i)==0)
         // this node hasn't been travelled yet.
         {Construct the conditional IFP-tree of a_i, and obtain the tree-R
            If (tree-R still has several routes)
                        {Call MINE-MAX (β, b_i, MFS) for each
      branch,}
            Else {
            // r_i is the last node of tree-R.
            The MINE-MAX(R, r_i, MFS) shall be called for tree-
   R.}
         }
      }
   }
// The realization process of MINE-MAX is shown below (conditional IFP tree β of b_i, the last node b_i and the maximal frequent subset MFS).
      MINE-MAX(β, b_i, MFS)
   {If (T α is null), then produce the candidate item C_{max}=b_i of the maximal frequent pattern
   Else C_{max}= $\beta \cup b_i$,
   //C_{max} supporting degree is the supporting degree of b_i node as well.
      If (the original MFS does not contain any b_i, or the sequence of b_i in the candidate frequent pattern is not less than that of b_i in MFS)
      //it means that C_{max} is not the subset of existing maximal frequent pattern MFS.
      { MFS=MFS $\cup C_{max}$, delete all subsets of C_{max} in MFS
      Alter the sequence of node in the new MFS, alter the flag value of all nodes in β to be 1.
      }
   }

6 Experimental result and performance analysis

The IFPmax algorithm mentioned in this paper is realized in the hardware environment with memory of 512M, CPU of Pentium2.1G, and the operating system of WindowsXP Professional as well as the compiling environment of Visual C++6.0. The experimental data are taken from two transactional databases (including records of one 15k transaction database and one 20k transaction database) of the network log file database. The mining time of different support is obtained based on the mining frequent pattern of FP-tree and IFP-tree, as shown in Tables 1 and 2.

Table 1: Contrast of Data Set Containing 15k Translations.

Time/s Support / Algorithm	Mining Algorithm Based on FP-Tree	Mining Algorithm Based on IFP-Tree
0.1%	–	10,260
0.5%	730	478
1%	128	105
10%	9.7	9.4
50%	3.1	3.3

Table 2: Contrast of Data Set Containing 20k Transactions.

Time/s Support / Algorithm	Mining Algorithm Based on FP-Tree	Mining Algorithm Based on IFP-Tree
0.1%	–	–
0.5%	–	609
1%	40.6	30.5
10%	13.7	11.6
50%	3.6	4.1

When the support is high (e.g., the support setting shown in the table is 50%), the operation time of mining algorithm based on IFP-tree will consume FP-tree. It is known by analyzing the algorithm that the complexity of IFP-tree construction algorithm is higher than FP-tree. It needs to conduct the support comparison and the dynamic ranking for the nodes inserted into the tree. When the support setting is relatively high, the frequent item set produced is low in number, the space compression rate is decreased and the performance of IFP-tree construction algorithm is decreased. When the minimum support IFP-tree is low, for example, the minimum support shown in the table is 0.1%. As the frequent item set is so large that the mining algorithm fails in the FP-tree, it is successful in the IFP-tree. It means that memory occupied by the IFP-tree is smaller than that of the FP-tree in the same transactional database. This embodies the memory compressing performance of the IFP-tree structural algorithm.

Meanwhile, seen from the operation time of mining algorithm listed in the table, the operation time of mining algorithm based on the IFP-tree is less if the database is large or the minimum support is relatively low. It means that the dynamic node insert technique used for the IFP-tree construction algorithm can increase the sharing performance of prefix branch and the number of branch to be traveled by the mining algorithm can be reduced. As a result, when the frequent item set is large, the IFP-tree has better adaptability than the FP-tree does.

7 Conclusion

On the deep research basis for frequent pattern algorithm and the FP-tree, this paper proposed the IFP-tree structure. The frequent mode tree can be constructed with the dynamic node insert technique to effectively compress the data space.

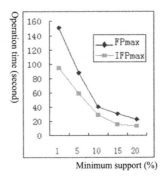

Figure 2: Performance comparison of FPmax and IFPmax algorithm.

Meanwhile, the mining architecture FPmax of the maximal frequent pattern shall be further optimized on the basis of IFP-tree structure. The IFPmax algorithm is proposed to conduct the prejudgment of node sequence before detecting the subset. The existing nodes can be marked according to the property of the maximal frequent pattern to effectively avoid the redundancy travel of node and increase the efficiency of mining algorithm of the maximal frequent pattern.

References

[1] R. Agrawal, T. Imielinski, Mining association rules between sets of items in large databases, *SIGMOD*, pp. 294–300, 1993.
[2] R. Agrawal, R. Srikant, Fast algorithms for mining association rules. In: *Proceedings of the 20th VLDB Conference*, pp. 478–499, 1994.
[3] Jiawei Han, Jian Pei, Yiwen Yin, Mining frequent patterns without candidate generation. In: *Proceedings of ACM-SIGMOD International Conference Management of Data*, pp. 1–12, 2000.
[4] N. Pasquier, Y. Bastide, R. Taouil et al., Discovering frequent closed itemsets for association rules. In: *Proceedings of the 7th International Conference on Database Theory*, Springer Verlag, Berlin, pp. 398–416, 1999.
[5] M.J. Zaki, S. Parthasarathy, M. Ogihara et al., New algorithms for fast discovery of association rules. In: *Proceedings of the International Conference on KDD and Data Mining*, pp. 283–286, 1997.
[6] R.J. Bayardo, Efficiently mining long patterns from databases. In: *Proceedings of ACM-SIGMOD International Conference Management of Data*, pp. 85–93, 1998.
[7] Lu Songfeng, Lu Zhengding, Rapid mining of maximal frequent item set. *Journal of Software*, **12**, pp. 293–297, 2001.
[8] Y.Q. Song, Y.Q. Zhu, Z.H. Sun et al., An algorithm and its updating algorithm based on FP-tree for mining maximum frequent itemsets. *Journal of Software*, **14(9)**, pp. 1586–1592, 2003.
[9] G. Grahne, J. Zhu, Efficiently using prefix-trees in mining frequent itemsets. In: *Proceedings of the Workshop on Frequent Itemsets Mining Implementations.* pp. 1–10, 2003.

Research on a fast calculation method and application for the radio wave propagation model

Shaoqing Wang, Jiyang Wang, Ning Zhou
The Electronic System Engineering Company of China, Beijing, China

Abstract

In order to enhance the real-time performance of the electromagnetic compatibility simulation experiment, this paper proposes a fast calculation method for the radio wave propagation model. We apply this method to the transmission loss calculation of the earth–space telecommunication systems which is explained in the ITU-R P.618 model. The simulation results indicate that the calculation speed of the ITU-R P.618 model is improved eight times by this method. Moreover, the maximal calculation deviation is 0.761 dB and the standard deviation is only 0.142 dB.

Keywords: radio wave propagation model, fast calculation, deviation.

1   Introduction

The use of radio wave propagation models to carry out the prediction of wave propagation attenuation is an effective means, which is used in analyzing effective coverage of the radio station, estimating the effective distance of radar and other equipments and determining the electromagnetic compatibility between the frequency devices and thus supporting their rational deployment [1]. When analyzing large-scale simulation of electromagnetic compatibility, predicting radio propagation attenuation resulting in cumulative amount of computation becomes one of the key points in restricting the computational efficiency of the simulation process, seriously affecting the real-time simulation analysis. Therefore, the study of the fast computing method for the radio wave propagation model is a very meaningful work.

Currently, research on propagation model fast solution methods are mainly based on data processing of radio wave propagation models. The main idea is to switch the calculation process of analytic expression based on the propagation model into the calculation process based on searching the data tables and interpolation, with plenty of offline results as the basis for the calculation to obtain the desired results [2]. This method can avoid complex analytical calculation to reduce the calculation time and improve the rapidity of the simulation when the simulation system is running.

Taking into account that the calculation quantity of a propagation model increases with the increasing of the model complexity, to meet the requirements of prediction accuracy condition, this paper presents a fast solution method for the simplified model and apply this method into the Star-ground link propagation model which is called as ITU-R P.618. Finally, the simulation results show the effectiveness of the method in enhancing the calculation efficiency of the propagation model.

The paper is organized as follows. In the next section, we propose the simplified model solving method. In the section "Simplification calculation for the ITU-R P.618," simplification calculation for the ITU-R P.618 is presented. The section "Simplification calculation for the ITU-R P.618" presents the simulation results and analysis. Finally, we conclude our paper in the last section.

2 Fast calculation method

According to Taylor's theorem, if the function $f(x)$ is the n order continuous differentiable function on the interval $[a, b]$ and is differentiable for $n+1$ times in the interval (a, b), so for the arbitrary x in the interval (a, b), we have

$$f(x) = \sum_{m=0}^{n} \frac{f^{(m)}(a)}{m!}(x-a)^m + R_n(x) \tag{1}$$

where the first polynomial on the right of the equal sign is called the Taylor expansion of the function $f(x)$, and $R_n(x)$ is the remaining term of the Taylor formula which is a high-end infinitesimal for the $(x-a)^n$.

It is found that with the increase of the order n, the order n polynomial approaches the function $f(x)$ better. However, the computation quantity of the polynomial will also increase, which reflects the contradictory relationship between computation and calculation accuracy.

According to the above-mentioned theory, we propose a simplified model calculation method for the propagation attenuation prediction. The basic steps of using the attenuation prediction method for solving the problem are as follows.

First, we analyze the effect factor of all kinds of ingredient in the propagation prediction equation, describe the tendency of the propagation attenuation change with their changes, and exclude the effect factor from the total propagation attenuation formula, which cause less impact or little change in attenuation value.

Secondly, for some computational complexity factor, the change trend of which is relatively regular; we use low-order polynomial to approximate the function or with the simple function. Curve fitting with piecewise linear is one of the effective means which reduce the amount of calculation for predicting the propagation attenuation.

3 Simplification calculation for the ITU-R P.618

ITU-R P.618 model is used to predict radio wave propagation attenuation for the earth–space link between telecommunication systems. On the basis of spatial diffusion losses, other factors considered in the model include attenuation due to atmospheric gases absorb, rainfall, cloud, and the beam spreading loss, radiance, multipath fading, and so on. Before solving model simplification, firstly, factors affecting the propagation attenuation are analyzed. Secondly, assess their significant impact on the attenuation values quantitatively. At last, simplify the calculation separately for significant and nonsignificant influencing factors.

3.1 The significance analysis of all kinds of propagation attenuation factors

Definition 1: The degree of significance of a factor affecting the propagation attenuation value is defined as the variational extent of the propagation attenuation value over the entire propagation path with changes of the factor.

In particular, it is assumed that the number of factors affecting the propagation attenuation value are both A and B, their values range of which is $[a_1, a_2]$ and $[b_1, b_2]$ respectively. The propagation attenuation value caused by A and B can be calculated by the function $F(A, B)$. If the expression (2) holds, then determine that the degree of A is more significant than that of B. Otherwise, the degree of B is more significant than that of A.

$$\left| F(a_2, b) - F(a_1, b) \right| > \left| F(a, b_2) - F(a, b_1) \right| \tag{2}$$

wherein a represents the typical value of the factor A and b represents the typical value of the factor B. If the expression (2) was established, in order to simplify the propagation model solution for higher computing speed, we can convert $F(A, B)$ to $F(A, b)$.

For the ITU-R P.618 model, the influence factors include the frequency of the radio wave f, propagation distance d, temperature t, atmospheric pressure p, rainfall factor $R_{0.01}$, radio wave transmitting station latitude Ψ, elevation angle θ_0, and the standard deviation of the signal amplitude σ_{ref} with the change of the refractive index of radio wave. Assumed in the current issue, the transmitting station's frequency is a fixed value of 12 GHz, σ_{ref} is a fixed value of 0.0086, and the value range of other factors is $d \in [200 \text{ km}, 20,000 \text{ km}]$, $t \in [20°, 25°]$, $p \in [1000, 10125]$, $R_{0.01} \in [20, 30]$, $\theta_0 \in [5°, 45°]$ respectively. When θ_0 is more than $5°$ and less than $53°$, the beam spreading loss can be ignored. Since latitude primarily affects the beam spreading loss, the changes of latitude factors can be ignored. As

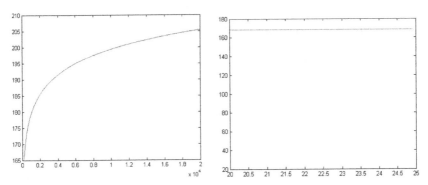

Figure 1: The propagation attenuation value vs. *d*.

Figure 2: The propagation attenuation vs. *t*.

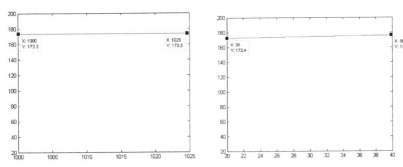

Figure 3: The propagation attenuation vs. *p*.

Figure 4: The propagation attenuation vs. $R_{0.01}$.

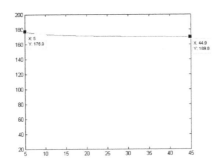

Figure 5: The propagation attenuation vs. θ_0.

seen in Figures 1–5, the propagation attenuation values change with the changes of these factors d, t, p, $R_{0.01}$, θ_0 respectively, which is predicted by ITU-R P.618 wave propagation model. The typical value of these factor is as follows that d is 500 km, t is 22°, p is 1013 hpa, $R_{0.01}$ is 25, and θ_0 is 10°.

We can find the following results from Figures1–5.

Firstly, the variation of the propagation distance results in the most dramatic changes of the propagation attenuation, the value of which presents logarithmic variation approximately as the distance increases.

Secondly, the variation of elevation angle in the range of between $5°$ and $45°$ causes that changes of the propagation attenuation is 7.1 dB, the effect of which is weaker than that of the variation of the propagation distance.

Thirdly, the propagation attenuation value is increased by 3.5 dB when rainfall increases varies from 20 to 40 mm/h.

Fourthly, the impact on the propagation attenuation are the weakest caused by atmospheric temperature and atmospheric pressure. Along with change within their value range, the propagation attenuation value hardly changes.

It is concluded that the taxis for the five significant factors from strong to weak is the propagation distance, elevation angle, rainfall, air temperature, and atmospheric pressure. However, from the description of the 618 model, it can be seen that the amount of calculation based on these factors to predict the propagation attenuation is on the contrary to their significance. For example, the role of atmospheric attenuation is weakest among these factors but spent a relatively large computation time. For the other, free space attenuation is the main form, but the most simple computationally.

Here, we simply divided these five factors into significant factors and nonsignificant factors, where the former includes only spread distance, and the latter include elevation, rainfall, air temperature, and atmospheric pressure.

3.2 The simplified calculation of significant factors

In the calculation based on the 618 model, the propagation distance is simple logarithmic relationship with the propagation attenuation value. If the radio wave frequency is determined, then the free space loss calculation requires only one addition, one multiplication, and one logarithmic computation, which is computational smaller and need not be simplified.

For the other applicable propagation models, if the calculation of a significant factor is more complex, we consider a piecewise linear approximation method or methods of calculating the data analysis.

3.3 The simplified calculation of nonsignificant factors

Both rain attenuation and scintillation decay are affected commonly by the elevation angle factor. When the 618 model is being simplified, it is necessary to consider elevation and rainfall as associated factors and establish the relationship function, where the total attenuation caused by rainfall and atmospheric flashing changes with the changes of elevation and rainfall. We can find that the total attenuation caused by rainfall and atmospheric flashing from the 618 model when elevation decreases or rainfall increases.

For a detailed analysis of and the relationship among the elevation, the rainfall and the attenuation value, we obtained the relationship function between attenuation values and the elevation factor θ_0 for different values of rainfall $R_{0.01}$, in the factor increases with the variation of the angle of elevation as well as the relationship function between attenuation values and the rainfall $R_{0.01}$ for different values of elevation factor θ_0.

For one side, the relationship function between attenuation values and the elevation factor θ_0 showed the exponential function relationship. For the other side, the relationship function between attenuation values and the rainfall $R_{0.01}$ presented the form of linear function. So we construct the predict model of rain attenuation and scintillation decay as

$$F\left(\theta_0, R_{0.01}\right) = ab^{\theta_0}\left(R_{0.01} - c\right) \tag{3}$$

In order to estimate the values of a, b, and c, the step-solving manner is used to calculate the approximation value of these coefficients.

The first step is to calculate the values of a and b with the methods of fitting a straight line and the nonlinear regression. As result, their values are 2.0186 and 0.9287 respectively.

The second step is to calculate the values of c with the method of parameter estimation. The value of c is 17.3442.

So the formula can be rewritten as

$$L_r + L_s = 2.0186 \times 0.9287^{\theta_0}\left(R_{0.01} - 17.3442\right) \tag{4}$$

Since the effects of atmospheric temperature and atmospheric pressure are very weak, the any constant in an effective value interval can replace them in the simplified calculation. However, since they only have effects on atmospheric attenuation, whereas the latter is almost zero, so just delete related calculations to the atmospheric attenuation.

At last, the ITU-R P.618 model can be simplified as

$$L_f = 32.78 + 20\log f + 20\log d + 2.0186 \times 0.9287^{\theta_0}\left(R_{0.01} - 17.3442\right) \tag{5}$$

4 Simulation

Simulation experiments with ITU-R P.618 refer to our meteorological satellite "China Star 6B." The purpose of the simulation is to predict the field strength coverage within the scope of our land and to verify the validity and deviation of the solving method for the simplified model.

4.1 Parameter settings

Taking into account the irregularity of national boundaries, in order to simplify the experiment, the coverage of the field strength is selected on the only part of the land area, where the range of the longitude and latitude range are (E90°, – E125°) and (N20°, –N40°). The satellite orbital altitude is 36,000 km. The transmitting band spans 800 MHz. Simulations are only carried out to predict the propagation attenuation at the frequency 3800 MHz. The rainfall factor is 25 mm/h, air temperature is 25, and the atmospheric pressure is the standard atmospheric pressure 1013 hpa. Attenuation prediction is based on the ITU-R P.618 model and the simplified calculation model proposed in this paper.

4.2 Simulation results and analysis

We calculate the time for the entire simulation process and the prediction error of the statistical results. In terms of computing time, during the simulation process, the other background programs are also performed on a computer such as drivers and security software, which have some effects on the performance of real-time calculation. Therefore, in order to obtain a relatively stable computing time, the same simulation task is executed many times, taking the average time as the result.

The simulation experiment results showed that using the 618 model took 0.125 s, but using the simplified model took 0.015 s. The maximum value of the prediction error is only 0.761 dB, and the error standard deviation is 0.142 dB.

From the experimental results, first of all, the time required to predict propagation attenuation reduced greatly and the speed is increased by more than 800%. Although the significant improvement in absolute time can't be reflected, but it is conceivable that this improvement will reflect some advantages during performing forecasting tasks in complex large scenes. Especially, when the same simulation platform commitments other computing tasks in less computing resource allocation, using this method is still in a relatively short period of time to complete all computing tasks. Accordingly, this improvement will be very significant.

Secondly, the prediction error is only 0.761 dB, which meets the capacity for prediction error for the vast majority of the receiving equipments.

5   Conclusions

In order to enhance the real-time performance of electromagnetic compatibility simulation experiment, on the condition of meeting prediction accuracy of wave propagation attenuation, this paper presents a fast solution method of simplified model and applies it to the wave propagation model ITU-R P.618. Simulation results show the effectiveness of this method to improve the efficiency of solving the propagation model. Solving the simplification will bring certain prediction error, so that the method can be used in the condition where extremely high solving efficiency is required, but the certain prediction error may be tolerated.

Acknowledgments

The research work was supported by National Science and Technology Major Project under Grant No. 2012ZX03006003.

References

[1] X. Yixi, *Theory and Application of Radio Wave Propagation*. The Post & Telecommunication Press, Beijing, pp. 7–9, 2008.
[2] J. Peinan, Z. Zhongzhi, *Radar Environment and Wave Propagation Character*. Publish House of Electronic Industry, Beijing, pp. 420–426, 2007.

Simulation study of blind signal separation algorithm based on Simulink

Biao Wu, Shaoqing Wang, Yuwu Yan

The Electronic System Engineering Company of China, Beijing, China

Abstract

The basic theory and the characteristics of typical algorithm of blind signal separation *(BSS)* are introduced. Take example for AMUSE algorithm, the simulation implement methods of *BSS* algorithm on Simulink with blocking simulation platform, and the simulation model and the result analysis are performed. By way of analysis, the simulation achieves the function of AMUSE algorithm and also have preferable real-time, maneuverability and expansibility. So it can offers a effective means for the design of signal processing system in practical environment and the R&D of virtual instruments.

Keywords: blind signal separation, algorithm, simulation.

1 Introduction

Blind signal separation (BSS), according to the observed mixing data vector, determines a conversion to restore the original signal or the source. Its main purpose is to achieve the extraction of the source signal with the observation data which the receiving antenna outputs on the condition of unknowing the source signal and the transmission channel, thereby providing a more effective method of signal processing and recognition extensively. BSS plays an increasingly important role in the field of digital signal processing and has been widely used in communications, speech processing, seismic exploration, biomedicine, image processing, radar, and economic data analysis.

Since creating the BSS theory, people in this area have made a lot of research work and proposed many valid BSS algorithm from different angles. According to the statistics information used, BSS can be divided into three kinds of algorithms, where the first algorithm based on information theory or likelihood estimation (such as Informax algorithm [1] and nonlinear PCA algorithm [2]), the second algorithm based on second-order statistics (SOS) (such as AMUSE [3] algorithm, SOBI algorithm [4]) and the third algorithm based on higher order statistics (such as JADE algorithm [5], FastICA algorithm [6]). According to BSS mathematical principles BSS algorithms can be divided into full eigenvalue decomposition algorithm (such as AMUSE algorithm), half-eigenvalues half optimization algorithm (such as SOBI algorithm, JADE algorithm, and fully optimized algorithm (such as Choi algorithm [7]).

Although it made a lot of useful BSS algorithms, but because it is difficult to implement the practical analysis software, and even the part of the code written by the researchers themselves, which results in that it is difficult to assess and promote these BSS algorithms for application. So it is very necessary to develop an independent integrated simulation software system for BSS algorithms. The Simulink software is a powerful simulation software, which uses the method of combining module to enable users to quickly and accurately create simulation models of dynamic systems. Moreover, Simulink integration environment is also supported by MATLAB, so it can directly use the powerful scientific computing capabilities of MATLAB. Thus the simulation study of BSS algorithm is convenient with Simulink is very convenient and real time. Then, we will give an example which shows the specific implementation method of AMUSE BSS algorithm in the Simulink simulation environment.

2 BSS algorithm theory

2.1 BSS problem and its mathematical model

BSS problem is a traditional and challenging task in the field of signal processing, which refers to restore the independent source signal from only the mixed signals observed. The "blind" means that the source signal is unobservable, and the hybrid system is not known in advance. The core issue of BSS is the learning algorithm of the separation or de-mix matrix, which belongs to unsupervised learning. The basic idea is to extract statistically independent features as the input expression without loss of information. Then we introduce a mathematical model of BSS.

Suppose there are m unknown source signals $s_i(t)$ constituting a column vector $s(t)=[s_1(t),\dots, s_m(t)]^T$, where $i=1,2,\dots,m$ and t is a discrete time, the value of which is 0,1,2,....

Let A be one $n \times m$ dimensional matrix, commonly referred to as the mixing matrix. Suppose there are n observed signals $x_i(t)$ constituting a column vector $x(t)=[x_1(t),\dots,x_m(t)]^T$, which satisfies the following equation:

$$x(t) = As(t) \qquad n \geq m \qquad (1)$$

BSS problem is to solve $s(t)$ to arbitrary t, according to the known $x(t)$, in the condition that A is unknown. This constitutes a BSS problem without noise.

Suppose there are n white Gaussian statistics noise signals $n_i(t)$ constituting a column vector $n(t)=[n_1(t),\dots,n_m(t)]^T$. Let n is white Gaussian statistics column vector composed of independent noise signals, which satisfies the following equation:

$$x(t) = As(t) + n(t) \qquad\qquad n \geq m \qquad\qquad (2)$$

So BSS problem is to solve $s(t)$ to arbitrary t, according of the known $x(t)$, in the condition that A is unknown. This constitutes a BSS problem with noise.

The formulation of BSS problem is to determine the separation matrix W based on the observed data vectors $x(t)$ in the condition of unknowing mixing matrix A and the source signal, so that the output is transformed into

$$y(t) = Wx(t) \qquad\qquad\qquad (3)$$

which is the copy or estimated signal of the source signal vector $s(t)$.

2.2 The assumptions and ambiguity of BSS problem

As a kind of compensation of structure information on the unknown mixing matrix A, there must be some additional assumptions about the source signal, which is a necessary condition for studying BSS problem. The assumptions conditions of BSS include:

(1) The source signals $s_1(t)$, $s_2(t)$, ..., $s_n(t)$ are statistically independent.
(2) A is a constant matrix of full rank.
(3) Only one source signal is the Gaussian signal at most [7].

Assumption (1) is the key to solving the problem of BSS. Although this is a very strict statistical assumption, it is a very reasonable assumption on the physical sense. Because the source signals are usually sent from the different physical systems, it is always able to meet the independent condition with each other.

Assumption (2) is to ensure that the number of observed signals is greater than the number of unknown signals, where the mixing coefficients are assumed constant under normal circumstances.

For the assumption (3), if the source signals are Gaussian distribution, the linear mixed signal of them is still submitted to the Gaussian distribution, which has been proved that this is inseparable [7].

In practical systems, the three assumptions are also satisfied easily.

For the lack of transmitting channels information and the knowledge of the source signals, there are two uncertainties or ambiguities for BSS, which are one uncertainty of the separated signals order and the other of complex amplitude of the separated signal (amplitude and initial phase). Uncertainty for BSS represents the incomplete identification to the mixing matrix A. However, in practical applications, the identification to the source signal is usually not affected by the ambiguity character of BSS. This is because almost all the information in the

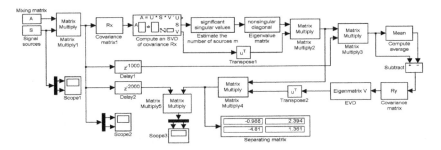

Figure 1 Simulink models of AMUSE algorithm.

source signals almost is already contained in the separated waveforms, which can meet the next step research on the BSS.

3 Simulink models of AMUSE algorithm

AMUSE algorithm is de-relation BSS algorithm based on SOS, which requires the source signal to be statistically unrelated. Also, the separation matrix is determined completely through the matrix eigenvalue decomposition by AMUSE algorithm, and therefore it is also full eigenvalue decomposition algorithm. The main advantage of AMUSE algorithm is simple, stable, and has small calculation amount, which can be applied to the source signals submitted to any probability distribution.

Simulink models of AMUSE algorithm is established as shown in Figure 1, where the observation data x is generated by simulation from the source signal module and the mixing matrix module.

The process flow is as follows with this model.

Firstly, the covariance matrix R_x of the observed data x is calculated through a covariance matrix module.

Secondly, the singular value decomposition is computed with the singular value decomposition module to obtain the eigenvalue and eigenvector matrix of R_x.

Thirdly, the number of source signals can be estimated based on the eigenvalues of R_x and thus we can obtain nonsingular eigenvalues diagonal matrix and whitening matrix T in order to implement robust whitening transformation to observational data and obtain data y.

Fourthly, solving the mean value of y by the mean module (mean). Then delay covariance matrix $R_y(\tau)$ of y is estimated by the covariance matrix module, where the delay τ equals 1.

Fifthly, carry out eigenvalue decomposing for $(R_y(\tau) + R_y^{T}(\tau))/2$ with eigenvalue decomposition module to obtain orthogonal eigenvector matrix V, by which we can obtain separation matrix $W = V^{T}T$. At last, the source signal can be separated from the mixed signal.

In Simulink models of AMUSE algorithm, in order to achieve the multiplication calculation among the whitening matrix T, the separation matrix W

and the observed data x, the observed data are processed in a delayed processing of different time periods, which will bring additional computational burden.

Simulation models of AMUSE algorithm built by Simulink has a strong versatility and scalability. It can be very easy to achieve separation of unknown source from sensors to achieve a multiuse effect. Meanwhile, according to the dynamic nature of Simulink, we can track variations in the signal processing in order to improve and optimize the model. Since Simulink in the interface hardware and software is also a great advantage, and thus the simulation model can be used with an external hardware device directly for data transmission and control facilitating real-time analysis and signal processing, which brings great convenience to the application of AMUSE BSS algorithms or other algorithms in the practical signal processing system.

4 Simulation results and analysis

In this section, ignoring the effects of noise, the simulation model of AMUSE algorithm established is tested by simulation and analysis. First of all, two signals of SSB and AM is simulated by blind separation. Let the carrier frequency of the two signals are 2 KHz, modulation frequency of which are 50 and 30 Hz respectively, and set the sampling rate 10 KHz with data processing length of 1000 sampling points.

The simulation results of the two source signals are shown in Figure 2(a). Supposing that the number of sensors is as many of the number of the source signals, waveform, and frequency spectrum of the two observed signals through mixing linear transformation matrix are shown in Figure 2(b) and (c), from which we can find that the distortion of each source signal is relatively large, and the spectrum also has a strong overlap and ambiguity. At this time, it is very difficult to separate the two source signals in signal processing methods of the frequency domain filtering. After performing AMUSE algorithm to the observed data of the two mixed signal, simulation waveforms and spectrum are shown in Figure 2(d) and (e), which showed that the AM and SSB signal are well separated, and signals spectrum has been completely separated so as to achieve a better BSS. It also proved the correctness of the Simulink simulation model of AMUSE algorithm proposed.

Then the simulation results are given for two-way voice signal simulation by BSS processing in real time. The waveform of two source signals of the speech signal, the mixed signal, and the signal after separation are shown in Figure 3(a)–(c).

As seen from the above simulation results, we can achieve better estimation of the unknown source signal under certain conditions obtaining a better BSS effect by Simulink simulation models of BSS algorithm AMUSE, which also prove that the simulation model has a strong real-time performance and operability.

5 Conclusions

In this paper, the basic principles and AMUSE BSS algorithm were studied and analyzed, and on this basis, we established AMUSE algorithm Simulink simulation model, which is verified to be valid by simulation.

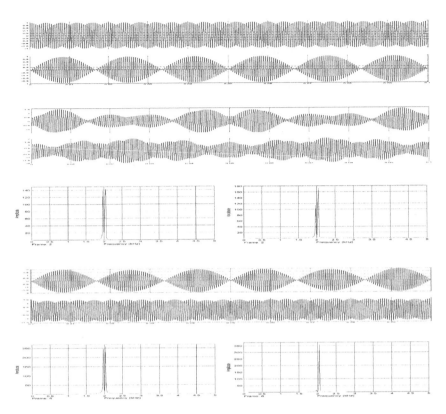

Figure 2: The simulation results of BSS: (a) waveform of SSB and AM signal, (b) waveform of the two mixed signal, (c) spectrum of the two mixed signal, (d) signal waveform after separating, and (e) signal spectrum after separating.

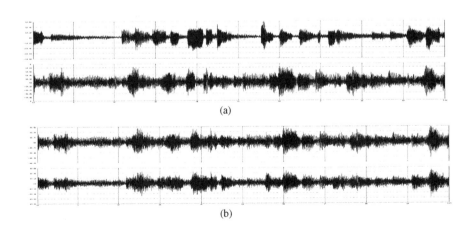

(a)

(b)

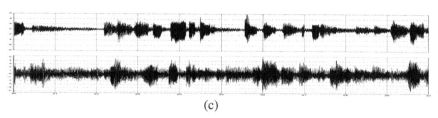

(c)

Figure 4: The simulation results of two-way voice signals: (a) waveform of two-way source signals, waveform of the mixed signal, and the signal waveform after separation.

Acknowledgments

The research work was supported by National Science and Technology Major Project under Grant No. 2012ZX03006003.

References

[1] A.J. Bell, T.J. Sejnowski, An information-maximization approach to blind separation and blind convolution. *Neural Computation*, **7**, pp. 1129–1159, 1995.

[2] J. Karhunen, J. Joutsensalo, Representation and separation of signals using nonlinear PCA typed learning. *Neural Networks*, **7**, pp. 113–127, 1994.

[3] L. Tong, R. Liu, V.C. Soon, Y.F. Huang, Indeterminacy and identifiability of blind identification. *IEEE Transactions on Circuits and Systems*, **38(5)**, pp. 499–509, 1991.

[4] A. Belouchrani, A.K. bed-Meraim, J.F. Cardoso, E. Moulines, A blind source separation technique using second-order statistics. *IEEE Transactions on Signal Processing*, **45(2)**, pp. 434–443, 1997.

[5] J.F. Cardoso, A. Souloumiac, Blind beamforming for non-Gaussian signals. *IEEE Proceedings-F*, **140(6)**, pp. 362–370, 1993.

[6] A. Hyvärinen, Fast and robust fixed-point algorithms for independent component analysis. *IEEE Transactions on Neural Networks*, **10(3)**, pp.626–634, 1999.

[7] S. Choi, A. Cichocki, S. Amari, Equivariant nonstationary source separation. *Neural Networks*, **15**, pp. 121–130, 2002.

Research on ripple-effect in software network

Zheng Liu[1], Qian Zhang[2]
[1]College of Information Science and Engineering, Northeastern University, Shenyang, China
[2]Technology Strategy & Development Department, Neusoft Corporation, Shenyang, China

Abstract

Aim at the problem that it is hard to measure large-scale software because of their complex structure, software structure was abstracted to network model, and ripple-effect of nodes in it was analyzed. Some open source software systems were selected as research objects and the distribution of forward ripple degree and reversal degree was analyzed. According to the analysis of ripple degree, vulnerable nodes, rigid nodes, and bridge nodes can be found in network structural which will provide guides for design and reconstruct of software system.

Keywords: ripple-effect, ripple degree, software structure, software network.

1 Introduction

Structure complexity has become one of the inherent characters of large-scale software due to its function complexity, which leads those traditional software quality control methods cannot fit for present software systems. The physiologists in Northwestern University in USA use functional magnetic resonance images to study the actions of human brain and the process of establishing contact between different parts in brain, and find that the structure of human brain is a complex network which presents typical small-world features. Software systems are fractal of human brain as the products of human brain, so the structure of software also present complex network features obviously. Some researchers in complex system science and statistical physics area have studied a large number of class diagram of OO software since 2002 and then started studying the overall features of software structure in network by abstracting diagraph from class diagram. It is

WIT Transactions on Information and Communication Technologies, Vol. 61, © 2014 WIT Press
www.witpress.com, ISSN 1743-3517 (on-line)
doi:10.2495/MIIT131121

the beginning of studying software structure based on complex network, and many new metric methods have been presented from then on [1,2]. More and more researcher identified the method study software structure using network model. They abstracted software system to a kind of artificial complex network and applied theories of complex network in study of structure and behavior of large-scale software system. The researchers studied the topological features of software network and reveal general characteristics of software structure, which provides strong support to researching the structural features of large-scale software system and also guide and help to studying metrics of them.

Researchers of software engineering paid more attention to analysis on the change of software function along with the further application of large-scale distributed software system based on Internet since 1990s [3]. Bohner [4,5] presented a process framework to analyze the software's changes and described these changes by "ripple-effect" for the first time. Ahmed Breech et al. studied the impacts that the change of software structural entities such as functions or variables have other relative entities in Orient-Object software systems [6–8]. Chen et al. [9] studied the relationship among design document, software component, external data and demand change, and built an impact model of software change based on objects and attributes. With the rising of software reuse and the wide application of UML modeling, Yinghui Wang [10,11] realized the analysis on architecture evolution of software and ripple-effect by reachability matrix.

The realization of complex function lies in the association and invocation between different modules in software system and the organization structure of modules will affect the system performance directly. It can reduce the risk of error and the cost of system maintenance by pay attention to the reasonableness of inner structure during software developing and maintaining. In this paper, the ripple-effect caused by node changes in Orient-Object software network is analyzed. According to the ripple range and rules of nodes, some critical nodes will be found to provide guide to software design and maintenance.

2 Building of software network model

Orient-Object software systems are main objects of study in this paper, and the process of building their network model is abstract the class diagram from original source firstly, and then regard the classes as nodes and the connections between classes as arcs to compose the software network. There are different relations between classes such as generalization, association, aggregation, and dependence, which have different closeness. In order to describe the software structure accurately, the connections are given different weights in network. The software network model is defined as follows:

$$N = (V, A, T, W) \tag{1}$$

where V(Vertices)=$\{v_i|\ i = 1, 2, ..., n\}$ represents the set of n nodes in network, and each node represents a class in software system. A(Arcs)=$\{(v_i, v_j, t)\ |\ v_i \in V,$

$v_j \in V, t \in T, i \neq j$} represents the set of arcs in network and each arc represents the relationship between two classes. There is usually not single relationship between two classes in real software system, for example, there is dependency and also inheritance between class A and class B, so t is a composite value. T(Type)={$t \mid t \in \{G, U, D\}$} represents the relationship between two classes. Here G means generalization, D means dependency, and U means usage including association and aggregation. W(Weight)={$w(a) \mid w(a)=f(t, \delta, N)$, $a \in A, t \in T, \delta \in (0,1), N \in \{0,1,2...\}$}represents the weight of each arc.

The value of weight is defined according to the closeness of connection between two nodes. In weighted software network, the larger the weight is, the closer two nodes connect, which meet the properties of similarity weight in weighted network. The similarity weight should be used in study of closeness of connections between nodes in complex networks and satisfy following conditions: the similarity weight is between 0 and 1. It means no connection if the weight is 0 and no network if the weight is 1 [12]. There are nine relations described in UML class diagram, but some of them including general association, limited association, association class, aggregation, and composition have no notable differences in UML structure, which can be distinguished only according to their semantics. So these relations are unified into usage, and inheritance, binding, and realization are unified into generalization. According to closeness defined in UML class diagram, weight of dependence is defined as 0.1, weight of usage is defined as 0.4, and weight of generalization is defined as 0.7. When there is more than one relation, the weight is defined as the larger one.

3 Ripple degree

According to the definition of ripple-effect, the node in network can be a producer or a consumer in the influence of ripple-effect. So the presentations of ripple-effect on nodes have two forms: forward ripple degree and reversal ripple degree.

3.1 Forward ripple degree

Definition 1: Forward ripple degree. It is the sum of weights on shortest paths starting from node v_i to all reachable nodes, which is denoted as

$$RF_{WG}(v_i) = \sum_{j \neq i}^{v_j \in TF(v_i)} W_{ij}, W_{ij} = \prod_{i \neq j}^{w_{mn} \in SP_{F(ij)}} w_{mn} \qquad (2)$$

where $TF(v_i)$ is the set of reachable nodes starting from v_i along forward arcs. W_{ij} is the weight of arc between v_i and v_j in $TF(v_i)$, which is the product of all weights on the forward shortest paths between v_i and v_j. When the out-degree of v_i is 0, $RF_{WG}(v_i)=0$.

Taking v_1 in Figure 1 as example, the weights on forward shortest paths from v_1 to other reachable nodes SP_F are $SP_{F(1,'2')}=\{0.7\}$, $SP_{F(1,'3')}=\{0.4\}$,

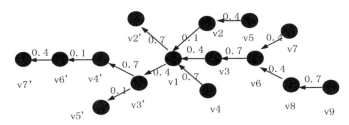

Figure 1: Example for ripple degree in software network.

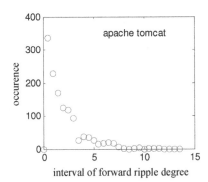

Figure 2: Occurrence distribution of forward ripple degree in apache tomcat.

$SP_{F(1,'4')}=\{0.4,0.7\}$, $\qquad$ $SP_{F(1,'5')}=\{0.4,0.1\}$, $\qquad$ $SP_{F(1,'6')}=\{0.4,0.7,0.1\}$, $SP_{F(1,'7')}=\{0.4,0.7,0.1,0.4\}$. Then add the products of weights on each path, that is $RF_{WG}(v_1)=0.7+0.4+0.4*0.7+0.4*0.1+0.4*0.7*0.1+0.4*0.7*0.1*0.4=1.4592$.

Forward ripple degree of node reflects the impact other nodes in network have on it, that is the possibility of being impacted when relative nodes are changed. The node with larger forward ripple degree is usually vulnerable and should be paid high attention to.

125 open source Orient-Object software are selected as sample to be analyzed on ripple degree. Taking apache tomcat as example, the distribution of forward ripple degree is shown in Figure 2.

The abscissa is the value of forward ripple degree and the ordinates is the occurrence of one forward ripple degree. The statistics of occurrence is done on the interval of 0.5, that is [0,0.5], (0.5,1.0], (1.0,1.5], (1.5,2.0], (2.0,2.5], etc. It is found that the occurrence is getting lower with the increase of interval value.

3.2 Reversal ripple degree

Definition 2. Reversal ripple degree. It is the sum of weights on shortest paths starting from all reachable nodes to node v_i, which is denoted as

$$RR_{WG}(v_i) = \sum_{\substack{j \neq i}}^{v_j \in TR(v_i)} W_{ij}, W_{ij} = \prod_{\substack{i \neq j}}^{w_{mn} \in SP_{R(ij)}} w_{mn} \qquad (2)$$

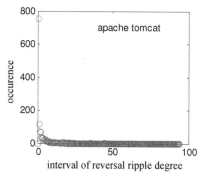

Figure 3: Occurrence distribution of reversal ripple degree in apache tomcat.

where $TR(v_i)$ is the set of reachable nodes ending with v_i along reversal arcs. W_{ij} is the weight of arc between v_i and v_j in $TR(v_i)$, which is the product of all weights on the forward shortest paths between v_i and v_j. When the in-degree of v_i is 0, $RR_{WG}(v_i)=0$.

Taking v_1 in Figure 1 as example, its reversal ripple degree is calculated as follows: first, get the weights on the reversal shortest paths from v_1 to other reachable nodes SP_R. $SP_{R(1,2)}=\{0.1\}$, $SP_{R(1,3)}=\{0.4\}$, $SP_{R(1,4)}=\{0.7\}$, $SP_{R(1,5)}=\{0.1,0.4\}$, $SP_{R(1,6)}=\{0.4,0.7\}$, $SP_{R(1,7)}=\{0.4,0.7,0.4\}$, $SP_{R(1,8)}=\{0.4,0.7,0.4\}$, $SP_{R(1,9)}=\{0.4,0.7,0.4,0.7\}$. Then add the products of weights on each path, that is, $RR_{WG}(v_1)=0.1+0.4+0.7+0.1*0.4+0.4*0.7+0.4*0.7*0.4+0.4*0.7*0.4+0.4*0.7*0.4*0.7=1.6208$.

Reversal ripple degree of node reflects the impact it has on other relative nodes when it is changed, which is the direct reflection of ripple-effect. The node with large reversal ripple degree is usually rigid and should be paid more attention to during development and maintenance of software.

Also taking apache tomcat as example, the distribution of reversal ripple degree is shown in Figure 3.

It is seen from Figure 3 that the occurrence is getting lower with the increase of interval value, which is similar with forward ripple degree.

4 Correlation between forward and reversal ripple degree

According to the definition of ripple degree, most nodes with large forward ripple lie in higher level of system and depend on many other nodes. They are vulnerable section of system because once any relative node is changed, they may be affected. So there can't be too many such nodes in system in order to avoid vulnerability appear. Correspondingly, most nodes with large reversal ripple degree are basic classes or interfaces that lie in lower level of system. They are associated with a large number of other nodes, and if they are changed, many relative nodes have to be changed too. The cost will increase. So it will lead to rigid if there are too many such nodes in system.

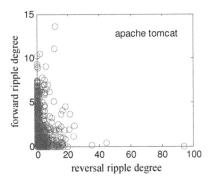

Figure 4: Joint distribution of forward and reversal ripple degree in apache tomcat.

The distribution of ripple degree reflects the design principles for software well according to the analysis on the front. As to a single node, if it has large forward ripple degree, it must depend on many basic nodes. It usually has rich functions, and its structure is complex. This kind of nodes is affected by others easily, so the probability of error occurring and changing in them is larger. In order to prevent error and changes from spreading wider in network, such nodes should not be depended and reused, that is the reversal ripple degree can't be too large. Similarly, the structural stability of nodes with large reversal ripple degree is very important for system because they are the basis of system. They can't depend on many other nodes in order to maintain the stability, so the forward ripple degree of them should be small. From this it might seem that there is negative correlation between forward and reversal ripple degree. In order to verify this conclusion, the joint distribution of forward and reversal ripple degree of sample software is analyzed. Still taking apache tomcat as example, the analysis result is shown in Figure 4

It can be seen from Figure 4 that most nodes have both small forward and reversal ripple degree, which is in the bottom left-hand corner of Figure 4. A few nodes with large forward ripple degree and small reversal ripple degree and those with large reversal ripple degree have small forward ripple degree are close to the axis.

5 Effects of ripple degree on software

The performance of ripple-effect is when there is error or change occurring in a node; this change will spread to other nodes associated with it quickly and affect other parts of system. Rigidity and vulnerability are two common features in corrupted software caused by the too large ripple range of nodes [13]. Rigidity means it is hard to change the software even single and simple change which will lead to chain reaction in other relative nodes. The larger the ripple range is, the more rigid the system is. In software network, rigidity is caused by large ripple-effect. When a node is changed, many other relative nodes have to be changed too, that increase the maintenance cost.

Vulnerability refers to if a module in software is changed, there will be problems in many other modules that have no relation with it. If these modules are modified, there will be more problems that appear. Vulnerability in software network appears in the nodes with large forward ripple degree because these nodes depend on many other nodes in structure and may be affected by any node's change easily. Thus it can be seen the rigid or vulnerable structure can be predicted by researching on ripple degree in software network, which provides guides for software maintenance of reconstruction.

According to the analysis on distribution of ripple degree, most nodes have small forward and reversal ripple degree both, a few nodes have large forward ripple degree or reversal ripple degree, and only few node, and even none, have both large forward and reversal ripple degree. At the view on software design, it is inevitable that a node has large unidirectional ripple degree. The nodes with large forward ripple degree belong to vulnerable nodes, so they should be checked first during error maintaining. The nodes with large reversal ripple degree belong to rigid nodes, and they should remain stable during maintaining or reconstructing. As to the nodes have both large forward and reversal ripple degree, they are bridge nodes whose structure may have hidden trouble. The number of such nodes in system should be limited.

6 Conclusions

Ripple-effect in software network reflects the internal connections between different modules or classes of system. If a module or class is changed, the change will spread to a large area through other relative modules or classes that are affected by the change. In software network, the forward ripple degree reflects the possibility of a node being affected by others, and the larger the forward ripple degree is, the larger the possibility is. This kind of nodes is vulnerable nodes. The reversal ripple degree reflects the possibility of a node affecting others, and the larger the reversal ripple degree is, the larger the possibility is. This kind of nodes is rigid nodes. Also a kind of nodes that has large forward and reversal ripple degree is bridge nodes. They are always critical nodes to connect different parts in structure, and also sensitive nodes whose structure may have hidden trouble. The research on these three kinds of nodes will provide guides to design of software structure and references to software maintenance.

Acknowledgments

The research work was supported by Fundamental Research Foundation of the Ministry of Education of China under Grant No. N110304003.

References

[1] R. Vasa, J.G. Schneider, C. Woodward et al., Detecting structural changes in Object Oriented software systems. In: *Proceedings of the 2005 International Symposium on Empirical Software Engineering*, Australia, pp. 479–486, 2005.

[2] R. Vasa, J.-G. Schneider, O. Nierstrasz, The inevitable stability of software change. In: *Proceedings of the International Conference on Software Maintenance*, France, pp. 4–13, 2007.

[3] P. Cheng, W. Liu, Y. Chen. Ripple-effect of software trustworthiness evolution based on matrix transform. *System Engineering—Theory & Practice*, **30(5)**, pp. 778–785, 2010.

[4] S.A. Bohner, Impact analysis in the software change process: a year 2000 perspective. In: *Proceedings of the 1996 International Conference on Software Maintenance*, Monterey, pp. 42–51, 1996.

[5] S.A. Bohner, Software change impacts: an evolving perspective, In: *Proceedings of the International Conference on Software Maintenance*, Montréal, pp. 263–272, 2002.

[6] A.E. Hassan, C.H. Richard, Predicting change propagation in software system, In: *Proceedings of the International Conference on Software Maintenance*, Chicago, pp. 84–293, 2004.

[7] B. Breech, A. Danalis S. Shindo et al., Online impact analysis via dynamic compilation technology, In: *Proceedings of the International Conference on Software Maintenance*, Chicago, pp. 453–457, 2004.

[8] H. Malik, A.E. Hassan, Supporting software evolution using adaptive change propagation heuristics, In: *Proceedings of the International Conference on Software Maintenance*, Beijing, pp. 177–186, 2008.

[9] C.Y. Chen, C.W. She, J.D. Tang, An object-based, attribute-oriented approach for software change impact analysis, In: *Proceedings of the International Conference on Industrial Engineering and Engineering Management*, pp. 577–581, 2007.[10] Y.H. Wang, S.K. Zhang, Y. Liu, Ripple-effect analysis of software architecture evolution based on reachability matrix. *Journal of Software*, **15(8)**, pp.1107–1115, 2004.

[11] Y.H. Wang, L.F. Wang, S.K. Zhang, A tracing approach of software requirement change. *Chinese Journal of Electronics*, **8(34)**, pp. 1428–1432, 2006.

[12] E. Ravasz, A.L. Somera, D.A. Mongru, Z.N. Oltvai, Hierarchical organization of modularity in metabolic networks. *Science*, **297(30)**, pp. 1551–1553, 2002.

[13] R.C. Martin, *Agile Software Development—Principles, Patterns, and Practices*, Tsinghua University Press, Beijing, pp. 88–132, 2003.

Survey of web backdoor detection and protection

L. Duan[1], L.H. Zhang[1], Z.F. Chen[1], T. Wei[2], X.H. Han[1]
[1]Institute of Computer Science and Technology of Peking University,
China
[2]BitBlaze Group, UC Berkeley, USA

Abstract

Web backdoors (also called webshell) are backdoors of web sites. By definition, web backdoors are hard to detect and are great threat to web users and web sites (especially PHP and ASP web sites). In this paper, we consider the problem of web backdoor detection and protection. We perform an in-depth analysis of varied install methods and hiding techniques that web backdoors used. We summarize web backdoor detection and protection mechanisms in three aspects: server configuration and reinforcement, intrusion detection systems, and static analysis. In addition, we propose a protection mechanism that combines white list with dynamic analysis to detect and prevent PHP backdoors. This mechanism can completely prevent web backdoors by detecting sensitive functions and has no false positive. Though current researches make it more difficult to make web backdoor attacks, there are still many limitations and unresolved issues that need both academia and industrial community to work on in the future.
Keywords: web backdoor, IDS, static analysis, dynamic analysis.

1 Introduction

According to Ref. [1], a backdoor is "a method of bypassing normal authentication, securing illegal remote access to a computer, while attempting to remain undetected." Backdoors are first proposed in Ref. [2].

Web backdoor attack, with the characteristic of high concealment, is one of the most important threats to the Internet. By constructing an ingenious web backdoor, an attacker can bypass system firewall, thus getting the control of a server and causing significant harm to web sites and web users. CNCERT pointed

WIT Transactions on Information and Communication Technologies, Vol. 61, © 2014 WIT Press
www.witpress.com, ISSN 1743-3517 (on-line)
doi:10.2495/MIIT131131

Table 1: The Roles of Detection and Protection Mechanisms in Three Stages.

Web Backdoor Stages	Server Security Configuring and Reinforcing	Static Analysis	IDS
Implanting	Y	N	Y
Concealing	N	Y	N
Bursting	Y	N	Y

out in Ref. [3] that the number of concealed attacks such as implanting backdoor was on the rise, and user information became attackers' key target. In 2012, CNCERT found out 52,324 web sites in China had been implanted backdoors, including 3016 government web site, separately increased by 213.7% and 93.1% monthly compared with 2011. The 360 company reported in 2013 China Internet conference that three out of ten web sites (about more than 1 million) in China were been implanted backdoors, of which some backdoors could survive up to 5 years. Web sites of medical treatment, government, enterprise, and education had the worst situation.

This paper presents that the complete web backdoor attack process includes three stages: backdoor implanting, backdoor concealing, and backdoor bursting. Existing web backdoor detection and protection mechanisms can be classified into three aspects: server configuration and reinforcement, intrusion detection systems (IDSs), and static analysis. Table 1 gives the roles of different mechanisms played in the stages of web backdoor attack process. "Y" means working and "N" means not working.

Server configuration and reinforcement is platform level protection which can prevent backdoor implanting and reduce loss.

IDS is a kind of web security device which monitors net transportation and will alarm or automatically take action when detecting suspicious transportation. There are two kinds of IDS: one is signature-based, which has a high accuracy but a high false negative; the other is anomaly-based, which has a stronger detection ability but a high false positive.

Detecting backdoor is the key and difficult point of web backdoor protection in backdoor concealing stage. The techniques of detecting and anti-detecting contest further between security researchers and attackers. Static analysis mechanisms, the major method used by traditional antivirus software and web backdoor scanning tools, fall into two categories: signature-based scanning and heuristic-based scanning. Dynamic analysis is not widely used in web backdoor detection. This mainly has two reasons: (a) Dynamic analysis policies are hard to define, which lead to high false positive, especially in web environment. (b) Dynamic analysis of script language is hard to implement.

Another contribution of this article is that, we proposed a method, which combines dynamic analysis with white list, to detect all web backdoors using sensitive functions. The combined method overcomes the limitation of high false positive rate of dynamic analysis.

The rest of this paper is organized as follows. The section "Technical features of web backdoors" summarizes and analyzes the implanting principle and technique features of web backdoors. The following three sections introduce server configuration and reinforcement, IDS, and static analysis mechanisms in sequence. The section "Discussion on PHP backdoors" proposes a new analysis method based on the combination of PHP dynamic analysis and white list to detect the backdoors. We summarize in the conclusion section.

2 Technical features of web backdoors

In general, there are two situations when web backdoors occur: one is that the backdoors exist when the web site is built; the other is that the attackers use vulnerability to implant web backdoors after that. In the former situation, the usual cause is that server system and the framework of web application have backdoors, or the web sites developers leave backdoors. This kind of web backdoors can be excluded by source code audit. In the latter situation, the precondition of web backdoor implantation is that attackers can compromise the web sites by exploiting known or zero-day vulnerabilities. We usually use defense in depth such as actively applying IDS to deal with zero-day vulnerability. As for known vulnerabilities, the web sites security maintainers should update the system in time.

Web backdoor implanting is the first step of attack. In the process of implanting, the system log can record suspicious events. If we detect the backdoors while attackers implanting them, the backdoors can be blocked from the beginning.

If attackers can implant backdoors, it means that they've already (at least partially) get control of the server by exploiting the vulnerabilities. In addition, attackers can modify last modification time and last access time to make backdoors stealthier. There are three ways for attackers to implant backdoors:

1. Uploading malicious files to server using the uploading vulnerability.
2. Create new files which include the malicious code.
3. Modify existing server-side files. Attackers can implant backdoors by modifying only a few lines, even just one line of the source file.

There are many techniques widely used in web backdoors. We can take advantage of these features in prevention and protection.

A. Using sensitive functions. There is one kind of backdoors called "one-line backdoor." In one-line backdoors, attackers just insert one single line of code to implant a backdoor by using sensitive functions, such as *system()*, *exec()*, *passthru()*, *shell_exec()*, *backtick operator*, and *eval()* in PHP.
B. Code obfuscation technique. Code obfuscation is a big topic. Limited by space, here we just list three common ways to obfuscate the backdoor code:
   - Using case sensitive code and string concatenate symbol.
   - Encoding and encrypting. There are already base64 encoding and decoding function in PHP library, so among all the code obfuscation methods attackers like base64 the most.

- Make use of *preg_replace()* function with */e* parameter to produce sensitive functions like *eval()*, and to fight against static code scanning based on function name.

C. Traverse server-side file directory and access/modify/delete server files. If the server doesn't protect the logs and configuration files very well, attackers will be able to delete or modify the server-side logs and configuration files. Then web backdoors will be harder to detect.

D. Hiding malicious shellcode logic by using get/post method, cookie, or uploading files (such as images). Malicious shellcode logic usually has signatures. Attackers can implant a backdoor without shellcode and the backdoor can receive messages from user input. Once the application sends user input to sensitive functions without correctly preprocessing it, there will be chances for attackers.

3   Server configuration and reinforcement

While server configuration and reinforcement isn't technically hard, it is quite necessary for improving server security. Web sites containing high-risk vulnerabilities are vulnerable to web backdoor attack and other security issues. Attackers can compromise a large number of web sites by simply running automatic tools.

Once the backdoor is installed in a web site, it is difficult to detect. The compromised web site is under severe danger, such as web pages tampering, traffic hijacking, Trojans planting, database data breach at any time.

Here we list five important and common ways to mitigate the problem:

1. Update systems and applications to the latest version and install patches in time.
2. Set permissions for ftp access. Never allow anonymous access.
3. Set permissions for sensitive server directory access, make sure the directory structure and file names are clear to the administrator.
4. Backup the logs, web site code, and other critical data in time, and stores them in a safe environment. This is useful to restore the server to a previous secure state when you cannot locate or completely remove the back door.
5. Language configuration: For example, disable sensitive functions in the PHP.ini to improve security in PHP severs.

4   Using IDS to prevent web backdoors

IDSs analyze the occurred events and produce reports about malicious activities or policy violations by monitoring network and system activities.

Zhang and Paxson [4] describe a method to detect a backdoor connection in a flood of legitimate network traffic. They assume that interactive traffic has characteristics quite different from most machine-driven traffic. So they develop a general algorithm and several protocol-specific algorithms that look for interactive backdoor signatures.

Borders and Prakash [5] put up Web Tap, a network-level anomaly detection system that detects covert communication, backdoors, and spyware. Web Tap takes advantage of legitimate web request patterns to detect anomalies in outbound traffic. Web Tap uses data of web traffic from 30 clients over 40-day period to evaluate the effectiveness. The results show that Web Tap is effective in detecting spyware and backdoor programs, while the false positive rate is manageable.

Juslin and Virtanen [6] propose an approach that combines NIDS with an integrated service checker to detect backdoors. They examine how an NIDS can be used as a trigger for service checking. The evaluation on detection of unauthorized SSH servers show that the combined approach reduces the amount of false positive.

Choi and Cho [7] propose a two-step hierarchical scheme for detecting detoured attacks to the web server. The first step is a signature-based detector and the second is an anomaly-based detector.

5 Using static analysis to detect web backdoors

Web backdoors are, by design, difficult to detect. Traditional antivirus software is basically based on file signatures or string signature scanning. Nowadays there are also many open source code-scanning tools (or scripts) [8–10]. These tools use principle and characteristics as features in static analysis.

Wysopal and Eng [11] describe a high level classification of backdoors and static analysis of source or binary code. They provide real-world examples of application backdoors, the techniques backdoors used, and strategies to detect these techniques. Xu et al. [12] summarize 12 features of ASP web backdoors. Based on the features, they introduce a program to detect ASP web backdoors automatically.

While signature detection can detect popular web backdoors, it is not that effective in detecting new backdoors and can be easily bypassed. Rahul Sasi [13,14] gives detailed idea of the effectiveness of antivirus software by detecting web backdoors. He describes the limitations and inefficiency of traditional antivirus software and code-scanning tools.

Hu et al. [15] propose a mechanism that uses machine learning in static analysis to improve the effectiveness. They use decision tree algorithm, which is a kind of supervised machine learning system. Combined with boosting, both the stability and accuracy is improved.

6 Discussion on PHP backdoors

PHP is the most widely used server-side open-source programming language. According to Ref. [16], PHP is now installed on more than 244 million web sites and 2.1 million web servers. After years of development, the PHP kernel is relatively safe. However, the third-party extensions, libraries, and tools are lack of security guarantee. PHP does not have any built-in additional security mechanisms; as a consequence PHP web site suffers more vulnerabilities than others.

PHP backdoor can be prevented in the aspect of the following three methods: the PHP package integrity, the PHP configuration, and the application layer protection.

(a) Check PHP package integrity: try to update to the latest version of PHP, only install and use extensions and third-party tools whose security can be guaranteed.
(b) Check the PHP configuration: e.g., make use of *allow_url_fopen* and *open_basedir* settings and disable the sensitive system function calls if the application itself does not need them.
(c) Application layer protection: popular PHP applications like PHPBB and Wordpress, which have a great amount of users, should be updated in time.

In addition to previously mentioned static analysis methods, we propose a new analysis method based on the combination of PHP dynamic analysis and white list to detect the backdoors: The PHP scripts are compiled into intermediate code before execution. Our dynamic analysis is achieved by modifying the system sensitive function handlers. In order to reduce the false positive rate, we use a white list approach: first we preprocess records of all sensitive positions in the source code of function calls and store the results in a secure location; then we check the white list at runtime dynamically, if the call site of a sensitive function is not in the white list, we can conclude that the call is a planted backdoor.

The combination of dynamic analysis and white list detection methods can completely overcome the limitations of false positives. Even if the PHP configuration is modified, as long as the attacker cannot disable the analysis extension by rebooting the server, the protection would be effective. The limitations of the protection method are: (1) the effectiveness depends on the safety of the white list. If the white list is modified, the protection will be compromised; (2) the backdoor can only be detected at runtime when the sensitive function calls are being executed.

7 Conclusion

In this paper, we define the three stages of web backdoor attacks. We also summarize and analyze the general techniques and features of web backdoors. Then we sum the web backdoor protection mechanisms up in three aspects: server configuration and reinforcement, IDSs, and static analysis. We analyze the strength and weaknesses of each above research. At last, we propose a protection mechanism that combines white list with dynamic analysis to detect and prevent PHP backdoors. In this way, we avoid the high false positive of dynamic analysis.

References

[1] Backdoor (computing), http://en.wikipedia.org/wiki/Backdoor_(computing)

[2] H.E. Petersen, R. Turn, System implications of information privacy. In: *Proceedings of the April 18–20, 1967, Spring Joint Computer Conference.* ACM, pp. 291–300, 1967.

[3] 2012 CNCERT report, http://www.cert.org.cn/publish/main/12/2013/20130320085931766172092/20130320085931766172092_.html

[4] Y. Zhang, V. Paxson, Detecting backdoors. In: *Proceedings of the 9th USENIX Security Symposium*, pp. 157–170, 2000.

[5] K. Borders, A. Prakash, Web tap: detecting covert web traffic. In: *Proceedings of the 11th ACM Conference on Computer and Communications Security*, ACM, pp. 110–120, 2004.

[6] J. Juslin, T. Virtanen, Automatic backdoor analysis with a network intrusion detection system and an integrated service checker. In: *Information Assurance Workshop, 2003. IEEE Systems, Man and Cybernetics Society.* IEEE, pp. 122–126, 2003.

[7] B. Choi, K. Cho, Two-step hierarchical scheme for detecting detoured attacks to the web server. *Computer Science and Information Systems*, (**00**), pp. 26–26, 2013.

[8] NeoPI, https://github.com/Neohapsis/NeoPI

[9] Linux Malware Detect, http://www.rfxn.com/projects/linux-malware-detect/

[10] PHP Shell Scanner, http://ketan.lithiumfox.com/doku.php?id=phpshell_scanner

[11] C. Wysopal, C. Eng, *Static Detection of Application Backdoors*. Black Hat, 2007.

[12] M. Xu, X. Chen, Y. Hu, Design of software to search ASP web shell. *Procedia Engineering*, (**29**), pp. 123–127, 2012.

[13] Effectiveness of Antivirus in Detecting Web Application Backdoors, http://www.exploit-db.com/wp-content/themes/exploit/docs/16082.pdf

[14] Web Backdoors, *Attack, Evasion and Detection*, http://www.garage4hackers.com/blogs/8/webbackdoors-attack-evasion-detection-258/

[15] J. Hu, Z. Xu et al., Research of webshell detection based on decision tree. *ISTIC*, **1(6)**, 2012.

[16] PHP Usage Stats, http://www.php.net/usage.php

An efficient remote user password authentication scheme for resource-limited environments

Zhonglin Liu, Jiayong Liu, Yong Fang
School of Electronics and Information Engineering, Sichuan University, Chengdu, China

Abstract

An efficient remote user password authentication scheme with higher security strength is proposed in this paper. The password authentication information is not stored in smart card to prevent sensitive data leakage. The introduction of random authentication factor and two-variant hashing operations are used to solve nonrepairable problems of the scheme. The scheme ensures that the authentication information is random to prevent replay attacks while avoiding the complex synchronization problems. The security analysis shows that this scheme can solve the security problem of being vulnerable against the off-line guessing and forged login attacks while holding the features of the low computational cost and the efficiency in implementation. And it can achieve better performance in security and practicality for resource-limited environment.

Keywords: smart card; nonce; authentication; guessing attacks.

1 Introduction

Authentication scheme based on password and smart card, which is the most commonly used technique to provide authentication between the legitimate users and remote server, is a two-factor mechanism. It is familiar remote user authentication scheme in resource-limited environments. The security of these authentication schemes rely on the confidentiality of user's password and sensitive data stored in a smart card [1–3].

However, Kocher et al. and Messerges et al. pointed out that the sensitive data stored in a smart card can be extracted by monitoring the power consumption or analyzing the leaked information [4–6]. Based on these studies, many previous schemes have been proved to be vulnerable to off-line password guessing attacks once the sensitive data stored in a smart card was extracted using above methods [7,8].

In 2007, Wang et al. [9] proposed a remote user password authentication scheme using smart cards and claimed that off-line password guessing attack is still inefficient even if a smart card was lost and the sensitive data stored in a smart card was extracted.

In 2008, Yoon et al. [10] pointed out that Wang et al.'s authentication scheme is still vulnerable to off-line password guessing attack and forgery login attack using lost smart card [11]. However, it is regrettable that they didn't give an efficient solution in their paper. By using time-consuming modular exponential computing, Chung et al. [12] proposed an improved scheme. But a great cost of computation is added, the scheme may be impractical in the resource-limited smart card scenarios.

In this paper, aiming at the weaknesses in the previous scheme to off-line password guessing attack, forged login attack, and its poor reparability, we propose an enhanced password authentication scheme against the off-line guessing and forged login attacks while still keeps the features of the low computational cost and the efficiency in implementation and have the reparability of the scheme.

2 An efficient remote user password authentication scheme based on nonce

In Wang et al.'s scheme [9], the password verification information is stored in smart card to increase the efficiency of identification in the use of the wrong login password and enhance the security of password change phase. However, the attendant costs followed by. The scheme is vulnerable to guessing attack, the forgery attack, the unrepairable problem, and other safety defects.

In addition, the problem of clock synchronism between the remote server and the smart card exists in the timestamp-based password authentication scheme. So in the open environment of the Internet, it will cost a lot to insure the strict synchronism, especially when the data transmission and processing delay is uncertain. If the setting of the interval of transmission delay is too short, it will cause the failure of the legal users' login. But, if the setting of the interval of transmission delay is too large, it will suffer from the replay attacks.

In this section, an efficient authentication scheme based on the smart card is proposed. In this scheme, the introduction of random number is used to solve nonrepairable problems, as reported in Refs. [3,7,11]. In the verification phase, usage of double hash operation will effectively prevent forgery and impersonation attacks. Password authentication information is not stored in smart card, thus guessing attacks and forgery attacks implemented by monitoring the power consumption or analyzing the leaked information is prevented.

The following notation is used throughout this paper.

U: the user.
ID: the identity of U.
PW: the password of U.
S: the remote server.
x: the permanent secret key of S.
$h(\cdot)$: a cryptographic unkeyed hash function.
$h_k(\cdot)$: a cryptographic keyed hash function with secret key k.
$\Rightarrow$: a secure channel.
$\rightarrow$: a common channel.

The scheme consists of four phases: the registration phase, the login phase, the verification phase, and the password change phase.

2.1 Registration phase

This phase is invoked whenever U initially registers to S.

R1. $U \Rightarrow S$: $ID, h(b \oplus PW)$.

U randomly selects a number b and computes $h(b \oplus PW)$. Later, U sends ID, $h(b \oplus PW)$ to S.

R2. $S \Rightarrow U$: smart card$[R, h(\cdot), h_k(\cdot)]$.

Upon receiving the messages, S generates a random number N, and the computes $k= h(ID \oplus x \oplus N)$, $R=k \oplus h(b \oplus PW)$. S sends a smart card containing R, $h(\cdot)$, $h_k(\cdot)$ back to U.

R3. S stores $\{ID, N\}$ into its registered user database.
R4. U stores b into the smart card so that U does not need to remember b after registration phase. U's smart card now contains R, b, $h(\cdot)$, $h_k(\cdot)$.

2.2 Login phase

This phase is invoked whenever U wants to login S for gaining the access right.

L1. $U \rightarrow$ Smart card : $\{ID, PW\}$

U inserts his/her smart card into the card reader and keys in ID and PW.

L2. Smart card checks the validity of ID.

Smart card rejects this session if the verification result is negative.

L3. Smart card $\rightarrow S$: ID

Smart card sends ID to S for login.

2.3 Verification phase

Upon receiving the login request, the remote system S performs the following steps to facilitate the mutual authentication:

V1. S checks the validity of ID.

According to the registered user database, S checks the validity of ID. S terminates the login request if the verification result is negative. Otherwise, S reads the corresponding N from the registered user database.

V2. $S \rightarrow U : \{c_1\}$

A random number R_S is generated by S, then S takes out the key x, computes $k =h(ID \oplus x \oplus N)$, $c_1 = k \oplus R_S$, and sends c_1 to U.

V3. $U \rightarrow S : \{c_2, c_3\}$

A random number R_U is generated by U, then U takes out R and b, computes $k =R \oplus h(b \oplus PW)$, $c_1' = c_1 \oplus k$, $c_2= h_k(c_1')$, $c_3 = k \oplus R_U$, and sends $\{c_2, c_3\}$ to S.

V4. $S \rightarrow U : \{c_4\}$

S computes $c_2' = h_k(R_S)$ and checks whether equation $c_2'\ ?= c_2$ holds or not. If not, S rejects login request. Otherwise, it means user is authentic and S accepts the login request. For the mutual authentication, S computes $c_3'=c_3 \oplus k$, $c_4=h_k(c_3')$, and sends c_4 to U.

V5. Upon receiving the message c_4, U computes $c_4' = h_k(R_U)$ and verifies $c_4'\ ?= c_4$. If they are equal, then user believes that the remote party is authentic system and the mutual authentication between U and S is completed, otherwise U terminates the operation.

2.4 Password change phase

This phase is invoked whenever U wishes to change his/her current password PW for some secure reasons.

C1. $U \rightarrow S : \{ID, m_1\}$

U inserts his/her smart card into card reader, keys in ID and PW, and requests to change password. Then the smart card generates a random number r_c and computes $m_1=k \oplus r_c$, and sends $\{ID, m_1\}$ to S.

C2. $S \rightarrow U : \{m_2, m_3, m_4\}$

According to the registered user database, S checks the validity of ID. If the verification result is negative, S rejects the password change request, otherwise S

reads the corresponding N from the registered user database. S takes out the key x, generates a random number r_s and N_{new}, then computes: $k=h(ID\oplus x\oplus N)$, $m_2=h_k(m_1\oplus k)$, $m_3=r_s\oplus k$, $k_{new}=h(ID\oplus x\oplus N_{new})$, and $m_4=k_{new}\oplus k$. And then sends $\{m_2, m_3, m_4\}$ to U in reply to the request.

C3. $U\rightarrow S : \{ m_5\}$

Upon receiving the response $\{m_2, m_3, m_4\}$, U computes $k = R\oplus h(b\oplus PW)$, $m_2'=h_k(r_c)$, and compares $m_2'?=m_2$. If not, rejects the password change, otherwise U chooses new password PW_{new}, and then computes $R_{new}= m_4\oplus k\oplus h(b\oplus PW_{new})$ $(=k_{new}\oplus h(b\oplus PW_{new}))$, and then stores R_{new} into the smart card and replaces the old values R with R_{new}.

Additionally, U should make a backup of copy of the old value R so as to relogin S using it when S fails to update N as following due to a network communication failure.

For responding to challenge from S, U computes $m_5= h_k(m_3\oplus k)$ and then sends $\{m_5\}$ to S in reply to the challenge.

C4. S : Update N

Upon receiving the response $\{m_5\}$, S computes $m_5'= h_k(r_s)$ and compares $m_5'?=m_5$. If not, rejects the password change, otherwise S believes that the user is authentic and have successfully received k_{new}. And then S replaces the N with N_{new} as new registration random factor in registered user database.

Now, user password PW and long-term secret k is synchronously updated in security.

3 Security analysis

3.1 Off-line password guessing attack

In the registration stage, the user chooses the login password PW freely and then sends to the server through the security channel. Compared to Wang et al.'s scheme, the password verification information is not stored in smart card. R is stored in smart card where $R= h(ID\oplus x\oplus N)\oplus h(b\oplus PW)$. Since x and PW are unknown to adversary, one can get neither $h(ID\oplus x\oplus N)$ nor $h(b\oplus PW)$ even if the adversary has successfully obtained R and b by monitoring the power consumption or analyzing the leaked information. Moreover, c_1, c_2, and R are all combined with two random or unknown-to-adversary items, as well as the isomerization, so that it is impossible to establish a valid guessing equation and the guessing attack on Wang et al.'s scheme will be defeated in our proposed scheme.

In the verification phase, even though an attacker intercepted the information such as $c_1 = h(ID\oplus x\oplus N)\oplus R_S$, $c_2=h_k(R_S)$, $c_3 =h(ID\oplus x\oplus N)\oplus R_U$ and $c_4=h_k(R_U)$, it is extremely hard for the attacker to obtain the information $k=h(ID\oplus x\oplus N)$, because of the property of the secure one-way hash function and the introduction of random number R_S and R_U. Using the challenge random will ensure that each of the identity information is random. Therefore, the improved scheme can resist the password guessing attacks effectively.

3.2 Impersonation attack

The scheme provides mutual authentication between clients and servers. For the client, the smart card, the user login password PW and identity ID constitute a two-factor authentication mechanism. Even if the attacker accessed to the smart card held by legitimate users, without knowing the correct login password PW and ID, he/she cannot impersonate legitimate users. For the server, even if the attacker obtained ID and N, without knowing the permanent secret key x, he/she cannot compute $k = h(ID \oplus x \oplus N)$ to impersonate the legitimate server. In the process of verification, even if the attackers intercepted authentication information $c_1 = k \oplus R_S$ and $c_3 = k \oplus R_U$, without knowing the secret information $k = h(ID \oplus x \oplus N)$, he/she will not be able to resume random number R_S and R_U. Thus, the authentication information $c_2 = h_k(R_S)$ and $c_4 = h_k(R_U)$ cannot be forged. Therefore, our improved scheme can effectively resist forgery attack.

3.3 Reply attack

The improved scheme introduces the challenge-response mechanism, using challenge random R_S and R_U to ensure that each of the authentication information is random. Even if an attacker successfully intercepted the last successful authentication information through some sort of attack means, he/she cannot use the last authentication information for replay attacks. Therefore, this scheme can resist replay attacks effectively.

3.4 The resolvement of reparability

For the problems of reparability, as mentioned in the literatures [7,11], suppose that the key $k = h(ID \oplus x)$ stored in smart card has been leaked, an attacker can pass the authentication successfully without using the password PW. And the legitimate user U is unable to prevent this attack even though he/she has discovered that the secret k stored in his/her smart card has been revealed and used a new password to re-register with S.

The introduction of random number N in secret information $k = h(ID \oplus x \oplus N)$ is used to solve unrepairable problem in the original scheme. If the legitimate user suspects that k or the password has been leaked, he/she is able to update synchronously the long-term secret k and his/her password by launching password change phase, where $k_{new} = h(ID \oplus x \oplus N_{new})$, N_{new} is random number generated by S. In other words, the problem of the reparability in the scheme can be resolved neither requiring the server to change the key x nor requiring the users to replace the smart card to change ID.

In addition, as long as the permanent secret key of S, i.e. x, isn't revealed, the secret information $k = h(ID \oplus x \oplus N)$ is still secure even if an adversary has obtained user's random authentication factor N due to the property of the secure one-way hash function. Of course, S should protect account-database from unauthorized modification in order to prevent from the denial of service attack resulted from unauthorized modification. But it is worthwhile to do so due to the reparability of the scheme.

4 Conclusions

In order to withstand off-line password guessing attacks and impersonation attacks and to solve the nonrepairable problem in the remote user authentication scheme, we proposed an efficient remote user password authentication scheme by introducing the user's random authentication factor N and double hash operation. The password authentication information is not stored in smart card, which can prevent effectively password guessing attacks implemented by monitoring the power consumption or analyzing the leaked information. Moreover, the proposed scheme still keeps the features of the low computational cost and the efficiency in implementation. Challenge random instead of time stamp ensures that each of the authentication information is random to effectively prevent replay attacks while avoiding the complex synchronization problems. And it can be easily realized in the practical resource-limited environment.

References

[1] M.S. Hwang, L.H. Li, A new remote user authentication scheme using smart cards. *IEEE Transactions on Consumer Electronics*, **46(1)**, pp. 28–30, 2000.

[2] H.M. Sun, An efficient use authentication scheme using smart cards. *IEEE Transactions on Consumer Electronics*, **46(4)**, pp. 958–961, 2000.

[3] H.Y. Chien, J.K. Jan, Y.M. Tseng. An efficient and practical solution to remote authentication: smart card. *Computers and Security*, **21(4)**, pp. 372–375, 2002.

[4] P. Kocher, Timing attacks on implementations of Diffie-Hellman, RSA, DSS, and other systems. *Advances in Cryptology*, **CRYPTO'96**, pp. 104–113, 1996.

[5] P. Kocher, J. Jaffe, B. Jun, Differential power analysis. *Advances in Cryptology*, **CRYPTO'99**, pp. 372–375, 1999.

[6] T.S. Messerges, E.A. Dabbish, R.H. Sloan, Examining smart-card security under the threat of power analysis attacks. *IEEE Transactions on Computers*, **51(5)**, pp. 541–552, 2002.

[7] W.C. Ku, S.M. Chen, Weaknesses and improvements of an efficient password based remote user authentication scheme using smart cards. *IEEE Transactions on Consumer Electronics*, **50(1)**, pp. 204–207, 2004.

[8] E.J. Yoon, E.K. Ryu, K.Y. Yoo, Further improvement of an efficient password based remote user authentication scheme using smart cards. *IEEE Transactions on Consumer Electronics*, **50(2)**, pp. 612–614, 2004.

[9] X.M. Wang, W.F. Zhang, J.S. Zhang et al., Cryptanalysis and improvement on two efficient remote user authentication scheme using smart cards. *Computer Standards & Interfaces*, **29(5)**, pp. 507–512, 2007.

[10] E.J. Yoon, E.J. Lee, K.Y. Yoo, Cryptanalysis of Wang et al.'s remote user authentication scheme using smart. In: *Fifth International Conference on Information Technology: New Generations*, pp. 575–580, 2008.

[11] W.C. Ku, S.M. Chen, Cryptanalysis of a flexible remote user authentication scheme using smart cards. *ACM Operating Systems Review*, **39(1)**, pp. 90–96, 2005.

[12] H.R. Chung, W.C. Ku, M.J. Tsaur, Weaknesses and improvement of Wang et al.'s remote user password authentication scheme for resource-limited environments. *Computer Stands & Interfaces*, **31(4)**, pp. 863–868, 2009.

Survey on the sensitivity of smart-phone users on QR codes security

Shiwu Chen[1], Shizhong Wu[1], Qin Li[2], Shoupeng Li[1], Yubo Deng[1], Tao Zhang[1]
[1]*China Information Technology Security Evaluation Center, Beijing, China*
[2]*Environmental Standards Institute, Chinese Research Academy of Environmental Sciences, Beijing, China*

Abstract

Quick response codes have been becoming important aspects in cities around the world. They are used to represent information in a compact form that can be scanned conveniently by mobile intelligent devices. With the popularity of mobile Internet and better equipped mobile devices, quick response codes offer a technique to increase the accessibility of mobile services. While this technology can also provide a new attack means for miscreants. To understand whether people are aware of this new threat, in this paper, we survey and analyze the safety consciousness of smart-phone users in Beijing city on security of quick response codes by a series of tests.

Keywords: quick response code, security, sensitivity, tests.

1 Introduction

Smart-phones have been playing an important role in our life. The comfort and convenience they provide undoubtedly made our life more comfortable and much easier than ever before. Modern smart-phones have two brilliant features: the integration of digital cameras and the ability to access the Internet anytime and anywhere, which enable us to seek information when we need it. But just like everything has two sides, the above two outstanding features of smart-phones can be god indeed, they can be devil either. One of those threats comes from two-dimensional (2D) codes, because 2D codes encourage mobile users to scan

Figure 1: An example of QR codes which leads to the home page of CNITSEC.

unauthenticated data from posters, billboards, and stickers, etc., thus providing a new attack means for miscreants.

A new sort of "bar codes" was originally developed for the automobile industry. But it is now used in much border fields [1]. There are at least 30 kinds of 2D codes in use now. For more information, one can read Ref. [2] where the authors introduced various 2D barcodes for camera-phone applications in detail, including their symbol structures and how they work. While in this paper, we mainly focus on quick response (QR) codes due to their obvious convenience in use. A QR code is a database 2D barcode invented by the Japanese corporation Denso Wave in 1994. QR codes have higher storage capacity than any other normal conventional barcodes. And QR codes can encode all types of data, such as symbols, binary data, control codes, and multimedia data. Specifically, a QR code can hold up to several hundred times more data than a traditional barcode, because information can be encoded in both the vertical and horizontal directions. The maximum data capacities of QR codes are 7089 characters for numeric data, 4296 characters for alphanumeric data, 2953 bytes for binary data, and 1817 characters for Japanese Kanji and Kana data. Therefore, QR codes are mainly used to represent or store messages, such as a web address, in a compact form. Then the massages expressed by a QR code can be accessed via capturing a photograph of the code using a camera (e.g., building into an intelligent device) and processing the image with a QR reader. An example of QR codes, which can lead smart-phone users to the home page of China Information Technology Security Evaluation Center (CNITSEC), is shown in Figure 1.

QR codes have rapidly gained international popularity and found widespread adoption, especially in Japan. In recent years, QR codes are popular with marketers because of their ease in deployment. Businesses display QR codes on advertisements to direct people to their web sites. QR codes can be normally found on store-front windows, magazines, newspapers, web sites, posters, mass mailings, and billboards to store URLs, addresses, and various forms of data.

In addition to the traditional applications, there are many other potential applications of QR codes. Early in 2004, Eisaku et al. showed new algorithms and the implementations of image reorganization for European Article Numbering (EAN)/QR barcodes in mobile phones [3]. In Ref. [4], the author proposed the notion of contextual QR codes that merge a public QR code and private information to provide data related to a particular context. Based on the idea of utilizing QR codes affixed to an object and scanned using a camera-phone equipped with QR reader software, Al-Khalifa [5] introduced a barcode-based system to help the visually impaired and blind people identify objects in the surrounding environment. In Ref. [6], potential applications of QR codes are identified and prototypically implemented in tourism and specifically within a cultural institution. Last year, Mihaela et al. [7] determined in their paper whether the massive implementation of QR codes would accelerate virtualized consumption and perform toward profitability as a new strategic resource. In the same year, Somdip [8] presented a new technique of using QR codes in the field of cryptography. Recently, via using QR code and without sacrificing user's privacy, Harini and Padmanabhan [9] presented a new two-factor authentication scheme that enhances secure usage of application information and preserves usability. One can find a lot of new applications from the Internet, such as in Refs. [10–12].

However, because the encoded information is designed to be machine readable only, one cannot distinguish between a valid and a malicious QR code. By positioning QR codes under false pretences, attackers can entice users to scan the codes and subsequently visit malicious web sites, install programs, or any other actions the mobile device supports. Thus humans might fall for phishing attacks, and automated readers are most likely vulnerable to SQL injections and/or command injections. The purpose of this paper is to test whether people are aware of this new threat.

This paper is organized as follows. In the following section, we survey and analyze the security susceptibility of people on security of QR codes by a series of tests. The last section ends up with some discussions and the conclusion.

2 Survey on the awareness of hidden danger of QR codes

The rate of people access Internet through mobile phones via reading the QR codes has reached 96% in Japan and Korea, but still in its infancy in China. However, it is believed that once this technology accepted by netizens of China, the applications of QR codes will render the explosive growth. The top 10 Android applications for reading QR codes are given in Table 1.

Based on the statistics data of the QR Codes Cloud Services Platform (as shown in Figure 2), up to June 2012, the number of QR code users has exceeded 20 million, and the people who scanned QR codes were more than 100 million per month, in which the top three contents that scanned by those people were web sites, downloads, and texts [13]. With the rapid increase in the amount of scanning QR codes, whether the contents encoded within QR code is safe and how to ensure that the results of scanning codes do not pose a risk for the users

Table 1: Android Applications for QR Codes Scan.

Rank	Application	Auto Visit
1	Barcode Scanner	No
2	ShopSavvy Barcode Scanner	Yes
3	QuickMark Barcode Scanner	No
4	RedLaser Barcode and QR Reader	No
5	ScanLife Barcode and QR Reader	Yes
6	Barcode scanner	No
7	i-nigma Barcode Scanner	Yes
8	AT&T Code Scanner	No
9	ixMAT Barcode Scanner	No
10	BARCODE SCANNER	No

Three of the top 10 free android applications automatically visit URLs scanned from QR codes. In this case, the user has no opportunity to visually inspect the URL prior to visiting that URL.

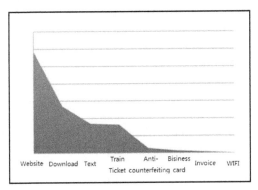

Figure 2: Scanning type list of QR code users according to the statistics data of the QR Codes Cloud Services Platform in second quarter of 2012. The top three contents that scanned by QR codes users were web sites, downloads, and texts.

have been becoming closely related doubts to users, even related to the development of the entire industry. Not long ago, it has drawn wide attention in China that QR codes on the real-name train tickets leaked information of users. With the popularity of smart-phones, applications of QR codes become more and more widespread, and its security issues will become increasingly prominent. So in this section, we test the general population's awareness on the safety of QR codes in Beijing through a series of experiments.

2.1 Methodology

The ease with which one can create and distribute QR codes may make them attractive to scammers seeking to direct people to phishing web sites. The

Figure 3: An example of the posters we used in this research, with the instruction for use.

purpose of this survey is to understand how users interact with QR codes in public spaces and to assess the susceptibility of smart-phone users to phishing attacks in Beijing city. Experimental procedures are as follows.

First of all, we looked for participants in public places (e.g., at bus stops, restaurants, coffee shops, saloons, movie theaters, subway stations, sight spots, shopping centers, supermarkets, KTVs, banks, gas stations, schools, hospitals, and post stations) randomly, and asked them to fill out our questionnaires. If we were refused, we found another one. The questionnaire stated the issues we want to investigate in detail, and in which we provide several possible answers; the only thing the volunteers need to do is to choose the appropriate options according to their actual situations. Of course, sometimes volunteers need to add and write their appropriate answers.

Then we posted our posters with QR codes in public locations. The poster we used is shown in Figure 3. All posters were posted in public locations where posters are routinely placed to attract the attention of people. To observe how people interact with the QR codes we posted in public spaces, we placed mini-camera in the vicinity of each poster. Then we could know how many people scanned the poster by the captured video. Each QR code on a poster represented a random and unique URL to our web server, allowing us to distinctly know in which location the participant observed our poster. Such URLs are commonly used in QR code advertising. Further, the use of random URLs is to minimize the risk that after scanning one poster, curious participants could easily determine and visit URLs associated with other posters. In the last month of 2012, we posted posters at 128 different locations. Each poster was checked weekly. If some posters were damaged, we replaced them with new ones in good time.

2.2 Results

Our questionnaires show that 58% of the participants are not familiar with the QR code function principles, and the ratio of participants who are very familiar with QR codes is only 17%. 67% of the participants said they have not contacted with the information related to mobile phone QR code business. Participants mainly saw QR code advertisings in the subway stations, which accounted for 60% to total number. 70% of the participants have used QR code services at least once, in which 50% is in the usage of coupons activities. 53% of the participants hope to employ QR code for metro and bus ticketing area in the future. 80% of the participants are interesting in using QR code. Our research has shown that Apple operating system phone users are more often to scan QR code, second is android phone users. This is consistent with the findings of the *Qrpix.com* web site. 35% of the participants had installed QR code viewers but do not use them frequently. Far more men than women concerned about QR codes, the ratio of male to female is approximately 9:1, and both of them in the age region 18–35. The occasions that mobile QR codes use more are sign in, ticket check at the station, online videos, and information browsing. The issue that most worthy of our attention is only 14.3% of the respondents worried that the use of QR codes may disclose personal information, while up to 42.9% of the participants does not understand that. In conclusion, our investigation imply that coverage of QR codes in China is far from Japan, Korea, the United States, and Britain, and most of Chinese people are not familiar with the potential danger from QR code, even are not aware of that.

By comparing captured video footages of people scanning the QR codes with server logs, we were able to identify the number of participants who scanned the code as well as the number of participants who actually visited the URL encoded in the QR code. In our study 80% (16/20) of people that scanned a QR code proceeded to visit the web site; however, our results may not be representative of a larger population.

3 Discussions and conclusions

Of course, the QR code in our research is a safe one. While just as we stated above, customers cannot distinguish a good and a malicious QR code. You can imagine: if the number of linkages increased and a malicious web site is employed in our experiments, there will be a lot of people access it and are likely maliciously attacked. Therefore, safety awareness should be maintained by everyone.

Then what should people do to avoid being attacked by the abuse of QR codes? The suggestive methods that we can do to raise security awareness to QR codes are as follows:

(1) One must identify the authoritative sources of the QR codes before scanning them. In particular, regular customers must not scan QR codes that are available on the web site with abandon.

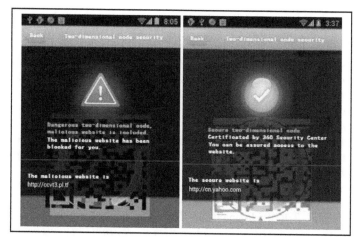

Figure 4: An example of a scanner which can visually inspect the URL prior to visiting it; therefore, user has the opportunity to avoid visiting a malicious URL.

(2) The protection programs, such as 360 phone guardian, should be installed in your mobile phone. Once your phone was under attack or received harmful information, this kind software can give a timely reminder. An example of that software is shown in Figure 4.

(3) Use the scanner provided by trusted software providers.

In summary, in this paper, we investigate and analyze the safety consciousness of smart-phone users on QR codes safety by a series of tests. Our research showed that most people in Beijing are not familiar with QR codes and/or are not fully aware of the potential danger. Thus malicious QR codes are likely to cause harm to them.

Acknowledgments

We would like to thank all the members of our cooperative group for various advices and supports.

References

[1] QR Code, http://en.wikipedia.org/wiki/QR_code, 2011.
[2] H. Kato, K. Tan, Pervasive 2D barcodes for camera phone applications. *IEEE Pervasive Computing: Mobile and Ubiquitous Systems*, **6(4)**, pp. 76–85, 2007.
[3] O. Eisaku, H. Hiroshi, A.H. Lim, Barcode readers using the camera device in mobile phones. In: *Proceedings of the 2004 International Conference on Cyberworlds (CW'04)0-7695-2140-1/04*, 2004.

[4] R. José, Contextual QR codes. In: *Proceedings of the 3rd International Multi-Conference on Computing in the Global Information Technology.* ICCGI 2008, Athens, Greece. © 2008 IEEE.

[5] H.S. Al-Khalifa, Utilizing QR code and mobile phones for blinds and visually impaired people. ICCHP 2008, LNCS 5105, pp. 1065–1069, 2008.

[6] C. Michael, H. Wolfram, F. Matthias, Application of QR codes in online travel distribution. *Information and Communication Technologies in Tourism*, pp. 137–148, 2010.

[7] I.M. Mihaela, M. Gabriela, B. Sandra, QR codes usage approach in the virtualized consumption. In: *Proceedings of the 11th International Conference on Informatics in Economy*, Vol. I, 2012.

[8] D. Somdip, SD-EQR: a new technique to use QR Codes™ in cryptography. arXiv: 1205.4829 [cs.CR], 2012.

[9] N. Harini, T.R. Padmanabhan, 2CAuth: a new two factor authentication scheme using QR-code. *International Journal of Engineering and Technology (IJET)*, 5(2), pp. 1087–1094, 2013.

[10] M. Max-Emanuel, D.L. Alexander, H. Alina et al., Long-term experiences with an iterative design of a QR-code-based payment system for beverages. *Human-Computer Interaction-INTERACT 2013, Lecture Notes in Computer Science*, **8120**, pp. 587–594, 2013.

[11] J.L. Ha-Kyung,Y. Young-Mi et al., Design of automatic paper identification system with QR code for digital forensics. *Mobile. Ubiquitous, and Intelligent Computing, Lecture Notes in Electrical Engineering Volume*, **274**, pp. 25–30, 2013.

[12] W. So-Min, K. Mi-Hye, K. Jin-Mook, Administration management system design for smart phone applications in use of QR code. *Multimedia and Ubiquitous Engineering, Lecture Notes in Electrical Engineering Volume*, **240**, pp. 585–592, 2013.

[13] According to http://nj.yesky.com/251/33294751.shtml.

Author Index

WITPRESS ...for scientists by scientists

Handbook of Communications Security

F. GARZIA, University of Rome "La Sapienza", Italy

Communications represent a strategic sector for privacy protection and for personal, company, national and international security. The interception, damage or loss of information during communication can generate material and non material economic damages from both a personal and a collective point of view.

Giving the reader information relating to all aspects of communications security, this book begins with the base ideas and builds to present the most advanced and updated concepts. The comprehensive coverage makes the book a one-stop reference for integrated system designers, telecommunication designers, system engineers, system analysts, security managers, technicians, intelligence personnel, security personnel, police, army, private investigators, scientists, graduate and postgraduate students and anyone who needs to communicate in a secure way.

The CD included with the book contains freeware cryptography and steganography Programs.

ISBN: 978-1-84564-768-1   eISBN: 978-1-84564-769-8
Published 2013 / 680pp +CD / £360.00

*All prices correct at time of going to press but
subject to change.
WIT Press books are available through your book-
seller or direct from the publisher.*

004B/25/P